ARCHITECTURAL DRAWING

American Sugar Refining Co.

A well-designed modern plant and office building.

ARCHITECTURAL DRAWING

Harvey W. Waffle, B.S., Ph.M., M.A.

STERLING TOWNSHIP HIGH SCHOOL, STERLING, ILLINOIS

[REVISED EDITION]

THE BRUCE PUBLISHING COMPANY ■ MILWAUKEE

Library of Congress Catalog Card Number: 62–19085

© 1962 THE BRUCE PUBLISHING COMPANY

Made in the United States of America

Introduction

This book is intended for the beginning classes in architectural drawing, after the students have had the basic and exploratory courses offered in mechanical drawing. Architectural drawing is usually offered as an elective subject with vocational interest, but it has its general and exploratory value in that most students electing the course are doing so because: (*a*) They believe they are interested in that particular type of drafting; (*b*) they have an interest in the building field; and (*c*) they realize the value of detailing, planning, and designing as presented in the basic course of mechanical drawing and particularly in the specialized course of architectural drawing as applied in the building field. Because of its exploratory value, as many as possible of the practical applications of the related vocations should be included so that the student acquires a well-rounded experience. This is particularly important because the student intending to specialize and receive further training in the subject should find out whether he is interested in the work and has the ability to succeed in it. Most students are able to make the elementary drawings involving line technique, views to be drawn, but dimensioning requires practical experience to know what dimensions the workman will need. Students may do a fine job in detailing but when they are required to render a perspective drawing they may be lacking the originality and artistry required of an architect. Happily the work in an architect's office is assigned according to training, interests, and abilities so that each person is given his specialty. In small offices the architect has to be able to do a good job in all divisions of the work.

This course is based upon a series of problems encountered in the four leading types of house construction — frame, stucco, brick, and stone. The drawings are supplemented by explanations and discussions of some of the fundamental principles of residence planning and construction. Effort has been made to teach the better principles of house construction, planning, and design, and to endeavor to develop some original student work along this line.

The material presented has been thoroughly tried out in the classes for which it was intended. There is enough material to allow for four semesters' work in the average school and it is flexible enough to permit the material to be fitted to any drawing course. The work is divided into sections, and under each section as many problems may be selected as time will allow. The drawings were purposely left incomplete so that the student would be required to do further study rather than following the line of least resistance and copying the drawings. Experience in the building trades is suggested for the student if no more than on a summer or part time basis. Observation is recommended of buildings in the process of construction, with class field trips where arrangements can be made. This practical experience is of decided advantage to the student in helping to determine the information to be given on the working drawings. Several methods of dimensioning are employed. Some will require the student to refer to catalogs for standard sizes; for others he must review previous constructions and drawings of experienced architectural draftsmen. Care has been exercised to prevent the student from being robbed of the opportunity to do his thinking and reasoning. All sections of the book are interrelated so that all of the material must be studied carefully and logically to complete the whole. The first section of the book is introductory and attempts to acquaint the student with the catalogs, handbooks, and reference books in the standard sizes and symbols used in architectural drawing. Its approach is that of "blueprint reading" important to all students whether they will intend to continue the study and specialize or not. All persons are closely associated with houses during their lifetime and can use the information given in the course whether they are choosing a house to rent; whether they are intending to buy a house and expect to receive full value; or, whether they are planning to build their house and incorporate their ideas in its planning. The section on house construction is of value to these same people that they may obtain the best construction for their money. There are several methods of construction, some good and some poor, which require consideration if a choice is possible. Information on this level of work can be obtained through actual work in the building trades, study of the sales features given in advertising literature and catalogs, reading of books and magazine articles, and gathering of opinions and information from experienced persons in this field of study. The section on house planning is an application of all previous study, providing further study on available information on good planning as exemplified in magazine articles and books, and offering the student the opportunity to make use of his original ideas. The last section of the book attempts to explore the artistic talent required of the draftsman and give the student a chance to evaluate his house plan for design, as well as practicability. The author is aware that this phase of the study is preliminary to the development of house planning as accomplished by the architect, but it is purposely placed in the course at this location because of the maturity of the student. This section is most beneficial to the advanced student, and is easier taught in this sequence. Each instructor has his particular organization of the course and it is intended that the material present in the book be kept flexible and adaptable to all variations. Some smaller schools must of necessity condense the course into one semester, at the same time still giving a sampling of the different divisions.

The author acknowledges with grateful appreciation the co-operation of all who have contributed toward the making of this volume — especially Dr. G. O. Banting, former Superintendent of Schools, Waukesha, Wisconsin, who encouraged the organization of the material for publication and offered most constructive criticism of all its phases; to Mr. J. E. Worthington, Principal, Waukesha High School, Waukesha, Wisconsin, who very constructively criticized the methods of presentation. In this present edition much credit must be given to Mr. Roscoe Eades, Superintendent, Sterling Township High School, Sterling, Illinois, for his constant encouragement and co-operation as well as his appreciated suggestions; and to Mr. U. R. DeVoe, Principal, Sterling Township High School, Sterling, Illinois, for his suggestions and loyalty which was always so evident. The early training received in drawing from his Professors J. E. Ray and Daniel Green of Stout State College, Menomonie, Wisconsin; and Mr. H. C. Thayer, Madison, Wisconsin, formerly of Stout State College, Menomonie, Wisconsin, and now retired from the State Board of Vocational Education, Madison, Wisconsin. He is especially indebted to Mr. John W. English, 36 York Road, West Hartlepool, England, F.R.I.B.A., who contributed his experience in architectural practice to the unit presentation on "Preliminary Sketches," and to Mr. Sylvester A. Snyder, Architect, Waukesha, Wisconsin who contributed his experience in architectural practice to the unit presentation on "Display Drawings." No statement of appreciation is sufficient to the students of Wisconsin Dells High School, Wisconsin Dells, Wisconsin; Plymouth High School, Plymouth, Wisconsin; Waukesha Senior High School, Waukesha, Wisconsin; Davenport Senior High School, Davenport, Iowa; Maine Township High School, Des Plaines-Park Ridge, Illinois; and Sterling Township High School, Sterling, Illinois, and especially to my wife and children.

HARVEY W. WAFFLE

CONTENTS

ARCHITECTURAL DRAWING III, HOUSE PLANNING

ARCHITECTURAL DRAWING IV

U N I T

I

The Architect

WHAT IS A CAREER IN ARCHITECTURE?

Architecture is the expression of a civilization through the medium of its buildings. Our cities are in fact architectural museums, reflecting in their skylines the use of materials, light, and space. Every type of building in our communities is the result of the architect's application of art, drawing, and science. Egypt's pyramids, Athens' Parthenon, the Forum of Imperial Rome, the cathedrals of Gothic France — all express the finest technical and cultural achievements of their time. In his designs the American architect no longer has to rely upon architectural forms and styles developed by earlier civilizations, whose primary materials were wood and masonry. The rapid growth of technology has greatly increased the materials and methods available for accomplishing today's building programs. Airports, terminals, shopping centers, and similar types of modern building have no historical development from earlier civilizations and reflect today's dynamic architecture as it deals with the movement, work, recreation, and distribution of people.

An architect is a person who professionally designs buildings and supervises their construction. While much of the process of creating the plan of a building is an indi-

vidual effort, architecture as a profession is generally a co-operative undertaking. The architect must play the role of a creative artist, professional adviser to his client, building technician, and businessman. Since such varied talents are rarely found combined to a high degree in one man, the architect frequently associates himself with others, differently gifted, as partners or associates. In few professions is there such an opportunity for self-expression as there is in architecture. An architect gains satisfaction by his services to the community, and in the knowledge that he is contributing work of a lasting nature. His buildings are lived in, and he has the satisfaction of knowing that his efforts contribute in creating places where people can better work and live.

WHAT ARE THE PERSONAL CHARACTERISTICS REQUIRED FOR A CAREER IN ARCHITECTURE?

The education of an architect cannot be confined between the covers of books but must grow from roots firmly planted in character, natural ability, and that all embracing characteristic — personality. The development of character and a willingness to continue to learn, combined with the ability to inspire confidence through the expression of opinions founded upon reasonable conservatism and sound judgment, represent qualities without which mere book learning becomes only a reservoir of facts and figures. Missing is that special something which makes of knowledge a living, moving force, and raises the technical and artistic skill in the design and erection of structures to the importance and dignity of a profession.

The development of the man in those qualities which make for good citizenship and leadership is but the beginning of the development of the architect, for amid the modern-day complexities of building construction, leadership is essential if confusion is to be avoided. The architect is logically such a leader and must qualify for leadership if the profession of architecture is to take its proper place in the confidence of the public, and secure for the architect the legal protection already accorded to the professions of medicine and law. The acceptance of leadership in any enterprise imposes responsibility and obligations, and the factors controlling leadership in the construction field must be carefully studied if the architect is to equip himself adequately as the master builder.

Even marked artistic ability will not alone suffice, for such leadership demands the bringing together of many diverse interests and the working out of problems involving property values, methods of finance, building economics, the co-ordinating of structural and mechanical details with the architectural design, the making of important contracts, and the general direction and supervision of the progress and completion of the work in the field.

Successful architects have sensitivity, agile minds, manual dexterity. They possess the ability to visualize and, although working mainly with ideas, develop skill in drawing as a means of studying their own ideas and designs and conveying them advantageously to others. Personal characteristics that seem to indicate desirable qualifications for success in the field of architecture include:

Scientific interest — an interest in the experimental method, scientific approach, and resulting scientific and technological conclusions.

Engineering knowledge — acquisition and mastery of knowledge of theoretical science, engineering principles, and mathematical and graphical analysis, along with the methods of descriptive representation employed in drafting.

Mechanical, structural, and aesthetic interest — an appreciable degree of interest in mechanical devices, principles of mechanisms, and principles of structural analysis, as well as artistic sense and appreciation.

Skill in the use of language — ability to convey ideas, facts, and data in a clear, concise, positive manner.

Creative ability, originality — talent for initiating ideas, discovering new facts, and inventing new procedures.

Energy and ambition — physical energy, will power, and drive.

Initiative — starting and finishing a problem of his own volition.

Aggressiveness — a competitive and assertive spirit or attitude.

Reliability and perseverance — reliability in carrying out an assignment regardless of personal inconvenience or obstacles.

Stability of emotion — emotional attribute of remaining calm and analytical under pressure or tension.

Mathematical competence — ability to use mathematics as a working tool.

General appearance and manner — factors contributing toward confidence in self, co-operation with, and respect for, others.

Getting along with people — delegation of responsibility, and inspiration of confidence. People depend upon his judgment.

Responsibility — a feeling that the over-all success of the project depends upon the individual's securing satisfactory results.

WHAT TYPES OF SERVICES ARE PERFORMED BY PERSONS IN THE ARCHITECTURAL FIELD?

A classification of work performed in the architectural profession demonstrates the significant differences and variations in the types of services performed in today's technological organization, and emphasizes the necessity of training young students with a great variety of interests, abilities, aptitudes, and skills.

The professional and technical classifications by functional areas are:

1. *Office boy* — performs any appropriate duties assigned.

2. *Student draftsman* — makes corrections to maps, surveys, and filing tracings, blueprints, specifications, and so on; examines and studies drawings made by others; takes care of samples and supplies; orders and trims prints, sends and delivers packages; makes experimental drawings and tracings, does minor lettering, and performs capably any appropriate, assigned duties.

3. *Apprentice draftsman* — looks up catalog references, files catalogs, cleans and trims tracings, mounts drawings; traces drawings made by others of minor buildings; does simple layouts of properties, plans of buildings, lettering, and titling; assists in taking measurements for architectural surveys of existing buildings; is of general usefulness in office routine and outside work.

4. *Apprentice detailer* — develops preliminary layouts of working drawings of plans, elevations, and sections of minor buildings, and prepares simple details from sketches and data by others; neatly traces or finishes drawings, and lettering; does incidental drafting of minor importance.

5. *Junior detailer* — makes corrections and alterations of working drawings; has familiarity with office routine and is of general assistance to others in translating ideas into architectural descriptions; makes visits to buildings under construction preliminary to submitting reports to inspectors or superintendents; independently takes measurements for architectural surveys of existing buildings.

6. *Assistant senior architectural draftsman* — does work of a more advanced nature in which experience is very important; makes sketches and prepares preliminary studies for plans, elevations, and sections of buildings of major importance; prepares actual working drawings of buildings from superior's sketches or layouts and accurately traces these drawings; makes sketches for and prepares and inks-in scale details and makes full-size details; has the ability to check in a preliminary way, dimensions, working drawings, scale details, contractor's shop drawings, and so on.

7. *Senior architectural draftsman or architectural designer* — is well equipped with a general knowledge of routine work in the office and the field, has a full spirit of co-operation with all associates, and possesses a certain amount of directional ability; prepares sketches and does renderings of drawings in various mediums; plans, designs, and details buildings, and is familiar with appropriate materials; co-operates with office technicians, engineers and so on, and has a knowledge of the crafts of building; designs and does full-size detailing of ornamental, sculptural, and other features of the building; outside the office, visits the sites of proposed projects, observes topography, local conditions, and natural and architectural surroundings; passes preliminary judgment on appropriate requirements, proposed materials, and so on.

8. *Technical draftsman* — specialized to enable him to be familiar with features of structural engineering, mechanical engineering, or electrical engineering to the extent that in planning and designing buildings he can regulate their features in proper accommodation to the necessary requirements as to spacing, size, arrangement, installation, application and satisfactory disposal of all component parts. He must be sufficiently capable in these architectural requirements to be a co-ordinator with any employed or consulting engineers, and on behalf of the architect to act as inspector or supervisor of installations and equipment at the site.

9. *Specifications writer* — possesses the ability to put into appropriate language the provisions which will insure complete, sound, workable structures and surroundings.

10. *Examiner or checker* — has the ability and foresight to discover whether or not all the component features are properly shown and provided for, and see that all drawings are complete before issuance of final estimates.

11. *Quantity surveyor and cost estimator* — keeps abreast of all costs applicable locally for materials, methods, and labor, and can make proper computations including comparisons as to maintenance.

12. *Superintendent or inspector* — has the ability and agility to cover all construction work as it progresses, and to see that the drawings, specifications, and all proper requirements are complied with.

13. *Assistant architect or chief draftsman* — investigates, plans, designs, and estimates with the staff members the first cost and the maintenance cost of building; takes charge of drafting and technical personnel, and maintains contact with all staff members doing outside work; directs the preparation of preliminary sketches, supervises the drafting room work and has general oversight of the preparation of drawings, details, and specifications; makes occasional field visits and renders final decisions with respect to the supervision of actual construction at the site.

14. *Architect* — completely responsible for the standards and methods applied, and for the technical soundness of the methods or work, and the accuracy and reliability of the results.

The occupational fields within the profession are partially listed as follows:

Architect
Architectural engineer
Building construction engineer
City planning engineer
Community planning engineer
Industrial architect
Landscape architect
Construction engineer
Planning engineer
Structural engineer
Production engineer
Sales engineer
Interior decorator

OCCUPATIONS IN ARCHITECTURE AND THE BUILDING INDUSTRY

The courses offered in architecture provide an integrated educational experience which, after a period of practical experience in an architectural office, will furnish a sound foundation for independent architectural practice or for careers as partners and project directors in the larger industrial firms.

The courses in building construction offer a preparation for business, management, and technical careers in the building industry. This industry — now the largest in terms of money spent and employment provided — offers a wide variety of opportunities in the area of building technology and in the fields of building material production, distribution, and marketing, as well as in the management and supervision of building construction, and contracting.

Courses in the areas of architecture and building prepare for the following professional careers:

Architect — practicing independently
Architect — partner in firm
Architectural consultant
Architectural delineator
Architectural designer
Architectural project manager
Design draftsman, architectural
Design draftsman, mechanical
Design draftsman, electrical
Design draftsman, structural
Structural designer, buildings
Industrial architect
Industrial designer
City planner
Construction estimator
Construction supervisor
Editor or author, architectural publications
Specification writer
Community planning consultant
Real-estate appraiser
Field inspector, construction
Government service, architectural
Housing consultant
Building appraiser
Building construction superintendent
Building inspector
Building contractor
Building department executive
Building maintenance consultant
Building maintenance superintendent
Building materials, production
Building materials, sales
Building materials, technologist

Land developer
Realty developer
Realty development consultant

WHAT THE ARCHITECT MUST KNOW

The architect should be a man of general knowledge and broad culture, interested in the affairs and development of the world about him and keeping abreast of the times in scientific, mechanical, and political activities as well as the field of his chosen profession and the allied arts. The base of his cultural knowledge cannot be too broad. "Let him be skillful with the pencil, instructed in mathematics, history, literature, and philosophy, understand music, have some knowledge of medicine, know the opinion of jurists, and be acquainted with astronomy and the theory of the heavens." — **Vitruvius.**

The development of personality and a willingness to continue to learn, combined with the ability to inspire confidence, represent qualities essential to every successful architect. He has to deal with draftsmen, clients, contractors, and subcontractors. This demands the bringing together of many interests and the working out of problems involving property values, methods of finance, building economics, the co-ordinating of structural and mechanical details with the architectural design, the making of important contracts, and the general direction and supervision of work in the field.

The architect should have a broad general education: he should have a knowledge of the history of art and of political and economic history; he should have a knowledge of physics, especially as bearing on engineering problems, and at least a rudimentary knowledge of chemistry, geology, and horticulture. If he can speak in three languages he is that much better equipped to profit by reading and travel.

He should be a good businessman, for a large part of his time is taken up with business problems. He should know how and when to buy and how to adjust satis-factorily to the differences which arise between the buyer, or owner, and the seller, or contractor. And more important he should know how to sell his services advantageously — when to yield a point and when to stand firm; this requires that he be a shrewd judge of men.

He must be a very practical person, with a good deal of common sense, for as he practices his profession he will find that it is not all aesthetic design and beautiful conceptions, but it embodies decisions concerning comparative costs, utility, durability, proportional sizes, and similar considerations.

The architect must be an artist, never satisfied with what he has designed but, even to the last stage before they are completed, to scrap his drawings if he feels the result can be improved. He should be able to convey ideas on paper to draftsmen, clients, or builders. If he can make artistic sketches so much the better, for they will help to impress the client. The preparation of the preliminary sketches marks a period of interesting study. At this time the designer and artist comes into his own, but from then on the work becomes more and more of a practical construction and engineering problem and much of the artistic color fades out of the picture.

He must have a talent for making friends and keeping them. He must have tact and no conceit or false pride and must remember what few artists do — that he is the servant of his client and his job is to give satisfaction without sacrificing his standards. This is not always easy, since clients may be unreasonable and contractors often find ways of interpreting the architect's plans and specifications.

While the contractor who erects the work must assume the responsibility for sound and honest workmanship, the architect must assure the durability of the structure and the economy of its upkeep through the wise selection of materials and methods of construction. His specifications must determine the character and quality of the materials. The architect must also be familiar with the laws, codes, and ordinances governing buildings if he is to make intelligent designs.

The architect should be able to save his fee to the owner by suggesting economies in planning, in construction, and in the use of materials which will not detract from the essential requirements. Some of the simplest examples are: grouping flues to save chimneys, planning for good traffic circulation and convenience, placing plumbing fixtures to save piping, and specifying materials which are most available and durable under local conditions. From the artistic point of view, either the architect should recommend to the owner the type of design best suited to the individual and the locality, or if the owner has determined in his own mind the character of the house to be built he should be able to point out and eliminate defects, and at the same time develop the individuality to be expressed, and emphasize the attractive features. From flat drawings he can visualize the house and feel the relationship of plans and elevation.

TRAINING OF THE ARCHITECT

Architects are usually trained in a specialized school of a university which requires from four to five years of professional study, after which an internship of usually a minimum of two years is spent in working in an architect's office. Regardless of the character and extent of the draftsman's academic and architectural scholastic training it is office experience which affords the only sure method of reducing theory to practice to the extent necessary properly to equip him to practice as an architect in accordance with the standards which should surround such practice. There can be no rule applied to the length of such office experience, for it is dependent upon the character of the experience, the natural ability and the educational equipment which the individual brings to the entrance of his office training.

A person can become a good draftsman, and some can become good architects, with no other professional training than that acquired through practical experience. The rise to professional recognition of many men who have lacked architectural training, aside from that gained through practical experience, should be an encouragement to any man who lacks the opportunity for such preliminary training; but it imposes upon such a man the added burden of acquiring as much training as he can while he is securing practical office experience. In all cases high-school training is recommended that he may have learned the fundamentals of drafting, and experienced some of the procedures and techniques employed in practice. High school graduation is a prerequisite for entry into professional architectural courses. A broad educational background with work in languages, social studies, English, art, physics, mathematics, and mechanical drawing is suggested.

All states and territories require architects to be licensed or registered before they can practice, because architecture involves the safety of life, health, and property. There are some differences in the requirements for licensing among the states but generally the requirements are graduation from a recognized professional school followed by three to five years of practical experience. Some states accept a long period of experience (New York State — 12 years) in place of graduation from an architectural school. Most state exams extend over a period of four days and the applicant works out his answers and solutions by himself. Tests cover mathematics, construction, mechanical equipment, history of architecture, artistic composition, and practical problems in design. If the applicant fails one portion of the examination he may repeat that portion the next time the exams are given. Information may be obtained from the licensing authority of the state in which the applicant desires to practice.

WORK OF THE ARCHITECT

The architect's definite duties, aside from being the advisor, philosopher, and friend of the owner are to consult with his client in preparing the preliminary sketches and estimates; to make complete working drawings and specifications; to obtain estimates; and, after passing on them with the owner, to draw up the contracts. At all times he is at the service of his client for consultation.

First are sketches or preliminary studies. These may be small and simple, but they should reveal all the elements of the plan and the essentials of the artistic treatment. They can be altered and even redrawn with comparative ease. The fact that the studies are not precise leaves the imagination free and the mind open for suggestions and changes.

Next he must execute working drawings. All the floor plans, elevations, and several sections should be carefully drawn to scale, with the materials indicated and with explicit dimensions noted on all drawings. Details like the swing of doors, location of electrical fixtures, switches, equipment, headroom under stairs, rainwater conductors should all be carefully considered and indicated. Such sheets require much time and skilled labor. Changes which in themselves appear trivial may involve rearrangements of supports or piping, doors or doorways, on each plan, section, and elevation, and cause considerable added expense to the architect. When plans are redrawn at this stage owing to the client's indecision or new ideas, he should pay for the cost of the unforeseen labor to which the architect has been put.

Third are specifications. Those which accompany preliminary drawings need to be only one or two typewritten pages, listing the most important materials in the walls, floors, roofs, and a line or two on heating, plumbing, and the electrical wiring. Working specifications should explicitly cover all the materials which are to be included in the construction, and the method of installing and finishing them should also be given. For example, if brick walls are called for, the common and face brick, their bonding and jointing must be described; their protection during inclement weather and their pointing and cleaning noted; the character of the sand, cement, lime, and coloring matter, and the method of mixing the mortar, and the tests and restrictions must be fully covered; the preparation of samples and the building-in of door and window frames, outside brackets, interior framing, nailing strips for applied woodwork, and flashing are all included if the specifications are to be complete. The specifications should clearly indicate which part of the work belongs to a particular trade; they should be arranged in the general sequence the construction is to follow, and should be presented paragraph by paragraph, for ease of reference and to avoid misunderstandings on the job.

Finally there are detail drawings. After the contract is let, large scale details are prepared for constructions on the job. Doors, windows, stairways, and other stock items are not detailed in residence construction since they are purchased as a unit ready for installation.

SUPERVISION OR INSPECTION

When the contractor takes possession of the site, the architect must begin his supervision of each part of the construction. To illustrate each batch of concrete which is mixed and poured may be inferior or defective, and unless both the contractor and his foreman are reliable the architect must give almost constant supervision. On the other hand a quarter of an hour's inspection can check several days' work of the carpenter, for a mistake in sizes or spacing can be readily detected and the correction ordered. The architect's duties require him to follow the progress of the work from the first excavation till the last workman is out of the house. Neglect of the contract requirements or slovenly workmanship can be corrected before it is too late, and where modifications are optional, such as the texture of the brickwork, the color of the paint, or the exact location of a light fixture, the owner can obtain what best suits his particular desire. The owner is not justified in demanding changes from the contract drawings and specifications without penalty on cost; and his experience in technical matters is more limited than that of the architect or contractor. A fussy and troublesome owner can break down the morale of an entire building crew and their boss, but a tactful and interested counselor may stimulate the contractor to friendly concessions and the workmen to quality workmanship. If the progress is not satisfactory, a frank conference between the owner and contractor, in the architect's office, will often clear up misunderstandings. It is best to avoid discussions on the job in the presence of workmen. Care should also be taken to give instructions to the foreman or contractor, rather than to individual workmen. Orders for any changes should go through the architect's hands and be confirmed in writing.

ACCOUNTING

Payments are made by the owner only on the written recommendation of the architect, who submits the statements as the work progresses. Before starting on the construction the contractor should submit to the architect a schedule showing how the total cost in the agreement is to be credited. The architect must keep careful records of the contract sums, all additions and deductions, and the amounts paid to the contractors, and also of the payments made to him on his commission.

EARNINGS OF THE ARCHITECT

After the first conference of the owner with his architect, a clear understanding should be had as to what services are expected from the architect and what his pay should be for the work done. The most commonly used method by which the architect sets his fee is by charging a certain percentage of the contract cost of the job. A fixed fee may be charged, plus the architect's office or production costs (his time, drafting costs, and overhead). Still another method is a fixed fee plus a percentage of excess (if the contract costs no more than 10 per cent beyond the first estimated cost). In practice, architects frequently charge 6 per cent of the building costs on all types of buildings except homes, on which they charge a 10 per cent fee. Remodeling jobs bring the highest fee of 15 per cent. His commission may vary on domestic design from 6 per cent for a house costing $10,000 or over, without unusual features or much ornamentation, to 10 per cent or more for a very small house, or for one where a great deal of special work is involved. This sliding scale is necessary, as the time involved by the designer and specification-writer is almost as much on a building costing $15,000 as on one costing $25,000. There are no more types of doors and windows to be detailed, the detailed, written description of the materials is no more complicated, and the client will expect as many hours of conference. Many architects who have made a name for themselves in domestic design charge 12 per cent or 15 per cent on all their work, since the demand for their services justifies the increased rate.

If unusual engineering requirements are involved, whether in the structure or in the mechanical equipment — such as bridging quicksand or an individual sewage-disposal system, requiring the advice of a specialist — the additional fee is paid by the owner. If radical changes are made, causing the redrafting of plans already prepared, or if the project is abandoned, the services of brain and hand rendered in good faith should be paid for.

On completion of the preliminary sketches, one fifth of the total estimated fee is due the architect; on completion of the working drawings and specifications, an additional two fifths; and the remaining two fifths is paid when the building is completed.

WORK OF THE ARCHITECTURAL DRAFTSMAN

The architect must depend upon the draftsman to carry out in detail the work he conceives and through his daily experience the draftsman has the opportunity to apply his skill, knowledge, and professional ability toward the goal of receiving his license to practice. It should be the duty of the draftsman to realize that such material profit as the architect may derive from his practice depends largely upon the ability and earnest application of the draftsman; for lack of knowledge or skill, time wasted or spent unnecessarily in repetitious work, or the development or rendering of drawings beyond the point required for the full and clear indication of the work — all add to the cost of production.

Architectural drawing is truly the language of the architect and the builder. It may be divided into freehand and working drawings. Pictorial representations are used as well as the projection form of drawing. Many freehand drawings are required of the architect, such as the details of carved stone and wood, ornamental iron, lettered inscriptions for the contractor, and rendered sketches to be submitted to the client. By a few strokes of his pencil, he must be able to express his ideas to the draftsman, or make some point clear to his client, or help the contractors visualize some matters not readily understood from the working drawings. He must be trained to make accurate drawings, mechanically. He, therefore, must have a thorough understanding of orthographic projection. Descriptive geometry is the basis of orthographic projection and is a worthwhile subject for the training of the architect's imagination. He also needs a thorough knowledge of perspective drawing, in order to show his clients the appearance of a proposed building, or to be able to study the design of the building for mass and proportion. To the builder, the architect conveys his ideas by working drawings. These drawings are to be made to scale, containing full dimensions and notes, and they must be accompanied by the specifications.

To qualify as an architectural draftsman, a student must possess knowledge of and be able to apply the following:

1. The symbols and conventions used in architectural drawing.

2. Lettering of the style used by architects and at a speed required by the architect.

3. The principles used in mechanical drawing such as the relationship of views, projections, intersections, and so on.

4. At least a brief history of architecture.

5. At least the elementary principles of design.

6. The strength, characteristics, and limitations of materials.

7. Pencil sketching, that he may pictorially express his ideas.

8. The principles of perspective drawing.

9. Working knowledge of shades and shadows.

10. Writing specifications and estimating costs.

11. Methods of rendering and applying wash to drawings.

STOCK PLANS

The procedure by which each house is designed and completed by the client's own architect, working on his individual problem from start to finish, is the ideal method, by which the most distinctive results may be achieved. It is the purpose of this text to have the student experience this procedure as nearly as possible. On a small house professional advice is available in other ways. By purchasing plans and specifications from the Small House Service Bureau, which is organized by the American Institute of Architects, a prospective home owner may procure economical, carefully considered plans, with designs of artistic merit. The construction of houses from stock plans lacks the intangible part of architectural service in adapting the house to the owner's personal requirements, and the constant supervision for which years of training have fitted the architect. On the other hand, some architects feel they cannot afford the time for painstaking preparation of small house plans that bring them such comparatively small compensation. Accordingly, a frequent practice nowadays is the employment of an architect to approve and supervise the construction of a house from a stock plan.

Many city building codes require a complete set of working drawings be drawn by an architect for any house to be built. These plans must be approved by the building inspector and copies are filed in his office.

PROBLEMS FOR CLASS DISCUSSION

1. List the qualities which an architect should cultivate.
2. Why is travel in Europe suggested in the education of an architect?
3. Why do you consider high school training necessary for a student who plans to study architecture?
4. Mechanical drawing is a prerequisite to the study of architectural drawing. Why?
5. List the trades, professions, and industries in which the study of architectural drawing is helpful or related.
6. What is the difference between an architectural draftsman and an architect?
7. Why are architectural offices usually organized upon a partnership basis?
8. This course is planned upon an exploratory experience. Can you explain the reason for this orientation?
9. Explain the correlations between architectural drawing and other academic subjects.
10. Why is practical experience necessary for the candidate for an architect's license?

Architectural Lettering

The lettering on architectural drawings is important because, by means of it, the draftsman supplies considerable information in the form of titles, notes, and dimensions. For this reason the lettering should be legible and conform to the character of the drawing. It also should be artistic and interesting, and express a definite character. Lettering is by far the most important element through which the draftsman's individuality may be expressed. Seldom do two draftsmen use exactly the same lettering forms. Usually each draftsman develops his own style. This is perfectly permissible so long as all the letters resemble each other closely enough to be of the same style. A beginning draftsman should adopt an alphabet which he can study and practice persistently.

Architectural lettering may be divided into two main divisions: (a) the lettering of titles and inscriptions on display drawings; (b) the lettering of explanatory titles and notes on working drawings. The lettering on display drawings is often included as a part of the design or ornament to be executed in stone, bronze, or other materials. The design of these letters must be in harmony with the style of architecture and adapted to the materials used. The lettering on working drawings must be legible and be made with speed. Lettering on display drawings requires more careful attention to details because the appearance of such drawings may be improved or ruined by the quality of the lettering. The selection of an appropriate style, the careful execution of the form and pro-

portion of the letter, and a studied mastery of the rules of composition all require careful study by the draftsman.

It is suggested that beginning architectural drawing students study the chapter on lettering in an advanced textbook on Engineering or Technical drawing to learn the fundamentals of single stroke gothic lettering. The scope of this text presupposes a background of these fundamentals so that emphasis can be placed upon application to the single-stroke Roman letters.

Practically all lettering used in display and working drawings has been derived from the ancient Romans, as modified and refined by the Italian architects of the Renaissance period. See Figure 1. The Old Roman alphabet may be varied considerably to meet the needs of each particular case, but no unnecessary flourishes or exaggerations should be used. The secret of good lettering is simplicity.

In architectural as well as in all other lettering, the use of guide lines is absolutely necessary to keep the lettering horizontal and the letters of uniform height. The most experienced draftsman, as well as the beginner, should use guide lines for every letter or figure on a drawing. The greatest mistake the beginner can make is to try to letter without them. All guide lines should be drawn very lightly so they will not interfere with the appearance of the lettering.

Students are inclined to believe that, after they have mastered the shape of the letters, there is nothing further to learn. The correct spacing of the letters and words is just as important as the correct formation of the letters, for, if the spacing is improperly done, the pleasing effect of the most carefully constructed letters is destroyed. Uniformity of effect is the element desired; that is, the letters in one part of a word or line should not appear more crowded than those in any other part.

In beginning the study of lettering, one should consider first, the spacing of letters in words; second, the spacing of words; third,

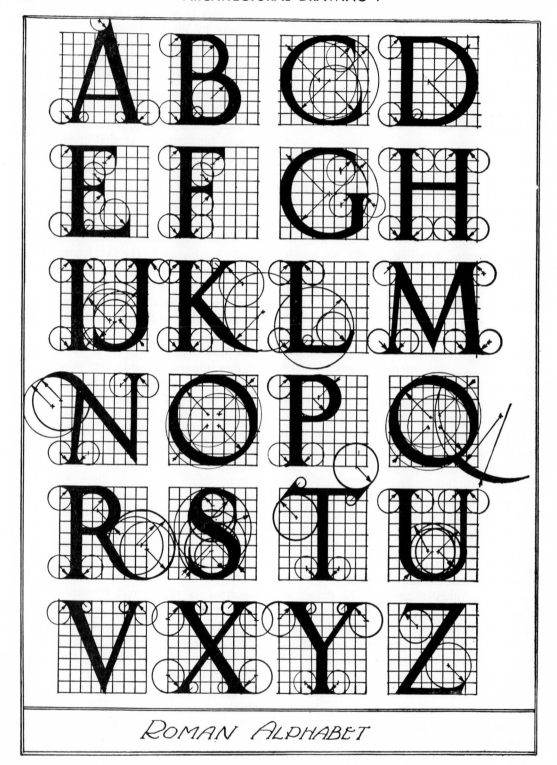

ROMAN ALPHABET

Fig. 1

the spacing of lines of lettering. All of this may be mastered only through constant practice and cannot be determined from a few rules which might be given. Success depends upon artistic judgment rather than upon rules.

Letters in words are not spaced at equal distances, but are made to appear uniform by keeping the irregularly shaped backgrounds between them to approximately equal areas. Thus, adjacent letters with straight sides are placed farther apart than those with curved sides, so that at times it is even desirable to overlap lines in such combinations as AT or LT. There is no set rule for the minimum or maximum distance between letters. One fact to be remembered is that the closer the letters are placed, the more difficult it is to adjust the inevitable irregularities.

In spacing the words in a line, the following rule should be observed: the clear distance between words should never be less than the height of the letters nor more than twice the height. No rule can be given for determining the vertical distance between lines. This height varies with every bit of lettering in order to meet the needs of the draftsman or designer.

In studying the alphabet, the letters should be considered in their family order, the rectangular letters, I, H, T, L, E, and F, taken first, then the diagonal letters, A, V, M, N, W, K, X, Y, and Z, and lastly the curved letters, O, Q, C, B, G, S, P, R, J, U, and D, which complete the alphabet. Most of the letters are made the same width, except the M and W, which are slightly wider because of their construction, and the I, which is narrower. In keeping the letters uniform, the use of a pair of dividers will prove helpful. The dividers are set to the desired width and two small marks are made to indicate how wide each letter is to be. The beginner should watch these widths very closely; as he becomes more experienced he will be able to gauge letters quite closely by eye.

The formation of the letters is very important, because it is necessary to keep all the letters in the same general style. A number of things determine the style of lettering, but only the most important points will be discussed:

Between the top and the bottom guide lines, the space is divided into three equal parts,' and two more guide lines are drawn very lightly. These spaces are used in fixing the proportion of the letters.

ARCHITECTURAL ALPHABET

A number of good alphabets are shown in Figure 2. The letter A is formed with its apex a little to the left of the center so that both sides appear to have the same inclination. The sides of the A may be made slightly circular with the crossbar on the lower third. The crossbar is made with a characteristic curve. The letter spreads out from the top toward the bottom so that the lower portion is wider. The sides curve outward to conform to the style, and to give the letter a suggestion of strength.

The bottom portion of the B is the larger. This letter has some of the characteristics of the E.

The E and F have their crossbars above center. The crossbars are given the characteristic curve, and the serifs on the lower and upper arms curve. These letters do not look well with the crossbars below center, and they would not follow the style if the crossbars were in the middle. Taste and style govern the formation of these letters.

For optical reasons, the letters O, Q, S, C, and G should be drawn so as to extend slightly beyond the upper and lower guide lines, because curved letters always look smaller than rectangular letters of the same height. The sides of these circular letters may be made slightly egg-shaped, the wider end being at the bottom. The sides of these letters are not perfect arcs, because the letters are not perfect circles; but the sides have a

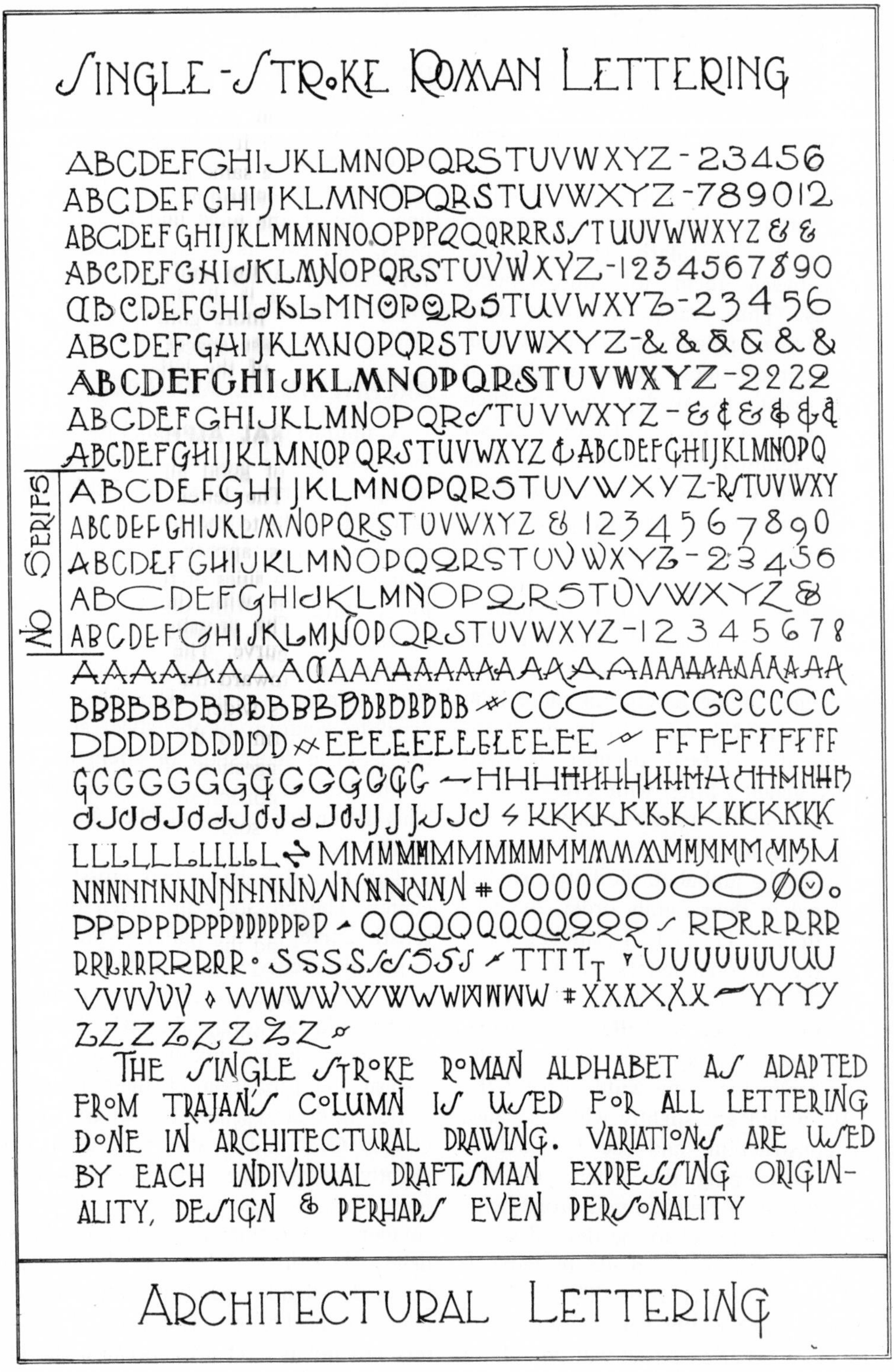

SINGLE-STROKE ROMAN LETTERING

ABCDEFGHIJKLMNOPQRSTUVWXYZ - 23456
ABCDEFGHIJKLMNOPQRSTUVWXYZ - 789012
ABCDEFGHIJKLMMNNOOPPPQQQRRRST UUVWWXYZ & &
ABCDEFGHIJKLMNOPQRSTUVWXYZ - 1234567890
ABCDEFGHIJKLMNOPQRSTUVWXYZ - 23456
ABCDEFGHIJKLMNOPQRSTUVWXYZ - & & & & & &
ABCDEFGHIJKLMNOPQRSTUVWXYZ - 2222
ABCDEFGHIJKLMNOPQRSTUVWXYZ - & ¢ & & &¢
ABCDEFGHIJKLMNOPQRSTUVWXYZ ¢ ABCDEFGHIJKLMNOPQ

ABCDEFGHIJKLMNOPQRSTUVWXYZ - RSTUVWXY
ABCDEFGHIJKLMNOPQRSTUVWXYZ & 1234567890
ABCDEFGHIJKLMNOPQRSTUVWXYZ - 23456
ABCDEFGHIJKLMNOPQRSTUVWXYZ &
ABCDEFGHIJKLMNOPQRSTUVWXYZ - 12345678

No SERIFS

AAAAAAAACAAAAAAAAAAAAAAAAAAAAAAA
BBBBBBBBBBBBBBBBBBBB CCCCCGCCCCC
DDDDDDDDDD EEEEEELELELEE FFFFFFFFFF
GGGGGGGGGGGGGGG HHHHHHHHHHHHHHHHHHHH
JJJJJJJJJJJJJJJJ KKKKKKKKKKKKKKK
LLLLLLLLLLL MMMMMMMMMMMMMMMMMMMMM
NNNNNNNNNNNNNNNNNNNN OOOOOOOOOØO.
PPPPPPPPPPPPPPP QQQQQQQQQQQ RRRRRRR
RRRRRRRRRR. SSSSSSSSS TTTT T UUUUUUUU
VVVVVV WWWWWWWWWWWWW XXXXXX YYYY
ZZZZZZZZ

THE SINGLE STROKE ROMAN ALPHABET AS ADAPTED
FROM TRAJAN'S COLUMN IS USED FOR ALL LETTERING
DONE IN ARCHITECTURAL DRAWING. VARIATIONS ARE USED
BY EACH INDIVIDUAL DRAFTSMAN EXPRESSING ORIGIN-
ALITY, DESIGN & PERHAPS EVEN PERSONALITY

ARCHITECTURAL LETTERING

Fig. 2

ARCHITECTURAL LETTERING

AS FAR AS APPEARANCE IS CONCERNED THERE IS NO PART OF DRAWING SO IMPORTANT AS THE GOOD QUALITY OF LETTERING.

ACCENT THE BEGINNING & ENDS OF ALL STROKES.

PROPORTION EACH LETTER CAREFULLY WITH EXTENDED OR CONDENSED STYLES BUT KEEP ALL LETTERS THE SAME STYLE WITHIN THE COMPOSITION.

SPACE WORDS WELL APART & LETTERS CLOSELY T o G E T H E R.

CONVEX CURVES INDICATE STRENGTH WHILE CONCAVE CURVES TEND TO SHOW WEAKNESS.

FANCY FLOURISHES ARE TO BE DISCOURAGED.

SERIFS ARE KEPT SIMPLE – NESLLLJWRR.

PLACEMENT & DESIGN OF CROSSBARS IS IMPORTANT–HHHHHH.

CURVED LETTERS ARE KEPT CLOSER TOGETHER – C O G, COG & COG – WHILE STRAIGHT LINE LETTERS ARE KEPT FARTHER APART – MINE, HIM, ILL – LA o VA o LT.

CIRCULAR LETTERS ARE EXTENDED ABOVE AND BELOW THE GUIDE LINES.

LETTERS ARE USUALLY PROPORTIONED TO APPEAR LARGER ON THE BOTTOM PORTION – BARS, RAH, KERMIT.

IN LIMITED SPACE COMPRESSED SINGLE STROKE ROMAN LETTERS ARE SOMETIMES USED WITH OVERLAPPING MONOGRAM COMBINATIONS.

THE THICKNESS OF THE STEM OR STROKE OF THE LETTER & PROPORTION OF WIDTH TO HEIGHTH MODIFIES DESIGN o   HHH HHH HHH 000 000 000 OOO 0.

ABCDEFGHIJKLMNOPQRSTUVWXYZ 234567890

ABOVE IS A GOOD ALPHABET FOR ARCHITECTURAL DRAWING.

ABCDEFGHIJKLMNOPQRSTUVWXYZ 23456789

INCLINED LETTERS ARE NOT COMMONLY USED IN ARCHITECTURAL DRAWING

TREATMENT of FORM & COMPOSITION

Fig. 3

circular tendency which is carried out in all of the letters.

The H may have slightly curved sides, a crossbar above center, and a larger bottom than top. K follows the same principle. In these letters, style determines the location of the crossbar and the intersection.

The letters M and W are made slightly wider than any of the other letters. These two letters conform to style with sloping sides and wider bottoms and tops respectively.

Five additional suggestions are necessary:

1. Those letters having distinct upper and lower parts require the upper to be a little smaller in size than the lower part. This reduction is made on the right side except in the cases of Z and M which contract toward the center line.

2. Crossbars are placed above the center except in the case of A, where it is placed below.

3. Curved letters, such as O, Q, S, should extend a little above and below the guide lines.

4. All heavy diagonal lines slope downward and toward the right except in the case of Z.

5. All light diagonal lines slope downward and toward the left.

The beginner will find lettering a real task which requires patience and determination. Skill cannot be obtained in any other way than by careful practice day after day. It is well to put a great deal of practice in lettering before attempting a drawing. At least fifteen minutes of outside time a day should be spent in lettering, for the more time spent the better the letters will be. The beginner should try to improve his lettering each day.

Use an HB pencil for lettering. Keep the pencil sharp and rounded, and do not bear down too hard on it. The lines should be

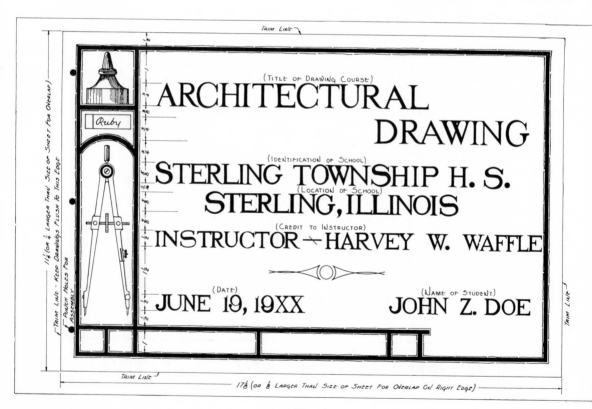

Fig. 4

made very lightly so they may be gone over until the letter has been correctly formed. Make an attempt to improve the shape of each letter when inking over lettering that has been laid out in pencil.

In cases where a tracing is to be made from a pencil drawing, be sure also to pencil in all the guide lines and lettering. Then when the tracing is inked, improvements can be made in the lettering. In order not to get too much ink on the pen, apply it to the pen with the quill from the ink bottle.

Some of the basic principles to be followed are shown in Figure 3.

ASSIGNMENT

Practice lettering daily for at least a fifteen-minute period upon either a lettering sheet or a lettering card, as assigned by the instructor. Be very careful to study the shape, order, and direction of strokes of the letters. Practice first upon the individual letters in their family order, then upon letters combined in words, and last upon sentences and paragraphs.

Sometime before you have completed the plates assigned for the semester you should design a cover using the Roman Alphabet as suggested in Figure 4.

PROBLEMS FOR CLASS DISCUSSION

1. Make up a booklet giving something of the history of the origin of the alphabet.
2. Why is the Roman alphabet used as a basis for architectural drawing?
3. Why is it necessary to analyze lettering into a study of forms, order, and direction of strokes?
4. What are the rules of spacing in lettering?
5. Why are letters proportioned so that the tops of the letters are smaller than bottoms?
6. Daily practice is necessary for proficiency in lettering. Why?
7. Lettering is taught by the family orders. Why is this so important?
8. Why are some of the circular letters made slightly higher than the rectangular letters?
9. Why is lettering in pencil taught before lettering in ink?
10. Why are guide lines used for all lettering?

U N I T

III

Architectural Technique

PAPER

White paper is generally used for architectural drawings, especially if a wash is to be applied or a drawing is to be rendered in ink. A cold-pressed paper is usually preferred. If a good grade of tracing cloth, tracing paper, or vellum is used, much of the work of laying out the floor plans and elevations is saved, because the sizes may be traced through without taking many measurements directly with the scale. On the floor plans, the outside line will be quite uniform, and changes need be made only in the partitions of the upper floors. For the elevations, the widths may be traced and measurement made only for height. A copy of the window elevation may be made on a small scrap of tracing paper which is shifted to the different locations and traced. This eliminates the drawing of so many separate window elevations, which takes time. The same time-saving copying may be done for dormer windows when several are alike.

PENCILS

The 2H and 4H pencils are generally used in schoolwork when the drawings are to be made on paper. Lettering is done with the HB pencil. When drawings are to be made on tracing paper or vellum, an H pencil is to be preferred.

CHARACTER OF LINES

More freedom of style is allowed in architectural drawing than in mechanical drawing. To a certain extent the student may develop his own style or technique. The result of this freedom, if not overdone, is that the finished drawings express more character, are more artistic and interesting than machine drawings. Lines, when meeting at right angles, or nearly so, are overlapped a short distance. This practice, if carefully done, adds to the appearance of the drawing and saves considerable time. Care must be taken that the overlap is rather uniform and not too long. Lines may be overlapped anywhere except when clearness might be sacrificed. See Figure 5.

In drawing, the thickness of a line should be uniform throughout its length. Lines may vary in different parts of the same drawing, and in different drawings, according to the amount of detail shown, but in all cases the lines must be fine, light, and clear. Sometimes in an elevation the lines representing parts of a building nearest to the spectator are drawn more heavily than those in parts which are set back farther from the observer.

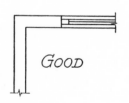 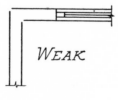 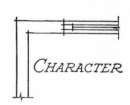

GOOD *WEAK* *CHARACTER*

Fig. 5

Thin lines in architectural drawing tend to express character and to elaborate design. The outline of curved moldings may be drawn freehand in the smaller details but should be drawn accurately in large sectional details.

Care should be exercised in the use of the compass so that holes are not pricked in the paper. The compass should be adjusted so that the needle and pencil legs are parallel and perpendicular to the paper at all times. When drawing circles, incline the compass in the direction in which the line is to be drawn. Small circles are drawn with the bow compasses.

The ruling pen should be held about an inch from the point and inclined slightly in the direction in which the line is being drawn. Light pressure should be used so that the nibs of the pen do not cut into the paper. If the pen is pressed too hard against the T square, the blades of the pen will be closed and the lines will not be of uniform thickness. The pen should be cleaned and filled frequently so that the flow of ink will be free. If the ink refuses to flow, it can be started on a moistened thumbnail, on the back of a finger, or by drawing the pen over a wiping cloth. On elevations, shadows may be indicated by drawing the lower and right-hand edges of the projecting surfaces a little darker and heavier.

Lines in different colors of inks may be used on working drawings to take the place of tinting; e.g., brown for brick, blue for stone, and orange for wood.

ACCURACY

An architectural drawing is made to help the builders visualize the building as it is to be erected and finished, and to give them all necessary information on sizes, shape, and the like, of its parts. The drawing must not only scale accurately so that missing dimensions may be found by measuring with the scale, but it must be accurate in every detail.

The dimensions should be very carefully checked to be sure that there are no errors. If the beginner can form the habit of drawing very accurately, and of checking his work very carefully, he will have learned a valuable lesson. It should be remembered that a small mistake on a drawing may cause a great waste of labor, time, and materials, and result in a heavy loss of time and money.

It is necessary that the connections between arcs and straight lines, rounded corners, and the like, be accurately drawn. Beginners are tempted to try these minor details freehand, rather than take the trouble of finding the exact centers and using a compass as should be done. The practice of being accurate in even the small details adds greatly to the beauty and finish of a drawing. The making of arrowheads requires skill which can be acquired only through continued practice. Arrowheads are a small part of the drawing, but if they are poorly made they detract greatly from the appearance of a drawing. The arrowhead is composed of two slightly curved lines which widen out just a bit more than the dimension line. The point of the arrow should not be heavier than the shaft line. Either the filled-in or the open arrowhead is accepted in architectural drawing.

TITLE BLOCKS OR STRIPS

Every sheet in a complete set of plans must bear a title block containing information used in recording and filing the drawings. The information contained should include the following:

1. Name and location of the structure.
2. Name of view; such as, basement plan, elevation, details, etc.
3. Name and address of owner of the property.
4. Date.
5. Scale.
6. Name and address of the architect.
7. Number of the sheet.

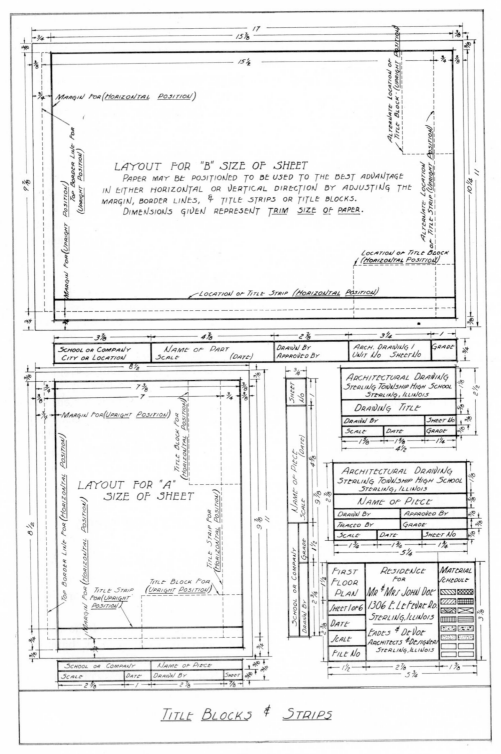

LAYOUT FOR "B" SIZE OF SHEET
PAPER MAY BE POSITIONED TO BE USED TO THE BEST ADVANTAGE IN EITHER HORIZONTAL OR VERTICAL DIRECTION BY ADJUSTING THE MARGIN, BORDER LINES, & TITLE STRIPS OR TITLE BLOCKS. DIMENSIONS GIVEN REPRESENT TRIM SIZE OF PAPER.

LAYOUT FOR "A" SIZE OF SHEET

TITLE BLOCKS & STRIPS

Fig. 6

8. Key to materials.

9. Office record.

The title block is always placed in the lower right-hand corner of the sheet. Accuracy is necessary in drawing the title block as well as in the other parts of the drawing. On the average drawing, the title block measures about 2 by 4 in. See Figure 6.

Border lines give a finished appearance to all drawings. These border lines should be the heaviest lines on the drawing, or they may be fine double lines which give the same effect.

Each plate should have a title such as "First-Floor Plan," "West Elevation," and so on. The letters for the title should be the largest on the plate, and they may be underlined if preferred. The titles for the room details should be placed where they will stand out, and they should be near enough to the details they name to prevent any possible error. Titles for rooms should not be crossed by other lines or lettering. The scale always should be given for all drawings.

SIZE OF LETTERING

The lettering on drawings should vary in size, not only to give contrast but also to show the relative importance of the various parts. The main title should contain the largest lettering. On the average drawing these letters are approximately ⅜ in. in height. The room titles are next in importance, and these letters are about ¼ in. high.

All other lettering should be about ³⁄₁₆ in. For main titles, such as "Window Schedule," the letters should be about ¼ in. The large lettering in the title block should be approximately ⁵⁄₁₆ in., and the small lettering not under ⅛ in. These lettering heights may be varied according to taste, but the beginner should follow some definite standard.

PROBLEMS FOR CLASS DISCUSSION

1. What differences exist in the techniques used by the mechanical draftsman and the architectural draftsman? Why?

2. Why is accuracy of even the small details so stressed?

3. Why are arrowheads given the importance they are in lettering practice?

4. What information should the title block contain?

5. Why is it necessary to give the scale used on all drawings?

6. Why should the lettering on a drawing plate vary in size? How is this proportioned?

7. Explain the process of adjusting the compass for use.

8. When are colored inks used in architectural drawing?

9. What is meant by the "character" of a drawing?

10. Why is it necessary in working with beginners to stress the correct order of procedure in making a drawing to the beginner?

Symbols for Materials

In learning to read blueprints, one should form a mental picture of the work to be done with respect to construction, appearance, arrangement, and similar considerations. This visualizing process requires a knowledge of the language and symbols used in the building trades. The drawings used in building construction naturally have to be made much smaller than the portions of the house they represent. The drawings, therefore, rely on symbols rather than actual measurements as to where each structural member of a house is placed. This is especially true in smaller-scale representations generally used for plans and elevations in working drawings. Although they do not represent the building accurately to scale, they contain all the necessary measurements, and thus are very useful to the building trades workman.

The draftsman or architect uses certain symbols or conventions, arrived at through common usage, which are understood by people in the building trades. These symbols are not standardized by any agency, but they are becoming generally accepted in the language of architectural drawing, and do represent the practice of the leading architects of the country (Plate 1). Each drawing office in reality adopts its own standard of symbols.

Various indications are used to represent the materials employed in the construction of a building. These conventional representations consist of lines, dots, triangles, circles, and other combinations forming a different symbol for each material. The reason for indicating the materials in this way is that these symbols may be made directly on the tracings and any number of blueprints may be duplicated from them. Colors are sometimes used to indicate the various materials, but colors cannot be printed by the blueprint process. If colors are used to emphasize the symbol or indication they should show as a light, uniform tint for any one color. Too heavy an application of crayon is not only difficult to apply uniformly, but will obliterate portions of the drawing. To overcome this tendency the crayon may be applied to the back side of the tracing which gives the effect of a tint showing through. Sometimes walls and partitions are shown in solid black when the plans are printed in magazines or newspapers; but these are designed more for display purposes than for actual use by tradesmen in construction work.

Simple pictorial symbols are used to represent the building materials on elevation views. Frame walls ordinarily have either siding or shingles on the exterior surface. The symbol shown for siding, or the one for shingles, is drawn in the proper location on the elevation drawing, either in patches or over the entire area. Artistic judgment must be exercised in indicating the symbol to give a pleasing effect on the drawing. The concrete symbol for elevations is the same as used for stucco and plaster. Consequently, when it is used this symbol should have a notation of the material lettered on it in one or more places to clarify it. Symbols for brick, concrete block, clay tile, and shingle are similar with the difference being in the size of the elements. Frequently draftsmen draw parallel lines to represent brick or shingles, since if drawn according to scale, the space between the lines is too small to indicate individual bricks or shingles. The glass symbol has very small patches in one or more panes of glass in the window or door represented; these patches are symbolic of the glare reflected by real glass.

Standard symbols for all kinds of insulation have not been conventionalized as yet because this material has been widely developed and used only in recent years. For instance, three general types of insulation have symbols which are becoming standard — loose fill, board or quilt, and aluminum insulation. The loose fill includes the various materials that can be poured, packed, or blown into place. The board or quilt type includes the various-sized rigid boards, or flexible materials quilted in several thicknesses between sheets of heavy kraft paper. The aluminum type includes all reflective insulations made of thin sheets of aluminum or other metals. In many cases it is difficult to draw these symbols in the small space available on the small-scale working drawings. Thus it is recommended that the specifications be lettered directly on the drawing, and the descriptions be written in the specifications. The exact type, thickness, and quality should be given, together with the specific areas which are to be insulated.

Walls can be divided into three main classifications — namely, foundation, exterior, and partition. The foundation forms the walls of the basement and supports the outside walls of the house. An exterior wall is the outside wall of the house as the name implies. Partitions are the interior walls which divide each floor into rooms, halls, and closets. The symbol for any type of wall is two parallel lines; the width of the space between them indicates (to scale) the thickness of the wall. If a wall is 12 in. thick, the parallel lines are drawn in with whatever scale is being used, to represent 12 in. A frame wall has two symbols: one is simply the parallel lines representing the thickness of the wall; the other has light wavy lines drawn freehand, which represent the end grain of wood. Concrete walls are used mainly for foundations, although in some modern homes the outside walls are constructed of poured concrete or of concrete blocks. Brick, brick veneer, and stucco are often used as outside walls of a house. Brick walls are of solid brick or hollow-brick construction. Brick veneer walls are half brick and half frame. Stucco walls are mostly frame. Brick and hollow tile may be combined for exterior walls, with the tile on the inside face and the brick forming the facing or veneer. Stone may be used in foundation walls or outside walls.

ASSIGNMENT

Plate 1, Symbols for Materials

Lay out the border lines of the sheet as assigned by the instructor. See Figure 6. The problems are designed for an 11 by 17-in. sheet but other border line layouts may be used to suit local requirements. Use either the title block or title strip on the following plates.

This problem is intended to acquaint the student with the material symbols used in the building trades. Representative symbols are used but no attempt has been made to make the selection complete. Several devices are used by draftsmen to give a comparison between the symbols used for the materials in plans and sections and those in elevations. Also there are many combinations of materials used in typical constructions. Many objectives may be accomplished through drawing a similar plate:

1. The student should be required to do some reference study from other source books to learn other symbols, or other symbols for the same material.

2. To learn other devices used by draftsmen to compare the same symbol as used for plan and section of a material and the symbol used in an elevation drawing.

3. To learn how to arrange or design the sheet for appearance.

4. To learn something about the lettering as used in architectural drawing.

5. To learn something about the technique and style as applied to architectural drawing.

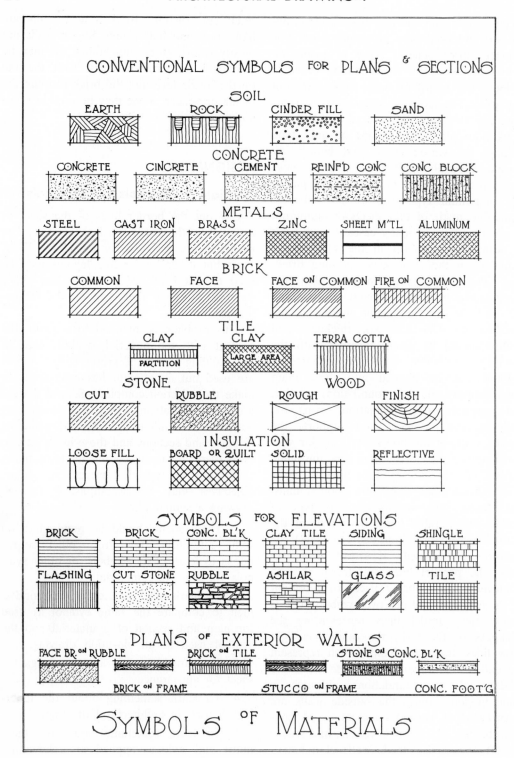

CONVENTIONAL SYMBOLS FOR PLANS & SECTIONS

SOIL

EARTH   ROCK   CINDER FILL   SAND

CONCRETE

CONCRETE   CINCRETE   CEMENT   REINF'D CONC   CONC BLOCK

METALS

STEEL   CAST IRON   BRASS   ZINC   SHEET M'TL   ALUMINUM

BRICK

COMMON   FACE   FACE ON COMMON   FIRE ON COMMON

TILE

CLAY   CLAY   TERRA COTTA
PARTITION   LARGE AREA

STONE   WOOD

CUT   RUBBLE   ROUGH   FINISH

INSULATION

LOOSE FILL   BOARD OR QUILT   SOLID   REFLECTIVE

SYMBOLS FOR ELEVATIONS

BRICK   BRICK   CONC. BL'K   CLAY TILE   SIDING   SHINGLE

FLASHING   CUT STONE   RUBBLE   ASHLAR   GLASS   TILE

PLANS OF EXTERIOR WALLS

FACE BR. ON RUBBLE   BRICK ON TILE   STONE ON CONC. BL'K

BRICK ON FRAME   STUCCO ON FRAME   CONC. FOOT'G

SYMBOLS OF MATERIALS

Plate 1

6. To gain some firsthand experience of the building trade.

7. To become more observant of the details of design, construction, and language in the building trades.

It is *not* intended that the student copy the plate as given but rather to design a drawing of his own, and in the process learn as much about architectural drawing as he individually can. Much will depend upon how much time and effort the student is willing to expend, how much originality he can show, how much firsthand experience he can gain from the building trade, and how observing he is about small details. The grade given to the student should be based upon these considerations. Neatness is a very desirable quality at all times but never more so than when making a drawing. Use the systems or procedures of laying out, checking, and completing drawings as taught in mechanical drawing.

PROBLEMS FOR CLASS DISCUSSION

1. How did the invention of the blueprint process change the conventional representation of material symbols?
2. Why are the symbols different for use on plans and elevations?
3. What procedures would you use in drawing this plate? Why?
4. Why are the border lines of a drawing drawn first? Why are they the darkest lines on the drawing?
5. Why should you plan the arrangement and spacing of your sheet before you begin your drawing?
6. Many students complete their drawing, later to find they could have used a larger or smaller scale. How do you find the correct scale to use on a sheet?
7. What is the relationship between the drawing and the lettering on this sheet?
8. Why are most of these symbols made freehand and by appearance rather than accurately to scale?

Standard Moldings

"Trim" is the name the builder gives to the elements of decorative woodwork. Door and window casings are known in architecture as "architraves." Exterior moldings are found in the cornices, molded casings around doors and windows, water table, belt courses, porch column caps and bases, and other ornamental details. Such trim has a utilitarian purpose, but through long use certain architectural styles have been developed in obtaining a decorative effect on otherwise bare wall surfaces. The projecting and receding planes create a play of light and shadow on the surfaces, softening the harsh construction lines.

Take for example the typical cornice: it serves as (1) a support for the gutter or eavespout which drains the rain water from the roof, (2) a protection from wind and weather under the eaves where the roof and walls join, and, (3) a partial shelter from the rain at the top of the walls. Such functions must be kept in mind when designing the cornices, but it is appearance which will finally determine its size, shape, and position. The chief precautions of proper flashing, thorough painting, and careful assembling must be taken to insure the preservation of the wood against the deterioration by weather, and the resultant expansion and contraction of the lumber.

Interior finish usually includes doors, windows, built-in cabinets, stairways, and baseboards and is known in the trade as "standing finish." Baseboards are used at the junction of the wall and floor, and are from 3 to 8 in. high, either with plain top or

with a strip of simple molding for a finish. These details are determined by the molding designs offered by the supply sources, the current trends in design influenced by professional designers, and the acceptance by the building public. "The simpler the better," is a safe rule from the point of view of both appearance and cost. Often all that is needed for the door and window trim is a plain board casing ¾ in. thick and 3 in. wide, slightly tapered on its face side and slightly rounded on the corners, applied to the wall surface with mitered joints.

Most moldings are based on the classic forms of curves used by the Greeks and Romans in the design of their buildings. These curves are mathematical formulae expressed graphically. Stock, or universal moldings are not always manufactured in the most pleasing shapes but instead depend upon how they can be run through the molding machine in production quantities.

Moldings are available in many different shapes. Each shape is designated by a number. But since the numbering system is not completely consistent, it is suggested that millwork catalogs be obtained from several sources, placed in the classroom library, and used for reference in the study of this and subsequent units of work.

The molding size is determined by the size of stock from which it is cut, as indicated in Plate 2. Some catalogs will give in addition the measurement of the projection of the molding and the drop. These facts will assist the student in his drawing. The curves of the molding may be obtained by the geometric constructions involving arcs of circles such as are used for an ogee curve but generally it is more practical to use a suitable French or irregular curve in the drawing of the detail. In practical application these details of moldings are drawn to an enlarged scale and used as removed sections on such detailed drawings as for the exact specification of members on doorways, windows, stairways, baseboards, and built-in cabinets. On small-scale drawings an indication is used and accompanied by a note specifying

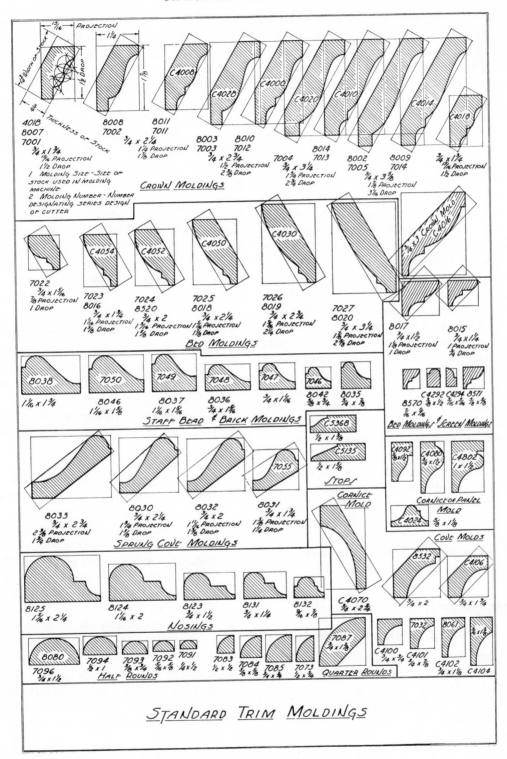

STANDARD TRIM MOLDINGS

Plate 2

the kind of molding determined by its purpose, its series number, and its dimensioned size. Since these moldings are standardized complete dimensioning is not required. The types of moldings in Plate 2 are commonly used in the construction of small houses:

Crown molds are used for the finish and decoration of cornices and the junction of vertical and horizontal surfaces.

Bed molds are used to cover the joints of surfaces joined at angles.

Quarter rounds are used in angles, usually where woodwork joins brick, stone, or plaster. A common use is at the junction of the baseboard and floor. It is mainly used to cover up irregularities, but it is also used where wall-to-wall carpeting is laid.

Casings are used for the trimming of window and door openings. The simpler forms are desirable, but these moldings may be had in an endless variety of shapes and sizes.

Stops are used on door and window frames. In doors they are placed on the jambs against which the door stops. In some constructions the jamb is rabbeted to serve the same purpose. They hold the sash in place on windows. In cabinetwork they are used in the place of putty, to hold the glass or panel in place. Screen molds cover the fastening of the wire to the frame.

Drip caps are used over the head of window and door casings to prevent water from running behind the frames. A form of drip cap is used in the construction of the water table in most houses.

ASSIGNMENT

Plate 2, Standard Moldings

Draw large-sized details of molding shapes. Represent the several kinds of moldings in use by drawing the various sizes and the variations of design for the same kind of molding. Carefully plan the sheet to give a representation of the different moldings in common use and to give a pleasing appearance to the sheet. The irregular curve may be used for careful representation of the curves, and the compasses for the drawing of the arcs.

Notice the method of cutting the moldings from the wood stock. Moldings are designed so that the maximum bearing surface may be had in the molding machine to eliminate vibration and chatter marks on the wood. These molding shapes are standardized and all companies carry the same shapes in stock. Some companies identify these moldings by the 8000 series of numbers, some by the 7000 series, and others by a 4000 series. Check this carefully in several millwork catalogs.

Draw the plate full size.

PROBLEMS FOR CLASS DISCUSSION

1. Why are interior and exterior moldings used?
2. Why are the moldings made to standard shapes and sizes?
3. Where are the drip-cap moldings used?
4. How are the moldings specified on a drawing?
5. Compare the uses of moldings as illustrated in catalogs, magazines, and books. How many different uses of moldings can you illustrate?
6. Where are crown molds used? Bed molds? Quarter rounds?
7. Sometimes these moldings go by different names in the different catalogs. Can you identify frieze moldings by another name?
8. Why are the simpler shapes of moldings more desirable for trim than the fancy shapes?
9. Why are quarter rounds used in preference to a cove type of molding on a baseboard?
10. What woods are used in making up moldings?
11. By what unit are moldings sold?

Symbols Used in Plans

Exterior frame walls are built with either 2 by 4-in. or 2 by 6-in. studs. On the outside of these studs, when siding is used, a surface of sheathing boards or composition sheathing panels about 1 in. thick is placed, over which finished siding is laid. On the inside of the building, the thickness of the plaster, including the lath, is a little less than 1 in. The thickness of the walls, when 2 by 4-in. studs are used, will thus be between 6 and 7 in., and between 8 and 9 in. when 2 by 6-in. studs are used. The thickness of frame walls is seldom given on the drawings since the measurement may vary according to the variation in the thickness of the materials. The dimensions are taken from some fixed point, such as the outside of the studs or outside of the sheathing. Actual thicknesses may be used but most architects use nominal sizes in their representation.

Frame partitions are built up usually of 2 by 4-in. studs with lath and plaster (or plaster board) on both sides, which actually figures up less but is taken as a nominal 6 in. The dimensions which locate the partitions are usually given to the centers of the partitions, which will be to the center of the studs, and any difference in thickness is divided between the rooms on both sides of the partitions. Closet partitions are often taken as 4 in., the studs being placed the narrow way.

Walls and partitions of wood-frame construction are indicated with freehand wavy lines to represent the grain of the wood. Some architects shade or darken the walls so they will appear a light blue or entirely white on the blueprints.

Stone walls are shown in the plan by bounding the masonry with parallel lines indicating the thickness and filling the space between with the symbol indication of stone. Dimensions are given for the nominal thickness of the walls. In masonry seen in plan or section no attempt is made to represent the individual stones, bricks, or pieces of material, it being understood that the work will be done according to the specifications or the indications on the elevations. Stone walls are usually laid 18, 20, 24 in., and so on, in thickness.

Brick walls are 9, 13, or 17 in. with 1-in. furring space and ¾-in. lath and plaster or plaster board on the inside. The thickness of a brick wall is determined by the number of rows of bricks in the wall, each row being 4 in. thick. A wall of two rows is between 8 and 9 in. thick; one of three rows is between 12 and 13 in., and one of four rows is between 16 and 18 in. thick. Bricks vary somewhat in size and therefore cause a variation in the thickness of the wall. In localities where the larger size of brick is used the thickness of the wall will be determined by the size of the brick. The wall is laid to the outside lines of the building so that any variation due to the size of the bricks or to the application of furring and plastering comes to the inside of the wall.

Hollow tile is used for walls and partitions in practically the same manner as brick. The walls may be from 6 to 16 in. or more in thickness depending upon the multiples used in the sizes of the tile.

WINDOWS

The windows in most common use today are the double-hung, casement, and variations of the single-sash using the pivot principle of hanging or a form of sliding sash. Different symbols are used for each type of window with the sash opening used as the width opening in the plan. This is 4 in. less than the width of the window installation in a frame wall. Window glass is cut in standard sizes, and to save money it is well to keep this in mind in determining the size of the openings. For example, a double-hung sash where the panes are 8 by 10 in., with three lights wide and four lights high, would have a sash opening 2 ft. 4 in. wide and 3 ft. 10 in. high. This allows for a sides-and-top rail 2 in. wide, bottom rail 3 in., and meeting rail 1⅝ in. wide. Most millwork catalogs give the necessary opening sizes so that it is usual to refer to them for the information.

When the sash is hinged at the sides to open either in or out, it is known as a casement window. A single sash may be hinged at the top or bottom as is often used in basement windows or over a door or window in the form of a transom. Sometimes this single sash is hinged at the top and used under a window in the form of an awning window, or these hinged sashes may be used in combinations to form the complete window. Sometimes they are arranged to slide horizontally in the wall opening instead. Multiple casement windows can be built on the principle of a folding screen, and very satisfactory hardware is placed on the market for just this use. The sashes run on light tracks or grooves, and can be folded back against the ends of the window frame. This arrangement gives a wide opening, well adapted for porches or where an unobstructed area or view is desired without the vertical mullions which would be required to form separate individual units. Practically no additional expense is involved for this kind of window, but care must be taken that the framing above the window is amply strong to prevent sagging of the framing around the window. Several forms of double glazed fixed sash are used in different combinations and are referred to as "picture windows." One ingenious form of casement-hinge pivots the sash near one end, so that when it swings open both sides can be easily reached for cleaning. Some double-hung windows are designed so that the sashes

may be easily removed for cleaning. Reference should be made to the millwork catalogs for all the symbols to be used as well as for the sizes in common use.

The sizes of windows are indicated on the symbols in plan by several systems as indicated in Figure 167. A center line should always be given since any change in the size of the window will not disturb its location. The size of the window is always indicated about its center location. When a schedule is used, numbers within circles are placed near each window, and corresponding numbers together with sizes appear in the schedule. For example, the windows numbered ① might be shown as 2 ft. 8 in. by 4 ft. 10 in. in the schedule with an indication of how many windows are needed. The sizes given are the over-all sash sizes in all cases.

The sizes of door and window frames are standard, for all mills make stock sizes which are the same in all parts of the country. This is done to lower the cost of the frames and allow the commonly used sizes to be carried in stock. Architects usually try to keep within these standard sizes because other sizes require special drawings and cost much more.

DOORS

Doors, like windows, are indicated by symbols on the plan. An arc and a line at an angle (usually 30 deg.) represent the swing of the door. Sometimes the line is represented perpendicular to the wall and an arc representing a quarter circle is used to represent a door at its full opening size. The dimension is given to the center of the opening and the door size given about this center. When the door is of the double-swing type then the swing in one direction is indicated by dotted lines. The dimensions are placed on the line representing the door with the first dimension given being the width, the second the height. Doors are usually purchased in stock sizes so that reference to a millwork catalog will give the needed information. Light wood doors are made up in stock designs for the conventional heights and widths of openings, at a saving over those made to order, and are recommended for the small house. The specification of the door itself should include the material, the number of panels, the type of moldings, and the direction in which it swings, that is, whether right- or left-handed. Notice that the sill is represented on the outside doors only.

FIREPLACES AND CHIMNEYS

It is imagined that the fireplace or chimney is cut through along a horizontal line which would cut through the vertical openings, and the top part removed so that the cut surface of the bottom part is represented. Fireplace drawings on the floor plan do not show the flue for the fireplace but may show the flue of the furnace continued from the basement level. The flue to the fireplace will show only on the floor above. Often the ash dump is shown on the first floor plan. Some architects state the size of the flue opening by figures inside the opening. The hearth is shown with the brick or tile pattern suggested either in patches or on a half of the symbol. The flue lining is represented by double lines which may be blackened in by some draftsmen. This tile flue lining comes in standard sizes and will be an indication of the inside sizes of the chimney. Chimney openings are designed to encourage the air currents called "draft" and require different sizes and shapes according to the flue used and other factors. Common sizes for wood or coal are 8 by 12 in. or 12 by 12 in., while gas furnaces usually use a circular shape of 6-in. diameter. Where building codes require chimneys to be lined, or where the lining is specified, it is not always indicated on the plan. Study of pages 184–189, Unit XI, will help the student in his understanding of the symbols used in representation of fireplaces.

In indicating the symbol for a fireplace, the first consideration is that the width of the opening must be in proportion to the size of the room. The widths range from 24 to 48 in., with the 36- and 42-in. widths being average for residences. The depth is usually 16- or 18-in. The depth runs straight back for 4 in. and is then angled or splayed until the width at the back will be ⅔ that of the opening width. The height at the front of the opening averages 30 in. If a mantel is used it is kept in proportional design.

See the table of fireplace openings, p. 184.

STORAGE CABINETS

Cabinets known as base units are those that rest on the floor, and whose tops form work counters. They may be purchased in pan units, tray units, drawer units, and for storage of utensils, electrical appliances, or food. Pan units usually have one or more drawers, with a larger space divided by one or more wire shelves. Drawer units ordinarily have three to six drawers of varying widths and depths. Wall units are placed above the work counters and usually contain two or three shelves. Small cabinets over refrigerators are often desirable. Sinks which leave areas for installation of sink and drainboards may contain shelves, drawers, and garbage receptacles, and may come in many sizes and qualities. Study these pieces of equipment in manufacturers' catalogs and literature, or by visits to dealers' display rooms and exhibits of model homes. The sinks may be purchased in a complete cabinet unit, or they may be purchased separately and installed in stock cabinets. Most cabinets are available in both metal and wood construction. Other cabinets designed for kitchens include broom cabinets, corner cabinet units, linen-storage units, bins, trays, ironing board units, and spice units. Cabinets are usually ordered by catalog number, and are delivered complete and ready to install. The symbols shown in plan should be to scale and represent a simple picture looking down from above. One should study carefully the proper swing of doors in their symbolic representation to eliminate any clumsy interference.

Kitchen ranges have been improved so radically that new ideas are constantly being presented. The range should have all the automatic features, as well as good insulation and some method of exhausting smoke and strong odors. Both electric and gas models are popular, and in localities where neither service is available the bottled gas and oil stoves give excellent performance. Most manufacturers' literature will give the student the necessary information and a suggestion for the symbol to be drawn.

Refrigerators are obtainable for operation with electricity, gas, or oil.

Base units, wall units, and over-units measure from 12 to 44 in. wide. Broom closets may vary from 18 to 24 in. in width. The depth of cabinets is generally about 24 in. for base units and broom closets, and 14 in. for wall and over-units. The height of base units is generally 32 in., while wall units are about 36 in. Over-units are about 16 in. for the most-used size. The average height for a broom closet is 64 in. Sizes vary slightly in the different makes of manufacturers so it is recommended that full information be obtained from manufacturers' catalogs.

ELECTRICAL SYMBOLS

All electrical symbols are standardized and may be obtained from any good reference book. Some of the more frequently used symbols are shown in Figure 9. The number found in the circle indicates the wattage of the bulbs used. Some knowledge of electrical wiring is necessary to plan the circuits and placement of the outlets and the switches. In small residences this may be planned with

the co-operation of the electrician. Usually this wiring is done by the electrician during the process of construction and much of it is planned during the time of installation. The planner can better control the locations of the electrical items by placing the symbol in the desired location.

HEATING, COOLING, AND VENTILATION SYMBOLS

Radiators for steam and hot water are usually placed under windows, the size varying according to the type, number of columns, and square feet of radiation required. Hot and cold air registers vary in size depending upon the heating system, the forced air systems requiring smaller registers than those used for gravity systems. It is advisable that consultation of a heating engineer be utilized in planning the heating, cooling, and ventilation systems. Usually the heating contractor will draw up the heating plans he needs from the working drawings. Since this planning is too technical for the average installation it is accomplished by trained engineers or contractors. It is desirable that the student become familiar with the symbols used and the considerations required in the planning.

Symbols used to represent heating, cooling, and ventilation units may be found in good reference books on drawing, or in the technical subject. Pipe symbols may be composed of symbolic lines or with a double-line representation. See Figure 8. The rectangular symbols drawn in the walls or partitions are drawn narrower so they can be more readily seen. Sometimes arrows are used with the symbols to indicate the direction of the air, steam, or water. Usually a separate plan is used for these features in the house but where the drawings are simple they may be placed in the plan representations. For hot-air heating the horizontal ducts and registers are indicated on the basement plan (Fig. 8). The dimensions specify the size of the ducts

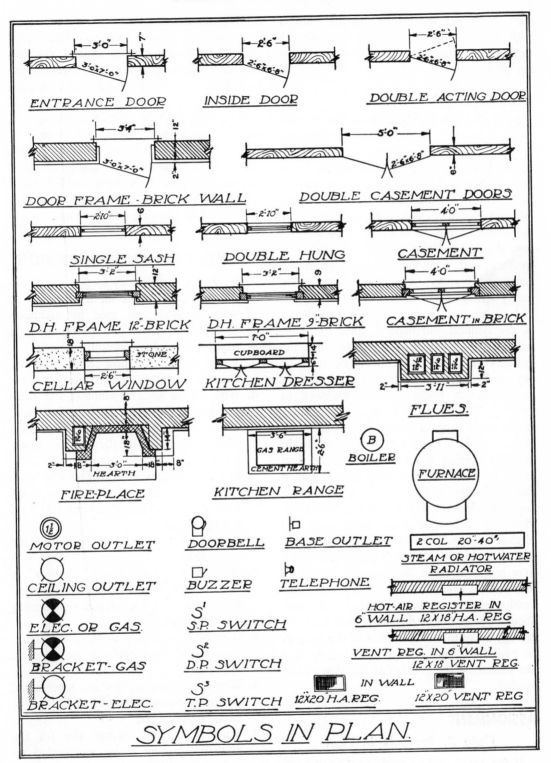

ENTRANCE DOOR INSIDE DOOR DOUBLE ACTING DOOR

DOOR FRAME - BRICK WALL DOUBLE CASEMENT DOORS

SINGLE SASH DOUBLE HUNG CASEMENT

D.H. FRAME 12"-BRICK D.H. FRAME 9"-BRICK CASEMENT IN BRICK

CELLAR WINDOW KITCHEN DRESSER FLUES.

FIRE-PLACE KITCHEN RANGE BOILER FURNACE

MOTOR OUTLET DOORBELL BASE OUTLET STEAM OR HOTWATER RADIATOR

CEILING OUTLET BUZZER TELEPHONE HOT-AIR REGISTER IN 6"WALL 12X18"H.A. REG

ELEC. OR GAS. S.P. SWITCH VENT REG. IN 6"WALL 12 X 18 VENT REG.

BRACKET- GAS D.P. SWITCH IN WALL 12"X20 H.A.REG. 12"X20 VENT REG

BRACKET- ELEC. T.P. SWITCH

SYMBOLS IN PLAN.

Plate 3

with the larger dimension running parallel with the ceiling. See Figures 82 and 83 for type drawings used in hot water heating plans.

CONVENTIONS

Symbols such as those used for electric fixtures, switches, windows, doors, cabinets, fireplaces, radiators, registers, furnaces, and so on have accepted representations based upon a simplified line symbol. These symbols evolve from common usage and are probably initiated through catalog representation by the manufacturer. In most cases these symbols should be drawn carefully to scale size so that wall accommodation, interference, economy of space, good traffic circulation, handy arrangement, visualization of the plan, and so on, can be carefully checked. Some of the symbols will depend upon the judgment of the draftsman, meaning that the symbols are easily understood or read by anyone in the building trades. A drop light fixture, which might actually measure as much as 24 in. will be represented to scale. If the scale used in drawing the plan were ¼ in. equals a foot, the symbol to be in good proportion should be no larger than ½ in. in diameter. Generally speaking then the circles used for the electrical fixture representation should be about ¼ in. in diameter. The four lines intersecting the circles are usually at 45 deg. and are all of the same length, although some draftsmen may represent these lines on the horizontal and vertical axes. The circles used for specification identification of windows and doors should be ⁵⁄₁₆ in. in diameter, and kept far enough away from the outline of the plan to be easily read and understood. Usually they are placed on the center-line location of the symbol.

ASSIGNMENT

Plate 3, Symbols in Plan

Reference should be made to the millwork catalogs for the standard sizes of doors, windows, and so on, and to the manufacturers' catalogs for information as to sizes, symbols, and other information regarding electrical installations, plumbing installations, heating systems and their installations, ventilation systems and their installations, cooling systems and their installations, and so on.

Draw these symbols to accurate catalog size using a scale which is commonly used on plan drawings. It is recommended that a scale of ¼ in. equals 1 ft. or ⅜ in. equals 1 ft. be used in drawing the symbols.

PROBLEMS FOR CLASS DISCUSSION

1. Why is it unnecessary to give the thickness of frame walls on a drawing?
2. What methods are used by architects to represent walls and partitions in a frame house? In a masonry house?
3. What determines how thick masonry must be in house construction?
4. Why are the sizes of windows and doors standardized? Where can you find these standardized sizes? What dimension of a window is used in the symbol representation?
5. In window representation, what size opening is represented on the plans of a frame house? What limit of accuracy is held for openings?
6. How are the sizes of wall openings given on a drawing?
7. What is meant by "good judgment" in the representation of symbols on a plan? How large are the circles representing the light fixtures?
8. Why is it necessary to have the representation of sinks, cabinets, etc., to exact scale?
9. Why is the fireplace flue not represented on the first-floor plan? How is the flue lining represented?
10. What is a good average size for the fireplace opening to be represented on a floor plan? What determines this size?

Elevation Drawings and Symbols

A person with very little technical knowledge of drawing can look at the symbols in the elevation drawing of most details used in houses and have a fairly accurate idea of what is represented. After the floor plans have been lightly drawn in the layout stage of the drawing and the conventional symbols for the doors and windows have been tentatively shown in their probable locations, the draftsman has something on which to start the drawing of the elevation. The development of the elevation drawings is carried on slowly, by trying out several design effects, until the appearance of the whole wall or side is satisfactorily represented. An elevation is a representation of a detail as it would be normally seen by the viewer (orthographically) when looking at one side of the house. It is necessary to keep all drawings lightly drawn in the planning or layout stage so that if the detail does not appear in good design, because of its location, changes can easily be made. Consideration must be given to the location of the symbol for convenience when drawing it in the plan, and from the consideration of good design and appearance when locating the symbol in the elevation.

A few typical considerations which should guide the preliminary thinking in the matter of designing a house are:

1. A square house is the most economical shape but the least attractive.

2. A low pitched roof costs less than a steep pitched one and makes the house appear to hug the ground better. The elevation representation of materials such as the shingles casts a more softening shadow for appearance. A dormer window serves a useful purpose in planning, gives a more interesting appearance if well designed, but increases the cost.

3. An inside chimney costs less to build than a decoratively designed one on the exterior wall.

4. Bay windows are beautiful and useful but the cost of construction is increased.

5. Elaborate cornice designs require more expensive materials and increase labor costs.

6. Architectural designing which uses standard millwork is less expensive; special millwork greatly increases the cost.

7. A rectangular shape is less expensive than a plan with wings or ells, and fewer outside corners economize on costs.

8. A two-story house requires less foundation, less roof, less cost than a one-story house with the same amount of living space.

9. Second story windows should be placed directly over those of the first floor for economy in framing construction. The windows on the second floor are proportionally smaller than those on the first floor. The size of the sash may be reduced in two ways — (1) by using smaller panes of glass or (2) by reducing the number of panes.

10. Openings in the wall must be designed for appearance from the outside without disturbing the amount of wall space needed on the inside for furniture and equipment.

DOOR AND WINDOW HEIGHTS

The average height from the floor level of the first floor double-hung window is 2 ft. 0 in., measured to the bottom of the sash. Kitchen windows should be at least 40 in. from the floor to allow for a cabinet or work table under them. Small windows over bookcases or buffets are approximately 5 ft. 0 in. from the floor depending upon the furniture and equipment heights. The height of the glass for the first floor windows average 28, 30, or 32 in. for each sash, making the total sash height 5 ft. 2 in., 5 ft. 6 in., or 5 ft. 10 in. This figure is found by adding 6 in. to the sum of the glass heights in the two sashes; the additional 6 in. is made up of 3 in. for the bottom rail, 1 in. for the meeting rail and 2 in. for the top rail. The second floor windows will average about the same heights, possibly a little less with 24-, 26-, and 28-in. glass being used, and a height from the floor given as 20 to 24 in. minimum. Check manufacturers' catalogs for the stock sizes of glass used. The glass size is usually indicated on the elevation symbol either by the individual pane size or by the overall glass size of the sash. Thus in a six-light sash the individual pane size might be 6⅝ by 8 in., the over-all glass size 20½ by 16¼ in., and a sash opening size of 2 ft. 0 in. by 3 ft. 2 in. The rough stud opening for this size would be 2 ft. 3½ in. by 3 ft. 5½ in., and a masonry opening of 2 ft. 4 in. by 3 ft. 6¾ in. The height of interior doors is usually given as 6 ft. 8 in. The height of exterior doors averages 7 ft. 0 in., although they may vary from 6 ft. 10 in. to 7 ft. 6 in. Usually the heights of doors and windows are lined up on the elevations which govern the height of the windows from the floor. Dimensions for the vertical heights of the windows and doors are indicated on the elevations.

SYMBOLS USED ON ELEVATIONS

The simple representation used for the elevation of a window is theoretically a vertical projection of the plan symbol for width, and a horizontal projection of a section of the window for the height. This is simplified to a single line representation of such details of the window as the muntins, rails, stiles, and so on. Actually the symbol is a simple orthographic representation of the appearance of the window in horizontal section. Sometimes a symmetrical center line is used and a half of the symbol is of the interior of the window, and a half is a view of the exterior of the window. Notice par-

ticularly the representation of the meeting rail crossing the symbol, for it extends across the bottom of the meeting rail in the top sash in an exterior elevation and across the top of the meeting rail in the bottom sash in an interior elevation. It is this close attention to detail which determines the quality of drawing in the representation of these symbols. Windows vary greatly in their general design. Notice that the symbol for wall material is indicated around the elevation symbol of windows. A center line should always be indicated in the symbol.

Where several representations must be drawn of the same size and design of window much time can be saved by drawing the symbol on a scrap of paper and sliding this paper under the tracing paper drawing of the house elevation. Then it may be traced through rather than drawn each time. Some draftsmen "tick" the horizontal measurements on a strip of paper so they may be transferred to the elevation drawing without individually scaling each symbol, and then repeating the process for the vertical measurements. Much can be learned by watching experienced draftsmen develop an elevation drawing, and the student can also think out ways of saving time and effort originally.

Doors vary greatly in their general design. A door symbol is drawn to illustrate the design of the particular door it represents, and hardware such as handles, knobs, and butt hinges may be shown if desired. The material symbol is represented around the door and window symbol.

On elevation drawings, areaways are represented showing the wall thickness, and the width and depth of the areaway. Dotted lines are used because the walls are below ground level and are thus invisible. Dotted lines are used to indicate the foundation walls, footings, and basement floors.

Sometimes elevation views of interior walls are drawn for one or more rooms to show the exact appearance of the wall. A device

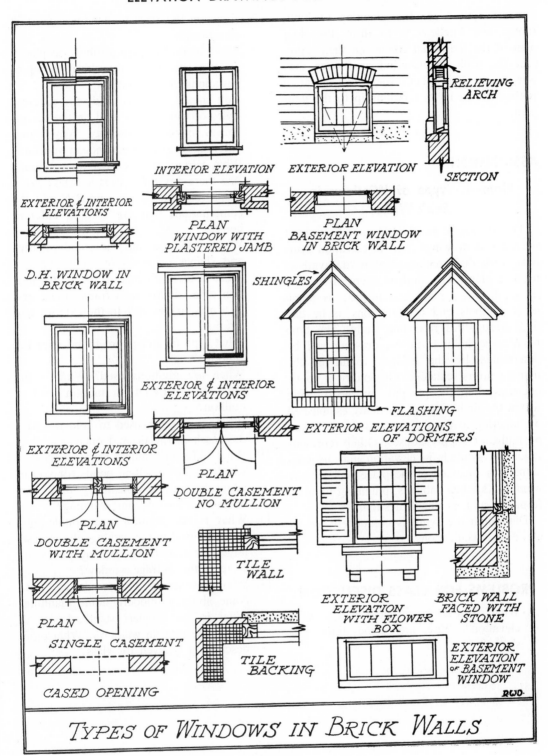

RELIEVING ARCH

SECTION

INTERIOR ELEVATION

EXTERIOR ELEVATION

EXTERIOR & INTERIOR ELEVATIONS

PLAN
WINDOW WITH
PLASTERED JAMB

PLAN
BASEMENT WINDOW
IN BRICK WALL

D.H. WINDOW IN
BRICK WALL

SHINGLES

EXTERIOR & INTERIOR
ELEVATIONS

FLASHING

EXTERIOR ELEVATIONS
OF DORMERS

EXTERIOR & INTERIOR
ELEVATIONS

PLAN
DOUBLE CASEMENT
NO MULLION

PLAN
DOUBLE CASEMENT
WITH MULLION

TILE
WALL

EXTERIOR
ELEVATION
WITH FLOWER
BOX

BRICK WALL
FACED WITH
STONE

PLAN
SINGLE CASEMENT

TILE
BACKING

CASED OPENING

EXTERIOR
ELEVATION
OF BASEMENT
WINDOW

RWO.

TYPES OF WINDOWS IN BRICK WALLS

Plate 4

sometimes used for the planning of bathrooms and kitchens is to draw the floor plan of the individual room and then represent the walls in elevation as though they were in the same plane. Each wall elevation is thus shown in its relationship to the floor plan.

ASSIGNMENT

Plate 4, Types of Windows in Brick Walls

The drawings in Plate 4 merely suggest the type of drawings used in elevation symbols, with their relationship to the symbols used in plans. The student is encouraged to design his own plate and include as many other symbols and combinations as he can find through his reference study. The type of window he uses in his drawing will be determined by the designs found in the manufacturers' catalogs. Originality is to be encouraged in the planning of the drawing within the limitations of economy established by adhering to the designs and sizes stocked by millwork supply houses. Other representations of symbols in elevation may be substituted or included in the place such as bay windows, kitchen cabinets, plumbing fixtures, furnaces, and so on, if desired.

Dimension the symbols completely for all elevation specifications.

PROBLEMS FOR CLASS DISCUSSION

1. What parts are represented in a window elevation? Why are some lines not shown?

2. How are the sizes of windows given in elevations?

3. Why should the plan symbols be placed directly underneath the elevation representations in this plate?

4. You should carefully study the different styles of windows as used on the several houses in your community. Why? What different types of windows can you find? What variations in design do you find? Are there any differences in sizes? What shapes of panes do you find? Notice the combinations that are used in different houses.

5. Where can you find the standard sizes and shapes or styles of windows?

6. What is the difference in the representation of a window in a frame house and in a masonry house? In the exterior and interior?

7. What type of arches are found over the windows?

8. When are mullions used? What is the difference between a muntin and a mullion?

9. What devices are used to hold the window sash at the desired open height?

10. What different features can you identify which might be selling points for you to adopt in your specifications for a particular window in your planning?

11. What is the smallest size double-hung window listed in the catalog? the largest? largest casement? How many panes are there in the average window?

12. What changes in window designs have come about in modern home planning?

13. What is the smallest standard size of glass pane used in windows? What other description is given for glass?

UNIT

VIII

Plumbing and Electrical Symbols

As a general practice, plumbing systems are not shown on the drawings for an average small house and are left to the judgment of the plumber. However in designing a house, provision should be made that the pipes may be run without weakening the framing structure. The thickness allowed in partitions where large plumbing pipes are run through them should be enough to allow the hubs (joints) of the commonly used 4-in. C.I. (cast iron) pipes to be covered smoothly without protruding through the plaster. The various line symbols show the location of pipes in horizontal position (horizontal runs), while a circular symbol should be used to indicate the diameters of the pipes in a vertical position in the partitions or on the floor plan. See Figure 7. Although the ordinary working drawings do not show all these symbols it is advisable for the student to be familiar with them.

Plate 5 shows the symbols for some of the common plumbing fixtures. These include bathtubs, shower stalls, lavatories, vanitories, water closets, kitchen sinks, laundry tubs, and so on. All such symbols are drawn accurately to scale, so that the space they require, and the space around them, may be judged accurately. A bathtub is installed to the inside of the studs so that this inside measurement must be sufficient to accommodate a standard size fixture. The sizes of these fixtures and their several designs are found in the manufacturer's catalogs. To identify the symbols further they are usually labeled for name, type, size, and other information. The student should carefully study good examples of architect's drawings to see the techniques generally used. Center lines are often located on these symbols.

The architectural draftsman should refer to the plumbing fixture catalog for sizes of the various fixtures when indicating plumbing symbols in the plan to insure that the fixtures will be drawn in true proportion, and that undesirable planning factors will be avoided when the actual construction work is done. (See "Considerations in Planning a House" and "Planning the Individual Room.")

HEATING AND AIR-CONDITIONING SYMBOLS AND PLANS

In small houses heating and air-conditioning symbols (Fig. 8) are seldom shown on the drawings, since the design of these systems is left to the heating engineer and contractor. Heating layouts resemble in form the drawings made for plumbing installations. The locations of the registers as well as the heating plant itself are indicated on the architectural plans. From these indications the heating contractor makes a diagram of the entire heating system for the workmen making the installation. This procedure is followed because the architect writes a clause into the heating specifications which states that the contractor must guarantee to heat the building to 70 deg. Fahrenheit at —10 deg. F. outside temperature. Doing this puts the responsibility for successful operation of the heating system squarely on the contractor. Therefore, it is proper that he should compute the size of radiators, boiler, pipes, and so on. If the sizes were specified, the contractor would not be able to assume full responsibility for efficient operation of the heating installation.

For the architectural draftsman, the work to be done in planning the heating system consists of showing the chimney and drawing the symbols which will show radiator and boiler locations and sizes. Sometimes detail drawings for radiator recesses may be necessary. There must also be pipe and duct spaces

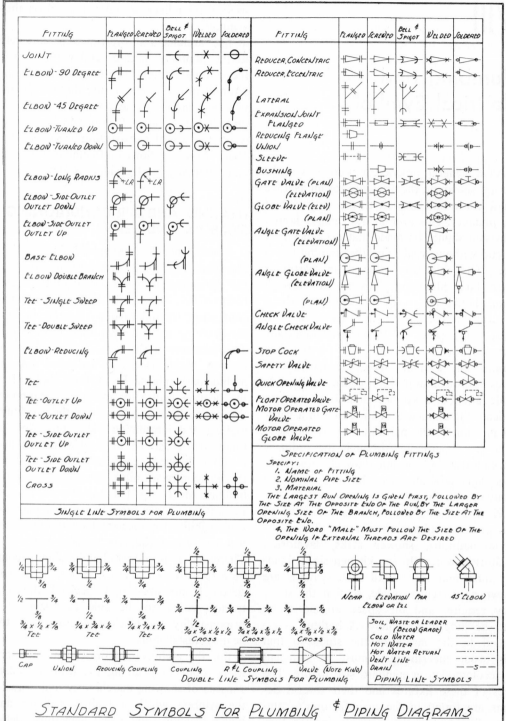

STANDARD SYMBOLS FOR PLUMBING & PIPING DIAGRAMS

Fig. 7

allowed for on the plans to accommodate circulation for the heating system to be used. The types of insulation to be used for walls, windows, doors, ceilings and roofs should be shown in the details and sections by means of symbols and notes. For small buildings, a 12 by 12-in. flue lining is almost universally used. None smaller is considered satisfactory except that a round 6-in. flue lining is used for gas-fired systems. This is done to stop the condensation which forms when gas burns, from soaking through the masonry of the chimney. For large sized flues, consult the heating unit manufacturers' catalogs since these give not only the proper size of flue lining to use for the boiler size indicated but also the required height of chimney above the boiler breeching opening. All chimneys should extend at least 2 ft. 0 in. above the ridge of the building, or higher if there is a nearby source for a downdraft. A 4-in. thickness of brick is considered the minimum around a flue lining. The building code governs the construction necessary for safety installations of heating plants. A cleanout door should be provided at the bottom of every flue.

The arrangement of the heating system in most houses is so similar that it can usually be reduced to a few simple rules. The heating plant is usually located as near the center of the house as possible to give a more even distribution of heat. Long runs of pipes or ducts are kept to a minimum, but with the newer designs which use force for this distribution, this consideration is not as important. In the newer designed plants the furnace may be placed at floor level and the heat drawn from the under-side of the heating unit, taken under the floor or encased in the floor, and distributed to the different areas for warm air units. Other designs take the heat from the top of the furnace and conduct it to the attic space, then bring it down to the individual rooms. Depending upon the type of furnace, a plan view is used to show the horizontal layout of the ducts and their

connection with the vertical stacks. The dimensions specify the size of ducts, with the greater dimension parallel to the plan. These sizes require careful calculation by a person trained in the specialized field. Each of the heating systems used has its limitations as well as advantages and disadvantages so that a careful study of them should be made before making a choice. Many heating manufacturers distribute catalogs and other forms of literature which describe their products and show applications of them.

The proper sizes used in the representation of heating symbols should be obtained from these heating catalogs. These symbols are drawn to a reasonable size simply as a means of indicating their location. For the draftsman or student who wishes to specialize in electrical, plumbing, or heating layout work, the information given in this text is merely suggestive. Since each of these specialized fields of work represents an independent phase of construction, an advanced study must be undertaken beyond the province of this book. The common symbols used are given in these reference books or may be obtained through the American Standards Association, 70 East 45th Street, New York 17, New York. (See "Considerations in Planning a House" — Heating.)

ELECTRICAL SYMBOLS AND PLANS

The outlines of walls, partitions, and door and window openings are traced from the working drawings by the electrical engineer and all of the electrical outlets and switches are indicated. He shows the layout of all conduit and indicates the number of wires to be contained in each. The electrical plan must observe the regulations of the building code, with consideration of economy of materials and labor. It is not intended that the architectural draftsman be trained as an electrical engineer, but he should be familiar with the conditions of the work which influence the location of outlets on the architectural

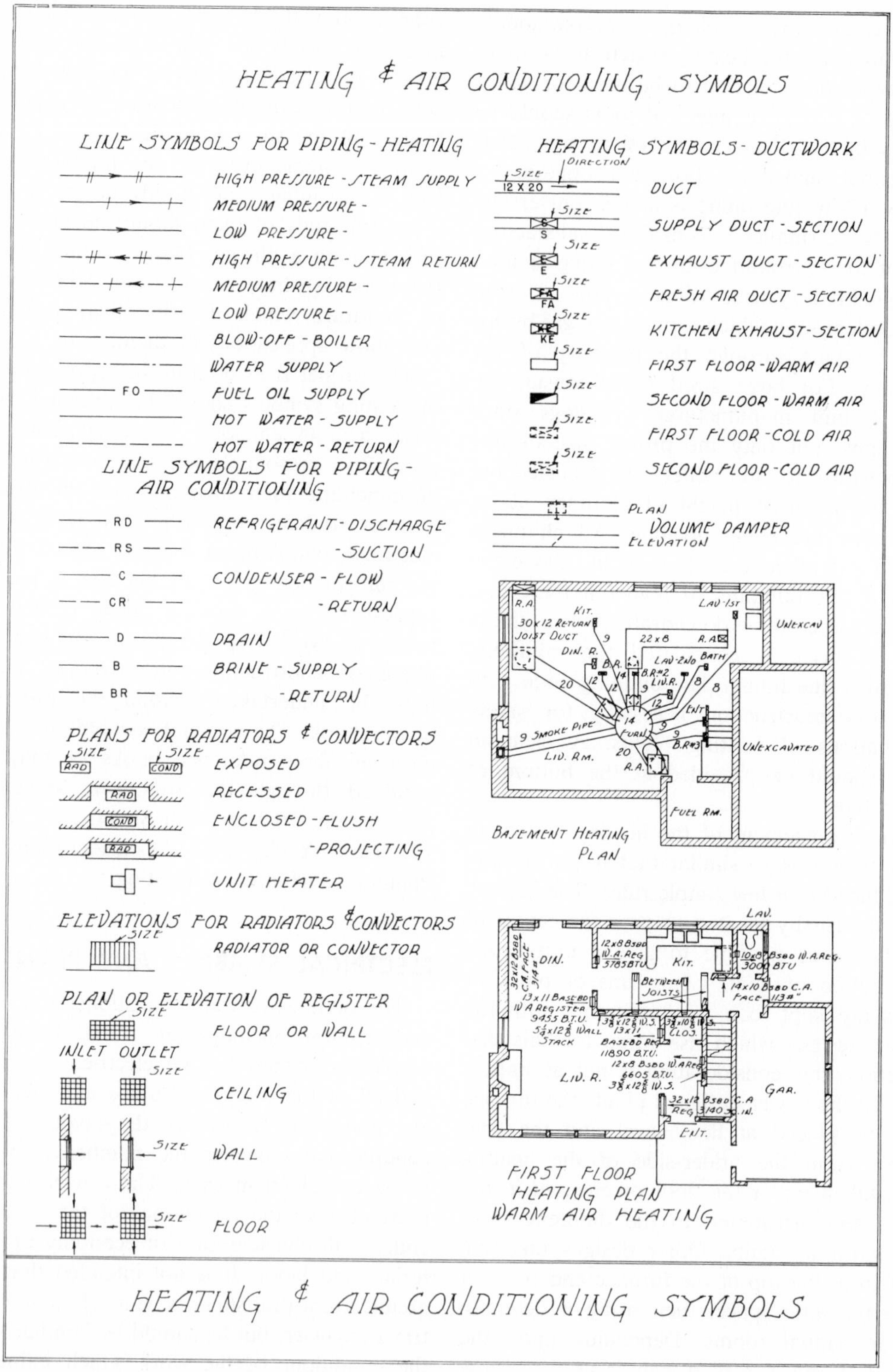

HEATING & AIR CONDITIONING SYMBOLS

LINE SYMBOLS FOR PIPING - HEATING

- HIGH PRESSURE - STEAM SUPPLY
- MEDIUM PRESSURE -
- LOW PRESSURE -
- HIGH PRESSURE - STEAM RETURN
- MEDIUM PRESSURE -
- LOW PRESSURE -
- BLOW-OFF - BOILER
- WATER SUPPLY
- FO — FUEL OIL SUPPLY
- HOT WATER - SUPPLY
- HOT WATER - RETURN

LINE SYMBOLS FOR PIPING - AIR CONDITIONING

- RD — REFRIGERANT - DISCHARGE
- RS — -SUCTION
- C — CONDENSER - FLOW
- CR — -RETURN
- D — DRAIN
- B — BRINE - SUPPLY
- BR — -RETURN

PLANS FOR RADIATORS & CONVECTORS

- RAD / COND — EXPOSED
- RAD — RECESSED
- COND — ENCLOSED - FLUSH
- RAD — -PROJECTING
- UNIT HEATER

ELEVATIONS FOR RADIATORS & CONVECTORS

- RADIATOR OR CONVECTOR

PLAN OR ELEVATION OF REGISTER

- FLOOR OR WALL
- INLET OUTLET
- CEILING
- WALL
- FLOOR

HEATING SYMBOLS - DUCTWORK

- 12 X 20 — DUCT (Size, Direction)
- S — SUPPLY DUCT - SECTION
- E — EXHAUST DUCT - SECTION
- FA — FRESH AIR DUCT - SECTION
- KE — KITCHEN EXHAUST - SECTION
- FIRST FLOOR - WARM AIR
- SECOND FLOOR - WARM AIR
- FIRST FLOOR - COLD AIR
- SECOND FLOOR - COLD AIR
- VOLUME DAMPER (PLAN / ELEVATION)

BASEMENT HEATING PLAN

FIRST FLOOR HEATING PLAN
WARM AIR HEATING

HEATING & AIR CONDITIONING SYMBOLS

Fig. 8

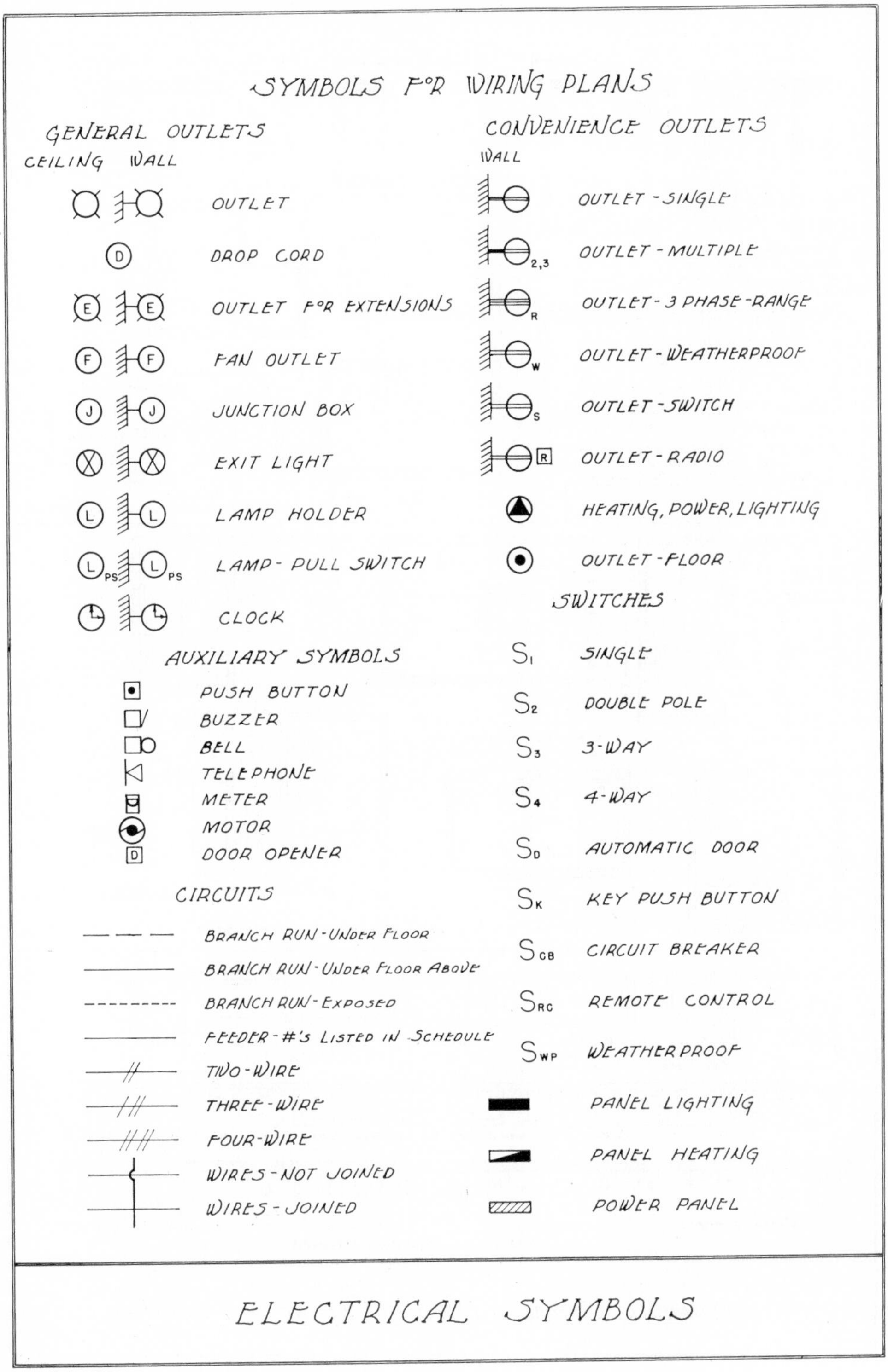

SYMBOLS FOR WIRING PLANS

GENERAL OUTLETS
CEILING   WALL

OUTLET

DROP CORD

OUTLET FOR EXTENSIONS

FAN OUTLET

JUNCTION BOX

EXIT LIGHT

LAMP HOLDER

LAMP - PULL SWITCH

CLOCK

AUXILIARY SYMBOLS

PUSH BUTTON

BUZZER

BELL

TELEPHONE

METER

MOTOR

DOOR OPENER

CIRCUITS

BRANCH RUN - UNDER FLOOR

BRANCH RUN - UNDER FLOOR ABOVE

BRANCH RUN - EXPOSED

FEEDER - #'s LISTED IN SCHEDULE

TWO - WIRE

THREE - WIRE

FOUR - WIRE

WIRES - NOT JOINED

WIRES - JOINED

CONVENIENCE OUTLETS
WALL

OUTLET - SINGLE

OUTLET - MULTIPLE

OUTLET - 3 PHASE - RANGE

OUTLET - WEATHERPROOF

OUTLET - SWITCH

OUTLET - RADIO

HEATING, POWER, LIGHTING

OUTLET - FLOOR

SWITCHES

S_1 SINGLE

S_2 DOUBLE POLE

S_3 3 - WAY

S_4 4 - WAY

S_D AUTOMATIC DOOR

S_K KEY PUSH BUTTON

S_{CB} CIRCUIT BREAKER

S_{RC} REMOTE CONTROL

S_{WP} WEATHERPROOF

PANEL LIGHTING

PANEL HEATING

POWER PANEL

ELECTRICAL SYMBOLS

Fig. 9

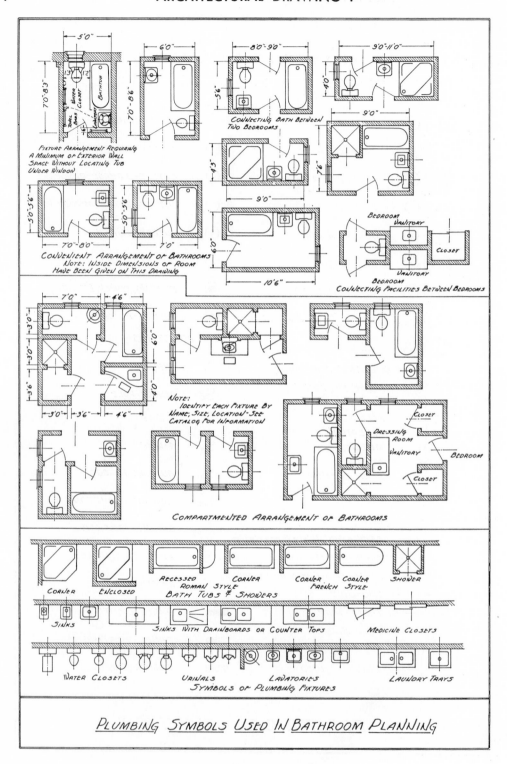

PLUMBING SYMBOLS USED IN BATHROOM PLANNING

Plate 5

plan. For residence work, a ceiling outlet and wall switch are usually sufficient for most rooms, together with enough wall outlets to accommodate the appliances, lamps, and electrical equipment. It is better to install too many outlets per room rather than too few with the growing popularity of electrical usage.

The draftsman should be acquainted with the type and wattage of the lamps, fixtures, or equipment to be installed. Spacing of the outlets must be done in such a way as to provide an even distribution of light. If this spacing is too far apart the lighting will be poor in areas between outlets. The fixtures should be spaced as regularly as possible throughout the room or work area. The switches for general lighting are usually located near the entrance to the room. Two-thousand watts are considered maximum for a circuit, and one switch should not control more fixtures than the number whose rated wattage adds up to one-half circuit, or 1000 watts.

The many types of lamps, appliances, and equipment in use require study if the draftsman is to gain a working knowledge of electrical technology. The principal electrical symbols are shown in Figure 9.

ASSIGNMENT

Plate 5, Conventions for Bathroom Plans

Indicate on the plate some of the symbols commonly used on plans and elevations for the representation of plumbing fixtures. Apply these symbols by drawing the plans of a bathroom and represent the symbols for plumbing fixtures for convenience, economy of space, and economy of materials and labor. It is suggested that the student plan a bathroom meeting minimum requirements of size, one meeting average home requirements, and one more elaborate which would be suitable for an expensive home. A compartment type of plan is to be recommended for experience. The instructor may assign the combinations expected of the student.

A variation in this assignment might require a diagram of the plumbing system required for the kitchen, bathroom, and utility room which might be required in making a vertical section of that portion of the house. This diagram may be drawn using the single line symbol, or by using the double line representations as required by the instructor.

Carefully plan the arrangement of your sheet for appearance. Use a suitable scale. Identify each symbol in your drawing and indicate each size by either a dimension or note. Indicate center lines where necessary. Do not copy plans given but study arrangements from other sources.

PROBLEMS FOR CLASS DISCUSSION

1. Why are the plumbing fixtures indicated on the plan drawings by conventionalized symbols?
2. Why are bathtubs usually built into a corner of the bathroom?
3. Why are the symbols drawn to catalog indicated sizes?
4. What influences have determined the design of the modern tub?
5. What is the smallest dimensioned tub listed in a manufacturer's catalog? the largest? What is the most commonly used size?
6. How are the sizes of plumbing fixtures indicated on the drawings?
7. How is the size of a kitchen sink given? How is the size of the drainboard given? What size of sink and drainboard is most commonly used?
8. How are shower baths represented on a plan? What types of showers are used in residence planning?
9. Why is the plumbing usually placed on an inside wall?
10. What type of lavatories can you find in the plumbing catalogs?

IX

Methods of Showing Fireplaces

Plate 6 shows a combination of plan, elevation, and sectional view fireplace symbols. The elevation view shows the fireplace as it would actually appear, and should be individually designed to indicate the student's taste. This drawing has been designed to show the general construction of the flues and how they are arranged in the chimney. The plans indicated for the several floors show the horizontal section as taken through the firebox of the fireplace, indicating its width and depth, and the arrangement of the construction materials. The vertical section shows the height of the fireplace constructions, the material arrangements, and the functioning of the fireplace as to distribution of its heat. Some consideration should be given to the methods of cleaning the fireplace and to the systems used for dumping the ashes. In some fireplaces the ashes are dumped into a drawer arrangement below the firebox which allows the drawer to be removed for emptying. In the more complicated arrangements the ash dump is connected from each fireplace to the ash pit in the basement. Even the arrangement of the cleanout door of the chimney deserves study.

Sometimes the elevation view and the plan view is drawn so the one side of the view indicates the exterior construction and the other half shows the construction features. Since there are so many variations in the ways these drawings are represented it is suggested that the student consult several reference books for ideas, as well as studying the chapter on the detail drawings required for fireplaces (Unit XI — Architectural Drawing II). The joist framing is often indicated around the fireplace and chimney in the plan view, with consideration being given to the fire-safety features of its construction.

On the first-floor plan representation, the rectangular hole in the brickwork proper is the symbol of the flue which comes up from the basement level. The flue for the fireplace starts above the fireplace and is not indicated on the first-floor plan. Three flues are shown side by side in the plan view taken at the ceiling and the plan at the top of the chimney. The double lines inside the flues indicate the tile flue lining required by most city codes as a safeguard against fire. The 8 by 12-in. dimension on the flue indicates that the flue is 8 in. wide and 12 in. long.

The ash dump shown in the first floor plan serves the same purpose as a grate in the furnace. It can be shaken, allowing the ashes or the complete bed of coals to fall into the ashpit. These ashes are removed through the cleanout door in the basement.

In the plan views the body of the chimney is shown crosshatched in one direction; the brick facing of the fireplace is sectioned in the opposite direction, or it may be double-hatched for contrast and better symbol representation. This symbol should indicate that the facing of the opening of the fireplace is constructed with firebricks. These bricks can better withstand the intense heat of the fire. Study their characteristics and proper application to construction. The hearths may be on the floor level or raised, and the bricks laid in several patterns to suit the individual taste.

In indicating the fireplace in the plan, the first consideration is the width of the opening, which is kept proportional to the size of the room. These widths will vary from 24 to 48 in., a 36 or 42 in. being the average for houses. The depth of the opening is 16 or 18 in., dropping straight back for the width of a brick (4 in.), where it is sloped or "splayed" so that the width at the back will be ⅔ that of the front of the opening.

The height of the opening at the front is about 30 in.

The proportions of all parts of a fireplace depend upon the size of the fireplace opening. The back wall should be pitched toward the front, throwing the smoke of the fire forward to the throat. This area should be ⅟₁₂ that of the fireplace opening, and the width from 3 to 4½ in. on the average. The back wall should rise vertically about 12 in., and the throat should be at least 8 in. above the opening, and should extend the full width of the opening. A metal damper is desirable for the control of the draft. Directly above the throat is the smoke chamber. This space is about the same depth as the flue and tapers at an angle of 60 deg. from the width of the throat opening at the bottom, to the width of the flue at the top. A back draft or smoke shelf is located just behind the throat to prevent down drafts from entering the fireplace heating chamber. The flue should center over the fireplace and be proportioned to ⅟₁₀ or ⅛ the area of the opening. Flue linings start at the top of the smoke chamber and carry up to 1 in. above the chimney cap.

Chimneys should be carried at least 2 ft. 0 in. above the highest point of the roof and be finished with a plain cement cap sloped from the edge of the flue tile to the outside brick edge. Ornamental chimney pots may be used and several designs of wind deflectors may be added when necessary. A chimney may consist of one or more flues surrounded with one width of brick, and lined with terra-cotta flue lining as a protection against fire. Exterior walls of the chimney should be 8 in. in thickness to prevent the cooling of the smoke which has a tendency to slow up the circulation of air currents. If the chimney is built with 8 in. brick walls the lining may be omitted. Two or more flues combined in one chimney should have a thin partition of bricks between the flues equal to the width of a brick. This partition, known as a "with,"* separates the flues and helps to

* Also spelled "withe" or "wythe."

bind the walls of the chimney together.

The hearth is the floor of the fireplace on which the fire is built. The portion in front of the facing which projects out into the room is built over a "trimmer" arch. It is usually made of brick, although sometimes a reinforced concrete slab may be used. On top of this a cement coating is used to hold the hearth tile or brick, as the case may be. The hearth may be flush with the floor or raised above the floor as desired. The ash dump is set about 4 in. from the back of the fireplace, and comes in stock sizes of 5 by 7 in. or 6 by 8 in. The facing of the typical fireplace is either tapestry or face brick, stone, or other suitable materials. Over the opening a flat arch supported by an angle iron is usually used, but other designs of self supporting arches may be used.

The foundations should be carried down to the same depth as those for the house, and should be large enough to distribute the weight over the soil according to its bearing capacity. A hollow space is provided for the ash pit into which the ash dump opens. Sizes of the cast-iron cleanout doors are 8 by 10 in., 10 by 12 in., and 12 by 14 in.

The brick mason works almost entirely from the sectional view and the plan, so that these views should show each construction dimension needed. The front elevation describes the design appearance and may be varied according to the wishes of the individual. The section should also give a complete description of the footing and foundation of the fireplace.

ASSIGNMENT

Plate 6, Methods of Showing Fireplaces

Notice in particular the arrangement of the flues in the chimney. The flue shown on the first floor plan is the flue from the basement and not that of the fireplace.

Study the unit on fireplace details of construction (Unit XI — *Architectural Drawing*

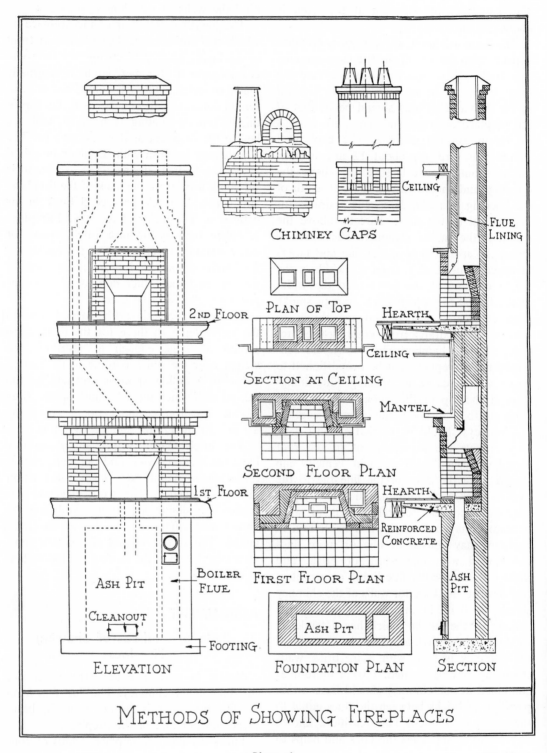

CHIMNEY CAPS

CEILING

FLUE LINING

PLAN OF TOP

2ND FLOOR

HEARTH

SECTION AT CEILING

CEILING

MANTEL

SECOND FLOOR PLAN

1ST FLOOR

HEARTH

REINFORCED CONCRETE

BOILER FLUE

FIRST FLOOR PLAN

ASH PIT

ASH PIT

CLEANOUT

ASH PIT

FOOTING

ELEVATION   FOUNDATION PLAN   SECTION

METHODS OF SHOWING FIREPLACES

Plate 6

II) and other reference materials to obtain the dimensions necessary to the construction of the plate, and draw the plate to convenient scale.

PROBLEMS FOR CLASS DISCUSSION

1. What is a "with"?
2. What is the purpose of a flue lining?
3. What does the double hatching of bricks on a fireplace drawing represent?
4. Why is the cleanout door of the ashpit placed above the floor level?
5. Which drawings furnish the construction information to the mason? Have you placed all the necessary dimensions on your drawing?
6. Under what conditions may the flue lining be omitted?
7. Why is the symbol of the fireplace given on the floor plan, when a detail drawing is required for construction of the fireplace?
8. What is the purpose of the ash dump? Where is it located?
9. What features of fireplace design help eliminate the tendency of fireplaces to smoke? Are you satisfied that you understand the scientific principles involved?
10. What purpose does the damper accomplish in the fireplace? Where is it located? Why is it placed toward the front of the fireplace?

Brick and Stone Masonry

BRICK MASONRY

Bricks are artificial stones. Because of the many different details connected with it, the process has become a separate branch of masonry called "bricklaying." Cornices, string and belt courses, capitals, panels, and window caps, which compose the ornamental portion of the building and are made of terra cotta, also are set in place by the bricklayer. Plastering also is considered a part of the mason's work and is classed as such in all specifications. Plastering may be interior or exterior work.

BRICKS AND BONDS

Common bricks are used for structural work and not for ornamental purposes. They are made in four grades according to their location in the kiln. The bricks in the inner layer and just above the flue are overburnt, brittle, hard, distorted, and often cracked. These bricks are used for paving. The second layer is made up of well-burnt bricks, fine in color and shape, and very hard. These are used as arch bricks. The third layer is soft and unfit for foundation work or for facework, but these bricks are used for filling in the inside partitions. The outside bricks are practically worthless.

Common bricks should be thoroughly burned, hard, straight, and uniform in size.

If two bricks are struck together they should give out a ringing sound; if the sound is dull the bricks are of an inferior quality. Bricks should be red in color; those light in color or salmon colored are likely to be too soft for use. The standard size of common bricks may be given as 2¼ by 3¼ by 8 in., but the size varies in different localities.

Face bricks are made in a variety of colors, textures, sizes, and shapes. The term *face brick* generally refers to bricks that have been pressed into a mold by machinery before burning, and are carefully shaped with square corners, smooth surfaces, sharp edges, and are of uniform size. Face bricks are very popular and are characterized by a more or less rough surface and a variety of pleasing colors.

Firebricks are used where great heat is to be resisted, as in fireplaces, furnaces, flues, etc. They are porous. The size is about 2½ by 4½ by 9 in. They are of a light cream color and are laid up with a mortar made of fireclay like that of which they are made.

Brickwork lends itself to some very interesting and artistic effects, which are produced by the various methods of bonding. Bond, in brickwork, is the overlapping of the brick one upon the other, either along the entire length of the wall or through its thickness, in order to bind the bricks together in a structural mass. The bricks are shifted back and forth so that the vertical joints in two successive layers or "courses" do not come into line.

In speaking of brick bonding, the two following terms are constantly used:

1. Stretcher. When a brick is laid lengthwise of the wall, thus showing its long, narrow dimension or "face" on the surface, it is called a "stretcher."

2. Header. If the brick is laid so that its length extends back into the wall, so that its short dimension shows on the wall surface, it is called a "header." The stretcher secures strength in the wall for length and the header for thickness. When a brick is broken as the case may require, the fragment is called a "bat."

The different bonds in common use are as follows:

1. Running Bond. The first and most obvious of these bonds is what is known as the "running" or "stretcher" bond. The wall surfaces are made up of stretcher courses, having at the corners a header which appears as a stretcher on the return side. This bond has the merit of being very strong longitudinally but lacking in transverse strength; consequently it is modified into the bond which is known as the "common" or "American" bond. This modification is accomplished by laying a course of headers every sixth or seventh course.

2. Flemish Bond. In this bond each course is laid in alternate stretchers and headers, the header resting upon the middle of the stretcher in successive courses. This produces a very attractive pattern of inlaid Greek crosses and is a favorite among builders because of its artistic effect.

3. English Bond. This is made up of alternate courses consisting of one course of all headers and then one of all stretchers. In both this and the Flemish bond it is customary to "clip" or use only one half of the header brick, except in the through bonding course, to economize in the face brick and make the adjustment of courses better if the face and backing bricks are not the same size.

4. Dutch or English Cross Bond. This is similar to the English bond, but with the vertical joints in the stretcher course alternating, instead of lining up with the ones in the stretcher courses above and below. If the variation in the color of the brick and the width of the joints are adjusted, the diagonal lines are emphasized in a diaper pattern.

Any one of these three special bonds gives life and variation to the blank wall spaces and decorative patterns to the spaces between the windows. They are well worth the slight increase in cost, unless the most rigid economy is demanded.

JOINT FORMS

Different jointings, by reason of their shadows or colors, emphasize or blend the patterns and colors of the bricks. These effects cannot be fully appreciated except in the examples of finished walls. Typical joints are as follows:

1. Flush. Where the surface is cut off level with the face of the brickwork.

2. Struck. Where the surface starts flush with the brick top, and is beveled to a point slightly back of the top edge of the lower brick.

3. Weathered. The reverse of the above, where the bottom is flush with the lower brick, and the top slightly back of the bottom edge of the upper brick.

4. Tooled. Where a joint is ruled with a rounded or a V-shaped tool or "jointer."

5. Rodded. Where the top and bottom of the joint are ruled with the trowel against a straight edge.

6. Raked. Where all the mortar is removed to a depth of about ¼ in.

TYPES OF BRICK WALLS

There are four ways of using brick which, when laid up in a wall, have a similar appearance. Three of these result in real masonry walls. The fourth does not. These four methods are as follows:

1. Solid Brick Walls. The thickness of a masonry wall is determined by its height and the load it must carry. In the case of a wall of solid brick, accepted practice has established the fact that in one- and two-family dwellings, where the walls are not over 30 ft. in height, they may be 8 in. thick, provided they are properly bonded. This wall is built with no hollow spaces constructed in it. The wall is substantial, easy to build, and appropriate.

2. Hollow Brick Walls. This type of wall in reality is a double-thickness wall built in such a way that a space is provided between the two walls. This space is intended to keep moisture from passing through, by maintaining a complete separation of the two walls. This dead-air space tends to keep a building cooler in summer and warmer in winter.

Such walls are accepted as desirable for dwellings up to 20 ft. in height and with an 8-in. thickness. They have not been very extensively used in this country, owing to the fact that for average dwellings a thicker wall must be used for this type than for solid brick, entailing consequently more space and more expense.

3. Brick Faced. Sometimes brick is used as a facing against other materials, most commonly hollow tile. Such a wall has proved to be satisfactory especially in localities where tile can be laid more cheaply than brick. When brick is so used, the minimum thickness of the wall, under the same conditions as noted for solid brick walls, is 12 in.

4. Brick Veneered. These have a masonry facing which is not attached and bonded to the backing in such a way as to become an integral part of it, and which does not therefore aid in its load-bearing strength. Brick is commonly used as a veneer against frame construction; when so applied it forms in no sense a masonry wall, but is used as an ornamental and fireproof coat, which costs more but requires less upkeep than one of siding or shingles. Although the wall has the appearance of brick, it has not all of its advantages.

STANDARD SIZES OF BRICK

Building brick	2¼″ x 3¾″ x	8″
Norman brick	2⅜″ x 4″ x	12″
Pressed brick	2⅜″ x 4″ x	8⅜″
Paving brick	4″ x 4″ x	8½″
Roman brick	1½″ x 4″ x	12″

COMMON SIZES OF BUILDING TILE

8″ x 5″ x 12″	8″ x 8″ x 12″	4″ x 8″ x 12″
4″ x 5″ x 12″	8″ x 12″ x 12″	4″ x 12″ x 12″

STONE MASONRY

Stone masonry entering into the construction of a building is divided into three classes: rubble, ashlar, and trimmings.

Rubble masonry is used for rough work, such as foundations, backing, etc. The stones used are those which are found in the locality. Field stones or quarried stones, granite, limestone, and sandstone are those most often used. With careful workmanship and a good grade of stone the rubble wall is very pretty. Quarried stone should be used wherever possible in preference to the common field stone, as a better bonding and bedding can be secured. The uncoursed rubble is composed of masonry of irregularly shaped stones set at random. Coursed rubble is composed of masonry of irregularly shaped stones set up in courses. The stones used in rubble masonry are shaped with a hammer. The wall varies in strength with the shape and character of the stone. If the stone has a marked stratification and can be split up into flat layers, a very strong wall can be built from it. If the common field stone is used, a very weakly bonded wall results, because of the cavities which must be filled with mortar or stone chips.

Ashlar is a facing of squared stones. The exposed surface of the stones is given any of the finer finishes. In order that a wall may be correctly classified as ashlar, the joints between the stones must run horizontal and vertical. There are two general classes of ashlar: coursed, and broken or ranged. Regular coursed ashlar has stones of uniform height and in continuous courses. The stones are 12 in. high and 18 to 24 in. long. Broken or ranged ashlar consists of squared stones but of different sizes forming a broken course. This type of wall takes more time to build but when carefully laid, presents a very pleasing appearance.

Masonry trimmings include moldings, belt courses, sills, etc., used for ornamental purposes. The tops of all trimmings should be beveled and on the underside, grooves should be provided.

In building a stone wall the least possible amount of mortar should be used. The thickness of the joints varies from ³/₁₆ to ⅝ in., depending upon the class of work. For ordinary work the thickness is about ¼ in.

FINISH

When stones are cut there are several ways of finishing the face, to which the following terms apply:

1. Rock Face. In this the surface remains about as it comes from the quarry, with the edges chipped down to a line.

2. Crandalled. This, on the softer stones, has the surface tooled into fine parallel lines or crisscrossed.

3. Bush-Hammered. In this finish the stone is dressed to a fairly even surface, and then is finished in parallel lines with a hammer, the face of which is made up of separate blades.

4. Vermiculated. This word, meaning "worm eaten," is given to the finish which consists of short twisting grooves gouged in the surface of the stone. It is expensive, and is used abroad more than in this country.

5. Rubbed. By this finish the face is brought to a smooth surface.

6. Polished. The rubbing in this finish is carried to an extreme degree, as with marble or granite.

VARIETIES OF STONE

In each locality the availability of native stone, the expense of transportation, or the local character of design will influence selection; but a few suggestions are here given on the use of the more common varieties of building stone.

1. Granite. Granite is an igneous rock; that is, one produced by the action of heat. It is the hardest and most durable building stone, but not the strongest. It varies in texture from very fine to very coarse, and in colors from white, through the grays, to green, pink, and red. Granite is a building stone, but is little used in domestic work except for the base course on city buildings, doorsteps, and window sills.

2. Limestone. Limestone is an aqueous rock; that is, one produced by the action of water, the product in most cases of large shell deposits. It varies in texture from fine to a coarse grade and is most commonly found in buff and gray shades. It is a softer stone than granite and is consequently more easily worked. It is cut from the ground in large slabs, which are then sawed into smaller blocks. Limestone is used principally for public buildings and for large residences, although it is not entirely confined to them.

3. Sandstone. The old "brownstone fronts" of fifty years ago were immensely popular in their time. They have given sandstone a rather bad name, however, because the material failed to resist frost and because the stone had such a dull rusty color. In northern states, where the natural strata were laid vertically, the carving and the exposed surface often flaked off, but when laid horizontally the rapid disintegration did not occur. Many quarries have since been opened up where the stone is harder, more weather resisting, and more attractive in color. The material, in both treatment and texture, is not unlike limestone.

4. Bluestone. This is a fossilized clay and varies considerably in hardness and formation. The most common formation in residential use is the ledgestone of Pennsylvania, where slabs are easily quarried in convenient sizes for masonry walls. The hardest deposits are particularly well adapted for flagstones and street crossings.

5. Marble. There are many native quarries of marble, which supply different colors of stone at a considerable range of price. For the residence of moderate cost this stone should be employed only for keystones, window sills, and the like, on the exterior, and

ENGLISH BOND

AMERICAN BOND

DUTCH BOND

FLEMISH BOND

BONDS IN BRICKWORK

UNCOURSED RUBBLE

BROKEN RANGE ASHLAR

BONDS IN STONEWORK

COURSED ASHLAR

BROKEN ASHLAR

SOLDIER COURSE

ROWLOCK COURSE

BONDS USED IN MASONRY

Plate 7

for fireplace facings, floor tiles, and similar minor details on the interior.

LINTELS

A lintel is a stone that supports the wall over a door, a window, or other opening. The ends of the lintels should not be built into the wall more than from 4 to 6 in. at each end since that gives sufficient bearing. Ordinarily the lintel is the same thickness as the reveal of the window, which, in the case of a brick wall, is about 4 in. Where the wall is of stone, this reveal may be from 6 to 8 in.

SILLS

Sills in masonry are the stones used to form the bottom of a window or door opening. These sills should be built into the wall from 2 to 4 in. at each end. Slip sills are made the width of the opening and are not built into the walls. All sills are beveled about 1 in. in 12 in. A drip groove always should be provided.

ASSIGNMENT

Plate 7, Bonds Used in Masonry

Draw isometric views of the bonds used in brickwork.

Notice the methods of laying bricks for longitudinal and transverse strength. Also notice the method of finishing the corners. Do not make the mortar joints thicker than ¼ in.

Scale: ⅛ in. equals 1 ft.

PROBLEMS FOR CLASS DISCUSSION

1. What tests are given for the quality of bricks?
2. How does the position of the bricks in the kiln affect their quality and use?
3. Bricks have been used for houses since the time of the Babylonians. Find out all you can about the history of brick-making and make up a booklet from the results of your study.
4. What is the difference between a face brick and a common brick? Between common bricks and firebricks?
5. What is meant by the term *bond* in brickwork? What is a "course"?
6. What is the difference between a "stretcher" and a "header"?
7. Name the principal bonds used in brick-work. How is each laid? What are the merits claimed for each?
8. What are the types of brick walls? What advantages and disadvantages can you give for each?
9. Name the three classes of stone masonry.
10. What requirements must be filled before a stone wall may be correctly classified as "ashlar"?
11. Why does common field stone make a weak wall?
12. What kinds of finish are given to stones used in building construction? How are these finishes obtained?
13. What is a "lintel"? How thick is it? How much bearing is given to a lintel?
14. What two kinds of sills are used? How much bearing is given? How much bevel is given to a stone window sill?
15. What is the purpose of the drip groove? Where is it placed?

Masonry Construction

OPENING SUPPORTS

The brickwork over all openings may be supported by a steel or a wood "lintel," or by a brick arch. Either the full thickness of the wall or the face brick only may be carried on a steel lintel or arch. Lintels are rarely used in combination with semicircular arches. When a steel lintel or an arch supports the brick, the backing usually rests on a wooden lintel, set higher than the arch or concealed by the frame. There should be a back-relieving arch above wooden lintels spanning more than 3 ft., bearing on the wall beyond the ends of the lintel, so that the brickwork will not be weakened should the lintel be destroyed by fire.

For a steel lintel over a small opening, an angle iron is sufficient. If the interior wall surface is also made of brick, the lintel is made by placing two angles, back to back, since the wood lintel would be unsightly. For openings up to 4 ft. wide, a 4 by 3-in. or a 3 by 3-in. angle is sufficient; wider openings up to 5 ft. would require a 3 by 5-in. angle. Lintels are usually made 8 in. longer than the width of the opening.

The brick arches generally used in small buildings are flat, segmental, or full semicircular. The segmental and semicircular arches are usually built of "rowlock" courses, their number depending upon the width of the opening. Flat brick arches over 2 ft. wide should be supported by steel, the brick being set in solder fashion or rowlock. As these bricks are slightly inclined from the vertical, their end edges should be ground or clipped

to make the joints on the faces of the arch come in a horizontal line. For either type of arch, the brickwork on both sides of the opening must be beveled in the form of skewbacks, to serve as beds for receiving the thrust of the arch. If these arches are properly handled as to design and execution, they add greatly to the appearance of the entire wall surface.

TREATMENT OF JOISTS

The brickwork should be stopped at the point where the floor joists are to rest upon it, and care should be taken to have the top course perfectly level, so that the joists may be set without wedging or blocking. The joists set by the carpenter should have, at intervals of approximately 6 ft., wrought-iron joist anchors solidly spiked to them and extending into the wall. Great care should be exercised in placing these anchors as near the bottom of the joist as possible in order to lessen the strain on the brick wall, in case a fire causes the joist to drop. For the same reason, the ends of all joists, with or without anchors, should be beveled so that, in like conditions, the joists will readily fall out without injury to the wall.

FURRING

The inside of all exterior brick walls should be furred, except where climatic conditions make this unnecessary. This furring may be of wood, hollow tile, or metal. The first, which is ordinarily used, consists of 1 by 2-in. wooden strips placed vertically on the wall and spaced 16 in. on centers. Either the strips are nailed to lath which has been placed in the joints of the brickwork by the mason, or they are attached by driving nails into the mortar joints. The grounds and lath are placed directly on these strips.

Hollow-tile furring is formed by splitting 3- or 4-in. "split furring" tile, which has been scored in manufacturing especially for this purpose. The webs are placed against the brick wall and are anchored by driving 10d nails into the mortar joints over every

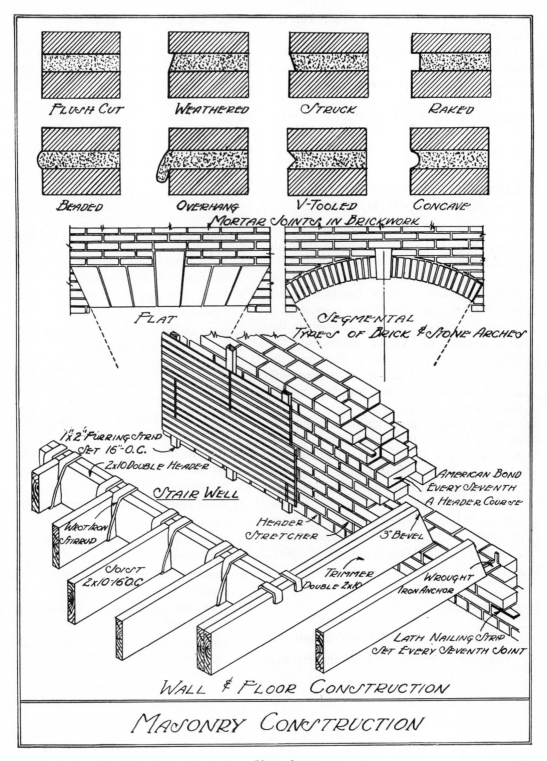

FLUSH CUT   WEATHERED   STRUCK   RAKED

BEADED   OVERHANG   V-TOOLED   CONCAVE

MORTAR JOINTS IN BRICKWORK

FLAT   SEGMENTAL
TYPES OF BRICK & STONE ARCHES

1"x2" FURRING STRIP
SET 16" O.C.
2x10 DOUBLE HEADER

STAIR WELL

WROT IRON
STIRRUP

JOIST
2x10x16 O.C.

HEADER
STRETCHER

TRIMMER
DOUBLE 2x10

3" BEVEL

AMERICAN BOND
EVERY SEVENTH
A HEADER COURSE

WROUGHT
IRON ANCHOR

LATH NAILING STRIP
SET EVERY SEVENTH JOINT

WALL & FLOOR CONSTRUCTION

MASONRY CONSTRUCTION

Plate 8

third tile in every second course. The tile should be laid without mortar so as not to make a solid connection, which would transmit moisture. This tile furring makes a good surface for interior plastering.

Metal furring is only used with metal lath and consists of small steel rods or other stiffening members placed either separately on the wall or as part of the metal lath.

SUPPORTING WOODEN JOISTS IN HOLLOW-TILE CONSTRUCTION

The joists are placed 16 in. on centers, which allows a 12-in. tile between the ends of each pair of joists. A row of brick stretchers is often used to support the ends of the joists, when the depth of the joist is less than the height of the blocks. Instead of a course of bricks being used to support the joists, a course of 1-in. tile which covers the entire thickness of the wall is often used. In each of these cases the space between the end of the joist and the wall is generally filled with concrete.

Special hangers are often used to support the floor joists. In this method the joist does not enter the wall and weaken each course where the tier of joists is placed.

Hollow-tile buildings, when not veneered, are generally finished with stucco on the outside, but tiles finished on the outside are obtainable. "Cincrete blocks," made of cinders, with a finished face in dull glazed colors, are similarly used.

ASSIGNMENT

Plate 8, Masonry Construction

Draw an isometric view of the framing around the stair well. Since this is the important detail on the sheet, arrange your drawings carefully to emphasize this feature. Show all of the details of construction. Orthographic views may be used if desired.

Label the brickwork joints according to the trade name.

Notice the construction of the several forms of brick arches. Be sure that you are drawing the bricks to scale when making the drawing.

Scale: 1 in. equals 1 ft.

PROBLEMS FOR CLASS DISCUSSION

1. What types of brick arches are used over window and door openings?

2. What is meant by a "soldier" course? Rowlock course?

3. Why are the bricks beveled in the arches? How is this accomplished?

4. Why are the joist anchors placed near the bottom of the joists? Why are the ends of all joists beveled?

5. What is the purpose of "furring"? Where is it used? When is it used?

6. What is the advantage in using hangers for floor joists? What styles of hangers are used for the purpose?

7. What kinds of joints are used in brickwork?

8. How much mortar is usually allowed for brickwork?

9. How far apart are the joists usually spaced?

10. How are furring strips fastened on a brick wall?

11. How are joists given support around openings?

Foundations

The word *foundation* is used to mean: (1) construction below grade such as footing courses, cellar walls, etc.; (2) the natural part of the earth's surface on which the construction rests; and, (3) the special construction such as pilings, piers, and so on, used to transmit the load of the building to firm bedding.

In this treatment of the study of foundations, the natural material on which the construction rests is referred to as the "foundation bed." Walls, columns, and piers below grade are called "foundation walls, piers, and columns," to distinguish them from the structure above grade. The lower parts of the walls, piers, and columns, which spread to provide a safe base are called "footings."

CHARACTERISTICS OF MATERIALS IN FOUNDATION BEDS

Solid Rock. The harder rocks, such as granite, slate, sandstone, and limestone, are capable of carrying the load of the ordinary structures. The softer rocks, such as shale and marley limestone, should not be overloaded. In loose rock or gravel it is best to increase the size of the footings.

Sand and Gravel. If compact, and if no underlying bed of poorer materials exists, gravel forms a most desirable foundation bed equal to sand or boulders in supporting power, and is not as liable to be disturbed by adjoining excavations.

Quicksand. This type of bed is objectionable because of the danger of its flowing in case it finds an outlet such as an adjoining excavation. In such cases some advantage may be gained by surrounding the excavation with driven wells and draining the soil by continued pumping.

Clay. Clay is not a reliable material on which to erect a building; first, because of its plasticity when wet, and second, because of its tendency to shrink upon losing its moisture. Where the foundation bed is of clay it is advisable to protect it from water action by a system of drains surrounding the wall, and of diverting the water from the building.

MATERIALS OF FOUNDATION WALLS

Stone. Where field stone or easily split rock is available it forms an excellent and economical foundation wall. A wall built of soft stones or of irregularly shaped stones is inferior to a concrete wall, or even one of brick. A stone basement wall should be at least 18 to 20 in. thick, both for strength and because the cost of laying anything less increases rather than diminishes, owing to the greater labor required in selecting and fitting the stone within narrow limits.

Brick. Brick is also a familiar material for foundation walls, of which the enduring qualities cannot be questioned. In some localities terra-cotta tile is used commonly. These materials are limited to use principally in the warm, dry climates. These walls are usually made to 12-in. thickness, depending on building codes or local practice.

Concrete. These wall may be built with concrete blocks, with the thickness of the wall determined by the standard sizes of blocks in use, or poured concrete fashioned with forms may be used. The minimum thickness of the poured concrete wall is usually considered to be 8 in. Concrete is better than stone work, in that: (1) in most parts of the country it can be built more cheaply, depending upon the local materials; (2) the finished interior surface will be more even, and therefore desirable if the basement space is to be utilized; (3) if properly constructed, and especially if reinforced by horizontal rods, it will resist local settlements because it is more homogeneous; and, (4) it can be more readily waterproofed if necessary.

The thickness of the walls increases from the two minimum sizes of 18 in. for stone and 8 in. for concrete to whatever thickness calculations or experience show to be required for the depth of the foundation wall below the grade and the weight of the building to be supported. It is advisable to have the foundation walls up to the first floor level at least 4 in. thicker than the walls above them. In all large cities the thickness of the foundation wall is governed by the building code. Where there are no existing codes the following table will serve as a guide:

DWELLINGS

Height of Building	Concrete	Brick	Stone
Two stories	8" to 12"	12" to 16"	20"
Three stories	8" to 12"	12" to 16"	20"
Four stories	8" to 12"	12" to 20"	24"

FOUNDATION WALLS

The simplest type of foundation consists of wooden piles driven into the ground to a solid footing. This type of support is acceptable in all parts of the country where strict economy is necessary, but it is imperative that the wood be treated to resist decay and termites. Hollow steel columns with poured concrete and reinforcing rods filling the shell may also be used.

Where a basement is desired, poured concrete gives the best performance of any material used for foundation walls if the proper proportions of cement, aggregate, and water are used and if reasonable care is taken in placing the concrete in the forms. See Plate 9. Concrete blocks are often used for basement walls, but special care must be taken to set up the blocks properly with waterproof joints to insure a dry basement. It is necessary that a block wall be coated on the outside with a cement-plaster and this be waterproofed with a coat of tar or asphalt. The inside surface may be painted with a

waterproofing paint as a further protection. A good poured concrete wall with only the asphalt coating is an effective treatment for moisture penetration. The great differences in the quality of the concrete blocks in different localities make it uncertain whether the blocks will be nonporous. This and the difficulty of securing watertight joints over the whole wall area are the main reasons for the suggested precautions.

The big advantage of concrete blocks lies in the fact that they can be laid economically even by a man not necessarily skilled as a mason. Costs of poured concrete foundations tend to be higher, although this varies by locality, depending upon the availability of various materials and labor. The biggest item in the cost of a poured concrete wall is the setting up and tearing down of the forms, which usually equal or exceeds the cost of the concrete itself.

MOISTURE AND VAPOR CONTROL

In all but the driest locations it is important to insulate a concrete floor, whether it is a basement floor or the first-floor slab (Fig. 10). A tamped gravel base about 6 in. deep will prevent water from coming into contact with the bottom of the slab unless the ground becomes saturated. In areas where there are heavy accumulations of ground water a few feet below the surface during wet seasons, basement walls should be tiled around the footings to allow this water to run off rather than stand against the outside of the walls. Sometimes the ground is so saturated that it is possible to dig a hole two feet below the surface and have water rise to within a foot of the surface. This means that the water table, or the level of water standing in the ground is but a foot from the surface. If you have a basement here with the floor level 6 ft. 0 in. below the surface, water is standing against these walls for a depth of 5 ft. 0 in., seeking to find its way in either through the walls or under

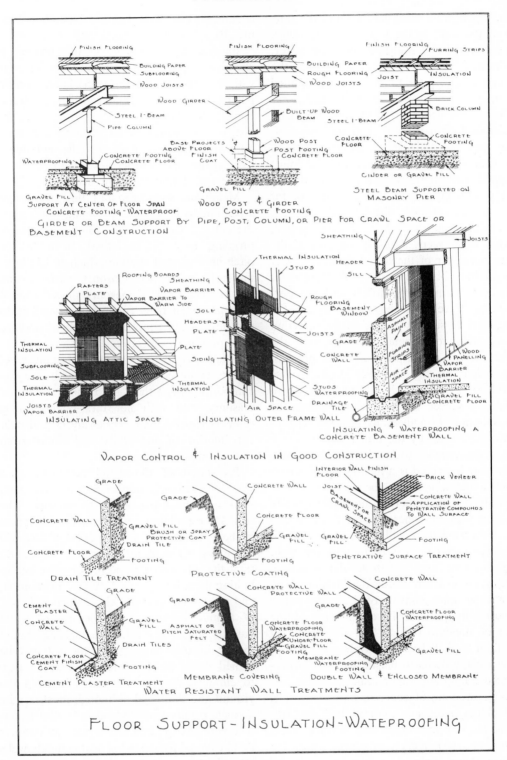

Fig. 10

them. Open drain tiling laid around the outside of the walls at the level of the footings, and connected to a sump pump, storm sewer, or drainage area at a lower level than the footings will keep the foundation bed drained within a foot or two of the walls and floor.

Terra-cotta field tile, 12 in. long and 4 in. in diameter, or perforated fiber pipe are generally used for drainage around the footings. The tiles are laid end-to-end, and the joints wrapped with copper wire screen or covered on top with pieces of asphalt shingle or tar paper to prevent loose dirt from clogging the openings. Since the joints are not sealed, ground water seeps into the tile around the entire perimeter of the foundation. The fiber tiles are joined by small collars allowing water to seep in through the joints and the perforations. Care must be taken to set the tiling level or slightly pitched in the direction of the sewer or drainage area so that the water will run off. A pitch of $\frac{1}{16}$ in. per foot is sufficient for this drainage slope. Coarse gravel, from 6 to 12 in. or more in depth should be placed over the tiling before the foundation is backfilled, to facilitate collection of the water by the tiling.

A recommended precaution before a concrete floor is poured is a membrane of waterproof material between the gravel and the slab. Even though there is no direct contact of water with the concrete, presence of moisture under the floor will cause condensation of water vapor on the bottom of the slab. The moisture may penetrate the concrete, causing damp floors inside the building. The membrane may consist of building paper made for the purpose. It consists of a double layer of standard roofing felt with a coating of tar or asphalt between layers and on top, an especially designed plastic sheet, or a premolded membrane vapor seal.

Waterproofing of concrete basement walls and floors may be accomplished by two methods: (a) membrane and surface treatments, and (b) integral treatment where the waterproofing material is blended with the concrete while it is being mixed. See Figure 10.

Integral dampproofing: in this process a chemical in powdered or liquid form is mixed with the concrete. These materials are usually patented and sold under different trade names. The simplest method is to use hydrated lime which is an efficient and economical method of making walls and floors tight against the normal amount of moisture in the soil during the rainy season.

Membrane waterproofing: this consists of a continuous impermeable coating which seals the entire floor and walls. Membrane waterproofing may be described as a tar or pitch-impregnated coating which is laid continuously upon one masonry surface, and has another layer of masonry placed against it to protect it from fracture and yielding to pressure. One simpler method of surface waterproofing is to cover the exterior of the foundation wall with a waterproofing, sold under various trade names with varying composition. Another is to mop the entire masonry wall with hot tar. Waterproofing cements can be used. These are coated over the interior of the walls and floors from $\frac{1}{2}$ to 2 in. thick.

Protection of the wood members of a house is extremely important wherever there is likely to be any exposure to moisture. The sills are especially vulnerable, for dampness in the concrete over a long period of time will cause the wood to rot. It is a good idea to treat the sills with a wood preservative before bolting them into place. A further precaution, and a necessity in areas where there is danger of termite infestation, is the use of metal flashing under the sill. The flashing should extend beyond the edge of the sill and be turned down at an angle of about 45 deg. to eliminate any access points between the ground and the wood. Although most termite damage occurs where wood is in direct contact with the ground, subterranean termites build covered passageways over concrete walls in order to reach the timbers. The turned down metal shield cuts off this passageway.

Where a basementless house is built with a crawl space over the ground, with wood floors rather than a concrete slab, the elimination of moisture is a major problem. Ventilation is one of the major factors in eliminating this trouble. Grilled ventilation openings are made in the crawl space walls equal to 2 sq. ft. per 100 ft. of building perimeter, plus ½ per cent of the building floor area. Thus a house 30 ft. 0 in. by 35 ft. 0 in. built over a crawl space should have almost 8 sq. ft. of ventilating area open in the crawl space at all times. Four openings 1 ft. 0 in. by 2 ft. 0 in. would provide this ventilation. With the improved furnaces in which the heat is distributed through pipes run under the floors in this crawl space area, a register may be provided for the crawl space. This register will provide warmer floors and tend to keep the crawl space dried out. In this method the ventilation openings may be closed during the heating season. It has been found that covering the soil beneath the crawl space floor with 55 lb. of heavy mineral-surfaced roofing paper can reduce the ventilation requirements considerably. Also polyethelene film will do the same thing. Where crawl spaces are used with the required ventilation, it may be necessary to insulate the floors to prevent their being cold in the winter months. Any exposed piping under the floors should also be heavily insulated, unless the crawl space is under an unexcavated wing of the house with a part basement. Here it is customary to provide the vent openings between the basement and the crawl space, keeping the latter warm and dry.

When a concrete slab is used as a floor in a basementless house in a northern climate, it is important to insulate the slab against excessive loss of heat. The actual temperature of a concrete slab on the ground is, or will become in time, somewhat higher than the temperature of an inadequately insulated floor over an unheated crawl space. The important thing to remember is that most heat loss in slab-floor construction is principally through the edge. This loss may be remedied by insulating the edges of the concrete slab laid on the ground and extending the insulation for a distance under the slab around its perimeter. Concrete slabs laid over crawl space require the insulation of the exposed wall of the crawl space. Rigid insulation board placed around the edge of the slab and the foundation wall, and also placed under the slab at the edge will effectively reduce heat losses. Insulating materials placed in or near the ground will probably be subject to attack by moisture, mildew, or termites. This, together with the pressure from the earth or the structural loading will compress or otherwise destroy the effectiveness of the insulating material. The following materials are used for this purpose:

1. Cellular glass enclosing sealed-in gas in thicknesses of 2, 3, 4, and 5 in.

2. Glass fibers with plastic binder, coated or uncoated and in thicknesses of ¾, 1, 1½, and 2 in.

3. Cane or wood fiber boards in thicknesses of ½, ^{25}⁄₃₂, and 1 in.

4. Hard cellular rubber or compositions enclosing sealed-in gas in thicknesses of ½, ¾, 1, 1¼, 1½, and 2 in.

INSULATION AND VAPOR BARRIERS

Because warm air is attracted to cooler surfaces and carries moisture along with it, discomfort, expense, and property damage may be caused by the varying temperatures between the inside and outside of a house. This problem is common to all climates and has made thermal and moisture insulation one of the most universally accepted features in modern home construction. See Plate 9. In cold climates the cold wall is the exterior wall, and warm inside air rushes to it, carrying dust-laden moisture through plaster, paper, wallboard, and paneling, and the result is cold, drafty rooms and dirt-streaked decoration. In warm climates the cold wall is inside the shaded wall, and outside air with its heat and humidity is drawn to it leaving dampness, mildew, and rot in the outer walls and musty condensation on the inner walls.

This condition may be cured by two types of insulation: thermal insulation which slows down the passage of heat and air and prevents a warm wall from becoming a cold wall; and vapor seals or barriers which stop passage of moisture into thermal insulation or into wall cavities where it may condense and freeze in cold climates. Both types of insulation should be used; often they are combined in one product that is easily applied. Thermal insulation is of two types: highly porous material which encloses insulating air spaces, and reflective material with mirror-like surfaces to reflect the heat.

Thermal insulation may be fiber boards, batts of mineral wool, glass, cotton or wool fibers, or small globules of fluffy material that pour freely into any space. These materials are easily applied to stud walls as sheathing, between-stud blankets or batts, or blown into spaces between studs and outer walls and plaster or other inside walls. Some insulating boards are impregnated with their own vapor-sealing materials and many of the batt or blanket types of insulation are enclosed in moisture-proof covers. Care must be taken that the vapor seals overlap tightly at all points exposed to cold walls, or much of the vapor barrier effect is lost. The vertical streaks of dirt on plaster or paper are spots that show up gaps in the insulation and vapor seals. The vapor-sealing material should overlap studs and be applied around joists abutting outside walls.

Reflective insulation may be thin metal cemented to fabric or paper, or thin metal sheets coated with alloys. It is important that the reflective surfaces of this insulation never touch other materials, or obviously they will have no chance to reflect the heat.

A good heavy building paper or felt should be placed over wood sheathing to cut wind infiltration to the minimum. Such a covering is generally not needed over insulation board or plywood sheathing, since these present unbroken surfaces which resist infiltration.

Insulating masonry walls presents more of a problem because there are no wide stud spaces to accommodate batts or loose insulation, and no sheathing. In masonry walls an insulating air space is provided by furring strips on which wall board or lath and plaster is applied. A vapor seal of waterproof paper should be applied over the furring strips, and the inner side of the masonry should be painted with asphalt or other waterproofing solutions.

Masonry veneer or brick or stone over a frame structure has value for appearance but very little insulating value, and does not add to the strength of the structure. The masonry layer is never used to carry the roof load. Care must be taken to keep moisture out of the house with this veneer construction, for it is subject to moisture penetration. Rain is frequently driven right through the masonry layer. Moisture will condense on the inside of the masonry and will run down between the veneer and the building paper over the sheathing. "Weep holes," openings in the bottom masonry course, must be provided to allow this water to run out.

The moisture problem also exists with stucco coatings, which are placed directly over sheathing or over open studs. To defeat the moisture problem it is important to place a waterproof building paper against the sheathing or over the studs to act as a backing for the stucco. Sometimes the stucco coating is placed on a wall or veneer of grooved terra-cotta tile, a grooved board sheathing, or on heavy wire which is fastened to the sheathing.

Where walls are of solid masonry, moisture is still a problem. If the brick is left exposed inside, which is frequently done for the architectural effect, moisture is likely to condense directly on the inside surface of the wall on very cold days. Wind-driven rain may penetrate too. The exposed brick wall is not recommended for locations where the winters are cold. The same is true where plaster is applied directly over the masonry, for condensation will form on the plaster on cold days. Furring strips should be anchored to the masonry and a vapor barrier placed inside of the furring before the walls are lathed and plastered. Such a wall should be insulated if possible.

FOUNDATION FOOTINGS

Every foundation wall should rest on a footing which projects beyond the wall on each side, unless the wall is built on solid rock or carries a very light load. Footings serve two very important purposes:

1. Distribute the weight over a larger area.

2. Add to the protection of the wall against the forces of nature.

The size of the footing is determined by the weight the foundation wall carries, and the nature of the foundation bed. If unusual soil conditions are encountered, or if the foundation walls and the building itself are of unusual construction and weight, the total load should be calculated and the footing designed to accommodate the problem. In ordinary house construction, certain practices are accepted and standardized by geographical localities. Often these practices are incorporated into a "building code." For a two-story house, built on a 10-in. masonry wall, the footing may be 8 in. thick and project 6 in. beyond the face of the wall to make the footing 1 ft. 10 in. For a one-story house built on an 8-in. foundation, the footing may be 8 in. thick and project 5 in. beyond the wall making a width of 1 ft. 6 in. A rule often used in determining the projection of a footing is shown with a 30–60 deg. right triangle laid out with the hypotenuse intersecting the bottom corners of both the footing and the foundation wall.

The weight encountered by foundation walls and footings in porches, garages, and small one-story buildings is light enough that adequate bearing is obtained with an integral footing. One form used commonly shows the foundation wall flared to provide suitable bearing on the foundation bed. Adequate bearing may often be obtained for a poured concrete foundation wall without a flared or projected footing, which in some communities reduces excavating and forming costs.

Sometimes the opposite is true. Then extra-wide or "spread" footings are required. In such cases it is necessary to have the footings project from 8 to 16 in. beyond the face of the fall, reinforced with ⅜ or ½-in. diameter steel rods running in both directions of the footing.

Where brick, tile, or concrete block foundation walls are used the footings are usually figured about the same as for poured concrete. The builder must consider soil conditions, thickness and type of wall, and then use good judgment in determining the size of the footing. Stone basement walls may have stone footings unless the walls are heavily loaded, in which case the footing is of concrete. If practicable, stone footings should consist of stones having a width equal to that of the footing. Stone footings should be hard, strong, durable stones laid on their natural bed and held solid by mortar. As a general rule the thickness of each course is made about equal to its projection beyond the course above. Where foundation walls are of brick, the footings usually are made of brick or concrete. Brick footings should always begin with a double course on the foundation bed and then be laid in single course for ordinary footings. No course should project more than one fourth the length of a brick, except in a 9- or 10-in. wall. The bricks used for footings should be the hardest and soundest obtainable, and should be laid in cement mortar.

For residences, where the load on the footing is usually very light, it is good practice to put a 1-ft. 6-in. footing under all walls where there is an average condition of clay and

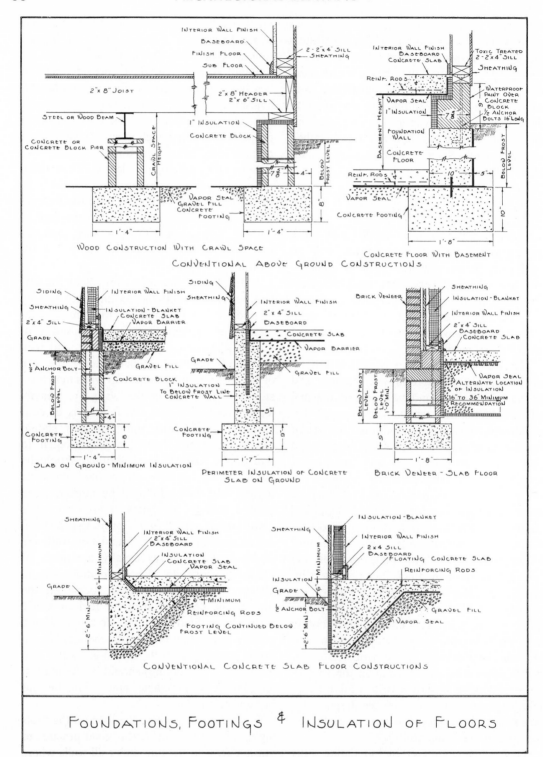

CONVENTIONAL ABOVE GROUND CONSTRUCTIONS

WOOD CONSTRUCTION WITH CRAWL SPACE

CONCRETE FLOOR WITH BASEMENT

SLAB ON GROUND - MINIMUM INSULATION

PERIMETER INSULATION OF CONCRETE SLAB ON GROUND

BRICK VENEER - SLAB FLOOR

CONVENTIONAL CONCRETE SLAB FLOOR CONSTRUCTIONS

FOUNDATIONS, FOOTINGS & INSULATION OF FLOORS

Plate 9

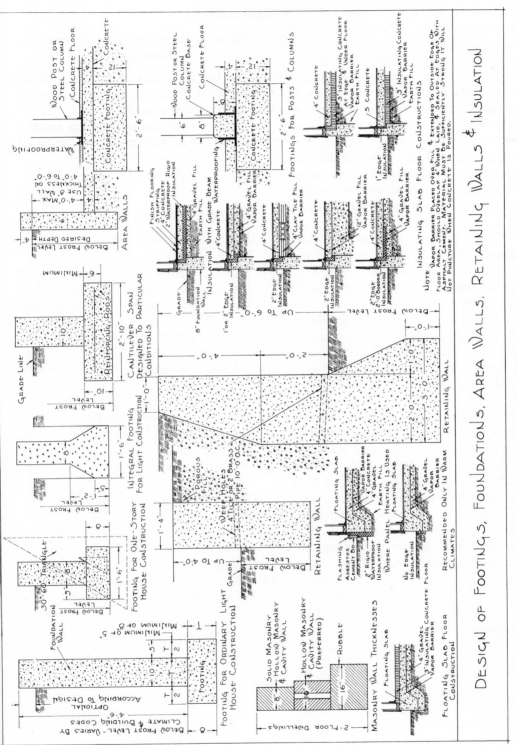

DESIGN OF FOOTINGS, FOUNDATIONS, AREA WALLS, RETAINING WALLS & INSULATION

Plate 9A

gravel. A 16-in. brick foundation wall requires concrete footings 2 ft. 0 in. wide and 8 to 12 in. thick. Brick footing should be 7 courses high, and stepped 1½ in. per course. Footing of stone requires 3 stepped courses of wide, flat, thick stones. A 20-in. stone foundation wall requires 1 course of flat, thick stones 24 to 30 in. wide and from 8 to 12 in. thick.

Footings of liberal size, made of stone or concrete, should be used under all basement posts, columns, or piers to prevent settling. The same is true of footings for chimneys and fireplaces. In most cases footings 1 ft. 6 in. square up to 2 ft. 6 in. square will be found of sufficient size to maintain the load put upon them. Cedar or locust posts 6 or 8 in. in diameter are the best wood supports. If brick piers are used they should not be less than 12 in. square; concrete piers should be from 8 to 12 in. square; stone piers usually measure to a minimum of 16 in. square because of the difficulty of bonding stonework in smaller sizes. The most commonly used column is the 6-in. diameter cast-iron type. Two methods of supporting the basement post are shown in Plate 9. Raising the wood post up off the floor is advisable since this method keeps the post dry and helps prevent wood rot. A metal dowel should extend from the concrete into the post, or a metal plate should be bolted to the concrete to prevent slippage of the post. When a steel post is used, it may rest directly on the footing with the concrete floor poured around it.

ASSIGNMENT

Plate 9, Foundation Walls and Footings

Draw the plate as directed by your instructor. Plan the arrangement of your sheet very carefully for appearance.

This plate shows foundations and footings in common use. Applications are given as found in common house construction.

Scale: ⅜ in. equals 1 ft.

PROBLEMS FOR CLASS DISCUSSION

1. What are the characteristics of several foundation beds?
2. How thick should a stone wall be built for residence foundation work? How thick should cement foundation walls be built?
3. What determines the thickness of the foundation wall?
4. What is the purpose of a footing in a foundation wall?
5. Where are retaining walls used?
6. Why are areaways used? What methods are used to stop the water from draining from the area into the basement?
7. What methods are used to keep basements dry?
8. Why aren't brick foundation walls commonly used? Stone?
9. What two kinds of cement foundation walls are used? What are their advantages?
10. What rules for sizes of footings are used for each type of foundation wall?

Garage Doors

Private garages may have doors of any style depending upon the space available for the doors, and the taste and needs of the owner. It is one of the most conspicuous features of the modern home which requires much thought and consideration in its design and planning. Manufacturers have developed several designs to meet an infinite variety of problems and tastes.

There are about six major types of garage doors on the market which can be roughly classified as: (1) roll-up or sectional door; (2) swing-up or panel type; (3) sliding doors; (4) hinged doors; (5) accordion doors; and (6) the upward-folding door (Fig. 11). Soon the old-type hinged door will be discarded in favor of the more satisfactory patented types. Upward-acting doors of one type or another are far in the lead in popularity with builders and home purchasers. Swinging doors are designed to swing out in order to economize on space. Where large swinging doors are used, a small wicket door is provided which works independently of the large door. Accordion doors are divided into several sections and hung on steel rails by trolleys. The tracks or rails are curved at the side of the door openings, and the door sections fall back against the side walls when they are opened. The upward-acting doors are built on the principle of the old-style office desk with the roll top. The door is built in horizontal sections which move up and down with trolleys operating in two steel channels installed at the sides of the door. The lift is assisted by strong steel springs. The sections of the door are attached by steel hinges and the trolleys are provided with ball bearings which reduce the labor necessary in opening and closing. The doors may be either wood or steel and are made in many pleasing designs (Fig. 11).

A necessary consideration in planning any garage for the installation of an upward acting door is the provision for headroom. There are doors available to take care of all kinds of headroom situations, with a number on the market which require no headroom, some only 2 or 3 in., or up the scale to others which require 15 to 16 in. Manufacturer's catalogs are to be consulted in these cases for the necessary information.

Minimum door sizes depend upon the ease with which a car can be driven into the garage. With a straight, unobstructed approach a 7-ft. 4-in. opening is practical for a minimum one-car garage. This allows a desirable clearance of 1 ft. 6 in. between the average small-car width and the door jambs. If entering the garage requires maneuvering or involves a curve near the doors, clearances should be increased and door openings enlarged accordingly. The extent depends upon the size of the car and its angle of rake in making the necessary entrance turns. For ordinary side-hinged doors clearance for hardware should be 6 in. minimum; for offset hinges or corner tracks, minimum jamb clearances range from 2 in. to 2 ft 2 in.; lifting doors require special hardware with clearances ranging from 2½ in. to 1 ft. 11½ in. Stock-door sizes range from the smallest listed, which is 8 ft. 0 in. wide by 6 ft. 6 in. high, on up to the garage width of 14 ft. 0 in., 15 ft. 0 in., and 16 ft. 0 in. (Fig. 12). The table on page 71 gives a partial listing which is approaching standardization.

There are sectional roll-up doors available with removable center posts; thus two or more doors can be installed to close a large opening, and if desirable the center posts between the doors can be raised up and taken out of the way to provide a full-width opening.

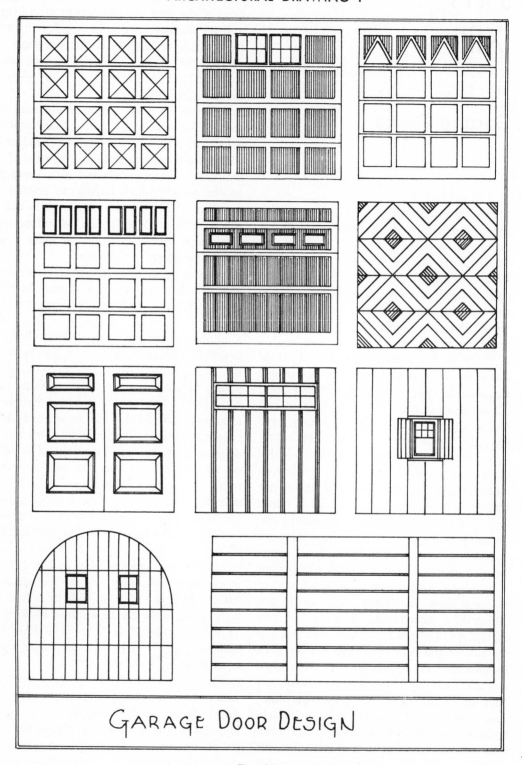

GARAGE DOOR DESIGN

Fig. 11

Door Size		Door Type	Panels	Sections
Width	Height	(Wood)	Wide	High
8'-0"	6'-6"	One-piece Sectional	2	
	6'-8"	One-piece		
	7'-0"	One-piece Sectional	3	
	7'-6"	One-piece Sectional	4	
	8'-0"	One-piece Sectional		
9'-0"	6'-6"	Sectional	3	
	7'-0"	One-piece	4	
		Sectional	6	4
10'-0"	7'-0"	One-piece Sectional		
14'-0"	7'-0"	One-piece Sectional	8	
15'-0"	7'-0"	One-piece Sectional		
16'-0"	6'-6" 7'-0"	One-piece Sectional		

Manufacturers are introducing reasonably economical remote control, by electricity or sound activation, to operate garage doors. The desirability and convenience of remote control lies in the fact that the garage door can be opened or closed by merely pushing a button on the instrument panel or floor board of the car. With garages fronting on the street and being used more extensively as utility or storage structures, the need of keeping the door closed at all times is obvious. It not only lessens the danger of theft but hides from public view miscellaneous equipment which might detract from the neat appearance of the premises. Since houses are designed to look their best with the openings closed it is desirable to have a garage door closed whether the garage is attached to the house or not. Basically the several different models of automatic door closers consist of a sending unit mounted in the owner's car with tuned wave length set to activate the door operator mounted in the garage. His wave length will not open other doors and no other owner can operate his door. These units make contact with a coil imbedded in the driveway or directly attached to the operating mechanism. There are units that activate the door operator with inaudible sound vibrations. Electrical switches inside the garage can be used to open or close the door, and the door can be operated manually in case of power failure.

Proper installation of hardware and fittings is essential to proper functioning of the doors. Decide upon the particular door to be installed before the rough opening is made so that the door will fit properly, and so that any necessary headers and jamb framing members can be built in to keep the door plumb and rigid. Hardware should be selected according to the style, size, and weight of the doors. Old garages are often remodeled with new doors or with new fittings. Hardware which will convert swinging or accordion doors to the upward-acting type can be bought.

The modern home implies compact space within the house itself, with the garage serving a multitude of purposes in addition to protecting the automobile from weather and other sources of damage. Garages should also be planned for storing other equipment required in the protection and maintenance of the home and grounds. Extra storage space as well as workshop space for the man of the house should be provided. Recreational facilities and play areas may be added. The garage may house such articles as lawn furniture, bicycles and outdoor toys, lawn hose, lawn roller, lawn mower, fertilizer, storm sash or screens, step ladder, extension ladder, firewood, garden tools, toboggan, sled, skiis, lumber, awnings, paint, shovels, plus the odd items accumulated to care for a family car. For single car garages it has been found feasible to add 5 ft. 0 in. to 6 ft. 0 in. to the length of the garage rather than widening the garage which may require a greater lot width (Fig. 13). A double-car 20 ft. 0 in. wide unit is desirable where space permits. A minimum clearance for passage is 1 ft.

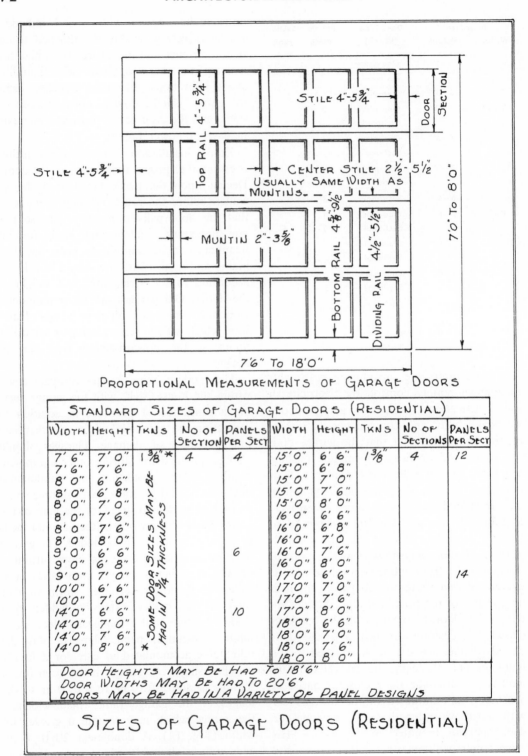

PROPORTIONAL MEASUREMENTS OF GARAGE DOORS

STANDARD SIZES OF GARAGE DOORS (RESIDENTIAL)

WIDTH	HEIGHT	TKNS	No OF SECTION	PANELS PER SECT	WIDTH	HEIGHT	TKNS	No OF SECTIONS	PANELS PER SECT
7' 6"	7' 0"	1⅜" *	4	4	15' 0"	6' 6"	1⅜"	4	12
7' 6"	7' 6"				15'0"	6' 8"			
8' 0"	6' 6"				15'0"	7' 0"			
8' 0"	6' 8"				15'0"	7' 6"			
8' 0"	7' 0"				15'0"	8' 0"			
8' 0"	7' 6"				16' 0"	6' 6"			
8' 0"	7' 6"				16' 0"	6' 8"			
8' 0"	8' 0"				16'0"	7' 0			
9' 0"	6' 6"			6	16' 0"	7' 6"			
9' 0"	6' 8"				16' 0"	8' 0"			
9' 0"	7' 0"				17'0"	6' 6"			14
10'0"	6' 6"				17'0"	7' 0"			
10'0"	7' 0"				17'0"	7' 6"			
14'0"	6' 6"			10	17'0"	8' 0"			
14'0"	7' 0"				18'0"	6' 6"			
14'0"	7' 6"				18'0"	7' 0"			
14'0"	8' 0"	*			18'0"	7' 6"			
					18'0"	8' 0"			

* SOME DOOR SIZES MAY BE HAD IN 1¾ THICKNESS

DOOR HEIGHTS MAY BE HAD TO 18'6"
DOOR WIDTHS MAY BE HAD TO 20'6"
DOORS MAY BE HAD IN A VARIETY OF PANEL DESIGNS

SIZES OF GARAGE DOORS (RESIDENTIAL)

Fig. 12

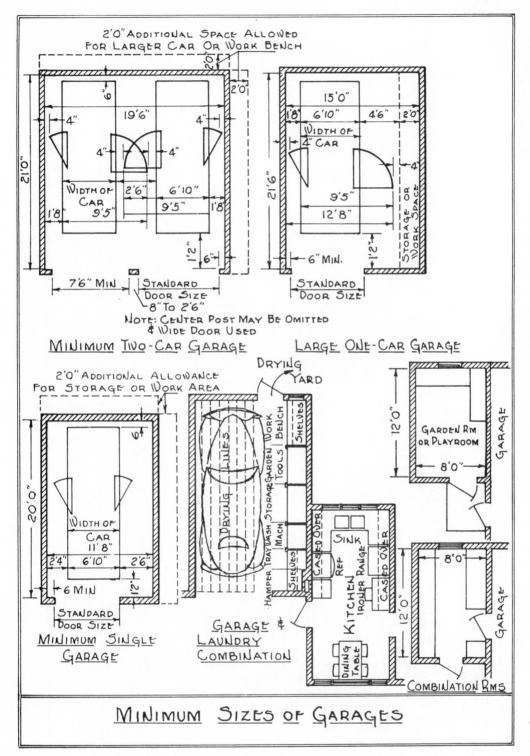

Fig. 13

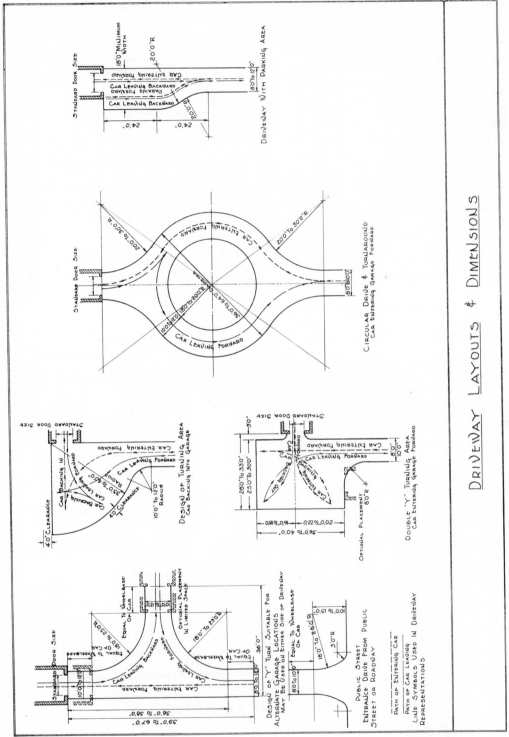

DRIVEWAY LAYOUTS & DIMENSIONS

Fig. 14

6 in., and 2-ft. 0-in. working clearance when the workbench is at the front end of the garage and 3 ft. 0 in. preferred in other conditions. The space for the car must be at least wide enough to permit car doors to be opened so individuals may comfortably get in or out when the car is in the garage. A 10-ft. 0-in. allowance is about the minimum for this accommodation. Allowance for length should be such that a person can get around the car when the garage door is closed, which means at least 6 in. in the front end and about 18 in. in the back of the garage. The ceiling or deck above the car should be at least 7 ft. 6 in. above the floor. Minimum requirements in many areas specify an inside garage width of 9 ft. 6 in. and a length ot 19 ft. 0 in.

Poor driveway planning results in tricky maneuvering, bad grades, obstructed views, accidents, and general grief for the home- owner. A one-car driveway should be at least 8 ft. 0 in. wide on the straight run and 11 ft. 0 in. wide on the curves (Fig. 14). The minimum width for a two-car driveway is 15 ft. 0 in., and wider if possible. If the driveway slopes there should be a level area the length of the car in front of the garage to prevent rolling if the brakes are not set. The smallest outside radius for a curve should be 29 ft. 0 in., and an 18-ft. 0-in. radius on the inside of the curve. The radius of the curve at the turn-in from the curb should be from 3 ft. 0 in. to 5 ft. 0 in. Sharp dips and abrupt changes in levels of the grade are other faults to avoid. A change in grade level of not over 1 in. per foot in any 10-ft. 0-in. stretch will allow adequate clearance for overhangs. The driveway should slope slightly to the sides for drainage.

ASSIGNMENT

Plate 10, Types of Garage Doors

Draw symbols for common types of garage doors. Scale ⅜ in. equals 1 ft.

Alternate plate assignment: Draw the de- tails of an overhead garage door, showing the elevation, vertical section, horizontal section, enlarged sectional view arrangement, and ex- planatory details necessary. Refer to a manu- facturer's catalog for particular details of construction and installation.

PROBLEMS FOR CLASS DISCUSSION

1. What types of garage doors are in com- mon use? Discuss the advantages and disadvantages of each type of door.
2. What arrangements are used for sliding doors to save space?
3. When and where are the wicket doors used?
4. What sizes are used in garage doors?
5. What patented mechanical devices are used on garage doors?

ARCHITECTURAL DRAWING II

UNIT

I

House Construction

After the site has been selected and a decision is made as to the style and type of house to be built, working drawings and specifications for the building are made. An architect is usually employed to do this work.

Specifications indicate how the drawings should be followed, what kind of materials should be used, and should give the carpenter and the owner all the information necessary to understand definitely and agree on the whole plan before the building is begun. Changes made in the building after the work has begun are costly to the owner and annoying to the contractor; therefore, before allowing the contractor to begin work, each detail of the drawing and all of the specifications should be studied carefully and be thoroughly understood. A set of working drawings should not be accepted from the architect until it satisfies the owner.

When the builder has received his contract, the first step in actual construction is to locate the house upon the land. The lot is "staked out" to indicate where the exterior walls should be placed and where the excavation should be made. This is known as the "layout." Generally this is accomplished in one operation, but occasionally the building is laid out twice, once for the excavation and again for the foundations. All buildings must be built with lines, the outside faces of the foundation walls of the structure are the

building lines, and the outside walls of the structure are represented by the main building lines. These lines are used as reference or base lines from which all secondary measurements of the building are obtained. The dimensions between building lines are shown on the plans, especially the foundation and plot plans, and these measurements must be transferred and located on the ground so that the construction of the building may follow them accurately. In order to lay out the building precisely, a system of stakes, lines, and batter boards is customarily used. These are placed after the topsoil has been stripped. Surveyor's instruments, especially the transit, are convenient for making the layout, but they are not essential and accurate work can be done without them.

The front building line is in many ways the most important because it is the starting point for all other measurements. Furthermore, in most cities zoning ordinances establish minimum distances from the front lines of the building to front lot lines, and if through error the building is not sufficiently cleared on this measurement, it may involve costly tearing down and rebuilding to correct the error. It is permissible to go back farther than the minimum, but often the owner attempts to stay directly on the line. Almost always the "front line" refers to the outside face of the foundation wall under the front wall of the house proper, exclusive of porches, stoops, areas, and so forth, but local zoning peculiarities must be checked for variations. The builder must have clearly defined lot boundaries from which to work. Generally these are defined by surveyor's stakes or bounds of some kinds situated at the corners of the lot. If such markers are not present, the builder should require that they be given to him; otherwise he cannot be responsible for errors in establishing house lines.

Houses are built on concrete slabs, foundation walls providing a crawl space under the floors, and with foundation walls deep enough that basement space can be utilized. Concrete blocks, poured concrete, brick, tile, and stone are the common materials used for foundations. The foundation walls have two primary functions: (1) to support the building with a minimum of settling, and (2) to keep water and dampness from entering basement. In many respects, foundations are the most important part of any structure. Once built, little can be done to change or improve them. If they are adequate, the building remains stable, level, and plumb; if not, settlement causes cracks and leaks in the foundation, sloping floors, binding windows and doors, cracked plaster, and general racking of the structure. Foundations normally consist of two principal parts — footings and walls. When the climate is mild and no basement desired, the foundation may consist of piers resting on footings and supporting grade beams upon which the house may be built.

Footings are generally used under foundation walls, piers, and posts, to distribute the weight of the wall (and the structure above) over an area of earth sufficiently large to bear the weight. In firm soils, such as compact sand and gravel, footings may be omitted if the foundation wall is poured concrete, continuous, and self-supporting. Walls of concrete block, brick, or stone should have footings no matter what bearing soil. Footings for foundation walls under houses are seldom computed for load but instead are built by rule of thumb (see pp. 65 and 67).

The seepage problem must also be studied in relation to the site. If the grounds are sloping, the side of the house facing uphill will be subjected to the pressure of the downflowing waters, especially after a rain. A tile drainway, properly placed beneath the ground and around the outside of the footings, will collect these waters and carry them away. These tile drains should be connected with the sewer or other drainage system. In any event, it is best to apply to the foundation walls one of the several types of good waterproofing that are on the market. A wet basement and a leaky foundation wall are not only annoying but definitely dangerous because of the harmful effect on the structure of the house and the health of the people living in it. In spite of all precautions, a basement remains a damp, cool place unless it is provided with windows that permit sunshine to enter sometime during the day. In crawl spaces used in some modern houses ventilators are used in the walls to help keep the space dry and help prevent the rotting of the wood members. If proper precautions are taken it is easy to make the basement suitable for use as playroom, workshop, study, or what have you.

Solid concrete foundation walls for dwellings are usually 10 or 12 in. thick, although 8 in. often meets requirements. Very thin walls and piers must be used with considerable caution, for while they may meet load-bearing requirement, they have a tendency to fail in shear or to buckle because of earth or water pressure. It is a good rule, therefore, whenever walls or piers less than 10 in. thick must be used, to reinforce them with vertical rods. Another useful rule is to limit the height of unreinforced walls or piers to ten times their thickness; if the ratio is greater, reinforcing rods should be used. Frequently the thickness of the wall is determined by the character of the structure above rather than by the load it is to support. The thickness of a frame wall is 5 or 6 in.; 1 in. for sheathing, 4 in. for studs, and another inch for outside finish if the latter does not extend beyond the wall. An 8-in. wall would do in this case. A brick wall, brick veneer, or brick with tile backing is at least 9 in. thick and at least 9 or 10 in. of foundation wall thickness must be provided. For stone face and tile backing 16 to 18 in. of foundation wall thickness may be necessary.

Provision must be made in the walls for openings such as doors and windows. Finished wood frames should not be set in the poured concrete because they are likely to swell and become distorted. Openings should be boxed and the frames set later. In the boxing there should be placed 2 by 4-in. wood blocks, best dovetail shaped, which remain in the concrete and to which the frames can be easily fastened. When steel frames are to be used, the frames are built into the boxes with the edges of the frames protruding. Concrete is poured and hardens around the frame thereby firmly anchoring it in place. Pipes for water, gas, oil, and electricity are brought through the foundation, and openings for these must be left in the wall. Openings are most conveniently provided by placing in the forms pieces of pipe or metal sleeves whose length equals the thickness of the wall and whose diameter is slightly larger than the pipes that are to pass through them. At the places where it is necessary to undermine footings, they should be either enlarged, or better still, reinforced with steel rods. This also applies to the vent line of the house trap.

If the construction is to be frame, it will have a sill which should be bolted to the foundation walls. These bolts, generally ½ by 15 in. provided with 2-in. washers at each end and spaced approximately 4 ft. apart, are suspended in the forms to the proper height and position. The concrete is then poured setting them in place. Later the sill can be slipped over them and fastened down by nut and washer.

Basements must be of such height that the proper pitch on the heating pipes may be obtained, if the heating unit is to be placed in the basement, and the sewer connections may be made properly. This height is ordinarily not less that 6 ft. 6 in. Preferably it should be 7 ft. or more. Basement walls should extend down below the frost line for that area; the height of the wall above the grade line is determined primarily by the style of the house.

Instead of poured concrete, walls are fre-

quently built of concrete block small enough to be handled by one man, and laid in much the same manner as brick. Although at one time there was a great multiplicity of sizes and shapes, concrete blocks have now been more or less standardized and those units commonly used are 7¾ by 15¾ in. on the vertical face with thicknesses varying from 8 to 12 in. in 2 in. multiples. With ¼-in. mortar joints all of these blocks are 8 by 16 in. on the face. To decrease weight and to save material, vertical open spaces are left in the interior of the blocks. For corners, special blocks with smooth end faces supplement the ordinary block with hollowed ends. Many special blocks are still made and these call for various interlocking and cross-tying systems, but they are all variations of the standard blocks. Smaller units much used and called "tile" are simply ordinary blocks reduced in size. Concrete blocks are customarily used for foundations only, but they may be used for the structure of the house, especially if they are faced with stucco, brick or some other masonry material. Sometimes blocks with a finished surface (commonly made to simulate roughly dressed stone) are employed with no further facing. In such cases they are used the same as cut stone, and must be made especially to conform to particular wall openings, or the openings must conform to the stock sizes of such blocks. The blocks are laid end to end "stretcher" fashion completely around the wall; the first course is leveled on top of the footing so that subsequent courses will also be true. The next layer is laid on top of the first but with the vertical joints offset half the length of a block. Therefore joints in every other course are directly above one another. Blocks lap over each other at the corners and provide a good bond. If walls are to be concealed below grade level, standard blocks may be used at the corners instead of the special, smooth-ended corner blocks.

Since blocks are 8 in. high including a ¼-in. mortar joint, any wall height which is not a multiple of 8 in. has to be obtained by (1) shimming with brick, (2) half blocks laid on the flat, (3) thickening all horizontal joints, or (4) combinations of the methods. Where doors, windows, or other openings occur, frames are usually erected before the wall is started so that the wall may be built tight against the frames. Nailing blocks are built into the wall directly adjacent to the frames, and the frames are spiked to these blocks for anchorage. If frames are erected subsequent to laying up the wall, openings of the correct size must be left and nailing blocks provided as indicated. Blocks are commonly pieces of 2 by 4-in. material. Strap iron anchors may be laid in the mortar joints and spiked to the frames when the frames are previously set. Concrete blocks are laid across the tops of openings on lintels. The lintel may be reinforced concrete, wood (2-in. thickness and laid on edge, or timber), or steel angles. Where changes in direction occur in a wall, care must be exercised to build the corners straight and plumb, and to make sure that no long vertical alignment of joints occurs. Such vertical joints are avoided by carrying the succeeding courses of blocks into the corner alternately from one side and the other. Pilasters are short sections of wall which are increased in thickness throughout its height, usually to carry concentrated loads such as posts and beams. Since there is a return at each side of the pilaster, the same precautions respecting long vertical joints hold as for corners. The pilaster may be built as an integral part of the wall by bonding wall and pilaster block together. To obtain odd dimensions, brick and half-blocks must be used. Piers are free-standing posts, usually square in cross section, which support structural loads. Frequently, voids or hollow openings in concrete block piers are filled with concrete to obtain a completely solid structure. Piers may also be constructed of poured concrete. For concrete block wall construction, anchoring is accomplished by carrying the bolts down some depth into the wall. In concrete block this should be equal

to at least two courses of block. The lower ends of the bolts are provided with steel plate washers approximately 4 in. square, which are embedded in the horizontal mortar joint. The bolts extend upward through the hollow openings in the block and are fixed in place by filling the openings with mortar.

In damp soil locations concrete block walls are apt to leak, so extra precautions must be taken to insure dry walls. Drain tile around the outsides of footings are essential to prevent a head of water from being built up against the wall. Drains lead into dry wells or into municipal sewerage systems. Even in relatively dry locations it is often desirable to "parge" or plaster the outside of the wall with a layer of mortar ¼ to ½ in. thick, troweled to seal the porous surface of the block. A heavy asphaltum is also painted on the surface to serve the same purpose. Membrane waterproofing consists of alternate layers of hot pitch and builder's felt. Advantages of block construction are elimination of the necessity for forms, which helps speed up production. Block walls are ready for upper level construction almost as soon as they are finished, and need not be allowed to stand longer than to allow the mortar to set. Solid concrete walls must be allowed to set before the forms are removed. Block walls offer poor anchorage, are more apt to allow seepage of water, and tend to crack through settling.

Several light-weight materials have been developed in the interest of economy and improvement of finished appearance, especially in the walls above grade. Cinder blocks, often known as "cincrete blocks," are made of hard-burned anthracite cinder aggregate. Since watertight walls are of prime consideration, the units must be used with attention to good workmanship, and the blocks carefully inspected for soundness, and the effects of freezing should be carefully considered. These walls contain a hollow space into which any penetrating water finds its way downward to the bottom of the wall and out through weep holes provided for the purpose. Wall ties must be of special design which will not transport water across the opening and into the inside of the construction. A lightweight block uses a special aggregate made by processing and burning shale into porous pieces ranging in size from coarse dust to crushed stone.

Since many dwellings are built entirely of stone, the information pertaining to masonry construction has previously been explained. Random rubble is the cheapest of the stone walls, and varies in thickness from 16 to 24 in. or more depending on the construction above. A closely knit wall depends upon the holding power of the bonding stones. These are stones which are laid in one piece extending through the thickness of the wall, and in good work should occur at least once in each 6 to 10 sq. ft. of wall surface. Stability is the important item in laying up the walls, which is accomplished by joints properly broken and bedded in good mortar. The walls should be leveled off every 2 ft. in height, if possible.

The basement floor is not poured at the same time foundation walls are built. It must wait until the house is framed and all the necessary underground service lines have been placed, but it should be poured as soon as possible to allow it to dry thoroughly before the finish lumber arrives. Otherwise dampness originating in the basement causes swelling and warping of the kiln-dried millwork used for interior finish. It is wise to put down a layer of cinders, gravel, or crushed stone, from 4 to 6 in. thick, before the concrete is poured. To avoid settlement the fill must be well tamped, preferably dampened at the same time to make it more compact. Concrete used in basement floors should be mixed quite stiff to reduce the amount of water which must be evaporated, to increase the density, and to provide a harder, more wear resistant surface. If floor drains are to be provided, the floor should be gradually but uniformly sloped toward the drains from all directions. To make sure that the slope is correct, stakes may be set in the fill and brought to the proper pitch with the carpenter's level and straight edge. Concrete is then poured and leveled to the tops of the stakes, which are removed during the process.

The exterior walls of the house may be, (1) frame, (2) frame and stucco, (3) frame and veneer, (4) solid brick or stone, (5) concrete block or tile, or (6) hollow tile with a veneered finish. Masonry veneer is similar to frame construction, except that the outside finish is of brick, stone, or some other material to give the appearance of solid masonry construction. The wall is built up of wood in the same manner as frame, or a hollow tile backing may be used. If built of wood frame a 1-in. air space is provided between the face of the wood sheathing and the back of the masonry veneer. The masonry veneer is then secured to the sheathing with metal ties. It is recommended that a layer of insulating paper be used between the framework and the masonry which with the dead air space furnishes good insulation and reduces moisture and condensation problems. This type of wall construction is favored by many builders and architects because it permits greater flexibility in the design of the house through the introduction of a number of different wall surfaces and textures.

Solid masonry walls in houses usually vary from 8 to 16-in. thickness, depending upon the height particularly. They can be built with either common brick or concrete block backing of 4 to 8 in. depth with 4 in. of face brick or stone backing. The inside face of solid masonry walls are furred to receive lath and plaster. In cases where basements are provided, the wall of the foundation should be at least 2 in. thicker than the wall above. A variation of the solid wall which has received widespread recognition is the cavity wall. This is made up of two separate brick or tile walls which are separated by an air space about 2 in. wide. The two walls, known as "wythes," are held together by rust-proof metal ties placed in the mortar joints at regular intervals (every six courses) as the walls are constructed. There should be no "bridge" between the inside and outside tier. The term bridge, as used here, refers to materials that may become lodged within the 2-in. air space, thus acting as a conductor for the transmission of moisture or cold air. In laying up this type of wall, the mason needs to be extremely careful to see that excess mortar does not drop into the air space and form a bridge. The exterior wythe is the exterior finish; the interior wythe may be used as the interior finish of the room, or plaster may be applied to the interior face of the wythe for variation.

Another type of wall is reinforced masonry. This is used wherever there is a heavy load or stress upon the wall. The reinforcing rods may be placed either in a vertical or horizontal position. Vertical reinforcing is recommended for any wall where there is excessive pressure distributed from the roof load, or water pressure in the case of foundation walls.

The all-steel house employs the use of steel channels for the vertical members and metal panels both inside and out for finish. The stressed-skin principle is applied in the manufacture of wall panels for prefabricated frame houses. Reduction in the size of the vertical framing members has been made possible through increased structural strength that is obtained with the use of glued-on surface panels. Indications are that the demand for glues will increase in home construction. The new durable glues are ideal for fastening of plywood and composition boards to studs and framing members. With the introduction of large window openings in the exterior walls, of large open areas within the house where several rooms are combined in one, and with the use of movable partitions which destroy much of the rigidity of the house, the question of immobility in the exterior walls with relation to wind pressure becomes of prime importance. This rigidity can be obtained in frame walls through the use of sufficient diagonal bracing at the corners of the house or wherever a break occurs in a continuous horizontal surface. The use of large rigid sheathing materials in houses of this type is essential as far greater bracing resistance is obtained than with the 6 or 8 in. width sheathing boards.

With the advent of the basementless house where a concrete slab is placed under the first floor area, the finished first floor line is usually placed from 6 to 8 in. above the grade line. Thus the wood members of the wall framing are placed dangerously close to the moist ground where they are subject to decay and termite attack. To guard against this condition it is well to adhere to the following practices:

1. Do not place wood in contact with moist ground.

2. Outside wood trim, water tables, etc., should be 8 in. or more above finished grade.

3. Provide dampproofing between wood and masonry where conditions may allow dampness to come in contact with the wood.

4. Avoid construction that permits condensation of moisture within the walls.

TYPES OF WOOD FRAMING

There are many types of house framing in use in the various sections of the country, but for practical purposes, they may be grouped into the following classifications; (1) braced frame, (2) balloon frame, and, (3) platform frame.

Braced Frame. The braced timber frame, "barn frame" and "old fashioned" frame (Fig. 15) is the oldest and is used primarily in the earliest settled portions of the country, particularly in New England. The early colonists brought with them a tradition of heavy, European half-timber construction, which was encouraged by the abundance of virgin timber at hand. Nails were hand forged; therefore, the early builders used them sparingly, and were most inventive in devising methods of fastening with mortises and tenons locked and fastened together with wood dowel pins.

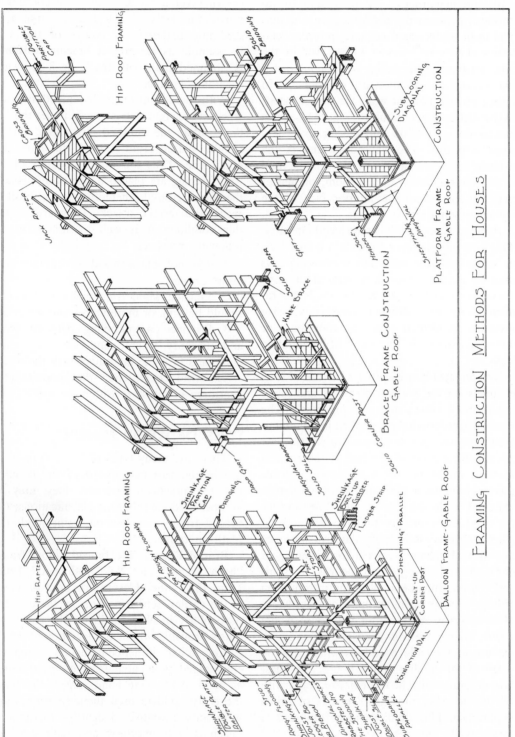

FRAMING CONSTRUCTION METHODS FOR HOUSES

Fig. 15

The principal framing members of the early constructions were hewn out of trees nearest at hand and of much larger dimensions than were actually required for strength and rigidity. Because of the amount of time used in this method of building the wood members were given sufficient time to air-dry thoroughly before being used. This method of construction produced an almost faultless house of which hundreds still standing (and in use) bear witness. Originally, this type was characterized by heavy timber posts at the corners, often with lighter posts between, all of which extended continuously from a heavy foundation sill to an equally heavy plate at the roof line. At the second story, were introduced heavy timber girts running from post to post, carefully mortised and tenoned and secured with oak dowel pins. The joists were notched over the girts while their inner ends rested on post-supported girders. The studs served merely as fillers, making what is known as a curtain wall, and were not intended to carry any weight. A fairly heavy piece, usually 4 by 6, was used as a plate. This plate served two purposes: first, to tie the studding together at the top and form a finish for the wall; and second, to furnish a support for the lower ends of the rafters. Braces were used as permanent parts of the structure and served to stiffen the wall, to keep the corners true and square, and to prevent the frame from being distorted by the wind. A brace was placed wherever a sill, a girt, or a plate made an angle with the corner post.

With the introduction of cheap nails, modern tools, and hardware, the construction has been modified and is still undergoing change. While still much heavier and costly than other methods of framing, it is lighter than in colonial times. Corner posts and girts built up of two or three pieces of 2-in. lumber now take the place of the solid timbers originally used. Nails replace mortises and tenons, and dowel pins for fastening. With the elimination of the heavy timber girts the intermediate posts required to support them have been done away with, and the studs have become an integral part of the structure, supporting the floors and roof about as they do in other types of construction.

Balloon Frame. The distinguishing characteristic of balloon framing (Fig. 15) is that the wall studs extend in one piece from the sill to the plate, with the ends of the second floor joists spiked to their sides and resting upon a false girt ("ribband board," "ribbon," or "ledger") which is notched into them on the inside. A box sill is ordinarily combined with this kind of framing. The elimination of the girts in the walls has brought about the necessity of placing fire-stops between the studs to prevent the walls from serving as a chimney with its updraft. Floor headers and fire-stops between the joists accomplish the same purpose. The subfloors are laid diagonally with the joists. The bearing partition studs rest upon the girders. Corner bracing is also required unless the sheathing accomplishes the purpose. Boards used for sheathing should be applied diagonally.

Balloon framing offers the advantages of speed and economy, and possesses excellent rigidity. Properly constructed, it is in every way recommended and most building codes require it. Builders have developed the method of construction in two diametrically opposite directions. Generally it has been improved to the point where it meets all the demands of efficient building practice. Some "jerry builders" through corner cutting have cheapened it to the point where it is a flimsy, short-lived structure.

In this construction the window openings on the second floor should be placed on the same vertical center lines as those used on the first floor for practical economy, as much as the appearance and design of the house will allow. In making plans for such frame structure, it is usual, then, to locate the windows by center lines measured from the corner posts. All studs about these openings should be doubled. Large openings are commonly spanned by large headers rather than by trusses. Trussing an opening is more difficult in this type construction because there is no girt or header at the second floor line against which the diagonals can bear, and a secondary header above the diagonals must be used. Since this makes the trussed opening even more complicated, and since the chief advantage of the balloon frame is economy and simplicity, this construction is not often used. It is, however, better than the simple large header with its tendency to shrink and swell.

Platform or Western Framing. The platform method of framing (Fig. 15) is the fastest and safest form of good construction and is gaining favor because of its economy. Interior and exterior walls are framed alike assuring that any shrinkage or settling will be uniform throughout the structure. Each floor is framed separately, with the subfloor laid before the wall and partition studs are raised. The fact that all studding is normally the same length permits the specification and use of ready-to-use lumber with consequent labor and waste saving on the job. Braced with diagonal sheathing, let-in bracing, the construction is adequately rigid to withstand all wind conditions.

In this type of framing, a box sill is used and the subfloor is laid to the outer edge forming a platform. The studs rest on a sill or "sole" which is spiked to the subfloor. The first floor studs support the second floor plates, joists, and flooring, where a second platform is begun for the second floor. This type of construction makes use of a series of these platforms to make up the full height of the structure.

The fault of this type of frame is that it accomplishes its end not through the reduction in the amount of cross-grained lumber but by the addition of more. It also lacks some of the strength found in the other methods, and therefore is not to be recommended for stucco, brick veneer, or with masonry walled buildings for either outside or inside construction. Special framing methods are required around chimneys, whether interior or exterior, and special precautions should be taken in flashing around chimneys and vents.

Quality of Construction. Quality in construction does not necessarily mean the use of the finest of materials available, but rather it does mean getting the best out of the materials at hand. Even the least expensive materials usually have their use and can bring about substantial savings. Good workmanship is the important factor in the use of good building materials, and consists of giving quality in places where it is important. This does not mean merely where it shows but allows taking a shortcut here and there where it is permissible. Even the best of carpenters, for example, will ruin a nail once in a while and if this happens in a place which does not show he will not bother to pull out the nail; he will hammer it over and drive another nail beside it. Precision in workmanship slows progress on a house and does not make for greater ultimate quality in the finished product; it would be just as absurd to use finish lumber for the framing of a house instead of the rough timbers commonly furnished for this purpose which are selected more for strength than for beauty.

In the basic framing of a house, precision counts most in level floors and plumb walls. This is a difficult job and calls for patience and exacting work. If you can lay a marble on a smooth floor, and the marble rolls from one end of the room to the other, the floor is badly off level. To achieve a level floor, the carpenter must see that the tops of all joists are exactly in a level line at the bearing points over sills and beams. To accomplish this may require shimming up joist ends at some points, cutting away from the bottom edge at other points. Plumb lines and carpenter's level are then used to make sure that the wall studs go up absolutely vertical and that corners are true. If masonry construction is being used, the mason must be constantly on the watch for deviations from a plumb wall. In either frame or masonry construction, if corners are not true right angles, and if the walls are not truly vertical, there will be trouble every step of the way in the remaining construction. An 8-ft. wall can be a full inch or more out of plumb in its height, without the error being apparent to the eye. If opposite walls are out of plumb, in opposite directions, the error can add up to 2 or 3 in., and the error may not show up until you try to put up wall paper or wood paneling on the end wall. Roof framing presents difficulties when walls are out of square. If the walls are put up properly, the angle cuts that must be made on each rafter are all identical and can be made quickly. If the walls are out of square, the angle cuts on every rafter may have to be slightly different to get a correctly framed roof.

DETAILS OF FRAME CONSTRUCTION

Posts and Girders. The outer ends of the joists which support the first floor rest directly upon the foundation wall, or on a sill, which in turn rests upon the foundation wall. The inner ends of these joists rest upon girders which are supported by bearing posts, masonry piers, poured concrete piers, hollow steel pipe, or steel pipe filled with concrete. If a building is wider than 14 or 15 ft. it is generally desirable (and often necessary), to use additional support near the center of the house to avoid the necessity of excessively heavy floor joists.

In determining the number and location of girders, consideration must be given to the permissible length of joists, to the room arrangement, to the location of the bearing partitions, and whether the girder is to be wood or steel. In most houses one girder will suffice; if a joist span exceeds 14 or 15 ft., for which a 2 by 10 in. is usually used, considerable increase in joist size becomes necessary in most wood species, thus making an additional girder advisable. Suppose the specifications call for 17 ft. 6 in. between inner faces of the bearing walls. If no girders are used, a 2 by 14-in. or 3 by 10-in. joist would be required in most cases. On the other hand, if a girder is to be used at the center of the building, the joist span would be one-half the length of 8 ft. 9 in., for which a 2 by 6-in. joist could be safely used. Furthermore, joists over 14-ft. lengths require two rows of bridging, so that economy of time and material is a consideration. Since joists are cut in 2-ft. multiples of length, the best spacing of girders is such as to allow full use of these lengths without waste. Usually, however, girders must be placed under important bearing partitions and these in turn are regulated in their spacing by room sizes. Sometimes it is desirable to place girders over basement partitions so they will not project into the ceiling space in finished basement rooms.

Most girders in houses and other light constructions are wood, but steel shapes are becoming more common. Wood girders may be either solid or built up. The built-up timber consists of pieces of 2- or 3-in. dimension stock set on edge and spiked or lag-screwed together to form a single piece. The solid timber is simplest and gives the most actual timber for a given cross section (a nominal 8-in. solid timber is actually 7½ in. whereas four 2-in. pieces are actually four times 1⅝ in. or 6½ in.). A built-up timber, therefore, would have to be made up of five 2-in. pieces to contain as much wood as the solid member. On the other hand, solid pieces run only from support to support whereas built-up girders can be made continuous from one end of the building to the other, thereby tying the entire frame more closely together and adding somewhat to the stiffness of the girder. Solid timbers are also apt to check badly. The larger sizes of timber call for an extra item in the lumber order whereas the built-up timbers are made of the same stock that is used for floor joists. Joints in built-up girders should be well "broken" and should occur at approximately the quarter-points of the span, not directly over the supports. If the total load on the girder, the span, and the allowable stress on the lumber to be used is known, it is possible by engineering formula to compute the necessary size of the girder. This information has been worked out in table form and can be found in the reference books necessarily at hand.

Steel beams used as girders in the I and wide-flange beams introduce new considerations, but are essentially the same as wood girders. Usually, because of their weight, they extend from support to support instead of being continuous, and are held in place by bolts which engage the cap plates of the steel pipe columns. They are spliced together by steel plates bolted to the ends of the two butted members.

Where the ends of girders, either wood or steel, rest on exterior walls, openings must be provided and the bottoms covered with steel bearing plates. The openings are made large enough and deep enough to provide ventilation around the ends of the girders, otherwise dampness causes the wood girders to rot and the steel girders to rust.

Joists supported by interior walls are carried on sills of the same type as found on the exterior walls.

Foundation Sills. The purpose of the sill is to provide support or bearing surface for the outside walls of the building. The sill is the first part of the frame to be set in place. It rests directly on the foundation wall and extends all the way around the building, being jointed at the corners and spliced where necessary. The sill is anchored to the foundation wall by means of ½- to 1-in. diameter anchor bolts set in the foundation wall. Holes are bored in the sill at proper intervals, the sill is slipped over the bolts, and nuts and washers are turned down tight. The sill must be level and straight if the rest of the frame is to be plumb and the floor joists level. Therefore, a bed of fresh, stiff mortar is strung along the top of the foundation wall

and the sill is tamped down on it, leveled with straightedge and spirit level, shimmed up if necessary with small stone chips. The sill must be recessed far enough back from the outside face of the wall to allow for the sheathing and water table. In balloon framing it is customary to build up the sill from a number of planks 2 or 3 in. thick and spike them together. A 6 by 6-in. sill can be made from three planks 2 in. thick and 6 in. wide. If the sill is built up, the corners and lapping are made much the same as two succeeding courses of brickwork. It is easier and cheaper to build up a sill in this manner than to use a large solid timber. When a sill of this kind is used, it should always be placed on the wall in such a way that the plank lies flat as a bed for the joists, but that a header is used at the ends of the joists to form a firestop. In the braced frame a solid sill is generally used, made up of a 6 by 6-in. sq. timber, but in better work it is usually 6 by 8 in. For porch sills a 4 by 6-in. timber or built-up sill may be used.

Where termites are known to be present, it is good practice to protect the sill against their attack by keeping the wood members at least 18 in. above the ground and use a noncorroding metal shield continuously around the periphery of the foundation wall. The shield should project on both sides of the wall and be bent down 2 in. at an angle of 45 deg. Where the shield fits around anchor bolts the joint is soldered or filled with an asphaltic mastic. The shield is bedded in mortar for tightness and the sill is in turn bedded in mortar on top of the shield. Special, tight shields are provided around water pipes and all other points of access.

Chemicals, and methods of chemical treating have so improved in recent years that no longer is the cost of obtaining treated wood a prohibitive factor. Wood preservatives now offer fungi and termite resistance; they are odorless, clean, and paintable. Thoroughness of application of the chemical is just as important as the kind of chemical used. Parts of a home where lumber treatment for termite or fungi control are:

1. Wood sills, caps, pier blocks, cross-bridging, foundation posts, girders, first-floor joists, plates, headers, and subfloor.

2. All lumber used in porch construction, including posts, girders, flooring, steps, and column bases.

3. Lumber used in basements, including stairs, bins, floors, sleepers, partitions, window frames, door frames, etc.

4. First floor studs which extend below the subfloor.

5. Sheathing and siding which extends to the ground or below the top of the masonry foundation. The lower 2 or 3 ft. of sheathing should be treated; however, less than this can be treated for economy.

6. Nailing strips for floors, window and door blocks embedded in concrete or laid directly on masonry.

7. Fence boards and posts, trellises, arbors, latticework, and decorative details which touch the ground or are exposed to dampness.

The wood preservative should have the following properties or characteristics:

1. It should be toxic to decay and stain organisms commonly found in the area, and it should be toxic to termites.

2. It should require a simple treatment and have a deep and speedy penetration.

3. It should have the ability to remain toxic for many years.

4. It should not have an objectionable odor.

5. It should be nonpoisonous and non-harmful to workmen.

6. It should be nonactive to paint and metals.

7. It should not be soluble in water.

Posts. The posts for balloon framing are built up of three 2 by 4-in. pieces spiked together and arranged so as to provide a return for nailing the lath or dry-wall board (Fig. 16). In the balloon frames, posts are found only at the corners of walls, not in intermediate points as in the braced frame.

They are never mortised and tenoned. In both balloon and platform frames they may run full height, but frequently in the platform framing they run one story or floor height.

In braced framing, posts are usually 4 by 6 in. but occasionally a 4 by 8 in. is specified or required by building codes. Posts are placed at all corners of the exterior walls and at intermediate points where important partitions join the exterior walls, or where it is necessary to make a joint in the girts. The posts run the full length from sill to plate. At all corners, it is necessary to provide two surfaces at right angles to each other to which lath or other inside finish material may be fastened. To obtain this nailing surface it is necessary to spike an additional 2 by 2-in. piece to the middle of the 6-in. face, with the inner edge of this piece kept in line with the inner edges of the studs. Because posts are erected first in framing they must be well braced in position. This is accomplished by 1-in. boards being tacked to the posts just below the second floor line and again at the sills (Fig. 16). The posts are set up, spiked to the sill, plumbed both directions with straightedge and spirit level, and finally braced. They must be straight and plumb because they line up the rest of the frame.

Girts. In braced framing the girts were proportioned strong enough to carry the entire floor loads, but today they depend instead upon support from the studs below. Their purpose is to act as horizontal ties holding the frames together laterally. Originally the girts were mortised and tenoned and extended continuously from post to post. In the modern adaptation the mortise and tenon is often omitted and a single step joint is substituted to save on labor costs, although it does not provide a good lateral tie. Girts which run parallel to the direction of the floor joists are set with their top edges at the same elevation as the tops of the joists. This permits floor boards to run out and be nailed to the girts which helps tie the floor and wall together. Girts which run at right angles to the

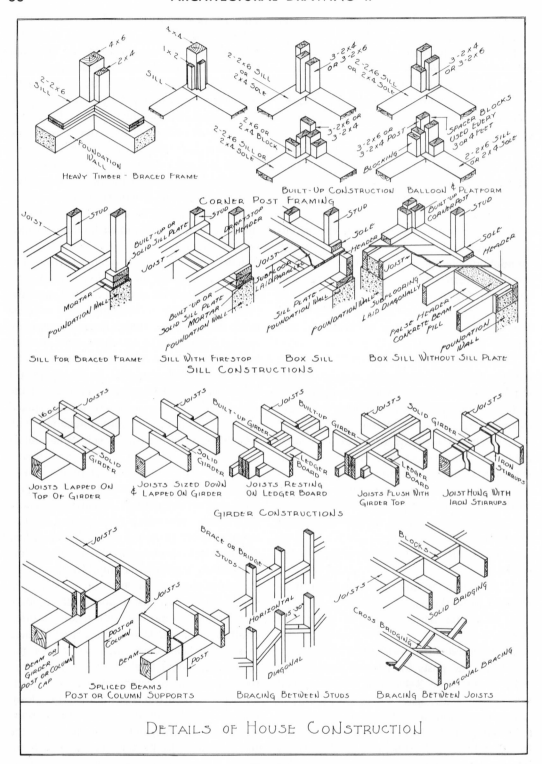

DETAILS OF HOUSE CONSTRUCTION

Fig. 16

joists are set with their top edges at the elevation of the joist bottoms, and joists rest directly on these girts. Girts are set at different elevations to stagger the mortises in the post. Usually these members were made the same width as the posts, being flush with the face of the post both inside and outside, and the depth was usually 8 in. although a 6-in. timber might be used.

In the balloon frame, light pieces called "ledger boards," "ribbons" or "ribbands" are substituted. The member is about 1 in. thick, 6 to 8 in. wide, which is notched into the studs so that its top is at the elevation of the bottom of the joists. The joists are set on the ribbon and spiked to the studs. The ribbon occurs only in those walls which run at right angles to the direction of the joists since it would have no function in the other walls. The disadvantage of the ledger board is that as a tie between the corner posts it is less effective than the girt.

Plate. The plate serves to tie the studding together at the top, forms a finish for the wall, and furnishes a support for the rafters. Occasionally the plate may be a solid 4 by 4-in. timber but more commonly and preferably, two 2 by 4-in. pieces are used. The lower piece is put in place all around the building first, and is so arranged that all members rest directly on the posts. Studs are inserted and fastened in place by spiking through the plate into their ends. The upper piece is then placed with the corners half-lapped and all joints broken with at least a 2 ft. spacing interval. The two layers are then securely spiked together.

In the balloon frame the solid timber is never used. The studs on the gable end are carried to the plate, and gable studs extend from there to the rafters. This is necessary because studs would not be obtainable in sufficient length to run from sill to rafter.

In the platform framing a second-floor header with the joists butting to it is used in the same manner as at the sill. Therefore, the box construction occurs again at this point

and at every subsequent floor level which exists in the building. Also, the second-floor subflooring is carried out to the edge; the second-story sole rests on the subflooring and studs on the sole, as before.

Braces. Braces are used to stiffen the wall and to keep the corners true and square. In the balloon frame, light strips are nailed across corners while the framework is being erected, but they are usually removed as the outside finish is put on. Sometimes, however, light braces 1 by 3 in. are used as permanent parts of the balloon frame. They usually consist of 1-in. boards notched into the studs at the corners of the house and run diagonally from post to a point on the sill approximately 4 ft. away (three stud spaces, if possible). For best construction, this member should join post, girt, and sill in a stepped joint, but excellent bearing is more easily obtained at the post by fitting the lower story braces into the intersection of post and girt, and the upper story braces against a 2 by 4-in. block securely spiked against the upper end of the post. The lower ends of the braces are best fitted against blocks spiked to the tops of girts and sills, although common practice is to fit them against the lower ends of studs.

Knee braces are short 4 by 6-in. struts set into the corners at 45 deg. angles to engage sill and post, post and girt, or post and plate. In the most exacting workmanship the members are all fastened with mortise and tenon joint, but more commonly the braces engage the posts and other members in a 1-in. step joint and are securely spiked in place (Fig. 10).

Bridging. Bridging consists of short pieces set in to stiffen long spans of joists or studs and prevent them from twisting. This bridging may be placed between studs to form a broken horizontal line across the wall by placing every other piece a little above the next piece. The pieces are 2 in. thick and the full width of the studding. Bridging is commonly 1 by 2 in. or 1 by 3 in. for joists up to 2 by 10 in. inclusive, and 2 by 2 in. or 2 by 3 in. for deeper joists. The bridging may be placed diagonally, in such a way that each piece connects with the pieces on each side of it. Sometimes a solid block bridging is used instead. There should be a line of bridging for each 6 to 8 ft. of unsupported length of joist (Fig. 16).

Studs. Wall studs are almost always 2 by 4 in. although studs 2 by 6 in. are sometimes required to provide a wall thick enough to permit the passage of waste pipes with their heavy hubs. Even in this instance the 2 by 4-in. studs may be increased in width with the addition of 2 by 2-in. strips. A rule often applied is that a supporting column should never have its height exceed fifty times its least dimension. To keep within this ratio, an ordinary 2 by 4 standing unbraced should not be more than 6 ft. in height. The stud is braced along its weakest dimension, however, by sheathing and siding outside and by the interior wall on the inside, so that it is possible to use the 2 by 4's as long as 15 ft. with reasonable safety. For buildings over three or four stories the studs in the lower stories may need 2 by 6-in. or 3 by 4-in. studs for additional strength.

Because wood laths were originally cut 4 ft. long or some 16-in. multiple, it has become almost universal practice to set studs and joists 16 in. apart (or 16 in. on centers), although joists are frequently set at different spacings. In temporary work, garages, summer cottages where plaster is to be omitted, or some other material is to be used for a wall finish, wider spacing may be used; as for example, 24 in. Because of this standard stud spacing practically all wall boards and plaster bases are made in stock sizes which are multiples of 16 in.

Wherever an opening such as a window or door occurs, such an opening must be framed in the studs to receive whatever member is to be placed in it. Framing consists of horizontal members called "headers," vertical members called "trimmers," and short studs

called "cripples." Similarly there is a similar member which is termed the "rough sill" at the bottom of window openings.

There are two kinds of walls and partitions, bearing and nonbearing. A bearing partition or wall is one which runs at right angles to and supports the ends of joists, or a load from above. A nonbearing wall or partition acts only as a screen or enclosure, with the headers running parallel with the joists of the floor above. Header sizes will be determined according to whether they are load-bearing or not. Unless the opening in a nonbearing partition is more than 3 ft. wide, a single 2 by 4 is satisfactory as a header. It often happens, however, that the trim inside or outside is so wide it prevents satisfactory nailing over openings with a single 2 by 4. In such cases it becomes necessary to double the header primarily to make provision for a nailing base. On load-bearing partitions or walls the header should be doubled even over narrow openings, especially if a short stud occurs near the center of the header. If the 2 by 4's placed over the opening are laid flat, they should be thoroughly spiked together to help support the load. If the 2 by 4's are laid on edge the nailing is not quite so important. It will be noted, however, that the two 2 by 4's laid on edge will measure only 3¼ in. instead of the actual width of the 2 by 4 when laid flat (3⅝ in.). Consequently it will be necessary to insert fillers (small pieces of lath) between the 2 by 4's in order to make the header line up with the studs.

If the opening is more than 3 ft. wide, the header will need additional strength to carry the weight imposed upon it from above. This additional strength may be secured by using material of greater cross section than 2 by 4's. For openings ranging from 3- to 6-ft. lengths of 2 by 4's should be used to form "trusses" on the same principle as that used in bridge construction. These lengths of 2 by 4's will in general be arranged in the form of triangles, which will not change shape unless the corners become disjointed or the members give away. For distances over 5 or 6 ft., or where unusually heavy loads must be supported, it is advisable to use a girder.

The size and number of studs on either side of wall openings will be determined by several factors. It may be necessary to double studs to provide ample support for the frames of windows and doors and provide nailing for plaster base, grounds, and exterior finish where it joins the opening. In door openings, doubling may be necessary on one side only, or on both. It is considered good policy always to double studs on the lock side of a door, thus forming a solid support for the door when slammed. However, the studs should be doubled on the hinge side with doors larger than 2 ft. 8 in. by 6 ft. 8 in. to provide a solid support for the weight of the door. Where additional studs are necessary for the support of headers or trussing, it is good practice to cut any additional stud so that the top of it comes underneath the header or truss. It is usually good practice to have openings planned so that one or both sides come near to the regular studs. In other cases, the sides of an opening may occur in the center between two regular studs. In balloon framing, all studding is carried up from the sill to the plate, so that, if there is an opening in the wall of the first story, and no corresponding openings in those of the second or third story, the door and window studding must still be carried double up to the plate. See Figure 15. In designing for balloon frames, therefore, it is well to take care that window openings come directly above those of the first story wherever possible.

Door sizes are specified by over-all dimensions of the door, consequently the opening must be framed large enough to admit the door frame plus sufficient additional room to allow for setting the door with its adjustment, blocking, and leveling. Outside door frames are ordinarily 2-in. softwood stock rabbeted to 1¼ in., with nominal 2-in. hardwood sills, therefore the opening must ac-commodate these dimensions plus space in each direction for blocking and adjustment. Horizontally this amounts to 3 or 4 in. greater than the door size, vertically 3 or 4 in. measured from the tops of the floor joists.

Window openings must be framed large enough horizontally to admit the window frame and provide space between the frame and trimmer for a pocket in which window weights may move up and down. In the newer windows other tension devices are substituted which allow the window to open to any desired height and remain in that location, which eliminates the need for the space allowed for the weight pocket. Vertically, the opening must be large enough to admit the frame. Since window sizes are specified by the size of the glass panes (called lights), the horizontal opening dimension is made enough larger (usually 11 in.) to allow for the two sash stiles, two frame thicknesses, and two weight pockets. Five 1-in. allowances are used for spring-balanced windows. The vertical dimension is similarly increased (usually 10 in.) for three sash rails, the window sill, and the head of the frame. The foregoing dimensions are for double-hung windows. The allowances for dimensions of openings for other types of windows are figured similarly.

The vertical spaces between studs are likely to act as flues to transmit flames in case fire breaks out. At the various floor levels, the flames may find their way horizontally across the building in the space between the floor and the plaster. Fire stops are important in preventing or retarding fire from spreading through the building by way of the air passages in walls and partitions. Similarly, fire stops should be provided at each floor level to prevent flames from passing through walls and partitions from one floor to the next, and should be provided over bearing partitions to prevent fire in partitions and floors from passing across the building. In the platform and the braced frame the construction itself provides the necessary stops at all floor levels. Additional stops are needed only in the floor space over the bearing partitions. In general, obstructions in the air passages may be made of 2-in. lumber, which will effectively prevent the rapid spread of fire. Fire-stopping at the sill may consist of brickwork laid up in mortar so as to fill the space between studs from the sill to a point just above the floor line. A form board may also be nailed across the joists, and concrete poured into the space between the studs, sheathing, and form board. Various sill constructions are designed to give the necessary fire protection. Additional firestopping between the sill and girt, and the girt and plate takes the form of horizontal 2 by 4-in. blocking between the studs halfway up the story height. The blocking may be inserted alternately sloping in between the studs in which case it is called "herringbone" stopping, or the blocks may be placed horizontal and staggered in level to facilitate nailing.

Sole. In platform framing, directly on top of the subfloor is a horizontal member called the "sole" or "shoe," which forms a base for the studs. The sole is made wider than the studding so that the plasterer's grounds may be nailed to the projecting surface. This sole is usually a 2 by 6-in. member for 4-in. studding, but it may be the same cross-sectional size as the studs and be spiked to the headers and joists below.

Joists. The standard length of lath, which is commonly 4 ft. (occasionally 32 in.), determines the spacing of joists. This limits the spacing to 12, 16, or 24 in. Since 24 in. is too great for proper stiffness between supports, especially on the ceiling, 16 in. has become the standard spacing for joists and studs except where special considerations require otherwise. Furthermore, 16 in. will fit either 4-ft. or 32-in. lath. Many building codes specify the sizes of joists, girders, and rafters for various conditions. A rule of thumb sometimes employed is to make the span in feet equal to one-and-one-half times the depth of the joist in inches, if the joists are

16 in. on centers and #1 common lumber is used. For #2 common lumber the span in feet is equal to the depth in inches. Thus a 2 by 8-in. #1 common joist could span 12 ft., and #2 common could span 8 ft. ordinarily. The length of each joist should be sufficient to allow at least a 3-in. bearing at each end, with 4 in. being recommended. This means that the length of the joist must be from 6 to 8 in. more than the distance between the faces of the walls or plates on which it rests. It is desirable that the joists are cut ½ in. short of the inside face of the sheathing so they will not project beyond the face of the studs. In masonry work the bearing should not be less than 4 in., with 6 in. to be generally recommended. For frame buildings it is not necessary that the end cut be exactly square as long as a satisfactory bearing is obtained, except where a box header or sheathing is to be nailed to it. In framing for masonry, the cut should be made at an angle for a safety release which would allow the leverage of a burning joist to cause the wall to fall inside the building. It is important to provide anchors at intervals of not over 6 ft. This effectively ties the walls of the building together and overcomes any tendency of the masonry to bulge outward. In balloon and braced framing the joists are spiked to the stud, while in platform framing they are toe-nailed to the plate. If there is a box header across the ends, it should be spiked securely into the ends of the joists.

The joists which run parallel with the two sides of an opening are usually doubled and are called "trimmers." Across the two other sides of the opening, at right angles to the trimmers, are set two other doubled joists called "headers" and into these headers are framed the shortened joists, known as "tail beams," "tail joists," or "header joists." Where spans are short and loads are light, this assembly can be spiked together, otherwise hangers are used, particularly to support the headers on the trimmers.

Framing around chimneys and fireplaces is commonly held 2 in. away and the space between is filled with incombustible insulating material.

Bathroom joists differ from other floor joists in that they are required to support unusually heavy loads imposed by plumbing fixtures, and are often weakened in installation of heavy waste and soil pipes. Bathrooms which occur over halls or where the joist span is short may not require additional strength. If a bathroom is over a living room, the joists must be proportioned as to their size and spacing to carry the heavier loads.

Sheathing. The rough boards which cover the outside of the frame and provide a base for the exterior finish are called sheathing. The same boards used on the roof are called "roofers," "roof boards," or "sheathing," and on the joists are called "rough flooring" or "subflooring." Since the eastern braced frame is resistant to sway and motion occasioned by winds, the sheathing contributes less to the stiffness of the frame than it does when bracing is omitted. In this kind of framing the sheathing may as well be nailed on horizontally which is the most economical and quickest way.

Because there are no braces in the balloon framing, the entire lateral rigidity of the house must be provided by the sheathing; otherwise the racking stresses are thrown into the lath and plaster, and cracks are almost certain to appear in the walls. With the sheathing applied diagonally the stresses are transferred directly down the sheathing boards to the sill and foundation. Diagonal sheathing is therefore a much more positive, stiffer, and more enduring type of construction and should be used on any frame which is not otherwise structurally braced. At diagonally opposite corners of the house, sheathing should run down from post to sill, and at the other two corners it runs up from post to plate. Bracing is occasionally employed in the balloon frame consisting of 1-in. boards let into the studs at the corners of the house and run diagonally from post to sill. Properly done and plentifully used, this kind of bracing adds a great deal to the rigidity of the frame, and eliminates the need for diagonal sheathing. It involves additional labor, however, and may well take as much time as setting the kind of bracing used in eastern framing.

The sheathing boards may be square-edge, shiplap, or tongue and groove. Unless end-matching sheathing is used, the joints must be made on stud centers and joints in successive tiers of boards should not be made on the same stud. Wood sheathing can be obtained in almost all widths, lengths, and grades. Generally used are widths from 6 to 12 in., with length selected for economical use. Almost all solid wood sheathing used is $1\frac{3}{16}$ in. thick and either square or matched edge.

In recent years there has been a strong trend toward the use of wood and composition panels for sheathing as well as for interior and exterior walls. Because plywood is applied in large sheets (usually 4 by 8 ft.), it can contribute to the rigidity of the wall. To economize, the plywood used is thinner than ordinary sheathing boards and should therefore be applied securely in nailing. If the plywood is glued, stiffness is greatly increased while the ultimate strength remains about the same. Because it is difficult to set the ordinary length sheathing boards at a 45-deg. angle, and because of the necessity for making the joints at the stud centers resulting in a high percentage of waste, it is recommended that short-length and end-matched sheathing be used for the purpose. This kind of sheathing can be in assembled tiers instead of the full wall height and the joints can be arranged conveniently with a resulting savings in both labor and material. Care must be taken to see that the boards are butted tightly at their ends and that the tongues are not so badly bruised in handling that they cannot be easily fitted together.

Fibrous wall boards, made of processed wood, cane, newsprint, and other materials manufactured with an "asphalt coated" or "asphalt impregnated" treatment have received a very wide acceptance in the building industry and are probably being used more than the traditional board sheathings. Most composition sheathings are fairly soft and porous to increase their insulating value but they are sufficiently rigid to withstand handling and do provide moderate nail-holding qualities. Half-inch thick boards of this type are frequently applied, and provide approximately the same insulating value as wood sheathing. Thicknesses of ¾ and ⅞ in. are better from the consideration of insulation. These panels (4 ft. by 8 to 12 ft.) are easy to handle in construction, cover large areas with a saving of time, have machined smooth edges producing even and tight joints, are windproof and waterproof, require no building paper, and impart a rigidity and stiffening strength greater than ordinary horizontally applied wood boards.

Gypsum-board sheathing is made by casting a gypsum core within a heavy water-resistant fibrous envelope. Each panel is a full ½ in. thick. Each 2 ft. by 8-ft. board is tongued and grooved. It is usually used with wood siding which can be nailed directly through the sheathing and into the studs. It can also be used in brick-veneer construction when metal ties are fastened to the studs to hold the veneer, leaving the regulation 1-in. air space between the brick and the sheathing. Gypsum sheathing is fireproof, windproof, water resistant, warp proof, and eliminates the need of the building papers.

DETAILS OF ROOF FRAMING

The roof (Fig. 17) serves to protect the house from the weather and its elements, but it also contributes to the styling and appearance of the house. The design and construction is influenced by geography, climate, and architectural considerations; but with the improvement in the materials being used, the climatic considerations become less important. Low roofs have been used in warm climates where only the run-off of rain was necessary, while steep-pitched roofs have been used in the cold climates where the shedding of snow was a factor because of its accumulated weight.

A roof may take many shapes, but the most commonly used are the following: (1) Shed or lean-to, (2) Gable, (3) Hip, (4) Gambrel, (5) Mansard, and (6) Flat or deck. Of these the mansard is least used in modern construction.

Rafters. Rafters serve the same purpose for the roof as do joists for floors in providing a support for sheathing and roofing material. There are several kinds — common rafters, headers, trimmers, and the like — which are similar in principle to the corresponding types of joists. In addition there are hip, valley, and other special rafters. The regular rafters are the straight-run rafters extending without interruption from eave to ridge, at right angles to the wall. These common rafters may be level as for flat roofs, or may be comparatively steep as for gable or mansard roofs. Since plaster is not generally applied to the underside of rafters, it is not necessary to follow the 16 in. spacing recommended for joists and studs. Spacing is determined more by stiffness of the sheathing applied to the rafters, weight load on the roof, and by the rafter span. Spacings from 16 to 24 in. are common, but for ordinary purposes 20 in. is often used. Greater spacing should not be used except where the sheathing is tongued-and-grooved flooring not over 4 in. wide or where extreme economy is essential. On the other hand, it is not usually necessary to space closer than 20 in. except where the roofing materials are heavy, or where climatic conditions require greater strength. If it is intended to plaster on the underside of the roof rafters, the 16 in. should be used. The rafter "span" is the horizontal distance be-

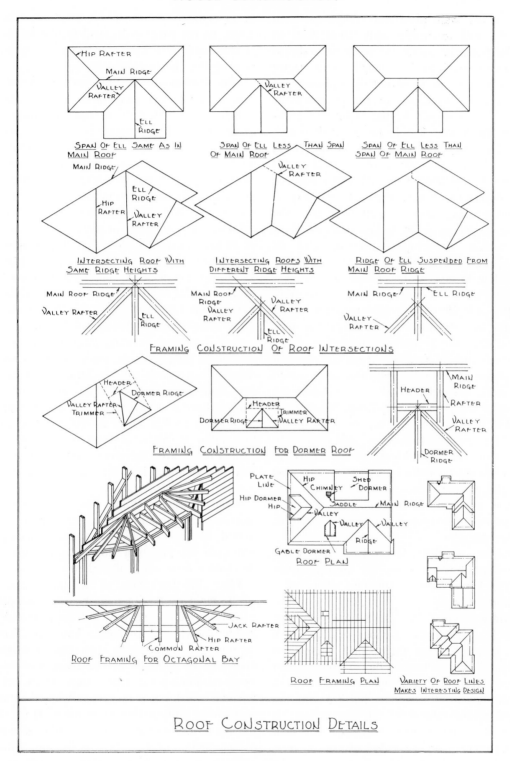

SPAN OF ELL SAME AS IN MAIN ROOF

SPAN OF ELL LESS THAN SPAN OF MAIN ROOF

SPAN OF ELL LESS THAN SPAN OF MAIN ROOF

INTERSECTING ROOF WITH SAME RIDGE HEIGHTS

INTERSECTING ROOFS WITH DIFFERENT RIDGE HEIGHTS

RIDGE OF ELL SUSPENDED FROM MAIN ROOF RIDGE

FRAMING CONSTRUCTION OF ROOF INTERSECTIONS

FRAMING CONSTRUCTION FOR DORMER ROOF

ROOF PLAN

ROOF FRAMING FOR OCTAGONAL BAY

ROOF FRAMING PLAN

VARIETY OF ROOF LINES MAKES INTERESTING DESIGN

ROOF CONSTRUCTION DETAILS

Fig. 17

tween the wall plate and ridge, or from inside wall to inside wall, from wall to collar beam or purlin, or from collar beam or purlin to ridge. The length of the rafter must be sufficient to permit the necessary cut at the ridge to allow for the projection at the eaves as shown by the architect's drawings. The rafters should be notched to give not less than 3 in. bearing on the plate. Wherever possible, ceiling joists should extend across the building to connect the base of the rafters at or near the plate. Rafters, if tied to ceiling joists, should be spaced the same as ceiling joists, unless the roof is so steep that ties at every second, third, or fourth rafter are sufficient.

Collar Beam. Collar beams are ties between rafters on opposite sides of the roof. If the attic is to be used for rooms, collar beams may be lathed as ceiling rafters, provided they are properly spaced. Sometimes they are placed partway up on the slope of the rafters but in this position they should never be depended upon as ties unless the slope of the roof is quite steep, because the nearer the tie is to the top or peak of the roof the greater the leverage action upon it. When the roof slope shows in the rooms, no floor should be placed on joists not resting on the plate or heel of the rafter. Collar beams are considered sufficient generally when they are spaced on every second or third rafter.

Purlin. A purlin is the horizontal member which forms the support for the rafters at the intersection of the two slopes of a gambrel roof.

Ridge Board. The ridge board or ridge pole is a horizontal member against which the rafters rest at their upper ends, and which forms a lateral tie to make them secure. Its function is unnecessary from a purely structural viewpoint, but it aids in the erection and alignment of the rafters. It generally is not necessary to use more than 1-in. lumber for the ridge except in relatively large houses. The depth should be about equal to the depth of rafter cut. The length of the ridge board will be the length of the building as measured from the inside face of the sheathing.

Hip Rafters. When the roof is shaped like a pyramid, sloping down on all four sides, a hip is formed where the two adjacent planes meet. The hip rafter is the one which runs from the corner of the building upward to the ridge. It acts as a ridge board, and when the pitch is low as a girder, supporting the ends of the jack rafters. Where hip rafters are short and the upper ends come together at the center of the roof, the hip rafter may be of the same size as the common rafter of equal length. For spans up to 12 ft., the hip rafter should be 2 in. deeper or 1 in. wider than a common rafter of the same span. For spans over 12 ft., the hip rafter should be doubled in width.

Jack Rafters. Framing into the hips are shorter rafters, running from plate to hip rafters, called jack rafters. Jack rafters are any kind of rafters which do not run full length from plate to ridge. They may run from ridge to hip, ridge to valley, plate to hip, valley to plate, or from hip to valley. Jack rafters are, therefore, found on any kind of roof which is broken up in interesting planes.

Valley Rafters. Where two roof surfaces meet at an interior corner, a rafter is required to carry such jack rafters as may rest upon it. The roof slopes down toward the valley from each direction.

Ells. Ells are framed in the same manner as the main roof, with ridge board, common and jack rafters, and so on. Usually the ell is not as wide as the main house so that its roof does not rise as high, and its ridge ends against the side of the main roof instead of joining the main ridge. If the ell is small and there is no reason why its attic space must be accessible from the main attic, the main roof rafters may be carried down to the plate, the roof boards on the main roof carried beyond the intersection of the main and ell roofs, and the ell roof may be rested on top of the main roof by fastening the valley members on top of the main roof and allowing the ell valley jacks to frame into the valley members. If, on the other hand, the ell is large and its attic space is to be continuous with the main attic, a valley rafter is first framed full length from plate to the ridge of the main roof and a secondary valley rafter on the other side is continued from the main roof to the first valley rafter. Jack rafters from both roofs then frame against these valley rafters, the ell roof framing is completed, and roof boards are carried into the valleys from both main and ell roofs.

Roof Boards. In cold climates, and where asbestos or composition shingles are to be used, the roof should be completely sheathed with roof boards. The manner in which roof boards are applied depends upon the kind of roofing material to be used. Usually the roof is tight sheathed with the boards driven up tightly against each other, with either ship lap or tongue-and-groove material. The boards are laid on a horizontal, starting at the eaves. The joints between board ends should be staggered so that no more than two of them fall on the same rafter. In warm, moist climates where wood shingles are used, it is customary to place the roofing boards with a space between them equal to the length of the shingle that is laid to the weather. Since wood rots when kept damp, and since water has a tendency to seep under shingles, sufficient ventilation should be provided under wood shingles to dry out any dampness as quickly as possible.

Plywood panels have many advantages over conventional sheathing boards; however there are some disadvantages. While the large panels have a tendency to cover the surface quickly, they are also more difficult to handle and fit into valleys, around dormers, and other irregular shapes. Plywood is resistant to shrinking and swelling, holds nails well, and in general provides a superior base for roofing materials. Panels ⅜, ½, and ⅝ in. thick in unsanded grades are used, depending upon the load to be carried and the spacing of the rafters.

Building Papers. Building paper is a special strong, heavy, waterproof paper used between the finish floor and the subflooring, between the sheathing and the finished outside walls, and between the sheathing and the finish roof. It helps prevent air and dust from sifting through cracks, and prevents moisture from the basement or any other source from entering the finish floor by absorption and thus guards against the swelling and buckling of floors, sheathing, and siding. It has some insulation and sound-absorption properties.

FRAMING AROUND OPENINGS

In the framing of floor joists, it is often necessary to cut away part of the joist to form the opening for stairways, or when framing around chimneys and fireplaces, and the weakening of the structural members must be compensated for in some way (Fig. 18). The joists which run parallel with the sides of the opening are doubled and are called trimmers. Across the ends of the opening are framed double members known as headers, and into these headers are framed the shortened joists, known as tail beams, tail joists, or header joists. When it becomes necessary to use headers more than 6 ft. in length, they should be fastened to their supporting joists by means of iron stirrups or joist hangers. Sometimes the tail beams are supported on ledgers by notching. In a building constructed so the second-story projects over the wall of the first story, longer joists for the second story are used where the projection is perpendicular to the second-story joists. If the overhang is parallel to the second-floor joists, then it becomes necessary to cantilever short joists. A similar situation exists in a bay window which

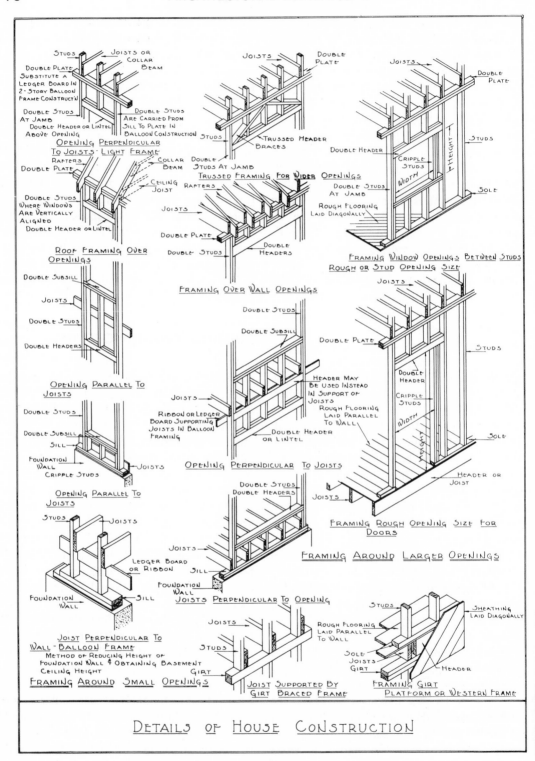

DETAILS OF HOUSE CONSTRUCTION

Fig. 18

has no supporting foundation underneath.

Framing around chimneys and fireplaces is commonly spaced 2 in. away and the space between is filled with fireproof insulation. Wood members should never be framed into the masonry of the chimney, although a pilaster or corbel may be built as part of a chimney to support the framing members.

Any one of several methods may be used for framing openings into vertical walls. Wherever an opening such as a window or door occurs, it must be framed in the studs and consists of the horizontal members called headers, vertical members called trimmers, and short studs called cripples. In balloon framing, all studding is carried up from the sill to the plate, so that, if there is an opening in the wall of the first story, and no corresponding openings in those of the second story, the door and window studding must still be carried double up to the plate. In designing for balloon frames, therefore, it is well to design the framing so that the window openings come directly above those of the first story wherever possible. The studs which frame the opening are doubled for the full height of the balloon stud. This waste of lumber does not occur in the other methods of framing because the studding in each story is independent of that in the story above or below. In the braced frame the door and window frames are made of 4 by 4-in. pieces. In all good construction a small truss is formed above each opening by setting up two pieces of studding over the opening, in the form of a triangle. This is to receive any weight which comes from the studding directly above the opening, and carry it to either side of the opening where it is received by the doubled studding and carried down to the sill. The header over the opening is usually laid on edge to gain advantage in stiffness, but on nonbearing walls a double header laid flat is strong enough to carry the load. The following sizes of headers are recommended for ordinary size openings:

Spans up to 4 feet in length — 2 x 4's doubled

Spans 4 feet up to 5½ feet in length — 2 x 6's doubled

Spans 5½ feet up to 7 feet in length — 2 x 8's doubled

Spans more than 7 feet in length — 2 x 10's doubled

This method, while simple, has the disadvantage that it introduces a large amount of wood which may shrink or swell across grain and cause cracks in the interior wall finish. A better way is to use the truss construction when the bearing requires greater stiffness.

PARTITION FRAMING AND INTERIOR WALLS

Inside partitions are usually made with 2 by 4 studs, and in the same manner as the outside walls for the western platform frame; that is, they require a shoe or sole, studs, and a plate or cap. Studs are usually spaced 16 in. on centers and may be stiffened with blocking, either herringbone or horizontal, set halfway up their height. Partitions are either bearing or nonbearing, they either help support the joists above or they do not. In bearing partitions the studs are 2 by 4's and the plate or cap is often a 3 by 4 or doubled 2 by 4, although a single 2 by 4 is sufficient if the joists bear on the plate directly above the studs. Nonbearing partition studs may be 2 by 3's turned facewise rather than edgewise since they function only as a surface for the interior finish and this method gives a little added floor space. Where plumbing pipes run in partitions, the studs may be 2 by 6's or 2 by 4's for a thick enough wall to accommodate the largest diameter pipes. Joists that support bearing partitions at right angles to, and near the center of, the joist spans are doubled with narrow blocking between them. Or the joists are single but deeper than would normally be used. For a nonbearing partition running parallel to the joists and over one, the joists are doubled and spaced with narrow blocking since there would be

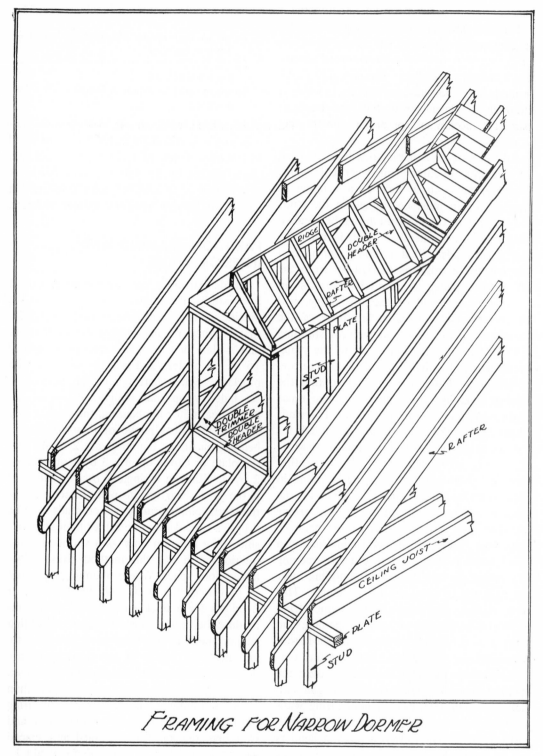

FRAMING FOR NARROW DORMER

Fig. 19

too much load for one joist to sustain. If the partition is located between two normally spaced joists, longer solid blocking is placed at 2-ft. intervals to distribute the load evenly to both joists.

Framing around door openings is the same as in the exterior walls and consists of doubled studs at the sides and a header across the top of the opening. For large openings the header is trussed.

Partition studs are set up in several ways, the simplest and probably the best method being to lay the subfloor over the entire floor area, tying the structure together horizontally at that level. Next frame the soles for the partitions on the subfloor, and assemble the studs to the sole. Some builders object to this method of construction because shrinkage occurs across grain involving the subfloor, sole, plate, and joist and that in better construction the sole should rest directly on the joists. This does away with the effect of shrinkage in the subfloor, but makes it impossible to lay the subfloor continuously. When the subfloor is laid diagonally extra blocking is required at the partition point, causing additional waste and labor. The quickest method is to assemble the partition — sole, studs, and plate separately — and raise them into place.

In the eastern braced and balloon frame, the partition studs for the first floor are framed on girders, joists, or blocking between joists. Second-floor studs are framed to the plates of the first-floor studs, if the partitions set over each other. This is good practice for bearing partitions in eastern and balloon frames because it equalizes the shrinkage in the outside walls and in the interior bearing partitions. In platform-framing it is better to have all partitions built in the same manner as the outside walls, starting with a sole on top of the subfloor and ending with a plate under the joists above. If the first-floor joists rest on ledgers at the girders, shrinkage is practically equalized throughout the structure. It is considered good construction to

extend partition studs down to a solid support since its use will prevent the cracked plaster and other defects caused by the shrinking and swelling of wood laid flat in bearing partitions. Adequate support of the bearing partition by means of a girder is recommended. In eastern cities it is common to use steel beams for the purpose, but in the West timbers are customarily used because of their availability and economy.

For nonbearing partitions it is not ordinarily necessary to increase the size or number of joists, but should the occasion arise the joists may be spaced at intervals of 12 in. instead of the usual 16 in., or the depth of all joists be increased 2 in., or the width of all joists be increased 1 in.

Where partitions join other partitions or exterior walls forming an internal corner, it is necessary to provide for the nailing of lath or plaster board just as it is at the corner posts.

FRAMING FOR DORMER AND BAY WINDOWS

The term *dormer window* is applied to all windows in the roof of a building, whatever their size or shape. In order to construct a dormer window (see Fig. 19), an opening must be made in the surface of the roof, and the window built over this opening. Headers are framed in between the rafters thus forming a rectangular opening in the roof frame. The rafters which form the sides of the opening are called "trimmers" and are made much stronger than the common rafters. Usually the trimmers are made by doubling the common rafters. The headers receive the ends of the rafters which are cut by the opening, and must be large enough to carry the weight which comes from supporting the walls of the dormer. Timbers, 4 by 8 in. to 6 by 10 in., are large enough for headers and often smaller timbers may be safely used. Where the front wall of the dormer is an extension of the main wall of the build-

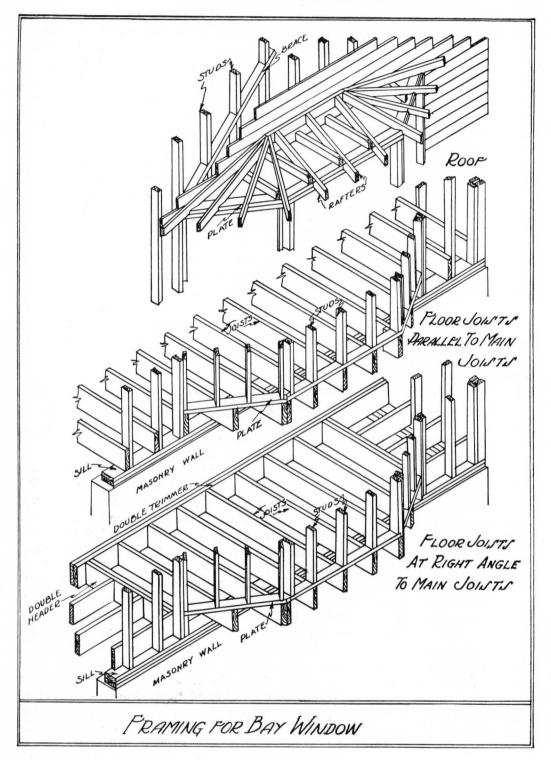

STUDS

S. BRACE

ROOF

RAFTERS

PLATE

FLOOR JOISTS
PARALLEL TO MAIN
JOISTS

JOISTS

STUDS

PLATE

SILL

MASONRY WALL

DOUBLE TRIMMER

JOISTS

STUDS

FLOOR JOISTS
AT RIGHT ANGLE
TO MAIN JOISTS

DOUBLE
HEADER

SILL

MASONRY WALL

PLATE

FRAMING FOR BAY WINDOW

Fig. 20

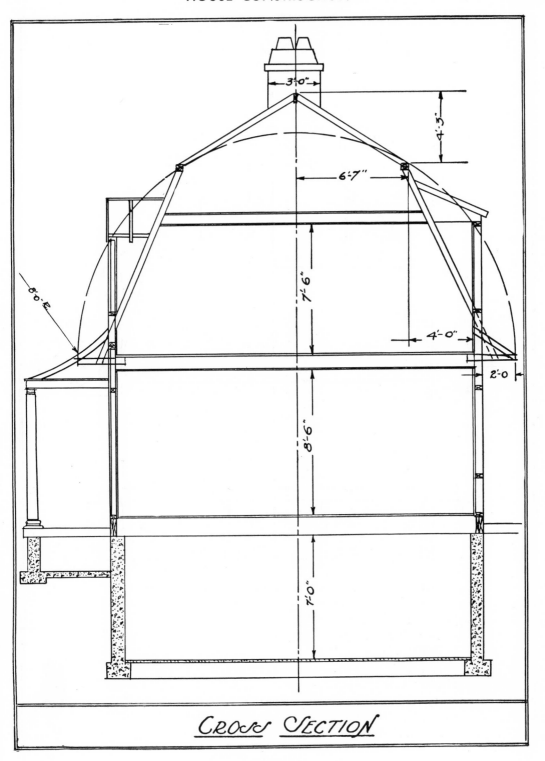

CROSS SECTION

Fig. 21

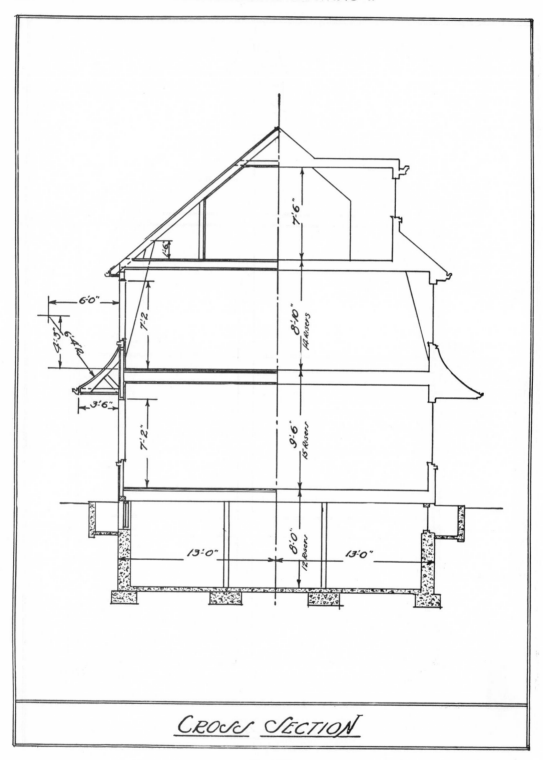

CROSS SECTION

Fig. 22

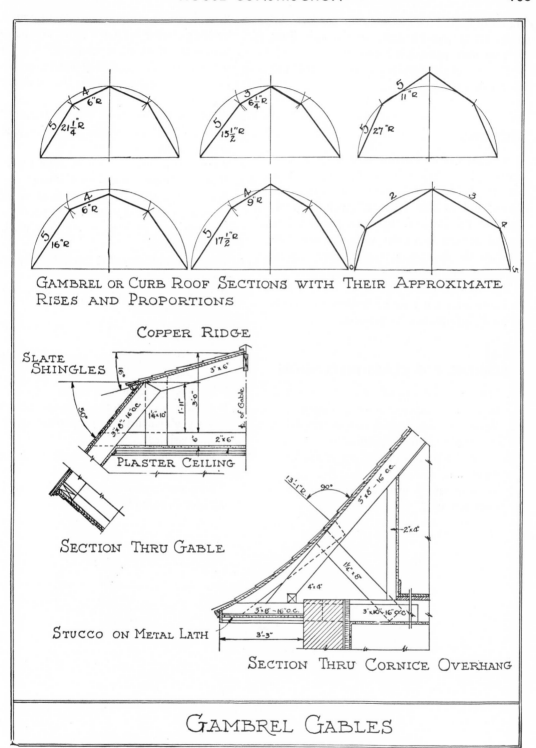

GAMBREL OR CURB ROOF SECTIONS WITH THEIR APPROXIMATE RISES AND PROPORTIONS

COPPER RIDGE

SLATE SHINGLES

PLASTER CEILING

SECTION THRU GABLE

STUCCO ON METAL LATH

SECTION THRU CORNICE OVERHANG

GAMBREL GABLES

Fig. 23

ing there is no need of the lower header. The studs are carried on down to the attic floor so they may rest on the trimmers.

The framing details for a bay window are shown in Figure 20.

SECTIONS

A section is an interior view on a vertical cutting plane, and is used primarily to indicate the heights of the floors, windows, and doors, and to show the architectural treatment of the interior. In a simple structure a wall section is shown with the elevation to show the floor heights and other vertical measurements. See Figures 21, 22, and 23.

The cutting plane line does not need to be continuous but may be broken to include as much information as possible.

PROBLEMS FOR CLASS DISCUSSION

1. Why are the drains and all pipes laid before the basement floor is poured?
2. What are the considerations regulating the height of the basement?
3. What determines the height of the basement wall?
4. What types of wall construction are in common use?
5. Why is balloon framing required by most building codes? Why is it more expensive than other methods of framing?
6. What is the distinguishing difference between the balloon and the western framing?
7. What are the faults of balloon framing?
8. How are fire and vermin stops provided in the house frames?
9. What two purposes does the plate serve?
10. How are braces placed in framing?
11. Why is the sill set back at least ¾ in. from the face of the foundation wall?
12. In what type of framing are girts used? Ledger boards?
13. Why are studs doubled around all openings?
14. What is the purpose of the bridging? Where is it used?
15. What spacing is used between centers in joists?
16. What is the difference between a sill and a sole?
17. Where is the cap used?
18. Why are second-story openings placed directly above first-story openings wherever possible?
19. What is meant by a header? By a trimmer?
20. Where are vertical sections used in architectural drawing?

Sill Construction

36 in. or about 1½ to 2 in. of actual shrinkage in the same story heights.

This shrinkage would cause settlement of all the floors and partitions, showing cracks and unsightly openings at junctures of the wall and ceiling, etc. Framing according to Method *A* will not cure all cracking ills but it can be easily seen that an area of about 30 in. of potential shrinkage is eliminated by this method.

Common framing does not consider this problem, but intelligent detailing does attempt to solve the problem and with encouraging success.

SHRINKAGE

Lumber, as ordinarily purchased, is seldom well seasoned. It shrinks perceptibly across the grain, whereas, the shrinkage occurring with the grain is so small that it may well be forgotten. All horizontal members of a frame, such as the sills, girders, joists, plates, rafters, and flooring, will shrink, and partitions resting on them will settle. The framing should be designed so as to equalize this settlement between these horizontal members.

In the framing shown in method *A*, Figure 24, a 2 by 6-in. nailer is bolted to the I beam, and the first-floor joist and studs are nailed to this nailer. The bearing studs are carried past the floor joists to rest directly on the main girder. On top of the bearing studs is placed a double plate which carries not only the second-floor joists but the bearing studs for the floor above as well. The only objection to this method is that the I beam extends below the basement ceiling.

The most common method of framing is shown at *B*, Figure 24. Instead of resting the studs on the girder they rest on a plate placed on the joists. The same condition prevails at the second-floor bearing. In method *A* there is a total shrinkage area of 5¼ inches across grain wood for the two floors, or about ¾₁₆ in. of shrinkage to be distributed at three points. In method *B* there is a total cross-grain shrinkage area of about

SILL CONSTRUCTION

The foundation sill is a plank or timber which rests on the foundation wall and provides a means of securing the superstructure to the foundation. As a rule the first-floor joists are nailed to the sill. In some constructions the sill is omitted entirely and the floor joists are permitted to rest directly upon the foundation wall. But then it is difficult to obtain a perfectly level surface on which to rest the joists, and difficult to align them correctly.

To anchor the house firmly to the foundation wall the sill must be more than just laid on the foundation wall. The first consideration in placing the sill is to see that it is perfectly level. It is good practice to spread a bed of mortar on the foundation wall and to lay the sill upon it at once, tapping it gently to secure an even bearing throughout its length. In all exposed situations the sill should be anchored to the wall by means of anchor bolts. These bolts are from ½ to 1 in. in diameter, and are built into the masonry of the wall with the threaded end projecting far enough above the wall to pass through the sill. Holes are bored in the sill to fit over these bolt ends and, after the sill is bedded and laid, the nuts are put in place over washers and are tightened gently with the fingers. After the mortar has set they may be drawn up securely.

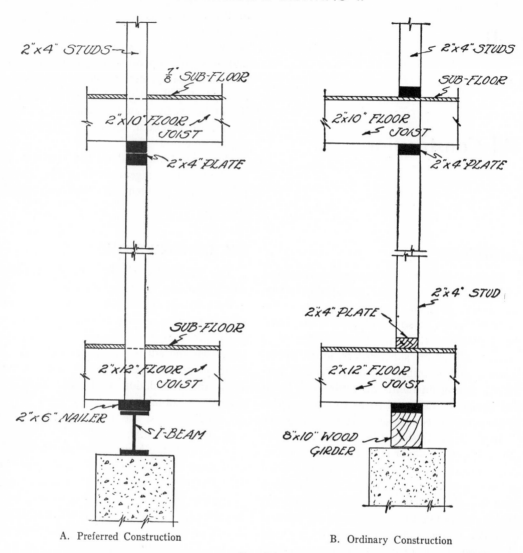

A. Preferred Construction   B. Ordinary Construction

Fig. 24

For light frame buildings, a 2 by 6-in. sill is large enough for the average condition. For two-story structures, particularly in localities subject to earthquakes and high winds, a sill 4 in. deep is recommended. When a basement or cellar window is so placed that the foundation sill is immediately over the frame, additional strength must be provided.

The length of the sill is determined by the size of the building. Dimension lines for the outside of a building are generally fig-

ured from the outside face of the sheathing. This means that the outside face of the sill will be approximately ¾ in. in from the outside face of the foundation wall.

ASSIGNMENT

Plate 1, Sill Construction

The drawings for the details of the sills usually consist of the vertical section for each sill. Include an elevation to show the water-

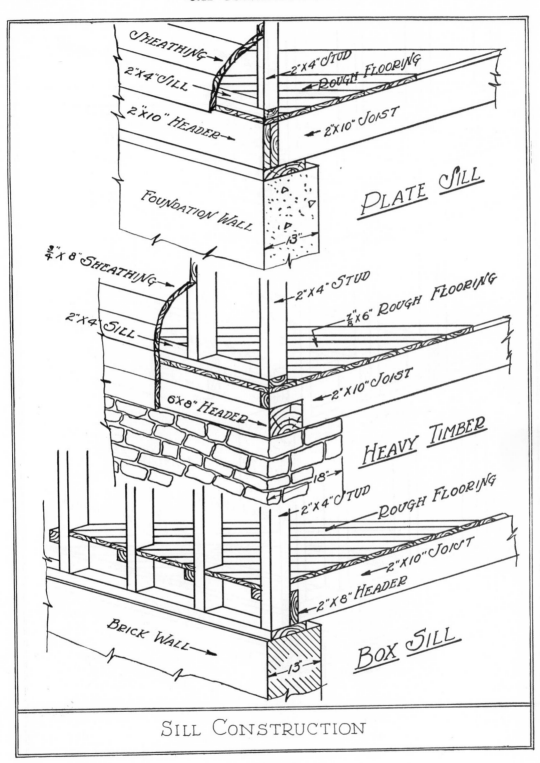

SILL CONSTRUCTION

Plate 1

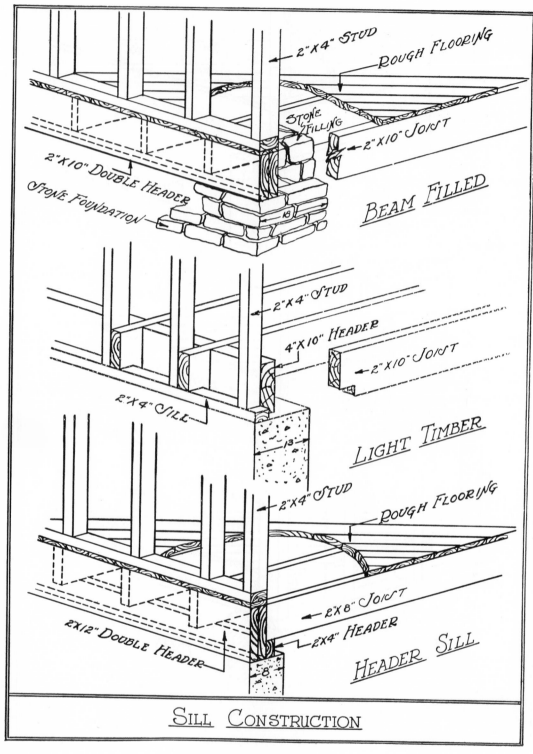

2"X4" STUD
ROUGH FLOORING
STONE FILLING
2"X10" JOIST
2"X10" DOUBLE HEADER
STONE FOUNDATION
18
BEAM FILLED

2"X4" STUD
4"X10" HEADER
2"X10" JOIST
2"X4" SILL
13
LIGHT TIMBER

2"X4" STUD
ROUGH FLOORING
2"X8" JOIST
2"X4" HEADER
2"X12" DOUBLE HEADER
8"
HEADER SILL

SILL CONSTRUCTION

Supplementary Plate 1A

table construction, the amount of siding to the weather, and the bonding if the wall is of brick. Draw these sill details in about the order in which they are constructed and follow the recommended practice as closely as possible.

Label each part indicating the size of the member and its trade name. Make no effort to memorize the names of these parts because you will become familiar with them through the repetition given in the following plates. The size of the separate parts may be given by the actual size which is ³⁄₁₆ in. less than the dealers' listed size, or by the dealers' list size as preferred by the instructor.

Make the drawings to a large scale, as for instance 3 in. equal 1 ft., or 1½ in. equal 1 ft.

Supplementary Plate 1A may be assigned to advanced students.

PROBLEMS FOR CLASS DISCUSSION

1. Why is shrinkage considered in the framing of a house? Where does it take place?
2. What is the purpose of the sill?
3. How is the sill anchored to the foundation wall?
4. Where are dimension lines generally given for the outside of a frame building?

STANDARD DIMENSIONS OF SOFTWOOD LUMBER

Thicknesses (S1S or S2S)		Widths (S1E or S2E)	
Nominal	Actual	Nominal	Actual
⁵⁄₁₆″	⁵⁄₁₆″	2″	1⅝″
⁷⁄₁₆″	⁷⁄₁₆″	3″	2⅝″
⁹⁄₁₆″	⁹⁄₁₆″	4″	3⅝″
1″	²⁵⁄₃₂″	6″	4⅝″
1¼″	1¹⁄₁₆″	7″	6⅝″
1½″	1⁵⁄₁₆″	8″	7½″
1¾″	1⁷⁄₁₆″	9″	8½″
2″	1⅝″	10″	9½″
2½″	2⅛″	11″	10½″
3″	2⅝″	12″	11½″
4″	3⅝″	14″	13½″
6″	5½″	16″	15½″
8″	7½″	18″	17½″
10″	9½″	20″	19½″
12″	11½″	22″	21½″
14″	13½″	24″	23½″
16″	15½″	26″	25½″
18″	17½″	28″	27½″
20″	19½″	30″	29½″
24″	23½″		

5. Check these details carefully for the elimination of excess shrinkage. Are there any suggestions for their improvement?
6. How is strength provided over basement window openings?

Floor Construction

When the sills and girders are in place, the first-floor joists are set. The joists form the framing construction on which the floors rest, and they are joined to the sills by the several methods of construction. These joists should be braced every 5 to 7 ft. with cross bridging, or herringbone bridging which consists of 1 by 2-in. or 2 by 3-in. strips nailed diagonally between the joists. See Figure 25. The purpose of the bridging is to keep all the joists in alignment, and to distribute to all the joists the exceptionally heavy, concentrated loads or sudden jolts that may be directly applied above one or two of them. The joists are usually 2 to 3 in. thick and from 6 to 14 in. wide, and they are spread from 12 to 16 in. on centers. They are spiked to the sides of the studs whenever possible.

The best method of laying the subfloor is to use the tongue-and-groove boards laid diagonally. These diagonal boards help to tie the structural timbers together, and it is very convenient to lay the finished flooring on top of the diagonal rough flooring. The finish floor boards are always laid across the underfloor and not parallel to it. The finished floor is always laid so that it extends lengthwise of the room.

The underfloors are sometimes stripped with 1 by 2-in. cleats, and the finished floor is nailed to these. The idea is to provide an air space between the finished floor and the underfloor, which is good insulation against cold and sound. Another advantage of the stripped floor is that it provides an excellent place between the two floors for running gas pipes and electric conduits. Heavy building paper is usually laid between the two floors, whether strips are used or not, because this layer of felt or paper helps to keep out the cold, acts as a sound deadener, and keeps the dirt from filtering through from the basement. Deadening materials are about ⅜ to ½ in. thick, made of two layers of building paper stuffed with hair, tow, or seaweed.

Finished flooring comes in several widths and thicknesses, from ⅝ by 1¼ in. up to ⅞ by 3½ in. A good size commonly used is ⅞ by 2¼ in. Oak flooring and maple flooring are most commonly used for all rooms except kitchens and other types of service rooms, for it is not much more expensive than the cheaper woods and it has the added advantage of being more durable. Thin, ⅝-in. flooring is often used in remodeling old houses because it can be nailed down over the old floors. The flooring ordinarily used is ⅞ in. thick and is tongued and grooved on the ends as well as the edges; thus when the joints are driven up tight they give a nicely finished appearance. Nails are driven through the grooves so that they are invisible after the floor is completed. When such a floor is finished, it is carefully scraped and sanded before a finish is applied.

Fir is an excellent wood for outside porch floors, 1¼ by 3½ in. being the size most used for this purpose. Such flooring may be tongued and grooved or it may be square edged; in the latter case the boards should be laid from ⅛ to ¼ in. apart. All porch flooring should be painted on the underside and on the joints before laying, to prolong the life of the wood.

WATER-TABLE CONSTRUCTION

Starting at the bottom of the wood structure, at the point where the foundation wall stops and the framework begins, the first part of the outside finish which meets the eye is the water table. The water table serves the purpose of shedding the water which runs

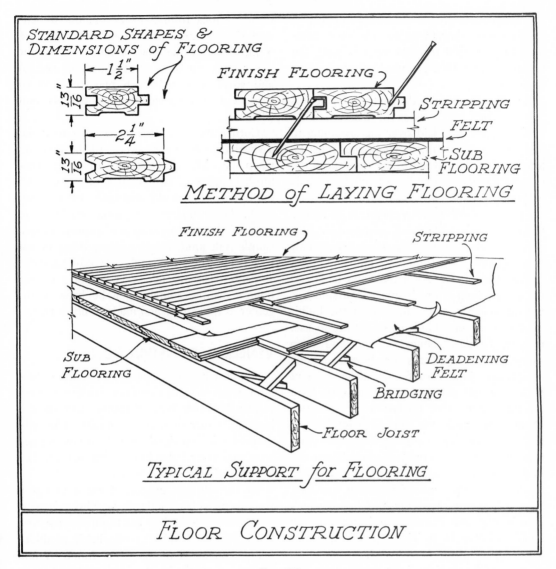

STANDARD SHAPES & DIMENSIONS of FLOORING

METHOD of LAYING FLOORING

TYPICAL SUPPORT for FLOORING

FLOOR CONSTRUCTION

Fig. 25

down the side of the house away from the foundation wall. This purpose is accomplished by several methods of construction.

WALL SECTIONS — FRAME CONSTRUCTION

Sheathing. The framework of a house is often materially helped by the outside board-ing, which contributes to the strength of the structure. The sheathing, which is about 1 in. thick and is dressed on one side, should be placed diagonally across the studding in the "balloon" type of frame. The sheathing is laid close, but need not be matched, and the boards may be 8 to 10 in. wide. In many sections of the country shiplap, laid hori-zontally or diagonally, is used in place of the tongue-and-groove boarding because it requires less labor to apply. The most common lumber used for this work is pine, but spruce and hemlock are used with very good results.

Building Paper. In the better built houses one or more thicknesses of heavy felt or building paper are laid over the sheathing to make the house warmer. This paper must be tough as well as waterproof, and must be easy to handle. A number of different kinds of building paper are on the market which are prepared with various chemicals to render them as nearly waterproof as possible. This paper is tacked around the window and door openings before the frames are nailed in place.

Wall Coverings. After the water table and the corner boards are in place, the siding is put on in horizontal courses over the building paper. Several kinds of siding are in use, namely, beveled siding, shiplap, and drop siding. The clapboards or beveled siding boards are about 5 or 6 in. wide and about 4 ft. long and are thicker on one edge than on the other. The thicker edge measures about ½ in. while the thin edge is about ⅛ in. thick. The clapboards lap over each other leaving a certain amount of each board exposed to the weather. This term "to the weather" is made use of in many specifications to indicate the amount of board which is to be exposed. The shiplap siding comes in lengths of 6 to 16 ft. This type of siding has a groove along the inside of the lower edge. This provides a tight joint and allows for expansion and contraction of the boards. The drop siding is uniform in thickness, from ¾ to ⅞ in., and 5½ in. in width.

Shingles are often used to cover the outside of houses. The advantages are in the appearance of the work, the variety of effects which may be obtained, and the fact that shingles may be dipped in stain thus producing a great variety of colors. Wall shingles should be laid with not more than 6 in. to the weather, although 5 in. is to be recommended. The width of the ordinary shingle varies from 3 to 12 in., but dimension shingles are cut to a uniform width of 6 in. Shingles may be obtained with their lower ends cut to a great variety of special and stock patterns which may be used to work out a large number of designs and effects.

Corner Boards. It is customary to make a special finish at the corners of the building when the walls are covered with siding. This finish consists of two boards, one 5 in. and the other 3⅞ in. wide, and both about 1⅛ in. thick. These boards are placed vertically at each of the corners and are finished with a simple butt joint, the two pieces being nailed together. When the walls are covered with shingles it is not necessary to have corner boards, as the shingles can be brought together at the corner and made to finish nicely.

VENEERED CONSTRUCTION

The brick-veneer house is simply a balloon-frame structure with a brick covering. It has the same type of frame, wall sheathing, and paper or other insulation. The only difference is that the door and window frames have no casing but a brick mold instead. The outside of the frame is set in about 4 in. from the outside surface of the foundation wall, to provide a footing for the brick veneer. The bricks are laid in the usual manner and the brickwork, which is one brick in thickness, is fastened to the wood frame by one of several methods. A simple method is to drive heavy nails into the studding through the sheathing, allowing about 2 in. of the nail with its head to be embedded in the horizontal mortar joint. These nails are placed every fifth or sixth course of brickwork with about one nail to each alternate brick. Another method is to nail heavy galvanized-iron wall ties to the studding and embed the ends of them in the horizontal brick joints. The same spacing is used as for nails. This method is better, since it allows for brick settlement and shrinkage of the wood frame.

STUCCO-WALL CONSTRUCTION

A similar frame construction as for brick veneer is used extensively as a base for stucco. Frequently wood laths are placed over the sheathing, and the stucco is applied directly to these. This is not a satisfactory method of construction because of the shrinkage of the base and the consequent cracking of the stucco. Metal lath often is applied directly to the frame and stucco is then applied to the lath. Another type of stucco base is formed of a dovetailed or grooved board which is nailed directly to the studding in place of the sheathing. It forms the sheathing and at the same time acts as a base for the stucco. Another commonly used stucco base is a patented lath in which strips with tapered edges are attached to an asphalt-felt backing, which resembles roll composition roofing. The grooves thus formed are dovetail in shape, and provide a good bond for the stucco.

One of the best stucco bases is masonry. This may be of stone, brick, hollow tile, or some form of concrete. Old stonework or brickwork forms an excellent base for stucco. Hollow tiles are extensively used as a stucco base in new construction.

STONE-WALL CONSTRUCTION

Stone is the most desirable building material because of its beauty and permanence, and because a house with stone walls is warm in winter and cool in summer. Stone walls for residences vary from 16 to 24 in. in thickness, with vertical furring strips anchored to the wall to which the interior wall surface material may be nailed.

BRICK-WALL CONSTRUCTION

Bricks may be used for the entire wall construction, including the footing, or they may begin slightly below grade and continue to the roof. Brick residence walls may be solid, 9 or 13 in. in thickness, or they

may be constructed with an air space, the faces being tied together at intervals with brick bonds or metal ties, known as the "hollow rowlock" which is popular in some sections of the country.

The walls of a brick house are tied together by the joists. These should have at least a 4-in. bearing on the wall, be "fire cut," and provided with a metal anchor securely nailed to the bottom of the joist and firmly embedded in the brickwork. Such anchors should be spaced 4 to 6 ft. apart. Fire stops, made by corbeling at the second floor, prevent fire communication from floor to floor. The roof should be fastened to the wall with ½ by 12-in. bolts built into the wall every 6 ft.

ASSIGNMENT
Plate 2, Water-Table Construction

Draw in the details of these wall sections to a scale of 3 in. equal 1 ft. or 1 in. equals 1 ft. An elevation often adds to the clearness of the detail.

Draw this plate following closely the order followed in construction. Be careful to keep all the parts to size and proportion.

The moldings included in this plate are all standard and must be looked up in a millwork catalogue for the number, size, and shape. The moldings which require reference are the base, base mold, floor shoe, and drip cap. Draw up separate detail sections of the moldings used in this plate. Label each molding as to name, number, and size as listed in the millwork catalogue.

Supplementary Plate 2A may be assigned to advanced students.

PROBLEMS FOR CLASS DISCUSSION

1. Why is the subflooring laid diagonally?
2. What are the advantages in stripping a floor?
3. Why is paper placed between the flooring?

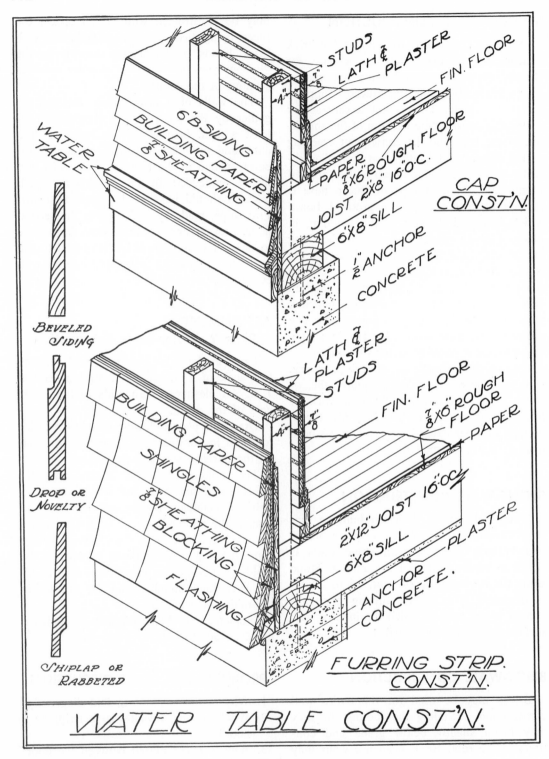

STUDS
LATH & PLASTER
FIN. FLOOR

WATER TABLE

6"B SIDING
BUILDING PAPER
7/8"SHEATHING

PAPER
7/8"X 6"ROUGH FLOOR
JOIST 2X8 16"O.C.

6'X8"SILL

CAP CONST'N.

1/2"ANCHOR

CONCRETE

BEVELED SIDING

LATH & PLASTER
STUDS

FIN. FLOOR

7/8"X6"ROUGH FLOOR

PAPER

BUILDING PAPER

SHINGLES

7/8"SHEATHING

BLOCKING

2"X12" JOIST 16"O.C.

6'X8"SILL

PLASTER

FLASHING

ANCHOR
CONCRETE.

DROP OR NOVELTY

SHIPLAP OR RABBETED

FURRING STRIP.
CONST'N.

WATER TABLE CONST'N.

Plate 2

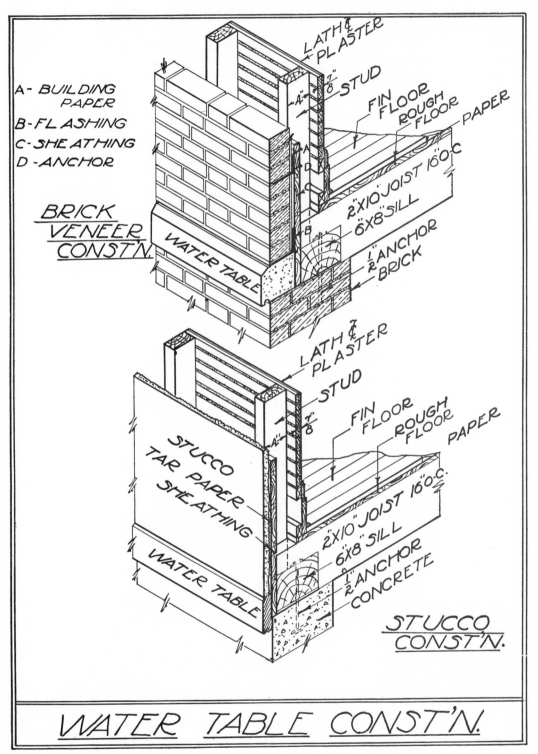

A- BUILDING PAPER
B- FLASHING
C- SHEATHING
D- ANCHOR

LATH & PLASTER

STUD

7/8"

A"

FIN FLOOR

ROUGH FLOOR

PAPER

BRICK VENEER CONST'N.

WATER TABLE

2"X10" JOIST 16'0"C.

6"X8" SILL

1/2" ANCHOR BRICK

LATH & PLASTER

STUD

7/8"

A"

FIN FLOOR

ROUGH FLOOR

PAPER

STUCCO TAR PAPER SHEATHING

WATER TABLE

2"X10" JOIST 16'0"C.

6"X8" SILL

1/2" ANCHOR CONCRETE

STUCCO CONST'N.

WATER TABLE CONST'N.

Supplementary Plate 2A

 4. Which direction of the room is the finished flooring laid?
 5. Why are hardwood floors to be preferred over softwood floors?
 6. What is the advantage of using thin ⅝-in. flooring in remodeling?
 7. What is the purpose of the water table?
 8. Where is the water table located?
 9. Why is the sheathing of a house placed diagonally on the studs?
10. What woods are commonly used for sheathing?
11. Why is building paper placed between the siding and the sheathing?
12. What kinds of paper are used for this purpose?
13. What kinds of siding are commonly used?
14. What is meant by the term "to the weather"?
15. What is the purpose of the corner boards?
16. What are the advantages in covering a wall with shingles? Disadvantages?
17. What are "dimension" shingles? What size are they?
18. What are the advantages of building residence walls of masonry?

UNIT
IV

Cornice Construction

STYLES OF ROOFS

Pitch or Gable Roof. The pitch or gable roof belongs to the simpler styles of roofs in common use. See Figure 26. It has two sloping surfaces, one on each side of the center line of the building extending up through the ridge. The gable roof is very simple in design and construction, so that it is very popular for all classes of buildings. The slope or "pitch" of the roof may be varied to suit the taste as well as the needs of the different climates.

Hip Roof. The hip roof slopes from all four walls toward the center. It is usually brought to a point at the top, but it may be finished with a small flat deck.

Mansard Roof. This roof is called by the name of the architect who introduced it. It is like the gable roof except that it slopes very steeply from all four walls toward the center, instead of from two opposite walls only, and it has a deck which is nearly flat at the top.

Gambrel Roof. The gambrel roof is a variation of the gable roof and serves to add more space immediately under the roof surface. This style of roof has a sort of gable at each end of the building, but the gable is not triangular in shape. The roof surface is broken near the middle on both sides of the building, with the portion just below the break at a steeper pitch, and the portion above the break flatter than that of a gable roof. The position of the break in the roof surface may be varied to suit the taste of the designer.

Lean-to. This is the simplest of the roof styles and is used mostly on small sheds, porches, ells, and in other places where appearance is not the chief factor. This roof consists of a plain surface, one end or side of which is raised to a higher level than the other end or side.

MATERIALS USED FOR ROOF COVERING

Wood Shingles. The wood shingle has long been a common roofing material, and its popularity is based on certain well-recognized merits. It has a definite artistic value, and for many types of houses, cannot be excelled in appearance. It is light in weight, can be applied easily, has excellent insulating value, and with a steep pitch it has durability. Shingles of cedar, cypress, and redwood give the best results.

Shingles are made in 16-, 18-, and 24-in. lengths and may be laid with various exposures to the weather. A 16-in. shingle, on a roof having a one-half pitch or greater should be laid 4½ in. to the weather; larger ones may have more exposure in proportion. Shingles for the roof are laid directly on the rough boarding, without the building paper which is needed for applying the shingles to vertical walls.

Asphalt Shingles. Asphalt shingles are made of felt, saturated with asphalt and surfaced with crushed slate or coarse sand, which renders them fire-resistant. They come in various colors — such as greens, reds, slate colors, and black. The durability of this type of roofing depends upon the pitch of the roof.

Asbestos Shingles. Asbestos shingles are composed of asbestos rock fiber and Portland cement, compressed under great pressure. They have been put on the market to meet the fire laws, and to compete with slate and tile in price or looks.

Slate. Slate is a natural rock which, because it can be readily split into thin sheets, has long been used as a roof covering. It is permanent and fireproof and, although ex-

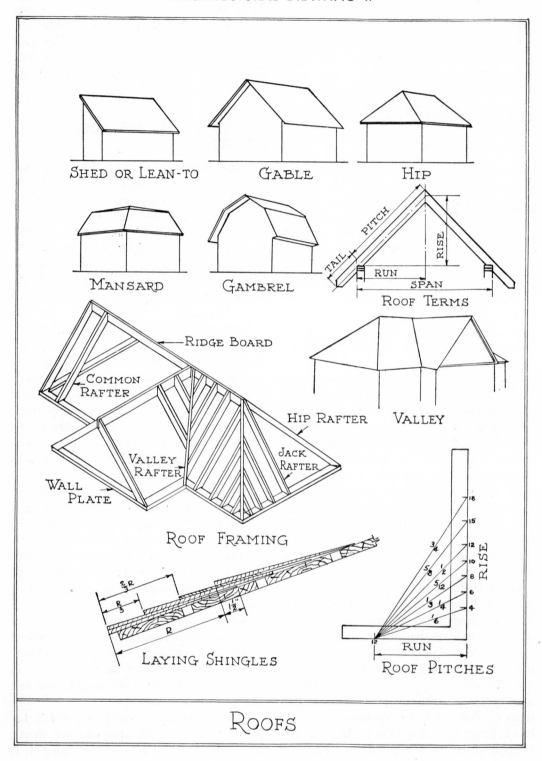

SHED OR LEAN-TO   GABLE   HIP

MANSARD   GAMBREL

PITCH
TAIL
RISE
RUN
SPAN
ROOF TERMS

RIDGE BOARD

COMMON RAFTER

VALLEY RAFTER

HIP RAFTER   VALLEY

JACK RAFTER

WALL PLATE

ROOF FRAMING

LAYING SHINGLES

RISE
18
15
12
10
8
6
4
RUN
12
ROOF PITCHES

ROOFS

Fig. 26

pensive in the first cost, is not prohibitive for the small house since its maintenance cost is negligible. Slate comes in black, blue-black, purple, mottled purple-and-green, green, and red. The charm of a slate roof depends as much upon a pleasing blending of colors as upon a varying texture.

For special purposes slate can be selected at the quarry both for color and for size. For ordinary service, slates are split to ¾₁₆ in. and range in size from 6 by 6 in. to 12 by 12 in.

Tiles. Tiles are usually of terra cotta, that is, burnt clay. They come in unglazed red or glazed in many colors; the latter are more expensive but more permanent in a climate with extremes of temperature.

The common trade name of "mission" applies to the primitive form of tiles, semi-circular in section like those used on peasant huts in warm climates; but this tile does not have an interlocking device which is needed in this country. The Spanish tile is S-shaped and is made in a form which is satisfactory for use in the United States.

The French model has a wavy surface and the method of interlocking is highly developed, coming from use in a wet northern climate.

The "shingle tile," as the name suggests, shows a flat surface, but two of the concealed edges are turned up to fit snugly in grooves on the adjoining and superimposed units.

In the Roman type, flat and arched tiles alternate, and in the Greek, flat and bevel-topped.

Specially molded forms are required for ridges and hips, and for their points of intersection, called "finials."

Metal Roofs. For a metal roof the average person is likely to be interested only in tin, copper, and zinc. The first, if on a flat roof, especially where it may be walked on at times, should have a flat seam, that is, the interlocking joint of two sheets should be folded down over the nails which hold the metal to the roof boarding, after which the joint should be soldered tight. If it is on a sloping roof, the appearance is enhanced by a standing seam. In this case the sheets of tin are double seamed and soldered together into strips reaching from the eaves to the ridge; their sides or sloping edges are turned up, held in place by cleats, and interlocked.

With sheet copper the procedure is about the same but the life of the roof and the cost are greater. Sheet zinc is also used, but more on public buildings than on residences.

Tar-and-Gravel. Roofing of this material is built up of three to five layers of tar paper, according to the quality which can be afforded; each lay is mopped with hot pitch and the top is mopped and then coated with screen fragments of slag or small stones which are embedded in the pitch. This roofing is effective but can be used only on flat surfaces because the materials will run in hot weather.

PITCH OF ROOFS

The "pitch" of the roof is the term used to indicate the slope of the sides of the roof surfaces or the inclination of these sides in respect to a horizontal plane. Evidently the pitch of any roof may vary to an almost infinite extent, because it may be absolutely flat, practically vertical, or it may be inclined at any angle between these two limits. There are several methods for indicating the pitch. The most simple, and yet the most accurate plan, is to give the angle which the roof makes with a horizontal plane. Thus the pitch of a roof may be 30 deg., 45 deg., or 60 deg. This system is recommended because of its accuracy, but it is not favored in use by architects or builders.

Another method of indicating the roof slope is to divide the rise by the span. The rise of the roof is the vertical distance from the top of the plate to the underside of the rafters at the center of the span, the span being the distance between the inside edges of the two rafters which come opposite to each other in the roof frame at the point where they intersect the top surface of the plate. The fraction thus obtained is used to express the degree of the slope of the roof. Thus: If the span of the roof is 20 ft. and its rise is 10 ft., then the roof is "half pitch." The angle which this roof surface makes with a horizontal plane is 45 deg. This slope is called a "square pitch" for the reason that the rise of the rafter is equal to the "run."

A two-thirds pitch would be a little less steep than the full pitch, and would have a rise of 16 in. for each 12 in. of run, so that if the span were 20 ft. the rise would be 13 ft. 4 in. When a roof pitch is steeper than a half pitch, the two-thirds pitch is used.

If the roof is one-third pitch, the rise of the rafter for each foot of run will be one third of 24 in. which is required to make a full pitch. Thus a one-third-pitch roof has a rise of 8 in. for each foot of run. If the span of the roof is 20 ft. the rise will be 6 ft. 8 in.

If the roof has a one-quarter pitch, the rise of the rafter for each foot of run will be one fourth of 24 in. Thus a one-fourth-pitch roof has a 6-in. rise for each 12 in. of run. If the roof has a span of 20 ft. the rise will be equal to 5 ft.

The pitches mentioned are the most commonly used, though any pitch may be used. Several factors enter into the problem of determining the most suitable pitch to give to a roof, and they must be carefully considered before coming to a decision. In the first place the appearance of the finished roof is to be considered. Personal taste is the determining factor in this case and no hard and fast rules are laid down. Another thing to be considered is the relative costs of the different pitches. A roof of a comparatively low pitch, say about 30 deg., is the most economical as far as the roof framing is concerned. This pitch, however, does not give any accommodation to the attic portion of the building. Consideration must also be

given to the factor of climate in which the proposed building is to be constructed. In colder climates where there is heavier snowfall, it is best to have a roof with a steep pitch so that it will shed the snow and rain as quickly as possible. In a warm climate where there is little or no snow, a roof of lower pitch may be safely used and will be more economical in construction. The character of the material to be used for a covering must also be considered in determining the pitch, since, if the covering is impervious to water, a lower pitch roof may be used.

FLASHING

Rain water has a habit of making its way inside the house, and every junction of different materials or different surfaces must be protected. Heat will cause unequal expansion between stucco and wood, brick and slate, tar and tin; water can also climb by capillary attraction. These factors make it possible for water to get under shingles and gutters, causing much damage. Certain measures should be taken to prevent this from happening.

Each exposed projection from the wall, even if only a window top, must be protected from seeping water. Where a cornice over the entrance or a porch "deck" joins the wall, offering a larger surface to the rain, metal flashing must be carried up under the clapboards, shingles, or stucco. If the wall is of brick or stone, metal flashing must be turned up against the masonry and then be counterflashed; that is, it must have a separate sheet of metal built into the joints above during construction, and then be turned down to cover the flashing below.

Valleys in roofs, which are formed by the junction of two downward slopes, may be finished open or closed. In a closed valley, the slates, tiles, or shingles of one side meet those of the other, and the flashing below them may be comparatively narrow. In an open valley, the flashing of zinc or copper is laid in a continuous strip, extending 12 to 18 in. on each side of the valley, while the tiles or slates do not come within 4 to 6 in. of it.

The ridges built up on a sloping roof, where it runs down against a vertical projection like a chimney or a skylight, are called "crickets." They are designed to shed the rain to either side. Since they are out of sight from the ground, they are covered with metal and the flashing is carried out well under the slates or shingles and up the vertical surface to counterflashing.

CORNICES

Cornices are used to crown the composition and are of more importance than the other parts of the façade. They may be very simple, consisting of a straight-hanging gutter, or they may have the more complex details of the molded cornices. In every case it is a matter of good taste and an expression of individuality to fit the cornice to the style of house. A well-designed cornice does much toward increasing the attractiveness of what might otherwise be an uninteresting design. Besides the ordinary hanging cornice there are those which are formed or built into the roof, finished with plain boards, and simply paneled. The simple cornices are inexpensive and may be made quite as attractive, though molded cornices are not necessarily expensive. It depends upon the amount of material rather than upon the shape.

The amount of overhang is quite important in that it must correspond to the other characteristics of that particular style of house. In the colonial style of house the cornices overhang very little and the type of moldings used on these cornices best fits this style. Plain cornices appear best when they project boldly beyond the wall of the building. Houses with steep roofs should be given a cornice with very narrow eaves. Roofs of low pitch look well with a projecting eave.

Houses of cement-plaster exteriors are usually covered on the underside of the cornice with the same material. There is something very pleasing about the simplicity of plaster extending up under the eaves without a variety of other materials used. On frame houses the eaves are boarded underneath with good effect. Plastered eaves in a projecting type of cornice help reflect light into the room. The maximum amount of overhang, to be practical, should be set at 3 ft.

First-story cornices on porch roofs, bay windows, and wings should be lighter and daintier than main-roof cornices. This is because these cornices are nearer the level of the eye. They should be of material and pattern very similar to the main cornices.

There are two types of cornices; the open or skeleton, and the boxed or closed. The type of cornice depends upon the style of house and the locality.

Open Cornice. This cornice is generally used on bungalows and allows a wide variety of designs. It is the more expensive type but is not so warm as the closed cornice. In the better constructions the main cornice stops at the plate, and false rafters, which are of better material, extend beyond the building and are sawed to the different designs. Huge brackets and wide boards are an expensive combination and, to say the least, are in poor taste. Dormers should have a cornice projection to their size.

Box Cornice. These cornices are entirely closed. The under part is covered with ceiling boards, and the front is covered with a fascia board. There are innumerable styles and designs in which cornices are made; and the profile and projection of cornice and gutter are left to the judgment of the architect.

GUTTERS

Gutters are troughs to carry off rainwater. They may be made either of metal or of wood. Care must be taken in the gutter to eliminate any leakage that may be caused by water backing up when the gutter is filled with ice or snow. It has been found that a 3-in. slope to 50 ft. is enough to insure a good flow. It is also known that a V-shaped trough carries the water faster than a flat-bottomed gutter. A gutter set at a slant detracts from the appearance of the building. This slope is obtainable in the better constructions by means of a false bottom.

The hung gutter consists of a semicircular trough supported every few feet by metal strips on the underside of the projecting eaves. This type of gutter is the simplest form and is used only on the cheaper constructions.

The built-in gutter is used where a cornice is built out beyond the projection of the eaves and is often incorporated in the top member. In this case the entire cornice and gutter may be made of sheet metal, or the ornamental parts may be made of wood and the gutter itself lined with metal, which should be carried up under the slates or shingles as flashing, to prevent the water from working up and in. If there is a masonry cornice, it is customary to have the gutter behind the parapet wall above the cornice; the conductors are brought down through the roof and back of the cornice, then out through the wall to a conductor head or box. This last feature lends itself well to decorative treatment and is often introduced as a juncture box below the "gooseneck" or curving pipe dropping from the gutter in the cornice and bending in toward the wall.

THE CONDUCTOR

This follows down the wall and is fastened securely to it. It may turn out at the bottom and discharge on a stone or concrete slab set flush with the ground to prevent erosion, or it may be connected to a cast-iron standpipe or conductor footing which goes underground to a dry well or to the storm sewer. In most communities rain water may not be discharged into the main sewer.

Conductors may be made of galvanized iron, copper, or zinc. If of galvanized iron they should be heavily painted. Copper and zinc are more durable and are well worth the additional cost. Zinc may be oiled or stained, but copper should be used only if an immediate color effect is desired. For strength and cheapness combined, the round corrugated form is the best, but for appearance the square or rectangular sections in stock designs are far more attractive; these are made plain or paneled.

Simple conductor heads or leader boxes are carried in stock, but special designs with monograms or dates are not expensive and add a distinctive touch.

ASSIGNMENT

Plate 3, Cornices

Draw in the main structural details first, such as studs, plates, and rafters. Then draw in the other parts in about the order in which they are constructed. A suitable scale is 3 in. equal 1 ft.

Include the drawing of the gable return for the closed type of cornice, and the elevation for the open or the exposed type.

Label the millwork details as to name, number, and size. Also include a detail section of the moldings, using a sufficiently large scale to show the exact shape.

Supplementary Plate 3A may be assigned to advanced students.

PROBLEMS FOR CLASS DISCUSSION

1. Name the several styles of roofs that are commonly used.
2. What is meant by the "pitch" of a roof?
3. What is the most simple method of indicating the pitch of a roof on a drawing? What is the common method?
4. How is the pitch of the roof figured?
5. What effect do these several roof pitches have in the cost of the house?
6. Define the terms *span, rise,* and *run.*

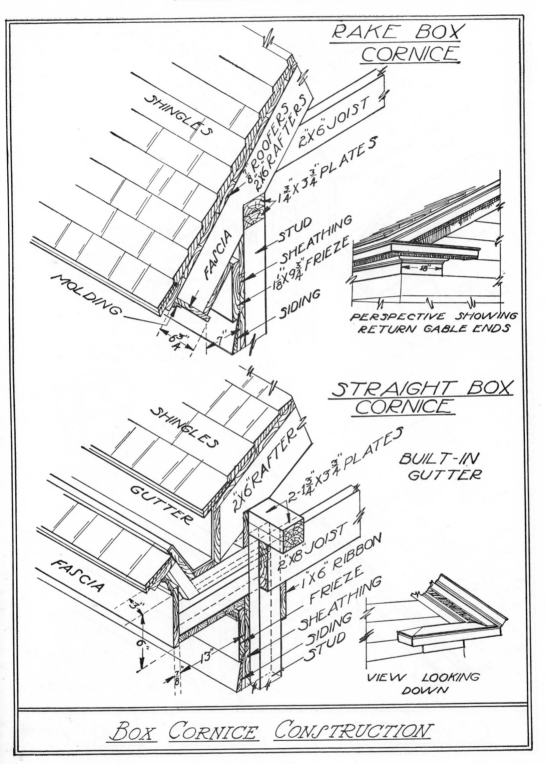

RAKE BOX CORNICE

SHINGLES

ROOFERS
2×6 RAFTERS

2"X 6"JOIST

$1\frac{3}{4}$" X $3\frac{3}{4}$" PLATES

STUD

SHEATHING

$\frac{1}{8}$"X$9\frac{3}{4}$" FRIEZE

SIDING

FASCIA

MOLDING

$6\frac{3}{4}$"

7"

PERSPECTIVE SHOWING
RETURN GABLE ENDS

18"

STRAIGHT BOX CORNICE

SHINGLES

2"X6"RAFTER

GUTTER

BUILT-IN
GUTTER

2-$1\frac{3}{4}$"X$3\frac{3}{4}$" PLATES

2"X8" JOIST

1"X6" RIBBON

FRIEZE

SHEATHING

SIDING

STUD

FASCIA

3"

6"

13"

$\frac{7}{8}$"

VIEW LOOKING
DOWN

BOX CORNICE CONSTRUCTION

Plate 3

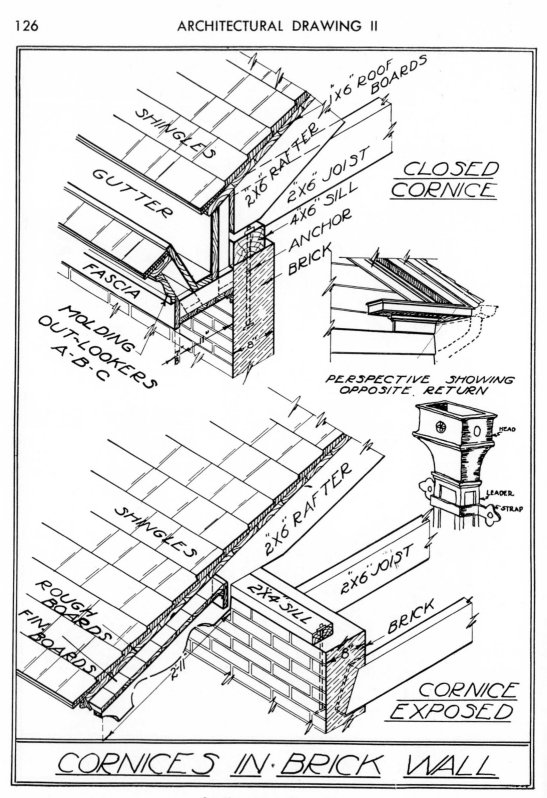

CLOSED CORNICE

PERSPECTIVE SHOWING OPPOSITE RETURN

CORNICE EXPOSED

CORNICES IN BRICK WALL

Supplementary Plate 3A

7. What factors enter into the problem of determining the proper pitch of a roof?

8. What is the proportion of the rise to each foot of run in a one-third-pitch roof? One-quarter-pitch? One-half-pitch?

9. In a one-third-pitch roof if the span of the roof is 20 ft., what is the rise in feet? In a one-quarter-pitch roof?

10. Where are the cornices used in house construction?

11. What types of cornices are commonly used?

12. What determines the amount of over-hang of the cornice?

13. What are the disadvantages of built-in gutters?

V

Windows

Windows are an important element in the design of a house. Whatever the style of the house, if the windows are poorly proportioned or badly grouped, the house will present an unbalanced, ugly appearance. Nothing tends to express the individuality of the owner of a house as the treatment of the walls with regard to openings. It is not so much a question of the kind of window used, but a question of fixing the amount of window space in proportion to the wall space. Plain windows with small lights above and a single large light below are always practical. The upper sash may be divided into six or eight equal lights, with small lights at either side, and larger lights in the center. In the colonial designs it is better to extend the small panes to the lower sash as well.

The disadvantage of using small panes of glass is that they are difficult to clean, because of the numerous small crevices next to the muntins. This disadvantage is more than offset by the added attractiveness to the house.

In colonial houses the windows are placed in perfect symmetry. In the dignified styles of houses it is safe to use this balanced appearance. The first consideration in placing windows should be the lighting of the room and, a very close second consideration, that of the outside appearance. In the kitchen where an extra amount of light is required, it is good practice to have a group of three windows with narrow mullions of wood between. In this arrangement it is well to center the group under those windows above, so that even though the windows below do not correspond with those above they at least do balance with them.

It is essential for the student to be able to weigh the features of the different manufacturer's windows and make a wise selection in the planning of his home. Each product manufactured has its faults and weaknesses as well as its strong selling features, and the student should be aware of this in his study of details of construction. Some windows slide vertically and are balanced by weights and cords or by some spring tension device, and some slide horizontally and need consideration for weatherproofing especially at the point where the sashes meet. Some windows are hinged so they swing out from the top, others from the bottom. Some swing on vertical pivots, or are hinged at the sides. These variations all differ as to advantage in ventilation from the opening size, ease of operation, ease of cleaning, accommodation of accessories, and so on.

GENERAL PROPORTIONS

If the house is two stories high, the windows are taller on the first floor than on the second. The panes of the second-floor windows may be less in height than those of the first, but the width of the panes should be maintained.

Area. 1. One eighth of the wall should be windows.

2. The area of the glass should equal at least $\frac{1}{10}$ of the floor area.

3. One square foot of glass should be allowed to 100 cu. ft. of the interior space to be lighted.

Design. 1. The height of the window should be approximately twice the width.

2. The glass line in residences should be about 2 ft. 6 in. from the floor in the principal living rooms, and about 3 ft. in the bedrooms.

3. The meeting rails should not be less than 5 ft. 9 in. above the floor.

TYPES OF WINDOW FRAMES

Double-Hung Windows. The common type of window frame used is the double-hung window. It consists of two sashes, fitted with balances or weights, thus permitting the raising or lowering of the individual sash. The essential features are the same in both frame and masonry, although the difference in the construction of the wall demands the use of different details in the frame. Double-hung windows are sometimes called "mullion" windows because the division between the sashes is called the "mullion."

Since the operation of the window does not interfere with either the swinging of a shutter or of a screen, this type of window is the more practical in a small house. Ventilation may be given by opening either the top or the bottom sash, but only half of the opening may be utilized.

Casement Windows. In casement windows the sashes are hinged at the sides so that they may swing either in or out as doors. The casement windows swinging in are less weatherproof than the double-hung windows and they take much room space. They may be easily opened, however, and they give the full benefit of the window opening. The casement window opening outward is the more weatherproof and looks well either open or shut. It is more difficult to open or close and presents a problem when screens or shutters are to be used.

Pivoted Windows. These windows are commonly used in factory buildings. The frames of such windows usually are of steel.

Tracery Windows. Stained-glass windows are commonly found in churches.

WINDOW FRAMES

The window proper consists of frame, sash, and finish, each part described separately in the specifications. The parts of the window which are exposed to the weather are preferably made of pine. The sides of the window frame are often made of hardwood to reduce the wear caused by friction. The movable frames which hold the glass in the windows are called "sashes." The pieces forming the top and the bottom of the sashes are called "rails"; and the sides are called "stiles." The small thin bars separating the lights are called "muntins." The pulley stile is made from 1⅛ to 1⅜ in. thick and is tongued into the blind stop which is made ⅞ in. thick. An open space of from 2 to 2½ in. is left between the back of the pulley stile and the rough stud thus forming the weight box. The parting strip is ½ or ⅝ in. thick and passes into a groove ⅝ in. deep. The thickness of the outside casing should be 1⅛ by 5 in. The inside casing should be sufficiently wide to cover the plaster joint. The sash stop is from ½ to ⅝ in. thick, and is secured with roundhead screws passing through slotted sockets. This stop should not be less than 1½ in. wide to take a window shade properly. The sill usually is made of 2-in. stock. The bevel that is formed on the outside of the lower sash and on the corresponding part of the sill tends to force the sash against the parting strip when the sash is closed. The sashes are made from 1⅛ to 1⅜ in. thick. Where 4-in. studs are used the sash should not be thicker than 1⅜ in. If thicker sash is required the studs should be 6 in. The meeting rails are 1⅛ to 1⅜ in. thick and may be double or single beveled. The lower rails may be from 3 to 4½ in. wide and should be accurately fitted to the sill.

Stone sills are generally made 5 to 6 in. thick and 4 in. longer than the opening. They have a 3-in. slope on top, and a drip stop on the underpart of the sill to prevent the rain from seeping into the building. The width of the brick jamb or reveal depends entirely upon the conditions of the setting of the frame, but usually the reveal is made the width of one brick measured from the stile.

Windows are indicated on working drawings by the size of their lights, that is, of the glass panes which form the window. In giving dimensions for glass the width is always

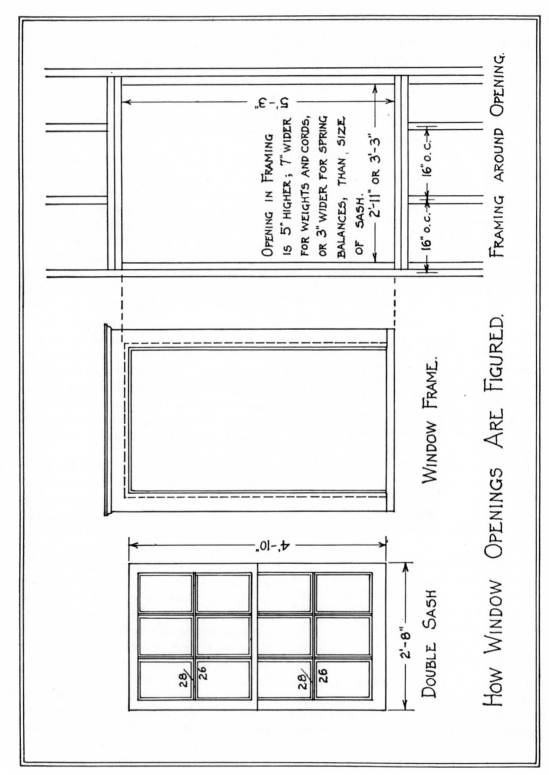

Opening in Framing is 5" higher; 7" wider for weights and cords, or 3" wider for spring balances, than, size of Sash.

5'-3"

16" o.c.   16" o.c.

2'-11" or 3'-3"

FRAMING AROUND OPENING.

WINDOW FRAME.

4'-10"

2'-8"

28   26   28   26

DOUBLE SASH

HOW WINDOW OPENINGS ARE FIGURED.

Fig. 27

given first. In figuring the width of a double-hung window sash, ¼ in. is added to the sum of the widths of the glass panes for each muntin and 4 in. for the two stiles. The corresponding brick opening is about 4 in. wider. Thus, for a sash containing six lights 10 by 14 in., there are three widths of glass at 10 in. plus the two muntins at ¼ in. each, plus the two stiles at 4 in. (30 in. plus ½ in. plus 4 in. equals 34½ in., or 2 ft. 10½ in.). The brick opening would be about 3 ft. 2 in. wide. See Figure 27.

To find the height of the window sash for double-hung windows add to the combined height of all glass, ¼ in. for each muntin, and 3 in. for the top and the bottom rails of the lower sash. The height of the opening in brick will be nearly the combined sash height plus the sum of the sill and the jamb, or 1¾ in. plus 2 in., less 1 in. overlap of the two sashes, or 2¾ in. Thus for the height of the same sash, six lights in two horizontal rows, each 14 in. high, gives the total height of the upper sash as 28 in. plus ¼ in., plus 3 in., or 31¼ in. The lower sash is 1 in. higher. The height of the brick opening will be 31¼ in. plus 32¼ in. plus 2¾ in., or 66¼ in., or 5 ft. 6¼ in.

The height of a casement window is about 1 in. less than that of a corresponding double-hung window, because the meeting rails of the double-hung window are replaced by a muntin; but the width is about 4 in. more for the two-sash casement window.

A basement-window masonry opening is in height and width about 8 in. added to the total width or height of the glass. Thus for a basement window with four 10 by 12-in. lights, the width of the opening is about 20 in. plus 8 in., or 28 in.; and the height is about 24 in. plus 8 in., or 32 in.

The tops of the outside doors and windows should line up, if possible. This determines more or less the height of the windows. Window sills should be kept low, 2 ft. 3 in. to 2 ft. 6 in., on the first floor and 2 ft. 4 in. to 3 ft. 0 in. on the second floor.

The standard sizes of sashes are as follows:

Size of Glass	Size of Window	Size of Glass	Size of Window
10" x 20"	2'1" x 3'10"	14" x 26"	2' 9" x 4'10"
10" x 22"	2'1" x 4' 2"	14" x 28"	2' 9" x 5' 2"
10" x 24"	2'1" x 4' 6"	14" x 30"	2' 9" x 5' 6"
10" x 26"	2'1" x 4'10"	14" x 32"	2' 9" x 5'10"
10" x 28"	2'1" x 5' 2"	14" x 34"	2' 9" x 6' 2"
10" x 30"	2'1" x 5' 6"	14" x 36"	2' 9" x 6' 6"
10" x 32"	2'1" x 5'10"	14" x 38"	2' 9" x 6'10"
10" x 34"	2'1" x 6' 2"	14" x 40"	2' 9" x 7' 2"
10" x 36"	2'1" x 6' 6"	14" x 42"	2' 9" x 7' 6"
12" x 20"	2'5" x 3'10"	14" x 44"	2' 9" x 7'10"
12" x 22"	2'5" x 4' 2"	14" x 46"	2' 9" x 8' 2"
12" x 24"	2'5" x 4' 6"	14" x 48"	2' 9" x 8' 6"
12" x 26"	2'5" x 4'10"	15" x 24"	2'11" x 4' 6"
12" x 28"	2'5" x 5' 2"	15" x 26"	2'11" x 4'10"
12" x 30"	2'5" x 5' 6"	15" x 28"	2'11" x 5' 2"
12" x 32"	2'5" x 5'10"	15" x 30"	2'11" x 5' 6"
12" x 34"	2'5" x 6' 2"	15" x 32"	2'11" x 5'10"
12" x 36"	2'5" x 6' 6"	15" x 34"	2'11" x 6' 2"
12" x 38"	2'5" x 6'10"	15" x 36"	2'11" x 6' 6"
12" x 40"	2'5" x 7' 2"	15" x 38"	2'11" x 6'10"
12" x 42"	2'5" x 7' 6"	15" x 40"	2'11" x 7' 2"
12" x 44"	2'5" x 7'10"	15" x 42"	2'11" x 7' 6"
12" x 46"	2'5" x 8' 2"	15" x 44"	2'11" x 7'10"
12" x 48"	2'5" x 8' 6"	15" x 46"	2'11" x 8' 2"
14" x 24"	2'9" x 4' 6"	15" x 48"	2'11" x 8' 6"

ASSIGNMENT
Plate 4, Double-Hung Window

Plates on window details call for vertical and horizontal sections through the window. Before starting the drawing, study the drafting-room practice for window details, and become thoroughly familiar with the names and the construction of the detailed parts of the window frame. Broken sections through the window are usually shown to a large scale, such as, 3 in. equal 1 ft.

First, work out the horizontal and vertical sections in the positions they are to take on the sheet, and project the elevations from these sections. Show one half of the elevation as an interior and the other as an exterior elevation. If the enlarged sections, horizontal and vertical, are drawn to a scale of 3 in. equal 1 ft., it is better practice to draw the

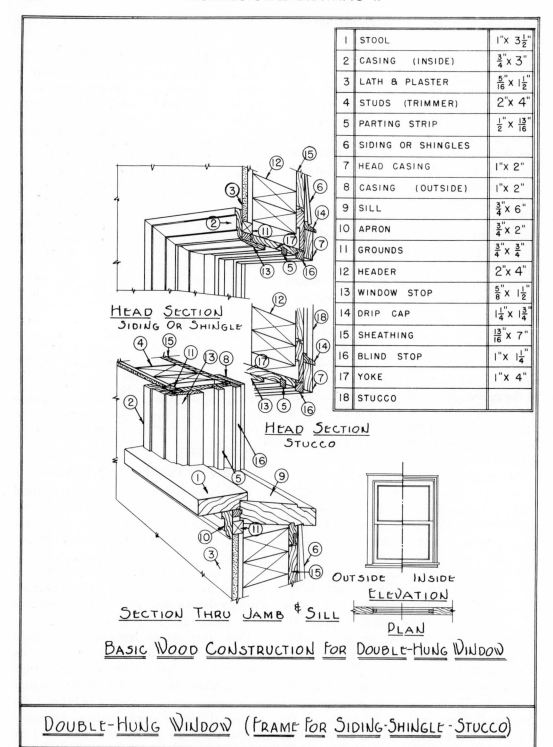

1	STOOL	$1"x\ 3\frac{1}{2}"$
2	CASING (INSIDE)	$\frac{3}{4}"x\ 3"$
3	LATH & PLASTER	$\frac{5}{16}"x\ 1\frac{1}{2}"$
4	STUDS (TRIMMER)	$2"x\ 4"$
5	PARTING STRIP	$\frac{1}{2}"x\ \frac{13}{16}"$
6	SIDING OR SHINGLES	
7	HEAD CASING	$1"x\ 2"$
8	CASING (OUTSIDE)	$1"x\ 2"$
9	SILL	$\frac{3}{4}"x\ 6"$
10	APRON	$\frac{3}{4}"x\ 2"$
11	GROUNDS	$\frac{3}{4}"x\ \frac{3}{4}"$
12	HEADER	$2"x\ 4"$
13	WINDOW STOP	$\frac{5}{8}"x\ 1\frac{1}{2}"$
14	DRIP CAP	$1\frac{1}{4}"x\ 1\frac{3}{4}"$
15	SHEATHING	$\frac{13}{16}"x\ 7"$
16	BLIND STOP	$1"x\ 1\frac{1}{4}"$
17	YOKE	$1"x\ 4"$
18	STUCCO	

HEAD SECTION
SIDING OR SHINGLE

HEAD SECTION
STUCCO

OUTSIDE INSIDE
ELEVATION

SECTION THRU JAMB & SILL

PLAN

BASIC WOOD CONSTRUCTION FOR DOUBLE-HUNG WINDOW

DOUBLE-HUNG WINDOW (FRAME FOR SIDING-SHINGLE-STUCCO)

Plate 4

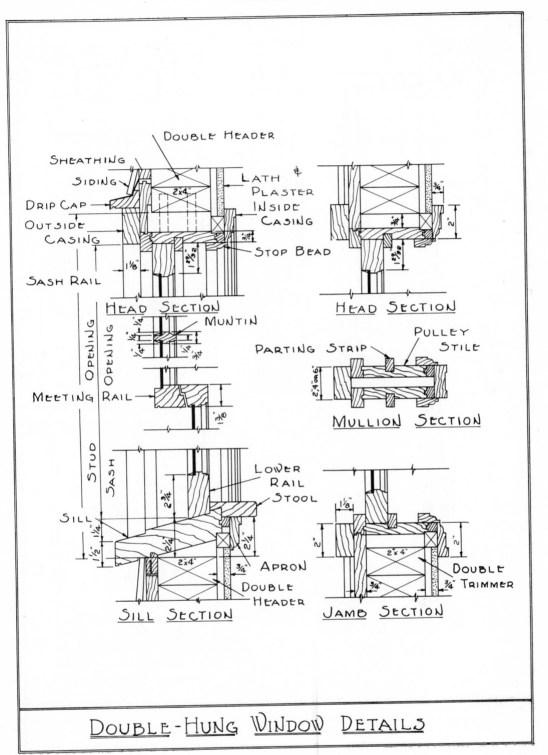

DOUBLE HEADER

SHEATHING

SIDING

DRIP CAP

OUTSIDE CASING

SASH RAIL

LATH & PLASTER
INSIDE CASING

STOP BEAD

2"x4"

HEAD SECTION

OPENING

OPENING

STUD

SASH

MUNTIN

MEETING RAIL

SILL

HEAD SECTION

PARTING STRIP

PULLEY STILE

MULLION SECTION

LOWER RAIL

STOOL

2"x4"

APRON

DOUBLE HEADER

SILL SECTION

1⅛"

2"x4"

DOUBLE TRIMMER

JAMB SECTION

DOUBLE-HUNG WINDOW DETAILS

Supplementary Plate 4A

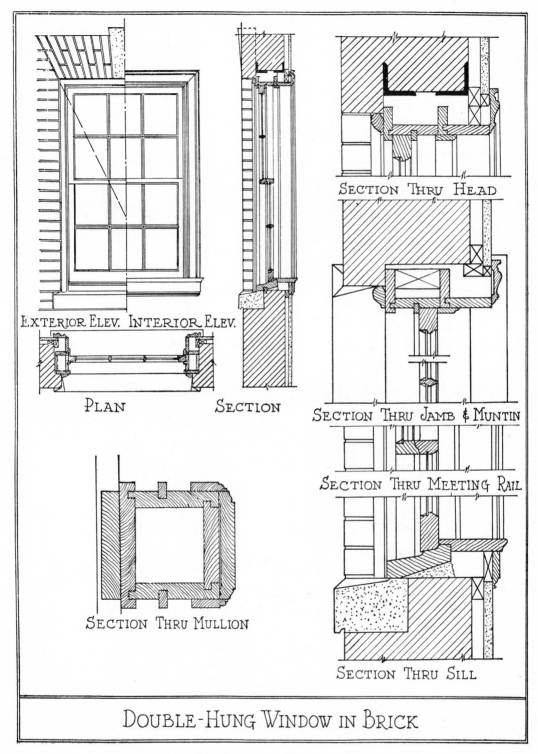

EXTERIOR ELEV. INTERIOR ELEV.

PLAN   SECTION

SECTION THRU MULLION

SECTION THRU HEAD

SECTION THRU JAMB & MUNTIN

SECTION THRU MEETING RAIL

SECTION THRU SILL

DOUBLE-HUNG WINDOW IN BRICK

Supplementary Plate 4B

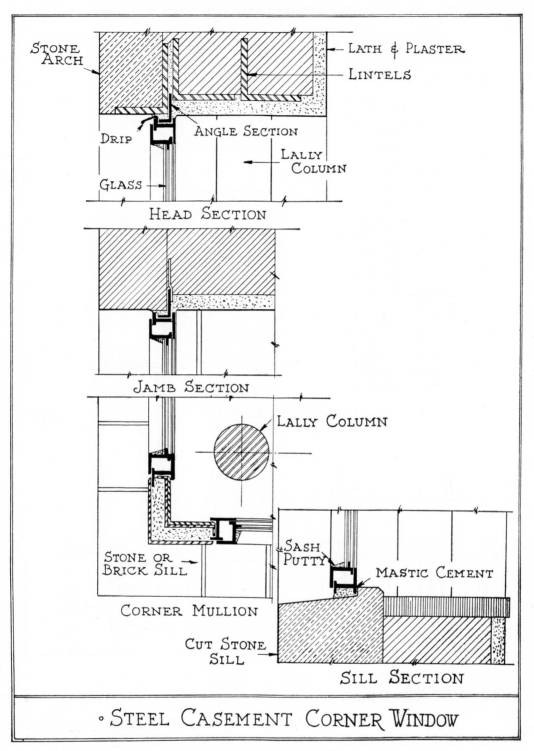

STONE ARCH

LATH & PLASTER

LINTELS

DRIP

ANGLE SECTION

LALLY COLUMN

GLASS

HEAD SECTION

JAMB SECTION

LALLY COLUMN

STONE OR BRICK SILL

SASH PUTTY

MASTIC CEMENT

CORNER MULLION

CUT STONE SILL

SILL SECTION

° STEEL CASEMENT CORNER WINDOW

Supplementary Plate 4C

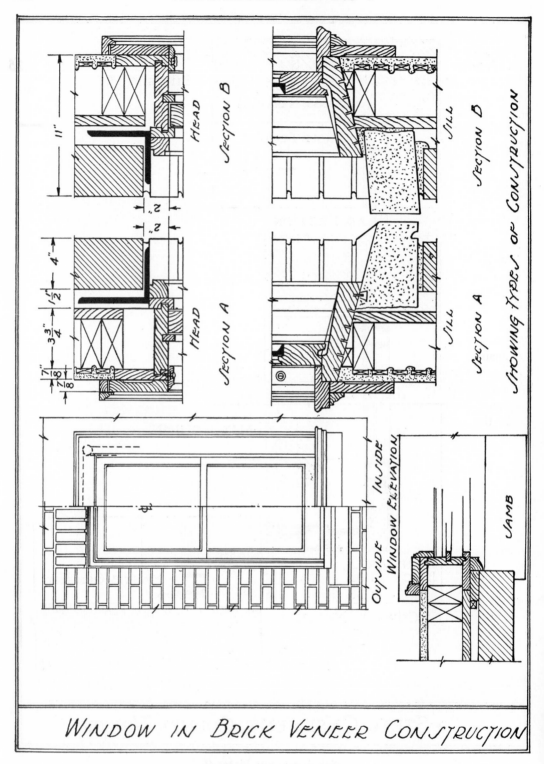

WINDOW IN BRICK VENEER CONSTRUCTION

Supplementary Plate 4D

orthographic representations of elevation, plan, and vertical section at ¾ in. equals 1 ft.

The enlarged vertical section of the head and the sill of the window may be broken and the enlarged horizontal jamb section inserted. Large-scale details of the mullion often are made.

Supplementary Plates 4A, 4B, 4C, and 4D may also be used to get a better understanding of the construction of the double-hung windows.

CASEMENT WINDOWS

There is a considerable difference between casement windows and the ordinary double-hung type. This is largely brought about by the practical requirements of each. Ordinary windows may be made as wide as desired and they will operate with a reasonable amount of effort and with a minimum amount of repair. Casement windows, whether opening toward the inside or outside, must be narrow so as not to prove too heavy for the hinges on which they are hung. To overcome this narrow effect the casement windows are usually grouped into two or three or more windows with narrow mullions separating each window. This adds to rather than detracts from the attractiveness of the house.

Casement windows are cut up into small lights which are separated by narrow wood muntins or by leaded strips or bars. Because of the necessity for screens in this country, the design of the casement windows has been somewhat changed from the original.

Windows should be as attractive from the inside as from the outside. Broad, low, ordinary windows are always attractive. So, too, are casement windows in pairs containing small leaded lights. Painting the leaded bars in colors to bring out the desired effects makes casement windows especially attractive.

Casement windows swinging outward, are called "outward-opening," and those swing-ing into the room are called "inward-opening." The outward-opening window is much more weatherproof and usually is the more favored construction by builders. Many building codes of cities, however, prohibit the use of the outward-swinging sash in exposed places because of the powerful leverage the wind may exert against them. The advantages of casement windows over the double-hung windows are as follows:

1. Full benefit of the window opening is obtained for ventilation.

2. There is an unobstructed view.

3. They are more beautiful in design and add to the appearance of the house.

ASSIGNMENT

Plate 5, Casement Windows

Make this drawing to a scale 1½ in. equal 1 ft.

Supplementary Plate 5A may be assigned to advanced students.

BASEMENT WINDOWS

A single-sash frame hung in a rabbeted frame is commonly used for a basement window. The head and the jamb are rabbeted to take the screen. A molding is used to finish the corner formed by the outside of the frame and the masonry jamb and to stop the entrance of wind and rain. The sill is also laid in mortar to prevent the passage of air and water. No trim is placed on the inside, but a quarter-round molding is used to make the window more weatherproof. A nailing strip is provided for holding the head and the jamb to the foundation wall.

The sash usually is hinged at the top of the frame and, when the window is opened, it is hooked to the underside of a first-floor joist. The basement windows usually are two or three light, and range in size from 8 by 10 in. to 14 by 20 in.

The frame usually is made of 2-in. planking and is set on a 9 by 5½-in. stone sill.

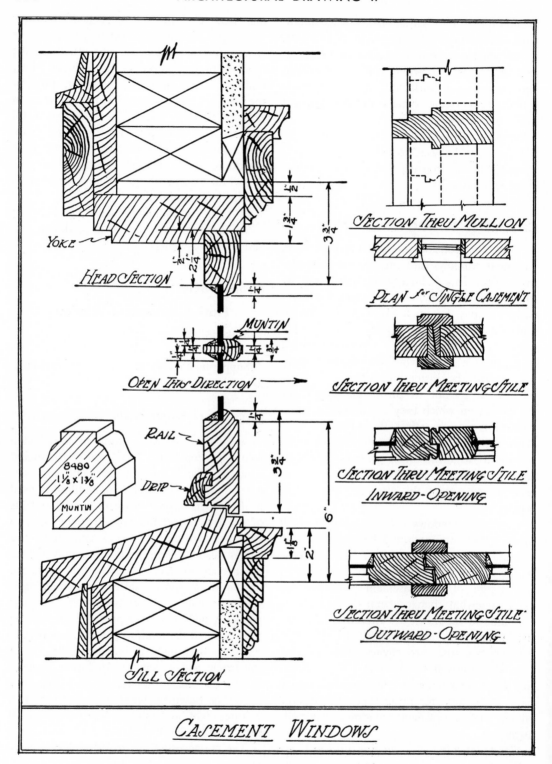

YOKE

HEAD SECTION

MUNTIN

OPEN THIS DIRECTION

RAIL

DRIP

8480
1⅛" x 1⅜"

MUNTIN

SILL SECTION

SECTION THRU MULLION

PLAN for SINGLE CASEMENT

SECTION THRU MEETING STILE

SECTION THRU MEETING STILE
INWARD-OPENING

SECTION THRU MEETING STILE
OUTWARD-OPENING

CASEMENT WINDOWS

Plate 5

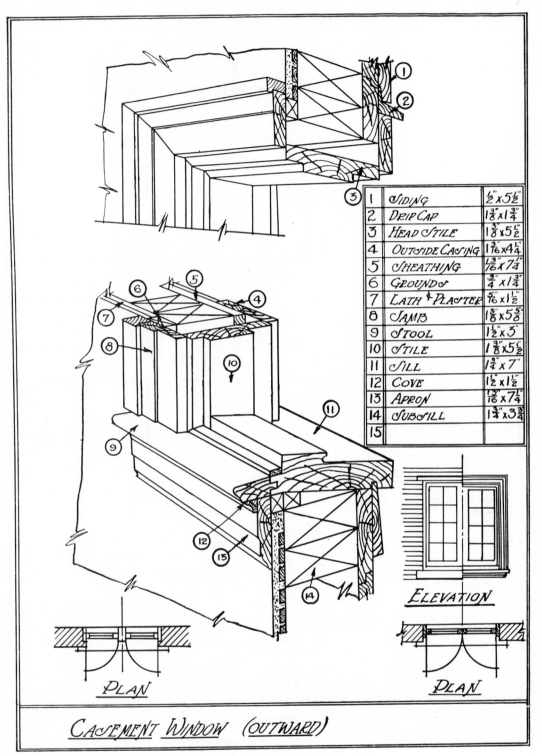

1	SIDING	$\frac{1}{2}'' \times 5\frac{1}{2}''$
2	DRIP CAP	$1\frac{3}{8}'' \times 1\frac{3}{4}''$
3	HEAD STILE	$1\frac{3}{8}'' \times 5\frac{1}{2}''$
4	OUTSIDE CASING	$1\frac{3}{16}'' \times 4\frac{1}{4}''$
5	SHEATHING	$\frac{13}{16}'' \times 7\frac{1}{4}''$
6	GROUNDS	$\frac{3}{4}'' \times 1\frac{3}{4}''$
7	LATH + PLASTER	$\frac{9}{16}'' \times 1\frac{1}{2}''$
8	JAMB	$1\frac{5}{8}'' \times 5\frac{5}{8}''$
9	STOOL	$1\frac{1}{2}'' \times 5''$
10	STILE	$1\frac{3}{8}'' \times 5\frac{1}{2}''$
11	SILL	$1\frac{3}{4}'' \times 7''$
12	COVE	$1\frac{1}{2}'' \times 1\frac{1}{2}''$
13	APRON	$\frac{13}{16}'' \times 7\frac{1}{4}''$
14	SUBSILL	$1\frac{3}{4}'' \times 3\frac{3}{4}''$
15		

ELEVATION

PLAN

PLAN

CASEMENT WINDOW (OUTWARD)

Supplementary Plate 5A

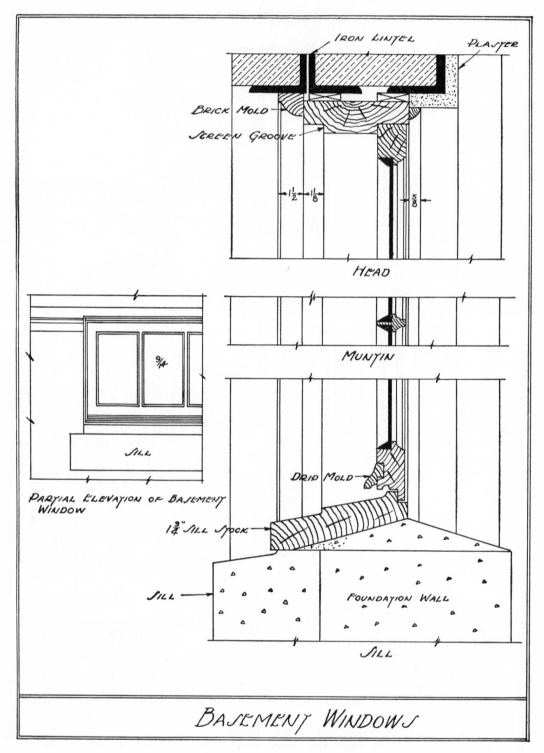

IRON LINTEL

PLASTER

BRICK MOLD

SCREEN GROOVE

$1\frac{1}{2}$ $\frac{1}{8}$ $\frac{5}{8}$

HEAD

MUNTIN

PARTIAL ELEVATION OF BASEMENT WINDOW

$\frac{9}{14}$

SILL

DRIP MOLD

$1\frac{3}{4}$" SILL STOCK

SILL

FOUNDATION WALL

SILL

SILL

BASEMENT WINDOWS

Plate 6

All lintels, inside and out, whether of stone, concrete, or wood, must have at least a 4-in. bearing upon both jambs over the openings. Lintels must have at least a ½-in. clearance over the frame to allow for the settling of the building.

ASSIGNMENT

Plate 6, Basement Windows

Make this drawing to a scale of 1½ in. equal 1 ft., and include a vertical section, a front elevation, and a horizontal or jamb section.

Supplementary Plates 6A, 6B, and 6C may be assigned to advanced students.

AREAWAYS

An area is an enclosed sunken space that is formed outside of the foundation wall of a building for the purpose of admitting light and air to the basement. The larger areas provide a means of access to the basement, usually in the form of outside stairways. The walls which directly enclose the sunken space and serve to keep the soil in place, are called area walls. Drains are often installed in the areas provided with concrete floors.

Area walls may be built of any building material such as tile, brick, stone, concrete blocks, or poured concrete. The choice of materials depends upon the materials available in the community. Brick area walls are constructed in the same manner as brick foundation walls, and are often built semi-circular for small windows which do not extend very far below the grade line. The walls are usually made a thickness equal to the length of a brick. Stone area walls are usually rubble bonded. When foundation walls of the building are to be of concrete, the concrete area walls should be poured at the same time so as to insure a bond between them. Small areas are usually poured with walls 6 in. thick.

Floors in areas in front of basement windows should be below the window sills, and should be provided with a water drain or a loose fill of gravel.

ASSIGNMENT

Plate 6D, Areaways

This is a supplementary plate which may be assigned to advanced students.

Draw a vertical section of the areaway to a large scale. The scale will depend upon the size of the areaway. Usually a scale of 1 in. equals 1 ft., or 1½ in. equal 1 ft. will be found convenient.

DORMER WINDOWS

Dormer windows, such as are shown in Plate 7A, admit light to the space under the roof, permit circulation of air in the room, and add room height at needed portions of the second-floor or attic plan of the house. The name refers to the sleeping rooms under the roofs in early times when such spaces were lighted by means of these windows. Whenever a vertical wall rises out of a roof, it is known as a "Dormer," and windows set in this wall are known as "Dormer Windows." Dormers may have a gable, or hip style of roof which is framed into the main roof, or a shed-style roof which blends into the roof proper. The wall of the dormer may be a continuation of the face of the main building, or set back from the face depending upon the type of dormer, appearance desired, and its construction advantages. Some dormers are extended almost the entire length of the house, providing almost normal ceiling light. The narrow dormer is preferred in residence work because it adds to the attractiveness of the house if it is carefully placed and proportioned. The wide dormer is used on buildings usually one story in height or built very low. It is the simplest style and is usually covered with a lean-to roof so as to allow enough vertical

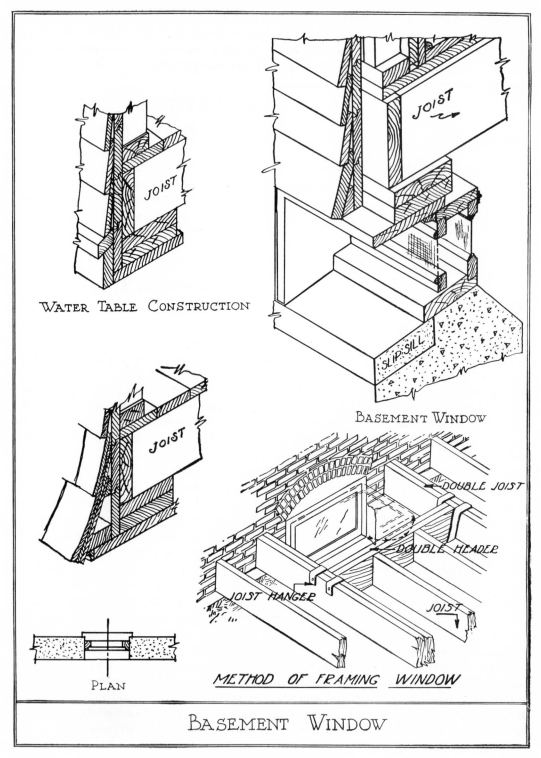

WATER TABLE CONSTRUCTION

JOIST

JOIST

SLIP SILL

BASEMENT WINDOW

JOIST

DOUBLE JOIST

DOUBLE HEADER

JOIST HANGER

JOIST

PLAN

METHOD OF FRAMING WINDOW

BASEMENT WINDOW

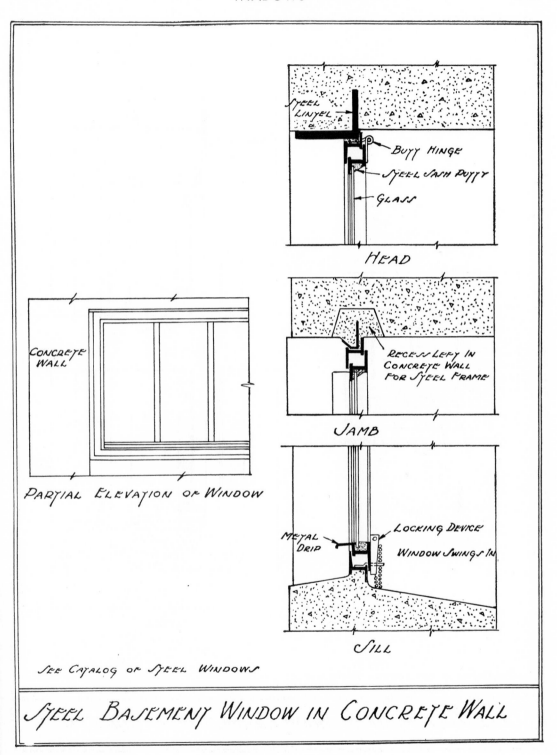

STEEL LINTEL
BUTT HINGE
STEEL SASH PUTTY
GLASS
HEAD

CONCRETE WALL

RECESS LEFT IN CONCRETE WALL FOR STEEL FRAME
JAMB

PARTIAL ELEVATION OF WINDOW

METAL DRIP
LOCKING DEVICE
WINDOW SWINGS IN
SILL

SEE CATALOG OF STEEL WINDOWS

STEEL BASEMENT WINDOW IN CONCRETE WALL

Supplementary Plate 6B

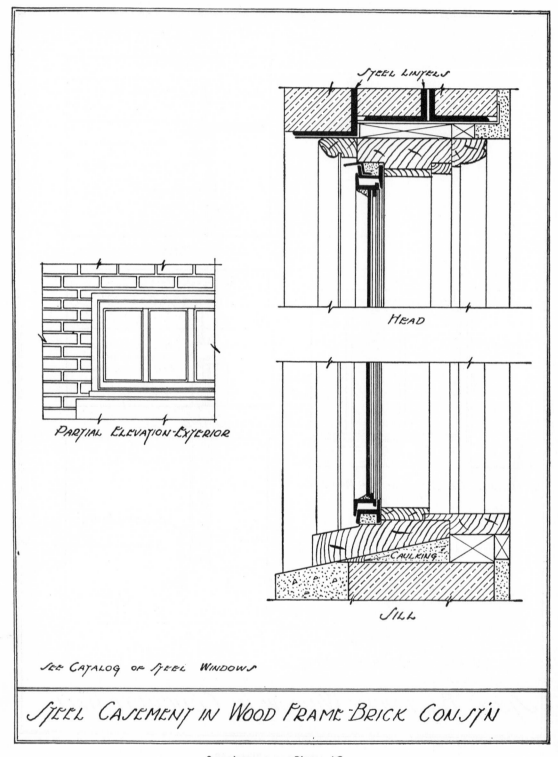

STEEL LINTELS

HEAD

PARTIAL ELEVATION-EXTERIOR

CAULKING

SILL

SEE CATALOG OF STEEL WINDOWS

STEEL CASEMENT IN WOOD FRAME-BRICK CONST'N

Supplementary Plate 6C

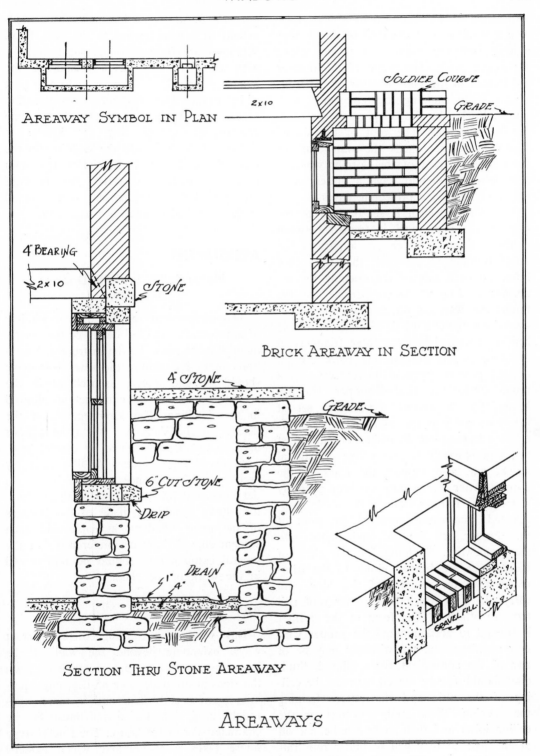

AREAWAY SYMBOL IN PLAN

SOLDIER COURSE

GRADE

2×10

4" BEARING

2×10

STONE

BRICK AREAWAY IN SECTION

4" STONE

GRADE

6" CUT STONE

DRIP

DRAIN

1'   4"

GRAVEL FILL

SECTION THRU STONE AREAWAY

AREAWAYS

wall in the front of the dormer to accommodate a window, and the roof of the dormer uniting with the main roof which allows for ample pitch. The walls of the dormer are treated in the same manner as the walls of the main building, being covered with stucco, brick, shingles, clapboards, or other suitable materials. The roof in the simple shed-type dormer sheds the water on the main roof in front of the dormer window, and therefore, should have a gutter along the front, and wide projecting eaves.

The dormer which is set back from the face of the main wall is framed between doubled trimmers which are a part of the rafter framing of the roof; that is, a roof rafter on each side of the opening for the dormer is doubled to compensate for the rafters that were cut out to make the proper size of the opening for the dormer. A double header is framed between these trimmers at the base of the dormer and placed in an upright position because it will serve as a rough sill for the window proper. The top header for the dormer opening is set at the same pitch as the roof. Main roof rafters are framed into these headers and must be large enough to carry the additional weight and also support the sides of the dormer. After the opening has been properly framed, the dormer framework can be constructed. The corner posts at the front of the dormer are doubled and nailed into the framework. Studding for the sides of the dormer are framed either to the trimmers or to the rough roof sheathing, and carry plates to which the dormer roof rafters are attached. The front of the dormer is framed to accommodate the proper window openings, and the windows may be of any of the convenient types offered. Studding should also be placed between the ceiling of the attic and the rafters framing the opening. These studs can rest on the ceiling joists and their ends can be cut off at an angle so they will fit under roof rafters and provide them with additional support. Some dormers have the wall studs extend to a sole framed to the attic floor. Windows are framed in the same manner, with trimmers and headers and, if the height is limited, the plate may form a part of the header. Dormers that are an extension of the main wall are basically of the same construction except that the header is omitted at the base, and the studding for the face of the dormer is framed to the main roof-rafter plate. The rafters for the roof are framed to a header and studs framed in the described manner. See page 149.

ASSIGNMENT

Plates 7, 7A, and 7B, Dormer Windows

The student may select a dormer window of appropriate style and detail, or the assignment may be made by the instructor. Variations in design among the several students should be encouraged, as well as in the accepted methods of construction allowed in the detailing. The arrangements of the details on the sheet and the combinations used should be determined by careful comparisons of representative details drawn by architects, by reference to good books on detailing, and by suggestions by the instructor. Study should be made of the features of the many windows available and each student should draw his preference, but the several combinations should be represented in the work of the class.

BAY WINDOWS

Bay windows are designed in different ways, extending beyond the wall of the house as a square-corner rectangle or with the sides at an angle. The 45-deg. angle permits more useful room and is more commonly used, but the design must fit the characteristics of the house. The English-type house takes a square bay which extends down to the window-sill height. Casement

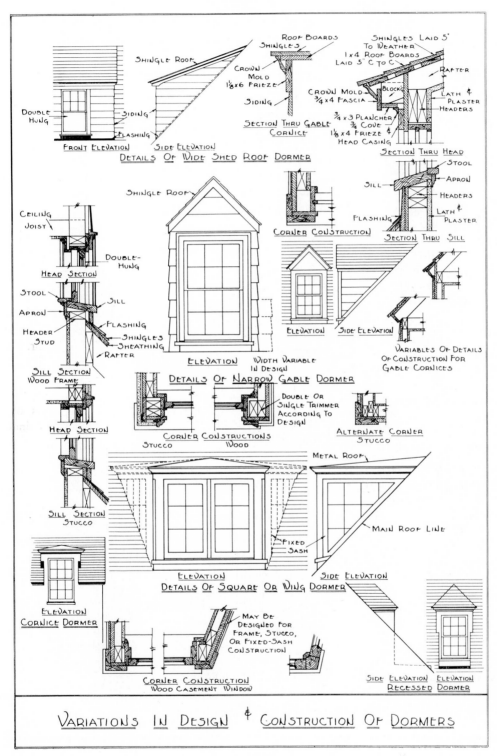

DETAILS OF WIDE SHED ROOF DORMER

DETAILS OF NARROW GABLE DORMER

DETAILS OF SQUARE OR WING DORMER

VARIATIONS IN DESIGN & CONSTRUCTION OF DORMERS

Plate 7

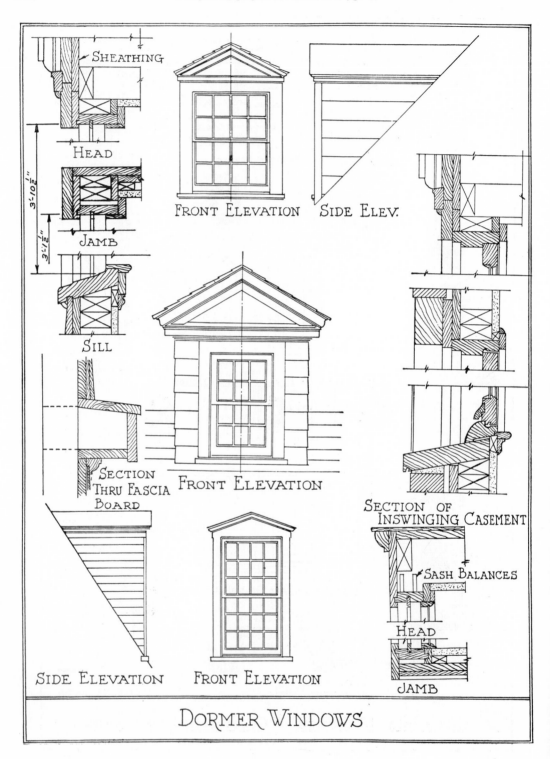

SHEATHING

HEAD

JAMB

SILL

FRONT ELEVATION

SIDE ELEV.

SECTION
THRU FASCIA
BOARD

FRONT ELEVATION

SECTION OF
INSWINGING CASEMENT

SASH BALANCES

HEAD

JAMB

SIDE ELEVATION

FRONT ELEVATION

DORMER WINDOWS

Plate 7A

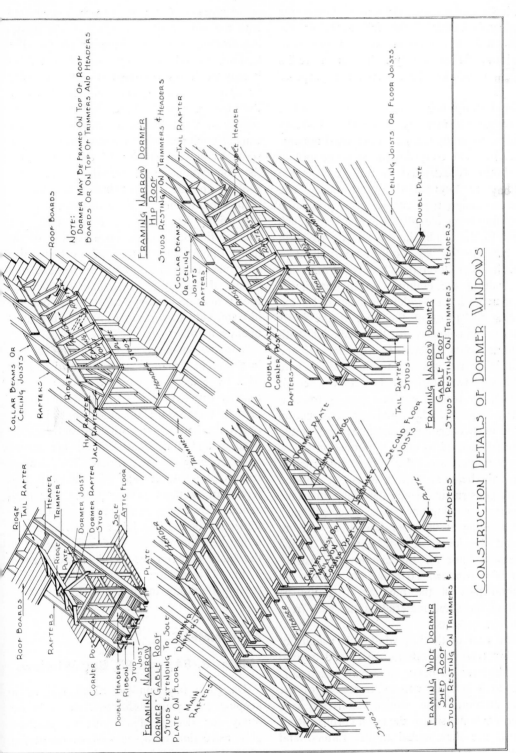

CONSTRUCTION DETAILS OF DORMER WINDOWS

Plate 7B

windows are usually preferred. Often the window is extended the full width of the room with a continuous row of casement windows. In some style homes a radial design of window best serves the purposes of style.

Single-story bay windows are the easiest to design satisfactorily, since the two-story window generally leads to a detached appearance. In a two-story design the main roof of the house is extended to project over the window to improve the appearance. The window design may consist of a projection extending from the sill line, or it may reach down to the grade line. If it extends from the sill line the bay requires no foundation since it is cantilevered or bracketed out from the wall of the building. In the cantilever construction, the window is framed by extending the joists of the floor if the joists run at right angles to the wall, or with separate joists framed to trimmers if the floor joists run parallel to the wall. Where the bay is two stories in height or where it extends up from the grade line, a foundation is required. The cantilever construction is the most economical since the cost of the materials needed to build a foundation below the frost line are saved. This construction can only be used with a house of balloon frame construction, since the platform frame requires removing the studs, sole, subfloor, and heading at the floor line to be able to extend the joists. A 4-ft. extension is the suggested limit for the cantilever construction of a window. To make the window an integral part of the building it should be built of the same material as the wall from which it projects.

The roof of the bay window is usually of the hip type. The rafters can extend beyond the plate for an open, closed or boxed cornice to match the cornice treatment of the main structure. The cornice details are kept in proportional size to the main cornice. Roof boards are then nailed to the rafters, and should be tongued and grooved lumber (or

wood veneer). The roof of the bay is covered with the same roofing material as the house, but flashing must be properly placed. The flashing should preferably be of metal, or it may be heavy roofing felt. The roof may be covered with the same material used on the main part of the house but may also be copper or a painted metal. Bay windows are usually equipped with a gutter and a downspout to prevent erosion of the soil around the foundation. In a one-story house the roof of the bay is just below that of the main roof. If there is little distance between the ceiling line and the roof rafters, the roof of the bay can be an extension of the main roof for that portion of the bay which is parallel to the face of the house. The roof rafters of the bay are extensions of the main roof rafters and are spiked to them, and the hip and side rafters are framed in the same manner as other bays.

Window openings are framed into the bay in the regular manner, with doubled headers of 2 by 4 members supported top and bottom by trimmers nailed to the corner posts, or near them, and short studs are nailed between the headers and sill, and between the headers and plate. The headers are set on edge or may be placed flat. The window frames of whatever type of window is preferred are then set in the opening, and horizontal sheathing is nailed to the studs. The underside of the bay joists are covered with a finished lumber. It is advisable to fill in the space between the bay joists with about 3 in. of insulation to prevent cold drafts from penetrating through the floor.

ASSIGNMENT

Plates 8, 8A, and 8B, Bay Windows

Design a bay window which will be in keeping with your preferred style of house. Study the details of the various methods of construction used, as well as the design of the appearance of the window. Make a

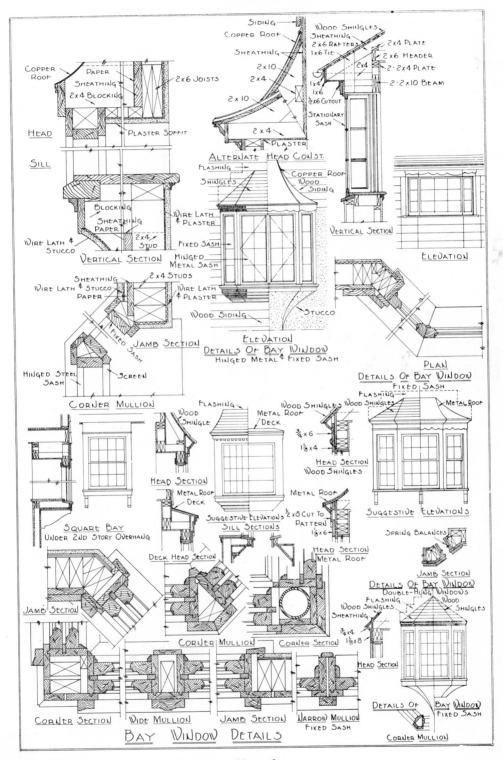

Plate 8

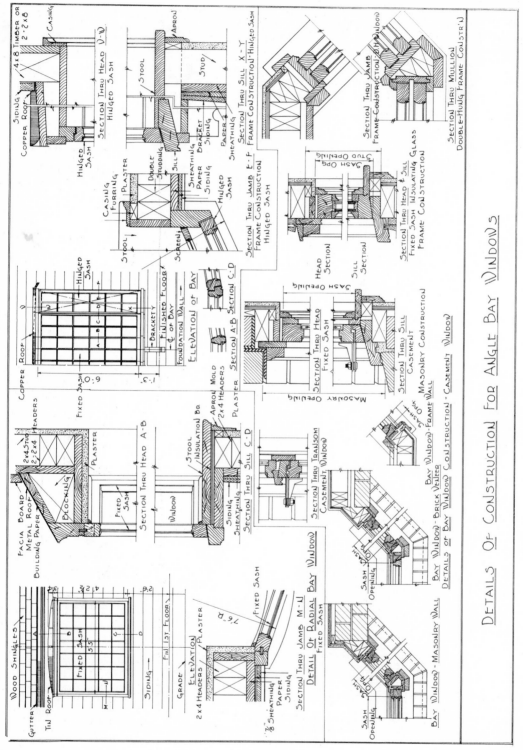

DETAILS OF CONSTRUCTION FOR ANGLE BAY WINDOWS

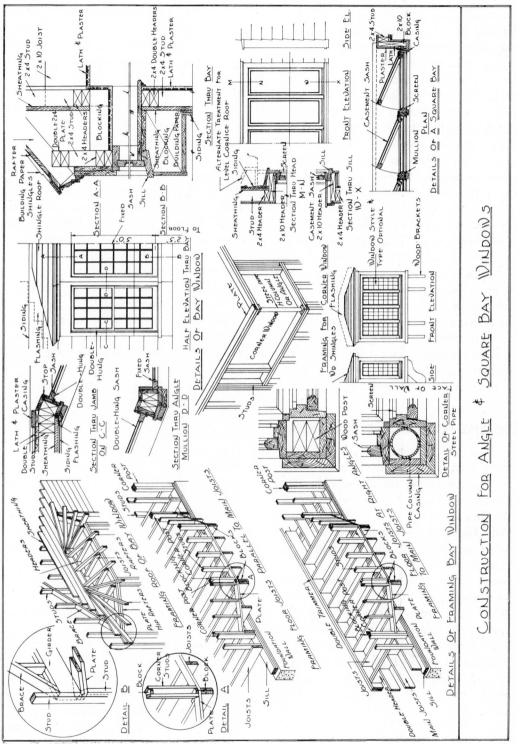

CONSTRUCTION FOR ANGLE & SQUARE BAY WINDOWS

Plate 8B

working drawing of this detail of the house. Use your judgment as to how to present the details and how to arrange them on your drawing. The instructor may advise the student or make a particular assignment.

The student should make reference to the several books on detailing in architectural drawing to study ideas of arrangement and presentation of the details of the window. Particular attention should be made to good construction practices, and use of standard millwork. Dimensions necessary to the workman may be obtained from a detailed drawing as made by an architect, from a completely dimensioned drawing illustrated in a book of details, from a completely dimensioned drawing illustrated in a textbook, or from a good example of a bay window as given in a building magazine. Remember the dimensions given on the detail drawing are the dimensions necessary to the workman in the construction. If variations are used by the several students as to design, kinds of windows, shape of dormer, the work becomes more interesting and valuable.

PROBLEMS FOR CLASS DISCUSSION

1. Why are the windows on the first floor taller than those on the second floor?
2. Why are windows on the second floor arranged directly over the windows on the first floor?
3. Why are windows standardized in size?
4. What are some of the standard sizes commonly used?
5. What are the general proportions given to windows?
6. What relationship exists between the area of the house and the number and size of windows?
7. Measure the size of the windows used in your home. How do these measurements correspond with the standard sizes? How high from the floor are the windows placed on the first floor? Second floor?
8. What styles of windows are used in the houses in your neighborhood? How many different variations can you find?
9. Why are the double-hung windows more practical in a small house?
10. What are the advantages of casement windows? Disadvantages?
11. How is the catalogue description given for casement windows?
12. Where are pivoted windows used?
13. How are the sizes of windows given on working drawings? How do you figure the width of opening from a double-hung sash? For a casement window? How do you figure the height of a double-hung window? A casement window? How are these sizes figured for a basement window?
14. What woods are used in the making of window frames? Sash?
15. Name and describe some of the common terms used in describing windows.
16. How wide is the reveal in a brick wall? In a stone wall?
17. What is the difference between an outward-opening casement and an inward-opening casement? What advantages and disadvantages?
18. How is the basement window hung?
19. What is the purpose of an area? Where are they used?
20. Why are dormer windows used?
21. Why are the narrow dormers much to be preferred over the wide dormers? How are dormer windows influenced by the style of house?
22. What variations are used in the styles of dormers?
23. What effect do bay windows have in the design of the house?
24. Why are bay windows built but one story in the usual design of the house?
25. Study the various styles and types of windows used in your neighborhood, as to the type of roof on dormers and bay windows, moldings and trim, size and type of pane, proportions, etc.

VI

Wall Sections

In a wall section one must imagine that the house is cut from the ridge of the roof down through the foundation. Such a drawing then indicates the heights of the different parts of the building. It is best to begin the drawing at the bottom of the house and work toward the top as is done when a house is actually being built. This gives the foundation and the footings first consideration. Concrete generally makes the best footing, but often stones and sometimes bricks are used for this purpose. The thickness of the foundation wall is determined by the building code of the city in which the house is to be erected, but for cases where no code is given, the table of thicknesses may be used. The thickness of the basement floor may be set at 4 in.

The lowest room height of the basement should be 7 ft., measured from the surface of the basement floor to the bottom of the first-floor joist. Since the first-floor joists, the flooring, and the basement ceiling take up 9⅝ in., plus 1⅞ in., plus ¾ in. or 12¼ in., the floor-to-floor height should be 8 ft. as the minimum height.

Because there is a 2 by 4 under the first-floor joist, 2 in. should be deducted from the 8 ft., which leaves 7 ft. 10 in. as the height of the foundation above the level of the basement floor. The sill is set back 1 in. from the face of the foundation wall to allow for the sheathing and the outside finish. The sill header is 2 by 10 in. laid vertically on top of the sill, with its outside edge flush with the outside edge of the sill. The sill is

bolted to the underpinning. The rough flooring is laid diagonally on top of the 2 by 10-in. joist. A 2 by 4-in. sole is laid on this rough flooring as a base for the next room-height studs. The distance from the top of the first floor to the bottom of the second-floor joist is 10 ft. The rough flooring is considered 1 in. thick and a 2 by 4-in. sole is laid on top of it. Immediately below the second-floor joist there is a 2 by 4-in. double header or plate. Adding 4 in. for the plate, 2 in. for the sole, 1 in. for the flooring, we get 7 in. Therefore, the length of the first-floor stud is 10 ft. minus 7 in. which makes 9 ft. 5 in. On this plate another header is continued for the second-floor height. The second floor is built up similarly to the first floor. The distance from the top of the second-floor joist to the bottom of the attic-floor joist is 8 ft. 11 in. The 2 by 6-in. attic-floor joist is nailed to the top of the upper plate and a 2 by 6-in. rafter is spiked to the attic-floor joist. The upper corner of the joist is sawed off when the rafter is nailed to the plate, so that the joist will not extend above it.

The ⅞-in. roof boards are nailed to the rafters and a covering of building paper is laid beneath the shingles. The rafters may extend past the wall of the house to suit the taste of the designer and fit the style of the house. Sheathing is nailed to the studding and is covered with building paper, and the siding is nailed on.

The laths are nailed directly to the studs and plaster is applied.

INSULATION

Wall construction has shown considerable improvement in recent years due to the improvements in insulation materials.

Insulation quilts are known by trade names and are made from seaweed quilted between heavy paper, wool-like wood fiber, hair, flax, and other vegetable fibers. In selecting such materials, inflammability, insect attack, and rodent damage should be considered; also cost and insulating value.

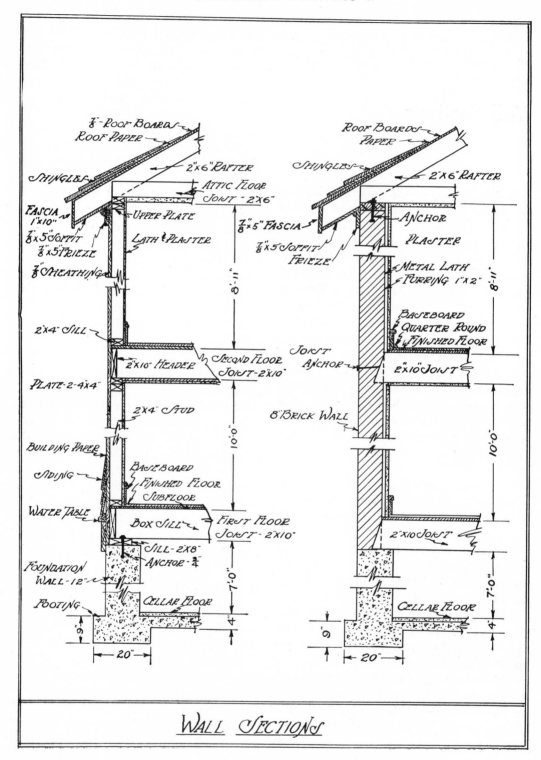

WALL SECTIONS

Plate 9

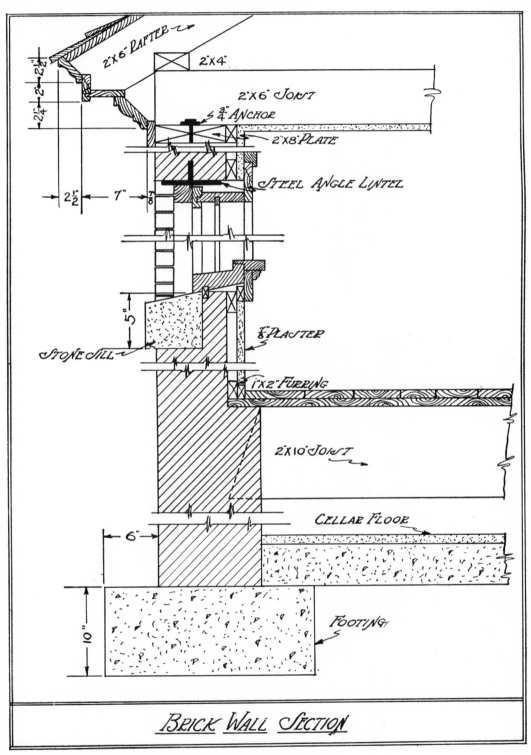

BRICK WALL SECTION

Supplementary Plate 9A

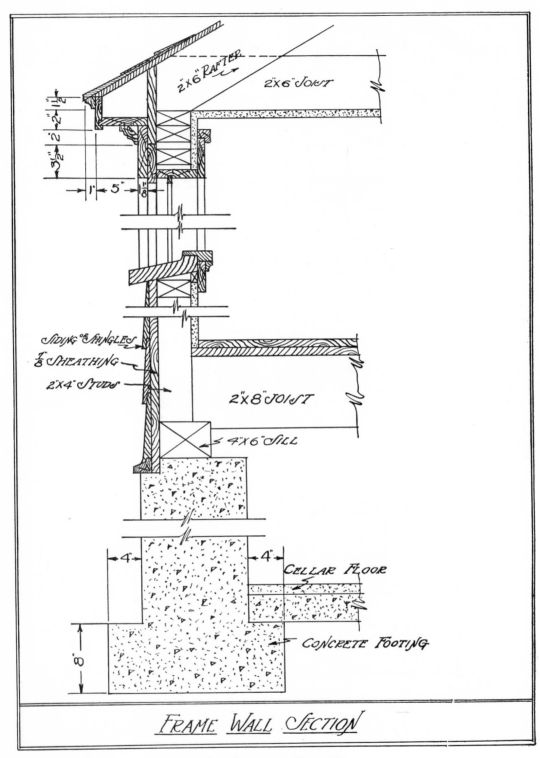

2"x6" RAFTER

2"x6" JOIST

3½" 2" 2" 1½"

1" 5" 1/8"

SIDING OR SHINGLES

7/8" SHEATHING

2"x4" STUDS

2"x8" JOIST

4"x6" SILL

4" 4"

CELLAR FLOOR

CONCRETE FOOTING

8"

FRAME WALL SECTION

Supplementary Plate 9B

The quilts are used between floors, rafters, and studding, and under siding and shingles.

Insulating boards are made from several kinds of fibers and minerals pressed into boards. Wheat straw, cornstalk pulp, and licorice root are commonly used. Corkboard is widely used as well as the wood fiber, exploded wood fiber, and the pulp from the sugar-cane mills. Boards made of minerals, such as gypsum or porous asphaltic materials, are likewise used. These boards are made 4 ft. wide and any length from 6 to 12 ft. They are used in place of sheathing, for a plaster base, and for the inside wall covering instead of plaster.

There are many fills such as "rock wool," sawdust, shavings, gypsum flake, etc. Other insulating materials are made by mixing various powders with water which forms a porous solid. Another insulating unit which fits between the studding is a pressed excelsior which is treated with chemicals to make it noninflammable. These materials are used between walls, under floors, above ceilings, and between rafters.

ASSIGNMENT

Plate 9, Wall Sections

Draw up the sections of a building, approximately in the order of their construction. A convenient scale to use is 1 in. equals 1 ft.

In drawing this plate, establish the sheathing line and the thickness of the cellar and the upper walls. Next, locate the floor and ceiling heights, and sketch in lightly the position of the window openings. You may use a broken drawing, but then these various heights cannot be located to exact scale. You may, however, establish the heights as near the proper locations as possible, with allowances made for breaks. Have the dimensions read full size. After these locations have been established it is an easy matter to draw in the various details by referring to the various plates which you have drawn.

Supplementary Plates 9A and 9B may be assigned to advanced students.

PROBLEMS FOR CLASS DISCUSSION

1. What is the purpose of showing a vertical wall section on the working drawing?
2. What room heights are commonly used in houses? Why do these room heights vary in different sections of the country?
3. Why is it necessary to keep the basement height above the 7 ft. minimum?
4. What determines the projection of the eaves in a house?
5. What materials are used in the construction of walls in the common residence work?
6. Why are these vertical sections drawn in about the order of their construction of a building?
7. Why is the house designed to "hug" the site? What factors determine the height of the house?
8. What changes in building construction are affecting the construction of walls?

Shutters and Blinds

Outside blinds accomplish two purposes: They make the appearance of the house more attractive, and provide a means of shutting out the sun in summer. Blinds are made with slats, either fixed or movable; shutters are solid and generally are paneled. Shutters are useful when the house is not being occupied as they may then be closed, affording some protection to the windows. Inside blinds consist of wooden slats through which a vertical cord extends, allowing the blinds to roll up like a curtain.

Both blinds and shutters are made 1⅛ in. thick and are hung on L hinges, which allow clearance for the outside casing or "reveal." They are secured by blind fasteners or blind adjusters. Outside blinds or shutters can be opened from the inside by using a patented opener. In the best type the shutter is operated by turning a handle, which communicates motion to the shutter by means of a rod extending through the window casing.

WINDOW SCREENS

Many improvements have been made in window and door screens. Screens may be made with metal frames constructed with a groove into which the wire screen is inserted, and then wedged into place with a metal spline. The best patterns of wooden screen are made in somewhat the same way, except that a molding of wood is used to hold the wire in place.

The cheapest screens have steel wire mesh and consequently need frequent painting to keep them from rusting. The better screens are covered with a mesh made of copper bronze, which is not subject to rust. The mesh is about 14 to 16 wires to the inch.

STORM SASH

Storm sash are sometimes provided for windows and are generally made 1⅛ in. thick. They are hung in the rabbet that is occupied by the blinds when they are closed.

ASSIGNMENT

Plate 10, Shutters and Blinds

Draw the elevations for this plate to reduced scale, and the details to full size. Draw the plans by projecting from the elevations. In the details include a section showing the stile-and-panel construction, the tongue-and-groove construction, and the finish-molding construction.

PROBLEMS FOR CLASS DISCUSSION

1. What is the difference between a blind and a shutter?
2. What is the purpose of blinds in a modern house? What purpose did they serve in the early houses?
3. What variation is used in the recent modern style of house? Have these ever been used before?
4. What is the purpose of storm sash?
5. How are screens used in casement windows?

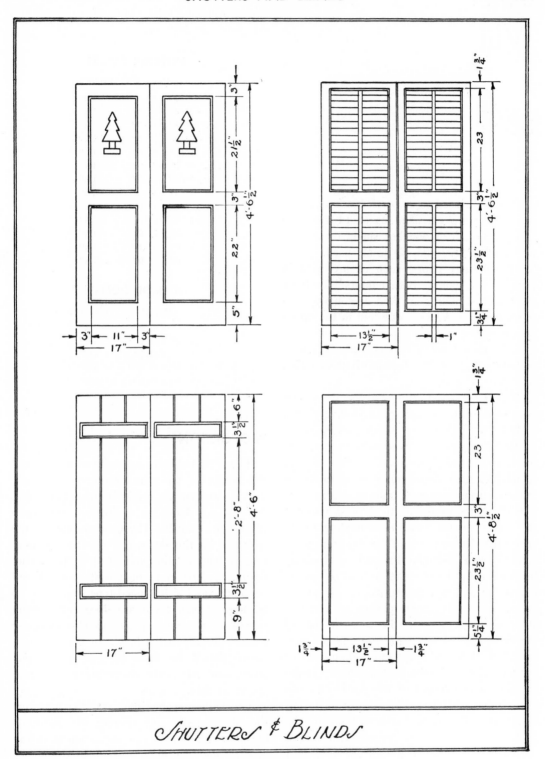

SHUTTERS & BLINDS

Plate 10

U N I T

VIII

Doors

Doors are used to close all kinds of openings. They are classified as to (1) method of operation, (2) whether single or double, (3) construction, and (4) joints used.

The cheaper doors, such as are used in garages, are called "batten doors." In these the matched boards are laid diagonally, with the boards on the rear side laid in the opposite direction to those of the front side. Usually they have a diagonal brace, and a wide board across the top and bottom which is called a "batten."

The better doors are usually of veneer construction. It is customary in every case to build up a frame of comparatively heavy pieces, then cover it over with veneer, and fill it in with lighter wood in the form of panels. Certain firms make a specialty of manufacturing patented built-up doors. The patents apply to the method of dovetailing the veneer to the core, thus tending to increase the glue surface and thereby prevent the veneer from peeling. In such a built-up framework for a door, the vertical pieces are called "stiles," and the horizontal pieces are called "rails." There are always at least two stiles and two rails, a stile at each side of the door, and a rail at the top and the bottom, but there may be more than two of each of these members. The stiles usually extend the full height of the door from top to bottom, and the rails are tenoned into them. After the frame has been built up, the door may be finished as desired, with sunken panels in the spaces between the rails and stiles, or with an inlaid veneer surface.

All millwork firms carry stock doors of the commonly used sizes. These sizes may be listed as follows:

EXTERIOR DOORS

Size	Thickness
2' 6" x 6' 6"	1⅜"
2' 6" x 6' 8"	1⅜"
2' 8" x 6' 8"	1⅜"
2' 8" x 7' 0"	1⅜"
2'10" x 8'10"	1⅜"
3' 0" x 7' 0"	1⅜"
2' 6" x 6' 8"	1¾"
2' 8" x 6' 8"	1¾"
2' 8" x 7' 0"	1¾"
2'10" x 6'10"	1¾"
2'10" x 7' 0"	1¾"
3' 0" x 6' 8"	1¾"
3' 0" x 7' 0"	1¾"

INTERIOR DOORS

Size	Thickness
2' 0" x 6' 8"	1⅜"
2' 6" x 6' 8"	1⅜"
2' 8" x 6' 8"	1⅜"
2' 6" x 7' 0"	1⅜"
2' 8" x 7' 0"	1⅜"
3' 0" x 7' 0"	1⅜"

PROPORTIONS

The ratio between the width of a door and the height of all main entrances is usually 1 to 2; that is, the height is twice the width. For single doors in residences the ratio should be 1 to 2½. The general rule for the width of interior doors is 2 ft. 8 in. for residences, and a minimum of 2 ft. for closet doors. A door more than 4 ft. wide should be made double if hinged-type doors are to be used. When there are doors of varying widths in the same room, to give a better interior treatment the height of the principal doors should be fixed by the proportions given, and the other doors made to correspond to those heights.

The width of the stiles and the top rails should be about one seventh the width of the door, the bottom rail about one tenth the height, and the muntins and lock rails ½ in. less in width than the stiles.

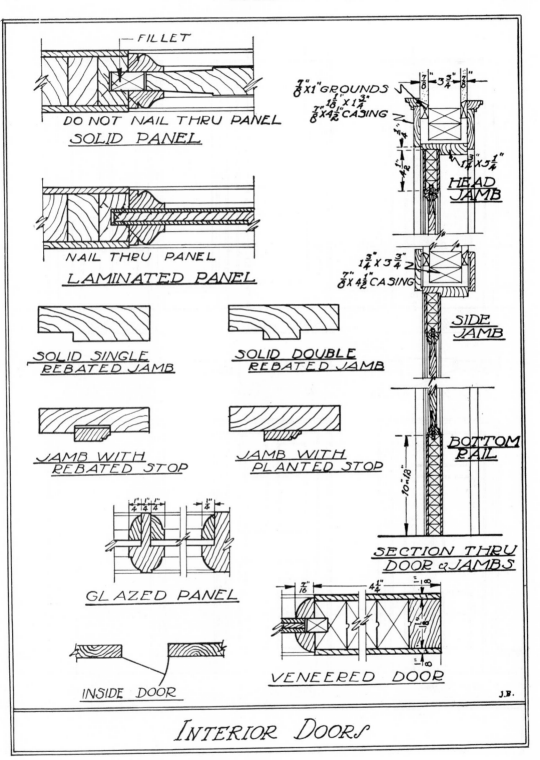

FILLET

DO NOT NAIL THRU PANEL
SOLID PANEL

NAIL THRU PANEL
LAMINATED PANEL

SOLID SINGLE
REBATED JAMB

SOLID DOUBLE
REBATED JAMB

JAMB WITH
REBATED STOP

JAMB WITH
PLANTED STOP

GLAZED PANEL

INSIDE DOOR

$\frac{7}{8}$"X1"GROUNDS
$\frac{1}{16}$"X1$\frac{3}{4}$"
$\frac{7}{8}$"X4$\frac{1}{2}$"CASING

HEAD JAMB

1$\frac{3}{4}$"X3$\frac{3}{4}$"
$\frac{7}{8}$"X4$\frac{1}{2}$"CASING

SIDE JAMB

BOTTOM RAIL

SECTION THRU
DOOR & JAMBS

VENEERED DOOR

J.B.

INTERIOR DOORS

Plate 11

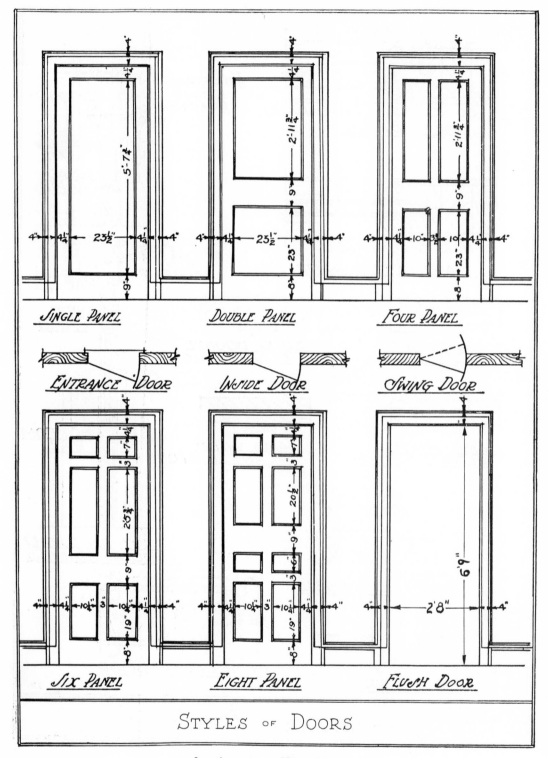

STYLES of DOORS

Supplementary Plate 11A

ASSIGNMENT

Plates 11 and 11A, Interior Doors and Styles of Doors

Draw a vertical section through the head jamb and the door rails, at a scale of 1½ in. equal 1 ft. Draw horizontal section showing the jamb at a smaller scale, ¾ in. equals 1 ft., and project from this section to obtain the front elevation. The elevation may show both interior and exterior.

Draw the plate on styles of doors to any convenient scale.

FRONT ENTRANCES

In building a new house or in remodeling an old one, no part of it deserves as much thought in planning as the front. The entrance should be correct architecturally, but it should be more than just correct. The doorway, or porch, or portico, or even the doorway of the city house which faces directly on the sidewalk, must have something in it to make it different from its neighbors; to reflect the difference between the people who live in this house from the people who live next door. The entrance should express the individuality of the owner of the house. The entrance door is a sign of the environment you create for your family; the symbol of your taste. Examples of front entrances are shown in Figure 29.

There must be absolute harmony between the main body of the house and the entrance to it. There are many variations of the charming architecture of the early American period, known as "colonial." Massachusetts furnished one kind, the Dutch settlers in New York another, and on throughout the thirteen colonies. Modern building has been influenced by all of these and by as many other factors as there are countries in the world. The colonial influence is still stronger than any of the others, but the variations have a hold everywhere, though distinct types prevail in sections, like Spanish varia-tions in California and other western states. Even today there is no distinctive American style and for some reasons the country is to be congratulated.

Nearly every home owner recognizes the type of architecture from which his house grew. There are houses of certain styles to which a New Orleans style of piazza or "gallery" cannot be added without giving the house a thrown together appearance, no matter how desirable the piazza may seem as a hot-weather addition to the dwelling. Similarly, a true colonial doorway will be very much out of keeping with a French Renaissance structure or a dwelling with a roof of Spanish tiles and the lines of the stucco-covered building.

The size of the plot on which a house is to set will have a great deal to do with the decision about the addition of a porch. In general, wide, spacious porches should be parts of wide buildings set on lots which give the harmonious picture an ample setting. For a dwelling on a small lot which has some lawn and landscaping, the portico seems to be quite desirable. A portico, as a rule, should not be the form of entrance for a house which sets high above the ground. Not more than three steps should lead up to such an entrance.

Nothing is so cheerful to the approaching visitor as a light at the entrance, and nothing so gloomy as the absence of it. In city and suburbs the entrance to a house should be lighted softly but definitely, and in no case should the entrance light fail to show the street number of the house. If access to a house is through the porch, there should be a light through the porch ceiling near the entrance door. If entrance is from the street or by way of a portico there may be twin lights, one on either side of the doorway, or a single light just above the door. In either case the lights should be so placed that they shine on the steps and that there are no deceptive shadows which might be the cause of serious accidents. In the city district there

FRONT ENTRANCES

Fig. 29

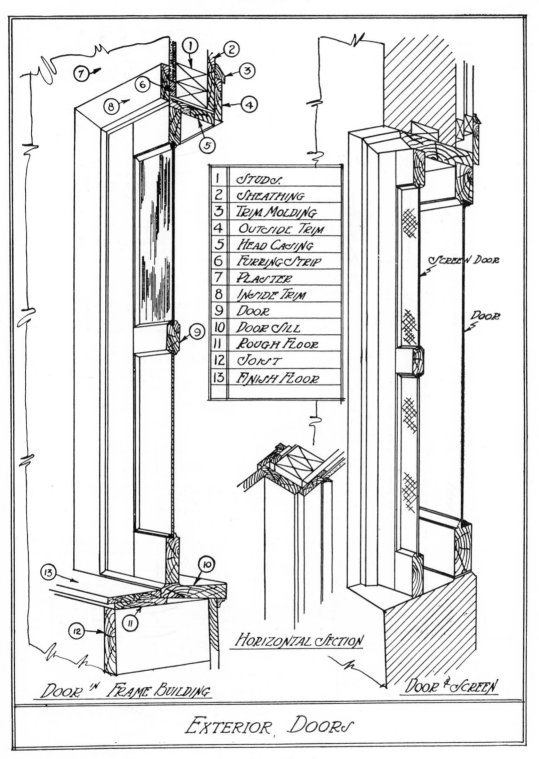

1	STUDS.
2	SHEATHING
3	TRIM MOLDING
4	OUTSIDE TRIM
5	HEAD CASING
6	FURRING STRIP
7	PLASTER
8	INSIDE TRIM
9	DOOR
10	DOOR SILL
11	ROUGH FLOOR
12	JOIST
13	FINISH FLOOR

SCREEN DOOR

DOOR

HORIZONTAL SECTION

DOOR IN FRAME BUILDING

DOOR & SCREEN

EXTERIOR DOORS

Plate 12

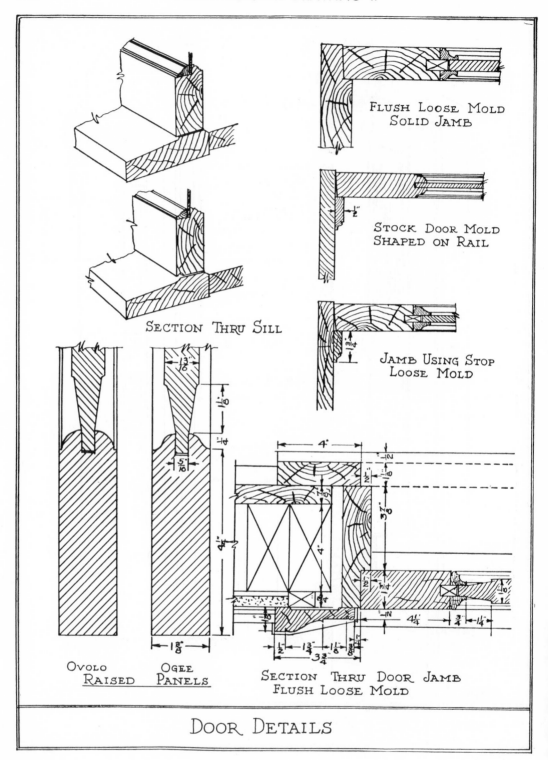

FLUSH LOOSE MOLD
SOLID JAMB

STOCK DOOR MOLD
SHAPED ON RAIL

JAMB USING STOP
LOOSE MOLD

SECTION THRU SILL

OVOLO   OGEE
RAISED   PANELS

SECTION THRU DOOR JAMB
FLUSH LOOSE MOLD

DOOR DETAILS

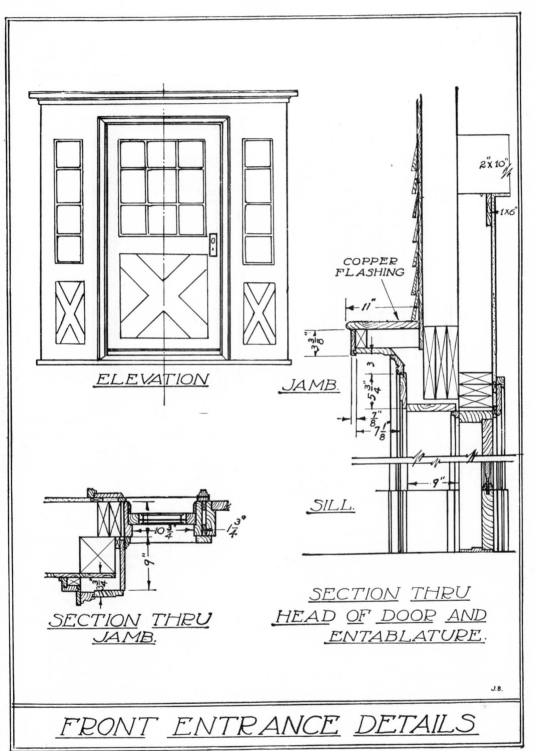

ELEVATION

JAMB.

COPPER FLASHING

SILL.

SECTION THRU HEAD OF DOOR AND ENTABLATURE.

SECTION THRU JAMB.

J.B.

FRONT ENTRANCE DETAILS

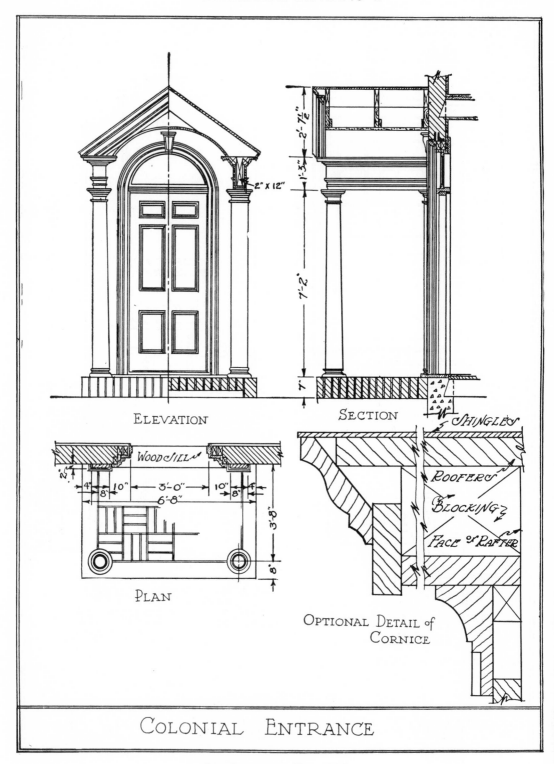

ELEVATION

SECTION

2" X 12"

2'-7½"

1'-3"

7'-2"

7'

PLAN

WOOD SILL

2"
4"
8"
10"
3'-0"
10"
8"
4"
6'-8"

3'-8"

8"

SHINGLES

ROOFERS

BLOCKING

FACE OF RAFTER

OPTIONAL DETAIL OF
CORNICE

COLONIAL ENTRANCE

should be a light switch to turn on the light at the door before the door is opened.

ASSIGNMENT

Plates 12 and 12A, Exterior Doors

Draw the plan for the entrance first. Then draw the section through the cornice to obtain the outline for the moldings in the elevation. You may also include details of the cornice and column base. Draw the elevation, plan, and section to the largest scale possible. Details are usually drawn to a larger scale.

The Supplementary Plates 12B and 12C may be assigned to advanced students. The students should become familiar with the different types of doors and door construction.

PROBLEMS FOR CLASS DISCUSSION

1. How are doors classified?
2. What construction is used in batten doors? Where are they commonly used?
3. Name and describe the parts used in the construction of a door.
4. Measure the sizes of doors found in your home. Observe the sizes and types of doors used in your neighborhood.
5. Why are the sizes of doors standardized? What are the common sizes of doors described in the catalogue? What variation of sizes are there in interior and exterior doors?
6. What are the general proportions used in door construction?
7. What variations are found in the styles of doors?
8. What characteristic of design is found in the front entrance of a Dutch colonial house? English colonial?
9. What is the rule of design for an entrance porch?
10. Why are entrance doors usually sheltered? How is this accomplished?
11. What is the difference between a right- and a left-hand door? Which is most commonly used? Which is used in your home?

U N I T

IX

Porches

When the floor of a porch or piazza is of wood, the joists supporting it should be framed parallel to the house so that the floor boards can be laid at right angles to the building and have a pitch of ⅛ in. per foot. All joists should be supported on girders which rest on the foundation of the house and upon piers of masonry under the front of the porch. A fascia board should cover the front and sides of the floor framing. The floor boards should be extended at least 1 in. beyond the fascia board and the edge should be finished with a semicircular profile, called a "nosing," under which a cove or other molding may be placed. The space between the fascia board and the ground is generally filled with lattice work.

The posts, columns, cornices, balustrades, etc., are designed in accordance with the style of the building. When a Gothic effect is desired the posts may be square and the sharp corners beveled off forming chamfers. This chamfer does not extend the full length of the post.

The railing consists of the top rail, the bottom rail, and the balusters. The rails are designed with a slight slope on the upper surfaces. A balustrade is frequently built around the roof of the porch.

Porches are often enclosed with sash and are used as sunrooms, sometimes provided with fireplaces. In summer the sashes may be removed and replaced with screens.

ASSIGNMENT

Plate 13, Porches

Draw up the porch detail as assigned by the instructor. Take into consideration the several methods of converting these porches into use for both summer and winter.

Study the construction of porches in your

PROBLEMS FOR CLASS DISCUSSION

1. How much slant is given to porch floors? Why?
2. Why are the joists of the porch laid parallel to the joists of the house?
3. What is the purpose of painting the underside of the porch floor?
4. Name and describe the parts used in the construction of a porch.
5. Why are sun porches usually located on the south side of the house?
6. How are these porches varied by the style of the house?

neighborhood for the details of construction.

7. What is the purpose of a porch on the second story? Where is it usually located?
8. What are some of the modern variations in the design of porches or verandas?

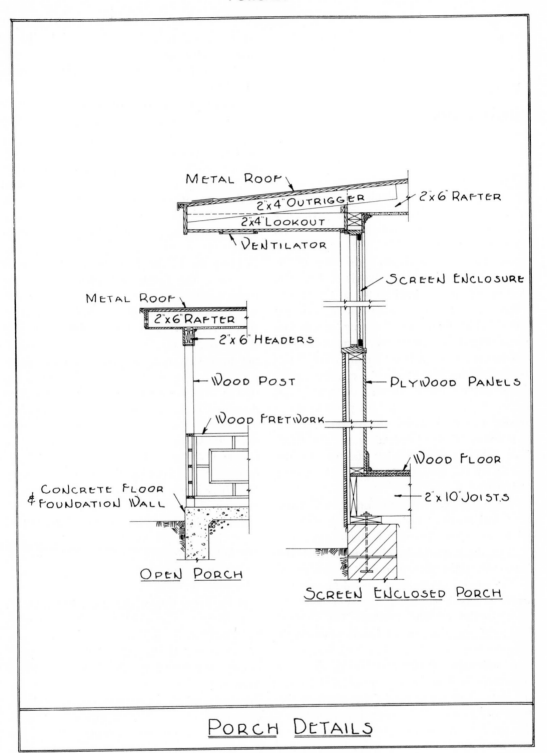

METAL ROOF

2"x 4" OUTRIGGER

2"x 6" RAFTER

2"x 4" LOOKOUT

VENTILATOR

SCREEN ENCLOSURE

METAL ROOF

2"x 6" RAFTER

2"x 6" HEADERS

WOOD POST

PLYWOOD PANELS

WOOD FRETWORK

WOOD FLOOR

CONCRETE FLOOR
& FOUNDATION WALL

2"x 10" JOISTS

OPEN PORCH

SCREEN ENCLOSED PORCH

PORCH DETAILS

Plate 13

U N I T

X

Stairways

The space through which a stairway runs is known as the "well." The two parts of a step are the "riser," which is the vertical portion, and the "tread," the part walked upon. The "nosing" is the projection of the tread beyond the face of the riser. The term *run* applies to the total width of the treads. (See Fig. 30.) The space wider than the steps, which constitutes resting places between flights, or which are terminations of the stairways, are called "landings" or "platforms." Winding, elliptical, circular, platform, curved risers, quarter cylinders with newels between, and half-turn platforms, are special forms of stairways. As one ascends a stairway, if the handrail is on the right, it is called a right-handed stairway; if the rail is on the left, it is called a left-handed stairway.

There are "closed" and "open" stairways. A closed stairway has a wall on each side, while an open stairway is built against a wall of the room in which it is located, the front and sides being exposed in the room.

The proportion between the riser and the tread is very important if the stairway is to be a comfortable one to climb. The average height of the riser in an inside stairway is 7 in., with a 10-in. tread. For back stairways, attic stairways, or cellar stairways the riser sometimes is 8 in., with a tread of 9 in. As the riser increases in height the width of the tread decreases; as the riser becomes lower the tread increases in depth. Following are architects' rules for proportions between the riser and the tread:

1. Two times the height of the riser plus the depth of one tread should equal 24 in.

2. The height of the riser plus the depth of the tread should equal 17 to 18 in. for inside stairways.

3. The product of the riser and the tread should equal 66 to 70.

Before the drawing for a stairway can be laid out, the height from the top of one floor to the floor above must be known, or the height from the top of the floor to the top of the landing. The height of the risers can be found by reducing the height in feet and inches to inches; dividing the height in inches by the height of the riser, which usually is 7 in.; the quotient thus obtained being the number of risers required; then dividing the height in inches by the number of risers, the result of which will be the exact height of each riser. The answer will not always occur in even inches, so the fraction is carried out in a decimal fraction, and then is reduced to linear measure corresponding to the nearest graduation on the scale. *Example:* Suppose the height from the top of the first floor to the top of the second floor is 9 ft. 6¼ in., and we want to find the number of risers, also the height of each riser. Reducing 9 ft. 6¼ in. to inches we obtain 114¼ in.; 114¼ in. divided by 7 in. equals 16%₂₈. Dropping the fraction we have 16, which is the number of risers corresponding to a 7-in. riser.

To obtain the height of the risers, 114¼ in. divided by 16 equals 7%₆₄ in. Since this can only be approximately set off from the scale each riser would be 7%₆₄ in. or approximately 7⅛ in. high.

If the total run of the stairs is limited to a fixed space, the width of each tread must be calculated in the same way as the height of the risers. If the run of the stairway is limited, say to 11 ft., the 11 ft. should be reduced to inches. Dividing the run in inches by the number of treads equals 132 in. divided by 15, or 8⅘ in. It should be remembered that the number of treads is always one less than the number of risers, because the landing or top floor forms the last tread.

174

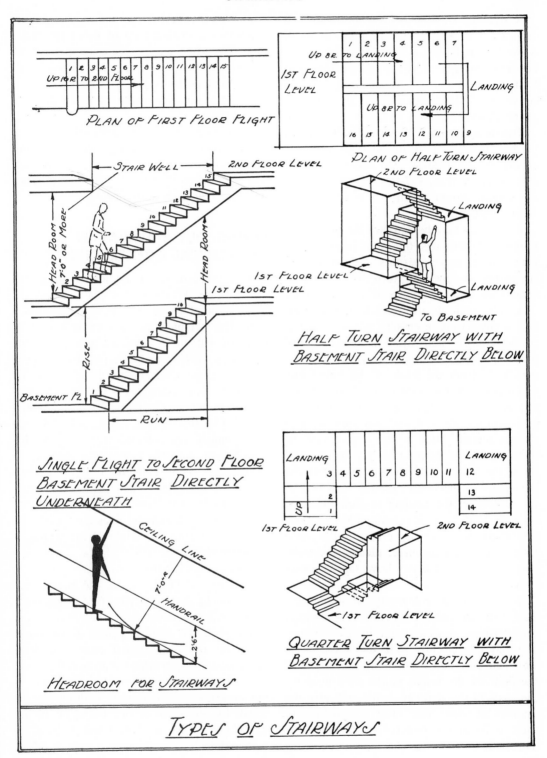

PLAN OF FIRST FLOOR FLIGHT

PLAN OF HALF TURN STAIRWAY

SINGLE FLIGHT TO SECOND FLOOR
BASEMENT STAIR DIRECTLY
UNDERNEATH

HALF TURN STAIRWAY WITH
BASEMENT STAIR DIRECTLY BELOW

HEADROOM FOR STAIRWAYS

QUARTER TURN STAIRWAY WITH
BASEMENT STAIR DIRECTLY BELOW

TYPES OF STAIRWAYS

Fig. 30

A stairway leading from an entrance hall should not be less than 3 ft. 6 in. in width while 4 ft. is better; a back stairway or cellar stairs may be 2 ft. 8 in. in width, but a stairway as narrow as this may not be convenient if large objects are to be moved up or down.

The headroom of a stairway should not be less than 7 ft. 6 in. figured from the ceiling to the nearest step. Sometimes the rule is given that a 7-ft. arc swung from the ceiling should touch the nosing of the nearest step.

A stairway may be run straight or may be broken with landings, the latter being preferable where space permits. Stairways are sometimes designed to turn by "winders," which are treads varying in width at their two ends. Such an arrangement is not desirable unless it is necessary to save space. In the circular stairways this type of tread must be used. A stairway in which one section leads from the back of the house and one leads from the front of the house, meeting at the same landing from which only one section leads to the second floor, is often a convenience. Such a stairway should be arranged in the house plan so that a view down the back stairs is impossible from the front part of the house; usually it is best to use a door at the landing to shut the back stairway from view. It is economical to place one stairway above the other in the same stair well; as for example, placing the stairway to the second floor above the basement stairway.

When a closet, a lavatory, or a passageway is to run under a stairway it is essential to determine at what point in the stairway one may conveniently walk under the steps. This can be found by dividing the height of the door by the height of the riser used for the steps in the stairway, which will give the number of steps one must ascend before there is headroom underneath the stairway. The same matter must be considered when determining at what point the second floor may extend over the stairway and yet allow headroom in walking up or down the stairway. The same number of steps down from the second floor as are required to give headroom under the stairway will indicate at what point the floor may be extended over the stairway.

A stairway should be well lighted, either by windows on the landing, windows in the entrance hall, or windows in the upstairs hall. The stairway should end on the upper floor in a well-proportioned hall.

LAYING OUT STAIRWAY BY GEOMETRICAL CONSTRUCTION

This problem is an application of geometry. Figure 31 shows the plan and elevation of the stairs at a scale of ½ in. equals 1 ft. The height from floor to floor is 9 ft. 0 in. or 108 in. A good average height for residence work is to make the riser as near to 7 in. as possible and the tread 10 in. To determine how many risers will be required, divide the floor-to-floor height by 7 in., which makes 15 risers. Select a scale with 15 divisions, which will coincide with the floor-to-floor height, with the zero at the intersection of the first floor and the first riser when placed at an angle. Each of these proportional parts will give a series of points through which horizontal lines may be drawn which will locate the height of the treads.

If 15 risers are required, 14 treads will be necessary. If the run of the stairs is limited to say 11 ft., repeat the geometrical operation by using a scale of 14 equal parts which will coincide with the run of the stairs when the scale is placed at an angle. Mark off the proportional parts and draw perpendicular lines which represent the risers of the stairway. If the run of the stairs is not limited to a given space multiply the 14 treads by the width of one tread, or 10 in., which gives 140 in. This result reduced to feet and inches would give a run of 11 ft. 8 in.

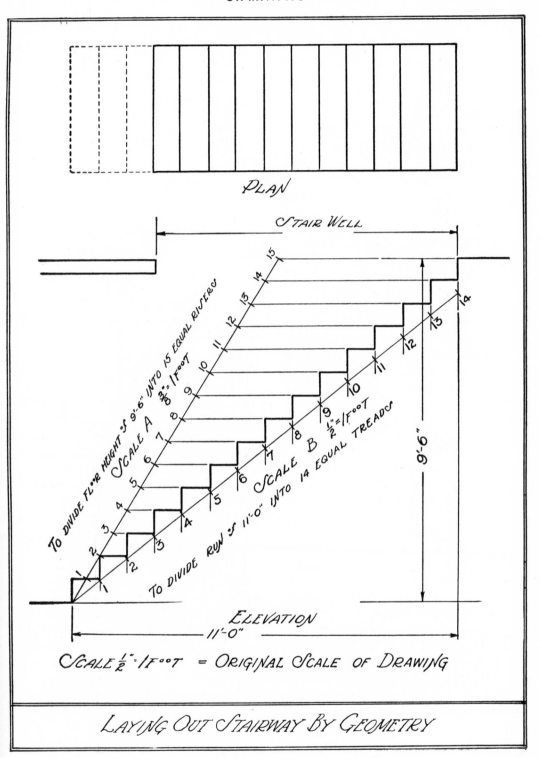

PLAN

Fig. 31

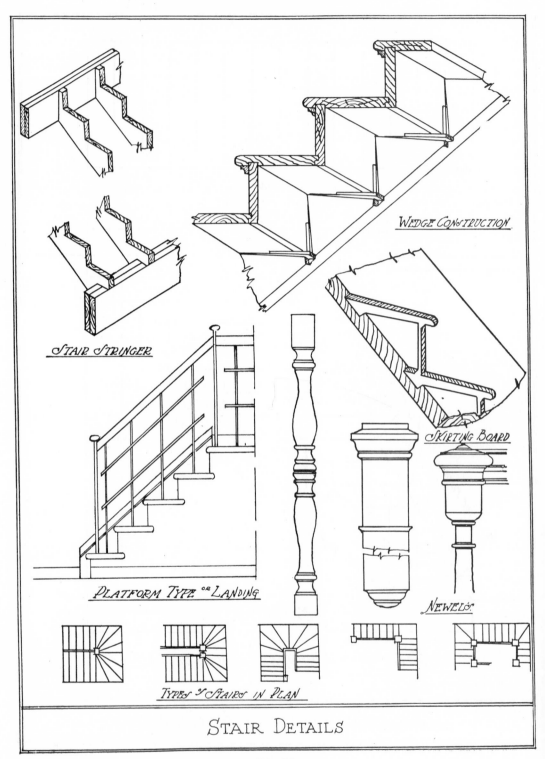

WEDGE CONSTRUCTION

STAIR STRINGER

SKIRTING BOARD

PLATFORM TYPE OR LANDING

NEWELS.

TYPES OF STAIRS IN PLAN

STAIR DETAILS

Fig. 32

DETAILS OF STAIR CONSTRUCTION

Almost all stairways built at the present time are made with posts at the angles, instead of easings and crooks which require an expert stair builder to lay and erect. The open treads with the spindles dovetailed into them make more work for the draftsman as well as for the carpenter and the millworker. Wood panels in the triangles and "soffits" add very much to the appearance of a stairway, but the expense is greater than if lath and plaster were used. The corner post should be housed out for the treads, risers, stringers, and panels. The string newel should be paneled or fluted, but the angle posts should be plain with a simple cap. The treads should be dovetailed out for the spindles, and the end nosings mitered on one end and returned on the other.

In most cases the contractor requires all of the work to be cut and framed, ready to be set into the building. The most frequent mistake in stair construction is a lack of headroom, which makes the stairs very steep, unless the headers are cut back more than originally called for in the plan. (See Figs. 32 and 33 for stair details.)

Stringers. Stringers support the risers and treads. The center stringer is cut to fit the under part of each riser and tread. Cut stringers are used in porch and cellar work, or where ordinary stairways are used. Cleated stringers are used in the very cheap constructions. The housed stringer is used in all fine work and is considered the best type for regular stair building. The finished risers and treads are generally housed into the stringer. The housing is usually tapered, wedges being used to drive up the treads and risers so that they make perfect joints with the stringers. The tapered cuts are called "rabbets" and they should be ½ to ⅝ in. deep.

Risers and Treads. There are two styles of risers and treads, classified according to the method in which they are joined together, as the "plain" and the "tongue-and-grooved."

The tongue-and-grooved are used in the better constructions. The tongue, if used at the top of the riser, is objectionable in that it weakens the end of the tread. The tongue should be ⅜ to ½ in. thick.

Skirting Board. The board placed on either side of the steps to finish off the rough work is called a "skirting board." This board is used in the average work instead of the housing stringer. The steps are supported by open stringers and the skirting board is used to finish off the job. Sometimes this skirting board is cut to fit over the risers and treads.

Newels. A square newel should be mortised and tenoned to the tread and should extend down to the floor if possible, so as to be securely fastened. Newels are used in stair construction in the average building, and may be square or round, and solid or built up.

Handrail. The purpose of the handrail is to assist a person in ascending or descending the stairs. The handrail runs parallel to the incline of the stairs and holds the balusters. The height from the top of the tread, on line with the face of the riser, to the top of the handrail should be not less than 2 ft. 5 in. nor more than 2 ft. 8 in.

Balusters. There are rectangular, square, turned, and circular types of balusters. The first baluster is always placed in vertical line with the face of the riser, the next is placed halfway between the first baluster and the face of the next riser; in other words, the space is divided into two equal parts. If three balusters were to be used, the space would be divided into three equal parts. More than three balusters are rarely used in a private dwelling for a 10-in. tread.

ASSIGNMENT

Plates 14 and 14A, Stair Details

1. Plan a stairway for a house with the first-floor ceiling height 8 ft. 6 in. with 10-in. second-floor joists. Have a landing at the lowest point which will permit a lavatory below it. Give necessary detail drawings.

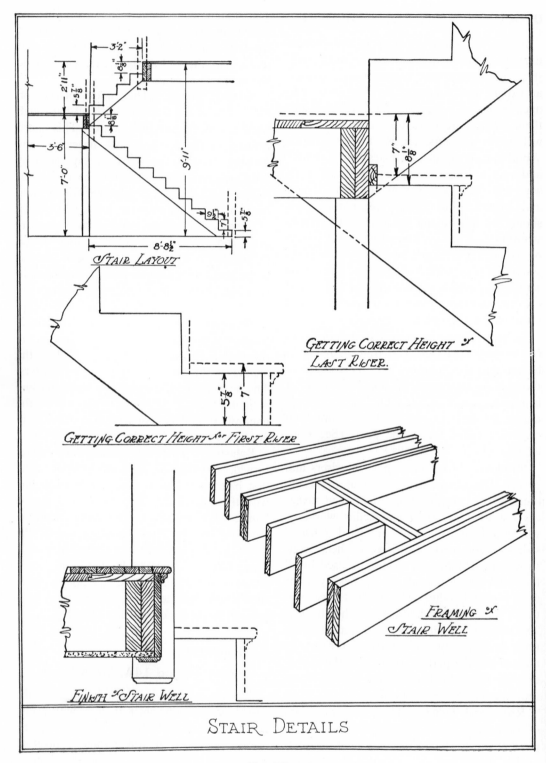

STAIR LAYOUT

GETTING CORRECT HEIGHT of LAST RISER.

GETTING CORRECT HEIGHT for FIRST RISER

FRAMING of STAIR WELL

FINISH of STAIR WELL

STAIR DETAILS

Fig. 33

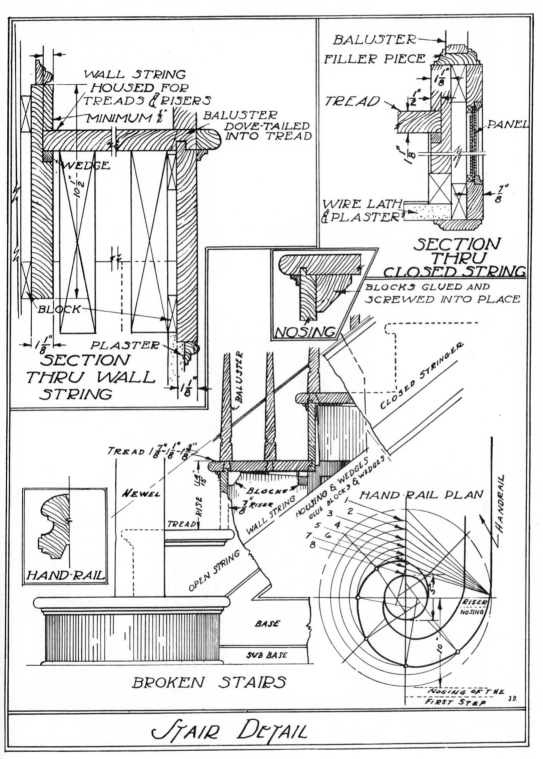

WALL STRING HOUSED FOR TREADS & RISERS
MINIMUM ½"
BALUSTER DOVE-TAILED INTO TREAD
WEDGE
10½"
BLOCK
1⅛"
PLASTER
1⅛"
SECTION THRU WALL STRING

BALUSTER
FILLER PIECE
TREAD
1⅛"
2"
PANEL
1⅛"
WIRE LATH & PLASTER
7/8"
SECTION THRU CLOSED STRING

NOSING

BLOCKS GLUED AND SCREWED INTO PLACE

CLOSED STRINGER

BALUSTER

TREAD 1⅞"-1⅛"-1¾"
NEWEL
TREAD
RISE
BLOCKS
⅞" RISER
WALL STRING
HOUSING & WEDGES
GLUE BLOCKS & WEDGES
OPEN STRING

HAND-RAIL

HAND RAIL PLAN

3 2
5 4
7 6
8

RISER
NOSING

BASE

SUB BASE

BROKEN STAIRS

NOSING OF THE FIRST STEP

HANDRAIL

J.B.

STAIR DETAIL

Plate 14

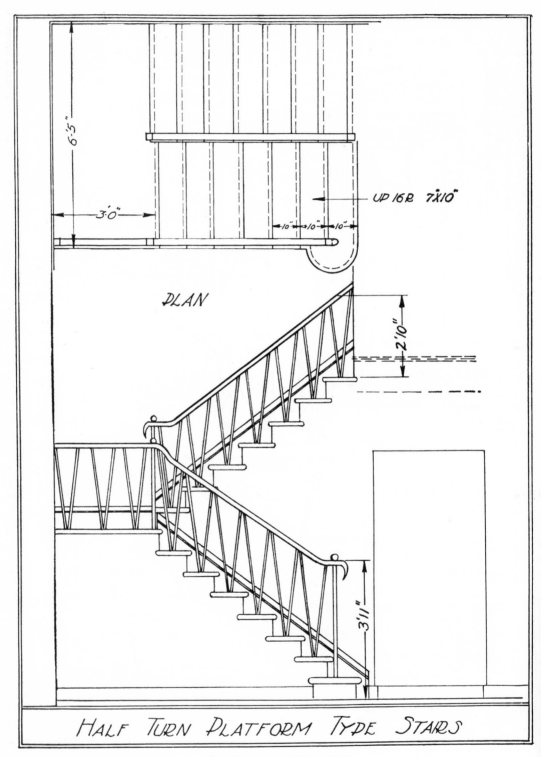

6'-5"

3'-0"

UP 16R 7"X10"

10" 10" 10"

PLAN

2'-10"

3'-11"

HALF TURN PLATFORM TYPE STAIRS

Supplementary Plate 14A

2. Draw a half-turn platform type of stairway as given in Plate 14A. Also draw the detail and sections which include newels, balusters, rails, etc. Draw them in such a way as best to show the stairway. Draw the elevations and plan of the entire stairway. In the detail drawings show the plan and elevation of the risers, the handrail, and newels, and a few general dimensions such as the rise, the run, the width to center line of handrail, and the height of the handrail. Sometimes the risers are numbered beginning with the bottom riser.

In making the drawing on stairways locate the floor levels the proper distance apart. Use a scale of ¾ in. equals 1 ft. Draw the large-sized details to 3 in. equal 1 ft. scale.

PROBLEMS FOR CLASS DISCUSSION

1. What is the difference between an "open" and a "closed" stairway?
2. What is the difference between a right- and a left-hand stairway?
3. Name and describe some of the common terms used in stair construction.
4. What formulas are given for the proportion between riser and tread of a stairway?
5. Describe the mathematics used in the drawing of a stairway.
6. How do you find the correct headroom for a stairway?
7. What variations in forms of stairways can you describe from your own observations?
8. Why are stairways usually located one above the other?
9. What minimum widths are established for stairways? Why?
10. How can the space below a stairway be profitably utilized?
11. Why do most building codes require a landing for every fifteen steps?
12. Why is the housed stringer used in all fine stair work?
13. What types of risers and treads are used in stair work? Why is the tongue on the top side of the riser objectionable?
14. Where are cleated stringers used in stair construction?
15. What dimension is given for the height of the handrail?
16. Make up a booklet of illustrations of stairways which can be found in catalogues and magazine articles.
17. How high have you climbed in going 10 ft. forward on your home stairway?

Fireplaces

A fireplace is the center of attraction in the modern living room. There is nothing that can make a home as cheerful as a few sticks or logs blazing on the hearth, especially in the fall or spring of the year. The hearth fire creates an atmosphere of comfort and cheer which distinguishes a "home" from a "house." An artificial log does not give this comfort, neither does a radiator. As a fireplace is the outstanding feature in a room the design and placement must be carefully considered.

DESIGN

A fireplace should be in proportion to the room, both in regard to width and height. Fireplace authorities have computed that a room with 300 square feet of floor space is well served by a fireplace 30 to 36 in. wide, 28 to 32 in. high, and 21 to 24 in. deep. If possible the fireplace should be placed in the far end of the room away from the door. If placed on the broad side of the average room, care should be taken to see that it does not reduce the practicable width of the room and force the rug over the hearth. If placed on an outside wall, it is better not to have a large flanking window, as that would mean facing too much light whenever the fireplace is used during the day.

A large room will take a projection of 17 to 21 in., while a small room permits a projection of 4 in. to 9 in. Building the fireplace flush with the inside wall sometimes gives a pleasing effect.

The average width of the modern fire-

place ranges from 5 to 8 ft., in proportion to the size of the room. A fireplace continued to the ceiling looks well in a large room but should be avoided in a small room. The distance from the floor line to the mantel varies from 4 ft. 6 in. to 5 ft. 6 in. The mantel should be in proportion to the size of the fireplace.

The following table gives the general proportions of fireplace openings:

(All dimensions given in inches)

Width	Height	Depth	Back Width	Back Height	Back Corbeled Height	Flue
24	28	16	11	14	18	8½ x 8½
28	28	16	15	14	18	8½ x 13
30	30	16	17	14	20	8½ x 13
34	30	16	21	14	20	8½ x 13
36	30	16	23	14	20	13 x 13
40	30	16	27	14	20	13 x 13
42	30	16	29	14	20	13 x 13
48	33	18	33	14	23	13 x 13
54	36	20	37	14	26	13 x 18
60	39	22	42	14	29	18 x 18
72	40	22	54	14	30	18 x 18

An elliptical or semicircular arch should be used with care because the curved line will not harmonize with the straight line of the mantelpiece. The flat arch, known as the "jack arch," harmonizes better with the straight lines of the mantel. Even though this is one of the weakest arches in masonry, it is strong and practical if supported with an angle iron. A "soldier course" takes away the plainness of the horizontal course. Although simplicity should be the keynote of the fireplace, one which continues to the ceiling may be ornamented with a plaster cast in the upper part.

SUPPORTS OF FIREPLACES

The support for the fireplace and the chimney should be of brick, stone, or concrete and in the form of a footing with at least a 6-in. projection and a depth of 8 to 10 in. according to the material. If there is a masonry wall to begin with, it may be utilized as one wall of the ashpit, but this is considered poor practice as the greater weight of the fireplace and the chimney results in the settling and cracking of both the wall and the footing. The walls of the ashpit should never be less than 8 in.

The size of the ashpit is determined by the depth and the width of the proposed fireplace. The cleanout door for the ashes is located in the center of the ashpit, and the bottom of the door is level with the bottom of the ashpit. A large cleanout door is most convenient.

FLUE CONSTRUCTION

Good draft depends upon the proper relationship of the fireplace opening to the size of the flue, the chimney height, and the position of the throat which determines the important matter of smoke shelf. Whatever the size of the fireplace, the actual inside area of the flue should be no less than one twelfth the area of the fireplace opening. Each fireplace should have its own separate flue carried full size to the top of the chimney, without connections of any kind from other sources. The chimney should be carried two feet above the highest point of the roof.

FIREBOX CONSTRUCTION

The firebox should be lined with firebrick laid flat. The common practice of laying the bricks on edge should be discouraged, because they burn out much quicker and require repairing oftener. Firebrick should be laid in thin fire clay by dipping them and setting them in place with a hammer.

The firebrick flooring may be laid first either rowlock or flat. The ash trap is set in the center of the firebox, 2 in. from the back firebrick wall. The bond should be laid out plumb for 14 in., then brought forward to allow for an 8-in. throat. This is done by tilting each course a trifle, keeping a smooth surface. This is a better practice than "corbeling." The forward curve of the back throws the smoke and flame forward to the throat, and at the same time forms a shelf

above, which is very effective as a means for deflecting any downdrafts in the chimney. The smoke-chamber sides should have a slope of 7 in. to each foot of height.

THROAT CONSTRUCTION

The throat is the vital spot of the fireplace, but with the present market of dampers designed for the several openings it is not such a difficult problem. All manufacturers of dampers and fireplace authorities agree that the damper should be placed against the front wall of the fireplace instead of at the back. There is a definite reason for the position. When the damper is placed at the front, the back wall of the fireplace opening must be sloped forward to support the back flange of the damper. This helps to radiate the heat into the room.

The throat should be at least 6 in. above the opening. The throat prevents the heat from going up the flue, and should be designed sufficiently large to carry off the smoke. The damper controls the draft and the amount of heat to be given off into the room.

THE HEARTH

The hearth may be regarded as consisting of two parts, the front and the back. The back hearth as well as the sides and back of the firebox usually are laid in firebrick. The ash trap and chute are located in the back hearth. The trap is of cast iron and works on a pivot in the frame so that it is a simple matter to dump out the ashes and clean out the hearth.

The front hearth is simply an extension of the back hearth beyond the chimney breast and, while serving the purpose of safety, is developed into a decorative feature. It is generally flush with the floor, although some people prefer to raise the whole hearth several inches above the floor and surround the hearth with a curb. The front hearth is usually treated in an artistic manner by using tile or brick in various patterns, on edge or flat, as suggested in the designs. The surface of the hearth should be smooth to facilitate cleaning, and, whether raised or flush with the floor, may be provided with a fender.

The hearth may be supported in two ways, either by a trimmer arch or by a flat concrete slab. A trimmer arch is simply a brick rowlock arch springing from the fireplace foundation and resting against the header joist. This arch is built over a wood center placed by the carpenter. On top of the form is laid a bed of mortar to level up and provide a bed for the finished hearth. If a concrete slab is used, it is laid on the fireplace foundation and on a flat form extending out in front as far as required for the hearth. It should be reinforced by light iron rods. This construction is used in the cheaper type of work. The trimmer arch, which costs only a little more, is the more satisfactory method of hearth construction.

ASSIGNMENT

Plates 15 and 15A, Fireplace Details

Draw in a center line to serve for both the plan and the elevation, either at the center of the sheet or on either side. Draw in the complete plan, which is a horizontal section through the fireplace. Project all points from the plan to the position of the elevation. Block out the vertical section and a horizontal section to a larger scale showing the detail of the mantel and the pilaster, and place these to the side of the sheet. Block out the vertical section of the fireplace to the right of the position taken by the elevation, and project all lines to the elevation.

It is necessary to work the plan, elevation, and sections in correlated procedure.

Draw all parts to the largest scale possible. Details may be drawn to a scale of 1½ in. equal 1 ft.

PROBLEMS FOR CLASS DISCUSSION

1. Why is brick generally used in fireplace construction?
2. By what reasoning would you justify a fireplace in a modern residence?
3. Why is it recommended that the fireplace be built at the end of the room rather than on the broad wall?
4. What determines the projection of the fireplace into a room? When should the fireplace be continued to the ceiling?
5. Why is the jack arch recommended for fireplaces?
6. What rule is given for the proportion between the flue and the fireplace opening?
7. How high above the floor is the mantel placed?
8. Why is the chimney carried 2 ft. above the highest point of the roof?
9. Where is the damper placed in the throat of the fireplace?
10. What purpose does the smoke shelf serve?
11. How high above the opening should the throat be placed?
12. Why are the bricks at the back of the fireplace corbeled or tilted?
13. What are the methods used for supporting the hearth?
14. Why is a separate flue necessary for the fireplace?
15. Make a booklet of sketches or pictures of several fireplace designs in brick and stone.
16. Make a booklet of sketches or pictures of the several designs used for chimneys.
17. Would you raise the hearth above the floor level in your house?
18. Some houses are planned to include an artificial fireplace with a gas log. Would you plan for one in your house?
19. Patented fireplace dampers are on the market. Would you advise the use of one?

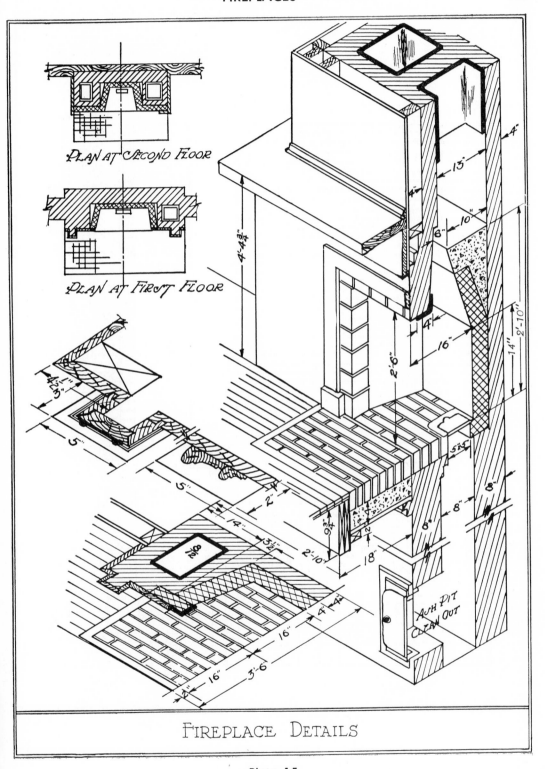

PLAN AT SECOND FLOOR

PLAN AT FIRST FLOOR

ASH PIT
CLEAN OUT

FIREPLACE DETAILS

Plate 15

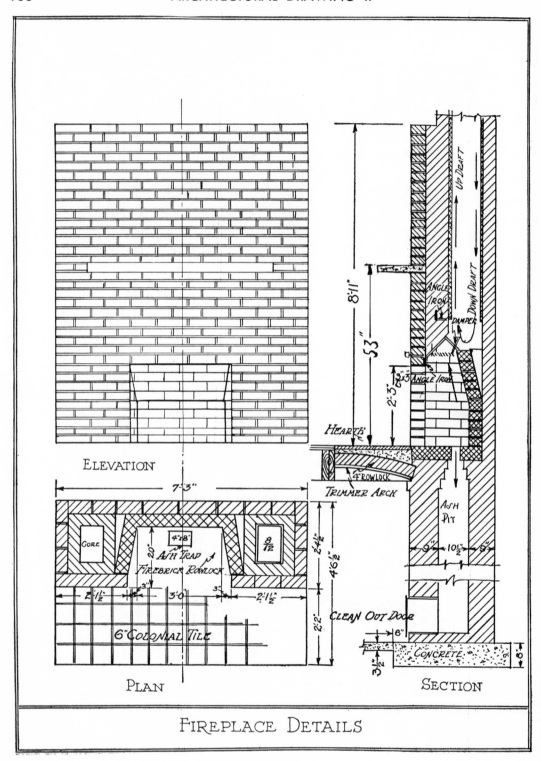

ELEVATION

PLAN

SECTION

FIREPLACE DETAILS

Plate 15A

XII

Built-in Equipment

One of the distinctive features of the small house as planned for the present-day client is the variety and originality displayed in providing for built-in conveniences. Standing equipment may be installed at any time and in any existing building, but built-in equipment must be placed when a structure is being built or remodeled. There is no better nor more logical time to decide upon the selection and location of such equipment than while the plans are being drawn. Comfort during its use should be a consideration, and of course it must be out of the way when not needed. Intelligent study will produce a compact plan, with total floor area unbelievably small in proportion to the rooms included.

BUILT-IN CLOSETS

1. Broom closets should be located in the service hall on both the first and second floors where possible. Space should be provided for a vacuum cleaner.

2. Cedar closets and drawer space lined with aromatic cedar usually are located in the master bedroom or in the bathroom.

3. A china closet for the better chinaware usually is located in the dining or breakfast rooms.

4. Linen closets should be located near the bedrooms and the bathroom, with storage space provided by drawers as well as by shelves.

5. Clothes closets should be located in all bedrooms, and there should be two in the master bedroom. Lights should be provided in all clothes closets.

6. Coat closets should be located near the entrance door.

BUILT-IN EQUIPMENT

These conveniences may be grouped under three classifications. There are those intended to be built into the exterior wall, those that are to be built into the partitions, and the electrical equipment which requires forethought in providing for the outlets.

1. Provisions for a built-in oven, refrigerator, television, or Hi-Fi must be made in advance to allow for gas piping or electrical wiring.

2. Whenever possible, the gas and electric meters should be accessible from the outside so that the meter reader will not have to enter the house.

3. Kitchen and bathroom accessories include paper-towel holders, soap trays, tumbler holder, toothbrush holders, toilet paper holders, towel bars, and so on.

4. Bell and buzzer push buttons should be located at the entrance doors. An intercommunication system and additional speakers for the Hi-Fi equipment may be recessed in the walls. The telephone and any extensions should be located conveniently with proper natural and artificial lighting available.

5. Bookcases may be located to suit convenience and may be in the form of either a case or a nook.

6. Cabinets:
   a) Kitchen — Should be carefully located in the plans; may be built-in or stock units.
   b) Bathroom — Often located over the lavatory.

7. Laundry chutes should be located with access doors in the service hall on each floor.

8. An ironing-board cabinet should be placed in the wall of the laundry or in the kitchen, where good natural light is available. This piece of equipment is set between the studs and is placed so that, when in an open position, the board is 33 in. above the finished-floor line.

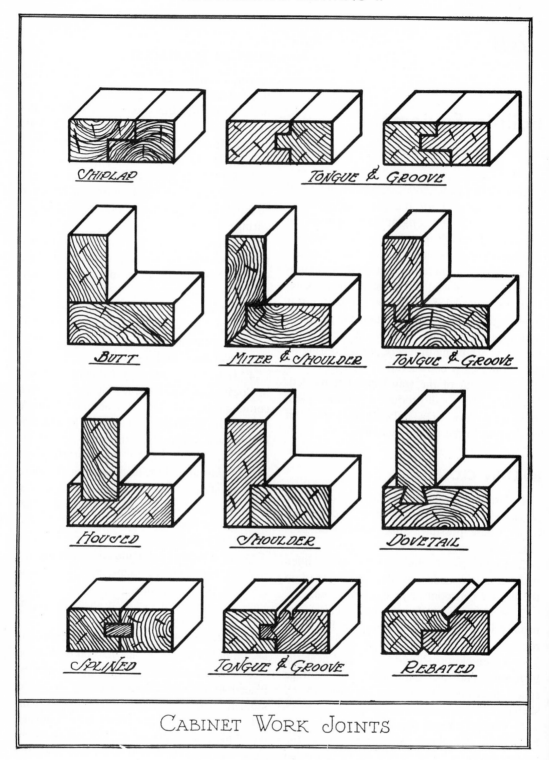

SHIPLAP   TONGUE & GROOVE

BUTT   MITER & SHOULDER   TONGUE & GROOVE

HOUSED   SHOULDER   DOVETAIL

SPLINED   TONGUE & GROOVE   REBATED

CABINET WORK JOINTS

Fig. 34

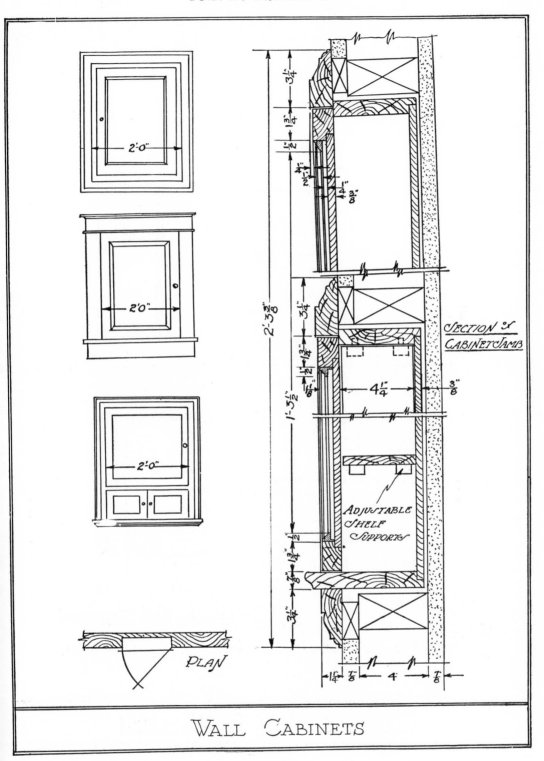

PLAN

SECTION °f
CABINET JAMB

ADJUSTABLE
SHELF
SUPPORTS

WALL CABINETS

Plate 16

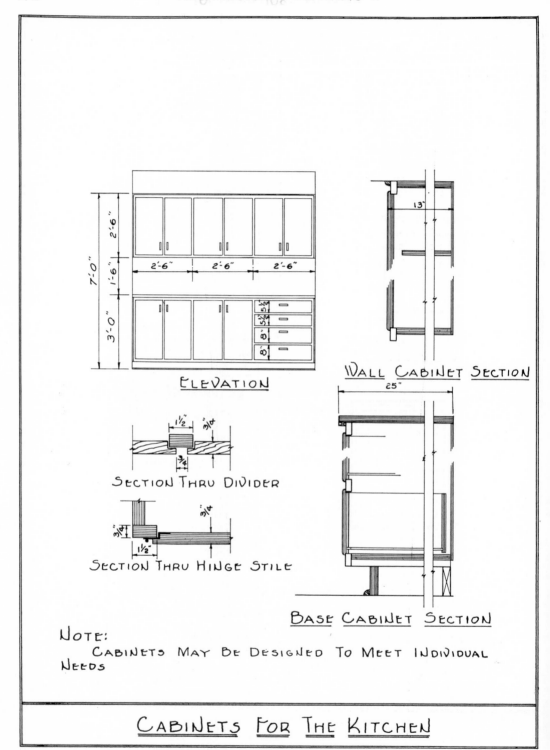

ELEVATION

WALL CABINET SECTION

SECTION THRU DIVIDER

SECTION THRU HINGE STILE

BASE CABINET SECTION

NOTE:
    CABINETS MAY BE DESIGNED TO MEET INDIVIDUAL NEEDS

CABINETS FOR THE KITCHEN

Plate 17

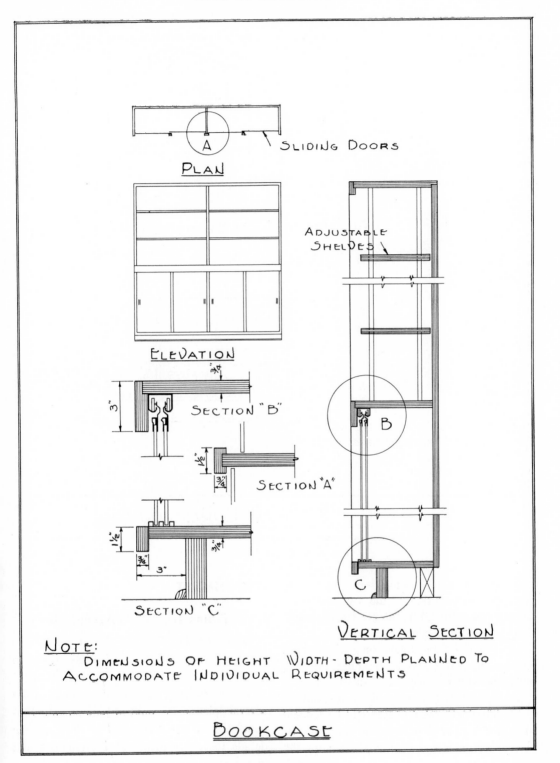

PLAN

SLIDING DOORS

ELEVATION

ADJUSTABLE SHELVES

SECTION "B"

SECTION "A"

SECTION "C"

VERTICAL SECTION

NOTE:
DIMENSIONS OF HEIGHT WIDTH- DEPTH PLANNED TO ACCOMMODATE INDIVIDUAL REQUIREMENTS

BOOKCASE

Plate 17A

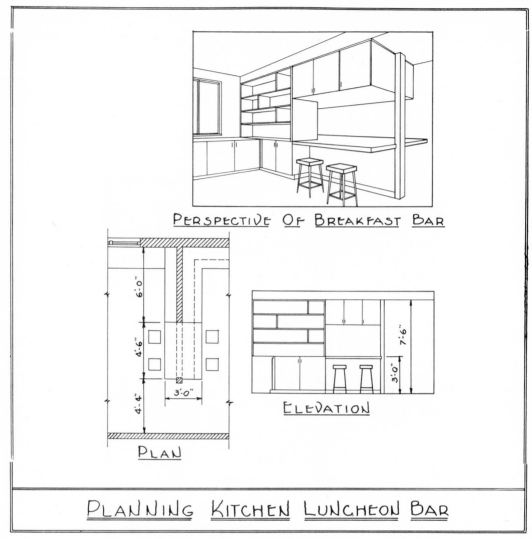

PERSPECTIVE OF BREAKFAST BAR

PLAN

ELEVATION

PLANNING KITCHEN LUNCHEON BAR

Plate 18

9. An electrical panel box should be placed in the partition of the service hall or kitchen; fuses for all of the electrical circuits should be located here.

10. For radio and television wiring, aerial and ground wires should be built into the partition, with the necessary outlets.

11. Fireplace. (See the unit on fireplaces.)

12. The incinerator flue should be located so that a hopper door into the flue may be placed in some wall of the kitchen on the floor above.

ASSIGNMENT

Plates 16, 17, 17A, and 18

Draw up the details assigned by the instructor. Study the kinds of joints shown in Figure 34.

These drawings are only suggestions of the several pieces of built-in equipment. Students are to be encouraged to draw up the details for other pieces of equipment found in the modern home.

BRIEF HISTORY OF DOMESTIC ARCHITECTURE

Architecture is the art and science of building structures which are beautiful as well as useful. Unlike the other fine arts, architecture arose out of man's needs. Much more than protection is involved in architecture, for men at all times have had an instinct leading them to beautify the buildings in which they lived or in which they worshiped their deities. Thus every historical period has produced temples and palaces as its finest type of building.

The requirements imposed upon the builders in the different climates and civilizations have given rise to architectural styles. The character of the building, if it is good architecture, is accommodated to the needs of the people who use it. The design and ornamentation of a house or church in a cold country, where steep pitched roofs are required to shed the snow, differ necessarily from the planning and decoration of a structure in the tropics, where protection from the heat and the shock from earthquake must be given first consideration. A nation devoted to hard work and simple living, will create for itself an architectural style that may be refined and beautiful, but which will certainly be less showy than that prevailing in a country whose people are wealthy and pleasure loving.

UNIT

I

Prehistoric Dwellings

Determining the origin of the house as a human habitation is partly a matter of speculation and partly the result of research. Those who have studied most about the early habitations agree that the Stone Age man, at least in temperate climates, frequently dwelt in natural caves. Even at this early age, man made distinct attempts to decorate his residence, as the cave paintings show. There are evidences, also, that forest-dwelling tribes, and those in tropical countries early developed some sort of hut construction, probably by planting sticks into the ground, in a circle, binding their tops together to form a cone, and covering the framework with a thatch of leaves. Such primitive constructions are still used in Central Africa and in other parts of the world.

Among the nomadic tribes whose place of habitation is dependent upon water supply and pasture, a movable dwelling was found to be a necessity. A small amount of wood to serve as a frame or support, and skins to be used for a covering, produced the lightness and ease of transportation which was required. For those people a tent proved a most desirable dwelling, and was in common use by many American Indians.

At some ancient time the cave dweller discovered that his residence could be enlarged and strengthened by constructing in front of it a wall of piled rocks, and covering the space between the wall and cave with logs or skins. Growing skill in this type of construction led to the development of such elaborate cave dwellings as those found on certain riverbanks in the southwest of the United States. The date when these dwellings were first used obviously antedates the pueblo constructions. Thus the hut is the parent form of the timber house, and the cave dwelling of the home built of brick or stone. Most of the ancient houses were of one room, but with the development of a more complex civilization, subdivision became necessary and the plan was expanded. At first this seems to have been accomplished by combining several units within a single enclosure. Many remains of floors and foundations of such groups of round, straw or unburned-brick huts, have been found throughout the Aegean world. Later, elliptical forms with subdividing partitions appeared like those of Crete and Mycenae. Another form of development characterizes the late Stone and Bronze Age villages of northern and central Europe, the so-called "lake dwellings" in which many rectangular houses, some of two or more rooms, were built upon a pile-supported platform over a lake. In European lake dwellings, not only does primitive frame construction, a development of the hut type, appear, but also crossed logs, overlapping at the corners, are used in the log-cabin construction.

Two other forms of dwellings are of interest to Americans. The first form is the pueblo. This name signifies a communal village, and is applied to the structure found in the Southwest. They consist of a compact mass of rooms built of carefully laid stone, the crevices being filled with mud and clay. The structure consists of from two to six stories with seventy or more rooms to each story. The buildings are both rectangular and circular in form with rooms connecting with each other by means of trap doors, and the outside rooms admitting light through openings left in the walls. The rooms can be entered only through the roof by means of ladders. These ladders may then be with-

drawn after the people have entered. The second form of habitation which resembles the pueblos is the cliff dwelling. The cliff dwellings were built in the recesses of cliffs at a height often of several hundred feet from the ground, and at the present time seemingly inaccessible, as the former paths that led to them have nearly all been destroyed by the crumbling away of the rocks. These dwellings sometimes consisted of many rooms, and in some cases were two or more stories high, hewn in the rock, with wood lintels in the doors and windows, which were probably closed with skins or blankets. The walls were finished with a plaster of clay, and showed considerable skill in construction.

The one requirement which the primitives have met has been that of protection and defense, yet sacrificing light, heat, and sanitation so necessary to modern civilization. Dwellings came to mean more than a mere shelter as civilization advanced and man domesticated animals, learned the use of tools, and the fine arts of weaving and of working with metal and wood. With the development of agriculture came a need for the protection for the group. Man first built walls and made openings in them. Later he protected these with gates. As he made his walls higher, he made openings at the bottom only and then had to support that part of the wall which came above the opening. From this need developed the post and beam of wood, then the pier and lintel of stone — a solution of the problem of support and burden which embodies the first principles of architecture.

The early buildings of stone had massive walls and piers, but as refinement in building grew, man decorated first the walls and then the piers. He learned to economize in his building construction by filling the spaces between the piers with lighter walls, until he developed less massive supports which finally evolved into the column and entablature. The column took the shape it did because it answered man's sense of beauty, as well as his religious and social instincts.

The evolution of architecture has proceeded with the evolution of civilization. Originating in necessity, it has been able to express the phases of civilization more closely and directly than the other fine arts. Since its materials for expression were of durable nature, the story it tells has survived throughout the ages, and may be used to trace the development of civilization. Definite sermons on religion, and lectures on character, conditions of life, and the methods and ideals of nations are to be found in the surviving examples of architecture. The Egyptian symbolized his belief in immortality by massive tombs and temples; the Greek expressed his ideal of perfection in temples.

Many factors have entered into the determination of historical architecture. Geography determined the type of material of which the structures were built. If stone was plentiful, stone structures were used; if brick and not stone was available, brick buildings were built. Climate, too, affected design. In the South where it is warm there were patios, courtyards, and terraces. In the North, where it is necessary to make provision against the elements, there were buildings with steep roofs. Religion has played and always will play an important part in the determination of architectural styles. The cathedrals of the Middle Ages were the expression of man's religious ideas. The type of government is also significant. A powerful, centralized government will have large and important public buildings, and the public buildings will be more important than the churches. If the government emanates from the religion of the people, the public buildings will take the form of temples.

Architecture began as a practical problem. As man's skill in building progressed, so likewise did his desire to make his buildings more expressive of his dignity as a human being. Civilization, age after age, has built, not only to meet the needs of life, but to express the ideals of the present and the hope of the future.

ASSIGNMENT
Prehistoric Dwellings

This unit is designed to arouse interest in the history and evolution of the house. A number of very interesting projects can be worked out in connection with this unit.

PROBLEMS FOR CLASS DISCUSSION

1. Look up the material at hand on the history of the "cave dwellers" and make a report to the class.
2. Develop an interesting topic on the communal types of dwellings, and report on this to the class.
3. Develop an interesting topic on Indian architecture as applied in the South American countries and Mexico. For example a very interesting report can be given on the Aztec civilization.
4. Make a model of one of the prehistoric dwellings such as the pueblo, cliff dwelling, or lake dwelling.
5. Of what value is the study of the evolution of the house to the student?
6. In what way does environment influence the character of the house?
7. How does the study of the early dwellings reveal the story of the civilization of the people?

Historic Dwellings

EGYPTIAN HOUSES

The history of Egypt may be traced through many dynasties, but seemingly the only remains of architecture are the palaces and temples and tombs. The earliest dwellings, as traced by a study of the relief pictures on the monuments of the period, were cut out of rock, but later huts were built of clay, with walls supported by reeds. These supports are typified in some of their columns which bear a conventional resemblance to reeds bound near the top with bands. Climatic conditions in Egypt made is possible for dwellings to be constructed with flat roofs supported by pillars. If clay walls were used between the pillars, colored decorations were placed upon the surface thus formed. The scheme for coloring was always strong and rich, consisting mainly of yellow, red, blue, green, dark brown, and black.

Supposedly, in front of each building was a walled court the object of which was to protect the entire establishment from the scorching wind and the swirling desert sand. The huts of the poor consisted of a simple square cell, sometimes of two rooms opening directly into each other, or separated by a small court. They were covered by a thin roof of palm leaves placed side by side, and were very low. This hut did not need windows nor doors. Probably the balcony and roof were much used at certain seasons of the year, since in such a place one might repose comfortably beneath an awning safe

from the tropical sun. The larger dwellings were invariably placed on the banks of rivers and canals, and each was equipped with a pump operated by oxen or slaves for supplying water to the household. Gardens were irrigated and made to produce a quantity of fruits and vegetables. Thus we may assume that each family lived within its walls on a narrow street that followed the watercourse. The cooking was done by means of an oven built in the open, and the meals were served perhaps in the shade of palm trees.

The larger houses or palaces of the time, an example of which is shown in Figure 38, were far more pretentious, consisting of extensive outer and inner courts surrounded by porticos, a solidly built ground floor surmounted by a terrace and two or three rooms, reached by a staircase placed against the wall of the court. The small dark rooms below were used as stables for the cattle, sleeping rooms for the slaves, and storerooms. The roofs and floors were made of trunks of palm trees, split in two lengthwise and laid side by side, a bed of beaten earth being spread over them. The family gathered on this terrace in the evening to enjoy the view and the fresh breezes. This idea of a flat-topped roof and an upper terrace is being used in modern homes to achieve a very similar purpose.

ASSYRIAN AND BABYLONIAN HOUSES

The people of Assyria and Babylon, living on the plains of Mesopotamia, were cut off from the supply of stone which the Egyptians had, hence they used sun-dried and burnt brick. They built very elaborate and gigantic structures (see Figs. 39 and 40), only possible by assuming that they had great numbers of captive workmen available to assist in the building. They developed the masonry arch, the barrel vault, and the dome. Typical features were their towers, with each story set back from the one below, and a winding ramp connecting the stories, sometimes as many as seven high. Since

Fig. 38. The Egyptian House. Front entrance, loggia, and storerooms; center, main hall, west loggia, and stairs to room; back, master's bedroom, toilet and bath, inner hall, and storerooms.

the building materials of these people were sun-dried bricks, their structures did not survive as did those of other civilizations.

The Babylonian house consisted of a series of apartments built around a courtyard into which each opened. These buildings were built upon great platforms and were approached by a ramp, up which the master could drive his chariot. A kind of veranda extended all around with posts planted in the earth supporting a light awning which was fastened to the wall. The rooms were narrow and oblong; a few were arched, and a few others were covered with a flat ceiling supported by the trunks of palm trees. Thick clay walls were faced with alabaster, enameled tile, and burnt brick on which, in low relief, were depicted hunting scenes, battles, and likenesses of the gods. The only structural decorations seem to have been the paneling of exterior walls and a form of parapet, but no characteristic molding capitals or cornices have yet been discovered.

Lighting and ventilation were seemingly minor considerations since many rooms were apparently windowless, depending upon artificial light or the scant rays of the sun which found their way through open doors.

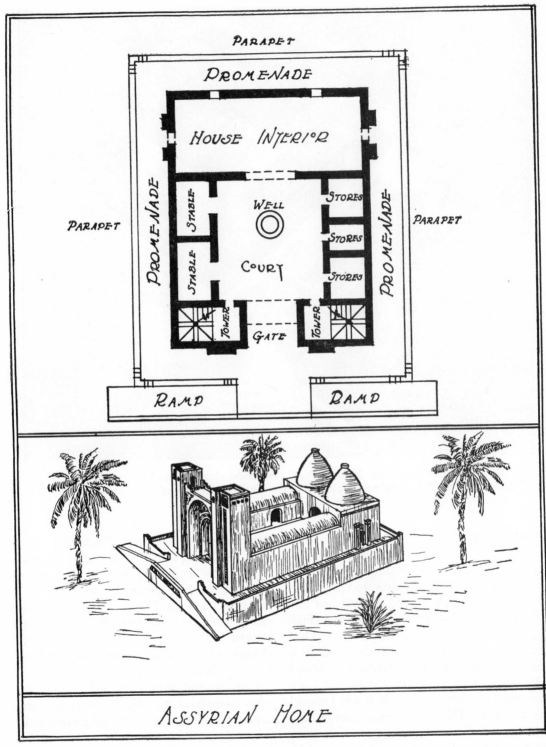

Fig. 39

Fig. 40.   Babylonian house model, from Ur of the Chaldees, c. 2000 B.C.

GREEK HOUSES

We are told that the earlier Greek houses were built of wood, roofed with leaves, and were of circular form. To provide for more space, the circular form gave way to an oval floor plan with posts of wood to hold up the roof. It is probable that the oval either became a rectangle or retained the oval at one end and became rectangular at the other.

The Greek house (see Fig. 41) differed most widely from our modern house in that it was built around an open court for the purpose of admitting light and air. The front of a one-story house toward the street was practically a blank wall covered with stucco, whitewashed or tinted in monochrome. Shops were often inserted into the street walls

somewhat as they are built in our modern hotels. The actual structure consisted sometimes of a framework of wood covered with stucco, sometimes of stone and marble, but generally of sun-dried bricks.

In the floor plan the entrance from the street led into a front vestibule beside which was the servant's quarter for the porter. This passage led directly into the court with the cloister and the mosaic floor. Passage from one room to the other was made through the court. The smallest rooms were the sleeping cells for the males. A large dining room was generally provided but the meals were usually served in the court. The court was used as a reception room, sitting room, and general gathering place for the family. Rooms

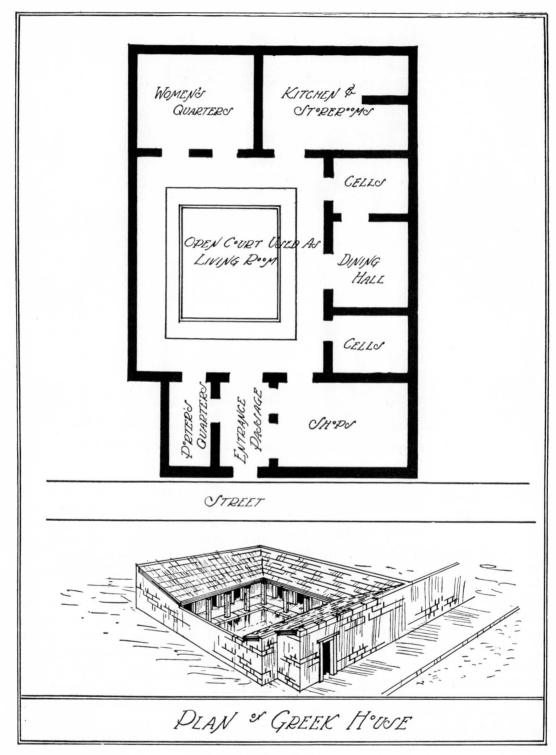

WOMEN'S QUARTERS

KITCHEN & STOREROOMS

CELLS

OPEN COURT USED AS LIVING ROOM

DINING HALL

CELLS

PORTER'S QUARTERS

ENTRANCE PASSAGE

SHOPS

STREET

PLAN of GREEK HOUSE

Fig. 41

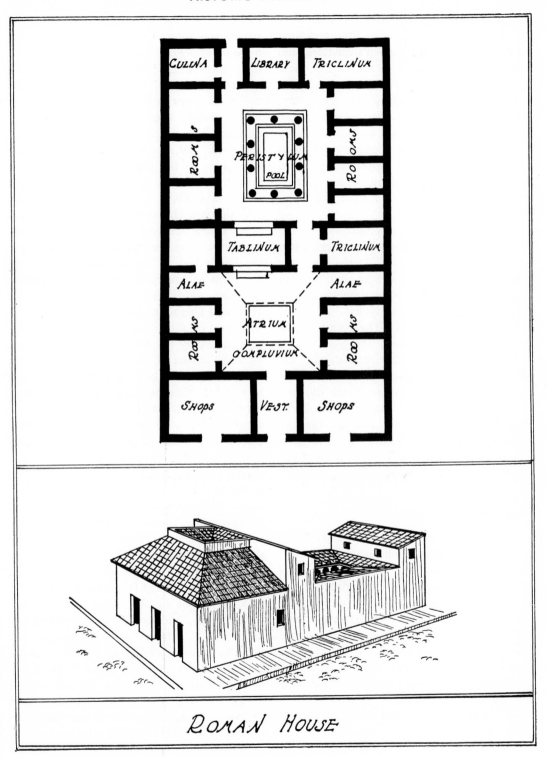

CULINA LIBRARY TRICLINUM

ROOMS

PERISTYLUM
POOL

ROOMS

TABLINUM TRICLINUM

ALAE ALAE

ROOMS

ATRIUM

ROOMS

COMPLUVIUM

SHOPS VEST. SHOPS

ROMAN HOUSE

Fig. 42

for the ladies were reserved separate from the main portion of the house. Strangers were never admitted to the women's quarters, and unmarried daughters did not leave these quarters without special reason or permission.

Usually the house was of but one story, but city houses often included a second story which overhung the streets as they do today in many European cities. Usually the women or slaves occupied this upper story; often this section was rented in which case a separate stairway was used from the street entrance.

Windows were practically unknown on the lower floor, but the upper floor was often provided with casements overlooking the streets. These casements were but wooden doors with no glass or other transparent material. The roof was usually flat but gables were sometimes provided. The better houses contained a cistern or well. The water which collected about the house was carried off by a drain into the street. Chimneys, such as are used at the present time, did not exist, but provision was made for smoke to leave through a hole in the roof and through other openings of the house. The fires were mostly of charcoal which was carried from room to room in braziers.

ROMAN HOUSES

The Roman house (Fig. 42) was typically a southern dwelling built around a court, getting its light and air with little dependence upon windows. The living room of the Greek house was expanded in the Roman style into a magnificent hall with the rooms leading from this court multiplied in number and vastly increased in size. Then through a series of passages one entered a second court even larger and handsomer, and with another array of dependent chambers.

The houses were entered directly from the street. The entrance door (ostium) opened immediately into the main hall (atrium) in the poorer houses. The refinement of later times led to the introduction of a hall or passageway which was later developed into a vestibule. This vestibule was formed by the walls of the shops which were open toward the streets. The atrium was a large, square chamber in the middle of whose floor was a shallow square basin called the "impluvium" into which the water from the roof was shed. The roof was sloped down on the four sides to the center of the room. The atrium was thus a spacious hall partly open to the sky. About it were the various living and sleeping chambers, and facing one another across the end that was farther from the street were the "alea" or wings, where the family history and records were kept in the form of masks, diagrams, etc. Between the alea and facing the entrance was the tablinum. This room was slightly raised above the floor of the atrium from which it was separated only by a balustrade or hangings. Here the master of the house kept the money chest and strong box, and made the room in fact his office or study. Here he received his business associates, clients, or friends; or secured privacy by pulling the curtain across the opening. Back of the tablinum, and separated from it by hangings or sliding doors, was the peristylum. Here the atrium was duplicated but on a much more elaborate scale. In the smaller house this space was planted with flowers and shrubbery; in the richer homes, an elaborately landscaped garden area fronted on all four sides by a colonnade supporting the inward sloping roof of tile. Doors opened from this area or court into the rooms of the slaves and members of the family, and into the dining rooms and kitchen. The dining room (triclinum) was not necessarily adjoining the kitchen (culina) because of the army of slaves kept in the household. It was customary to have several dining rooms for use at different seasons of the year in order that the rooms might be warmed by the sun in winter. The kitchen was placed on the side of the court opposite the tablinum. It was supplied with an open fireplace for roasting and broiling, and with a charcoal stove for baking.

The construction of the Roman house was quite similar to that used today. Walls of dressed stone were laid in regular courses. Over the wall was spread a fine marble stucco for decorative purposes, which gave it a finish of dazzling white. For less pretentious houses sun-dried bricks were used. The floors of the entrance and atrium and various other rooms were of cement-finished mosaic. The doors were exactly like those in modern times except in the matter of hinges. The door hinge was really a cylinder of hard wood terminating above and below in a pivot. To this cylinder the door was mortised. The construction of roofs differed very little from the modern method. They varied as much as ours do in shape, some being flat, others sloping in two directions, others in four. There were no windows opening on the street in the first floor, but in the upper floors there must have been windows because these rooms had no outlook upon the court. The windows were small and furnished with sliding shutters. Glass was known to the Romans of the Empire but it was too expensive for general use. The house as a rule was heated only by the rays of the sun. The atrium in winter received the light when the sun was high; the peristyle afforded a sunny promenade; solariums were provided in some houses; winter dining rooms were provided to alternate with those used for summer. In the more severe weather of winter charcoal stoves or braziers in which coals could be burned were used. These braziers had legs to keep the floor from injury, and handles by which they could be carried from room to room. The wealthy had furnaces resembling ours under their houses, the heat being carried to the rooms by pipes. In the richer houses, lead pipes in quite the modern fashion entered and supplied water to the kitchen, the bath, and the various fountains in the peristyle or atrium. In the poorer houses the water was carried from the running jets supplied by the city water supply system.

ASSIGNMENT

Historic Dwellings

This unit is designed as an informational unit which correlates with the studies carried on in the foreign-language classes and with the study of ancient history.

PROBLEMS FOR CLASS DISCUSSION

1. What do you learn from a study of these historic dwellings about the family life of these early people?
2. Make a working model of one of the historical houses. This would be a very worth-while project for several interested members of the class.
3. Develop an interesting topic on the domestic architecture of the Asiatic countries, and report on this to the class.
4. Trace the development of the heating systems used from early civilization through the introduction of the chimney to the present day.
5. Trace the development of the plumbing system used from the early civilization to the present day.

Early Domestic Architecture of Europe

GOTHIC ARCHITECTURE

The English had not progressed so far in the art of building as the people of southern and eastern Europe, but they led in determining the type of houses in most common use along the eastern shores of America (Fig. 45). The small cottages consisted of a hall and stable, or a hall and bower. The bower was the chamber or women's private room. In the poorer cottages there were no partitions between the parts of the building. Few of these cottages contained a fireplace. The fire was built on the hearth in the center of the room and the smoke left through a hole in the roof. Thatched roofs were common, while a few were shingled or covered with sod. A two-room cottage usually had two outside doors, and by the sixteenth century, it had two windows. The doors were of the batten type, and divided in the middle so that the upper portion could be opened independently of the bottom.

The fortified castle of the nobleman sprang up in Europe during the middle ages. It is probable that the earlier structures were built more for military purposes than for residences.

A pit, known as a "moat" surrounded some castles of this period. Crossing this on a drawbridge, one directly entered a great outer court surrounded by massive stone walls and towers. At the side of this court were servants' quarters and stables. An entrance led to the inner court from which access might be gained to the towers and parapets at the top of the walls. There was a mighty isolated tower with walls of great thickness known as a "keep" or "donjon," a great hall where the feudal lord and his retainers dined, he on a raised platform, and they about an open fire over which meat was roasted in great quantities. Sometimes, at one end of the great hall, were pantries for foodstuffs and at the other end the sleeping room of the noble and his intimates. On the rushes and straw littering the great hall slept the vassals, content to rest here safe from the enemy without.

The "Great Hall" in medieval times was the all-important and chief element of the plan; in fact, it was originally the house proper, all other rooms being merely additions for particular uses. The modern descendant of these great halls is the "living room." We are told that the great hall invariably stood with the gable ends to the east and west, and like the cave dwelling which preceded it, had no partition walls and but one story. Sometimes the entire structure was of wood, but in either case the roof was made by placing layer after layer of bark over the beams, which ran up to the ridge forming lofty gables in which smoke could rise from the fire, built to light and warm the one great room. Over the layers of bark, dirt was piled in so thick a layer that vegetation kept right on growing. The principal piece of furniture was the "long seat" which ran close along the walls on the north and south sides and often across the eastern end. In front of the seat was a table, long and narrow, which might be removed in some cases, but often was firmly fastened to stakes driven in the ground. In the center of the long seat was one "high seat" nearest the fire and occupied by the master of the hall and his wife. The family which occupied the hall was not as we think of a family today, but resembled a garrison for defense, consisting of real or supposed kindred of the house owner.

From this half-military life in the old hall

FEUDAL CASTLE

EARLY TUDOR OR PERPENDICULAR STYLE

LATE TUDOR - ELIZABETHAN OR ENGLISH RENAISSANCE STYLE

GEORGIAN

MODERN

THE ENGLISH HOUSE

Fig. 45

of Europe there came about a gradual change which was seemingly brought about by an era of peace. The transition from the old hall seems to have begun by the erection of supplementary houses for special purposes.

TUDOR ARCHITECTURE

With the fifteenth century a decided evolution in castle architecture ensued. (See Fig. 46.) The fire was moved from the center of the hall to a side wall, and a chimney was provided for carrying the smoke. It is interesting to note that the use of the chimney made possible the construction of an upper story in the hall, since this high space was no longer needed as a place in which smoke could rise. Gradually, the low side walls were raised and provided with openings which were first covered by shutters and later glazed. Stories were subdivided into rooms, the long seat was moved out from under the eaves and was replaced by the several different pieces of movable furniture.

The houses of this period may be exemplified by the town houses of the English. (See Figs. 47 and 48.) These dwellings often consisted of a shop on the ground floor with sleeping quarters above similar to the plan used by the Romans. The kitchen and service rooms were on the first floor behind the shops. The houses were built in rows without lawns between them much as our city blocks are built. In the neighborhood of good building stone, houses were built of stone. The treatment of style in these houses was very simple, and reflected the religious background and training of the builders, for they were experienced in church building, and transferred their methods of constructing churches into the construction of houses. Windows in these early houses had cusped heads and sometimes tracery, which gradually changed to the Tudor four-centered arch without the cusping, and finally to the plain square head. Transoms were introduced during this period, and the bay window was particularly featured in the English houses. A special method of construction was found in the forest districts

Fig. 46.　Tudor (fifteenth-century English house).

Fig. 47.   Medieval town house in Rome
(fifteenth century).

on an enlarged scale under Elizabeth, where the castle became a "mansion." (See Fig. 49.) The new nobility who profited by the confiscation of church property continued house planning on a new scale of magnificence. The house during this period received additions of drawing room, kitchen, servants' hall, breakfast room, library, laundry, etc. Planning on symmetrical lines steadily advanced, and the quadrangular plan was generally used. Building materials were stone, brick, and timber of the locality as in earlier days. The external treatment shows little improvement over earlier styles other than the decoration of the front entrance with pilasters and entablature, and in some instances of setting the doorway in a projecting porch. Details were emphasized for the gateways, balustrades, and even the rain-water leads. Square-topped, mullioned windows were universal, and the bay window maintained its popularity and was even enlarged to include the full height of the house. Hallways were improved to afford access to all rooms and featured the vestibule and great staircase.

RENAISSANCE ARCHITECTURE

The seventeenth century saw the establishment of Renaissance architecture in England, in which the form was modified due to the influence of Inigo Jones upon the architecture designed by Sir Christopher Wren. (See Figs. 50 and 51.) This translated the English house into the formal, symmetrical, Italianized type which later became the American Georgian or English Colonial of the early colonial period. Houses were rectangular in shape with a central doorway opening into a hall — now definitely an entrance vestibule. The roofs were hipped and without gables, and dormer windows took the place of gable windows. Stone quoins and window treatments were usual even on the brick houses. Sash windows were sym-

where an abundant supply of oak was available. The so-called "half-timber" houses were constructed with a framework of stout timbers, left visible with curved struts and braces, which gave a pleasing impression of strength and coherence. The spaces between the timbers were filled with lath and plaster, or bricks laid in a variety of patterns. The interior finish was elaborate with carving. Glass gradually came into general use for windows.

ELIZABETHAN ARCHITECTURE

The development in domestic architecture, so marked under the Tudors, was continued

Fig. 48. Medieval town house. Shop and kitchen on lower floor; living hall and bedroom on second floor.

metrically placed in the walls. The entrance doorway was given a formal treatment with pilasters, entablature, and a pediment such as is still used in this style of house. Doorways and fireplaces were emphasized in the general scheme which allowed the use of rich moldings. The door proper was divided into six or eight panels as still used. The fireplace opening was framed with marble or stone molding, a frieze and cornice forming the mantel shelf. The staircase, usually in a central position, was treated with broad, elaborate stair flights. Massive, carved newel posts, turned balusters, and elaborate scroll-

work marked the changes in detail. By the middle of the eighteenth century the practice of architecture had been systematized very much along the lines of our modern houses.

The sash window was now almost universal, and the ornamental doorway was an expression of prosperity; the choice of brick, stone, and stucco demanded personality on the same scale as the desire to be well dressed. This period provided originality of composition, beauty of detail, form of plan, treatment of materials, expression whereby the tradition of yesterday could be joined to the styles of architecture of the day.

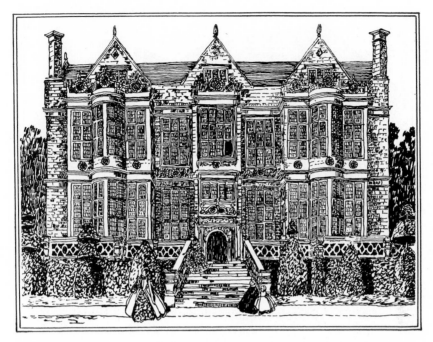

Fig. 49.   Elizabethan (sixteenth-century English house).

Fig. 50.   Renaissance (seventeenth-century English house).

Fig. 51. Georgian (eighteenth-century English house).

ASSIGNMENT

Early Domestic Architecture
of Europe

This unit is designed as an informational unit closely correlated with the study of modern history.

PROBLEMS FOR CLASS DISCUSSION

1. Trace the history of the stairway to the present time.
2. The invention of glass has influenced the history of architecture. Trace its history to the present day.
3. What historical events were influencing the architecture of this period?

Domestic Architecture in Colonial America

Turning our attention from the old countries to the new colonies in America, we shall observe that all of these colonists settled along the eastern shores of the new country. We know the influences of these various nationalities upon the crude architecture of the period. Only two alternatives lay open to them; either to evolve a new kind of building based upon the necessities of their locality, or to copy from memory the homes of the Old World. But, in any event, they needed immediate shelter from the rigors of the New England climate, and the colonists of this area built what was common among the peasants of Europe — huts of saplings filled in with clay. Very soon, however, frame houses began to appear, and it is to these early frame dwellings that we now turn our attention.

The Colonial Period in America extended over a length of time in which there were many changes in England; the Jacobean style, covering the reigns of James I, Charles I, Cromwell, Charles II, and James II, had succeeded the Elizabethen. William and Mary and Queen Anne followed, and after them the Georges. The influence of each of these monarchs is reflected in the architecture of the time. Each of these styles was exported to the colonies. Before 1700 the few buildings in America were crude, humble, and without decoration, and of the medieval Elizabethan style. After this period it is distinctly Georgian reflecting the influ-

ence of Inigo Jones, Sir Christopher Wren, and the brothers Adam. (See Fig. 52.)

COLONIAL ARCHITECTURE IN NEW ENGLAND

It has been said that, in rebuilding London after the fire, Sir Christopher Wren took Inigo Jones's book and erected a building from each picture until he ran out of illustrations; then he went over the pictures again with a series of modifications and changes to fit. In a very similar manner the colonial carpenter worked from available books of Vitruvius, Vignola, Palladio, and Alberti. The originals of these are still in constant use, and their plates illustrate the five orders of architecture and the details useful to the builder.

The first native-born architect of the United States was Charles Bullfinch of Boston. Thomas Jefferson was an architect, but he confined his designs to the University of Virginia and to his own home. Colonial architecture was a result of the owner's desires and tastes transferred into houses by local carpenters. These carpenters drew on similar experiences, and worked from books of design either brought over from England or copied from the English models. (See Fig. 49.) They departed from English practice and differed from each other chiefly as climate and available materials dictated. The houses in the South began early to have high ceilings and more spacious rooms than the Northern houses where the summer heat did not last so long. As might be expected with the early building activities spread over so large a territory, under climatic conditions that varied greatly, and employing workmen of several nationalities who must draw upon their own traditions for their methods and architectural forms, the Colonial period gave birth to many types.

In New England, some of the early residences served not only as living quarters, but also as fortifications and meeting houses. In many instances, the floor plan consisted of but two rooms, one on each side of a

EARLY GEORGIAN

GEORGIAN

EARLY COLONIAL

EARLY COLONIAL

NEW ENGLAND COLONIAL

SOUTHERN COLONIAL

THE COLONIAL HOUSE

Fig. 52

Fig. 53.   Early New England Colonial.

central chimney, while the roof construction was most simple, usually made with but one ridge and two end gables. The attic space was meagerly lighted by windows in the gable ends. The windows carried out the medieval picture for they were small, hinged with casement sash filled in with square and diamond-shaped panes, which were often of oiled paper or parchment. The great chimney often was built of wood, covered with clay. One of the outstanding characteristics of the earlier houses was the overhang of the second story finished at the corners with heavy carved pendants. The two-room plan was frequently enlarged by adding an ell. This ell was sometimes extended by repeated additions until the two-room plan was exactly doubled, and a central hall was added giving a symmetrical arrangement. The enlarged plan made the ridgepole so high that rooms could now be placed where there was but attic space in the earlier houses. At an early date, a cottage type was developed by extending the roof over a one-story part,

usually in the rear. Later, a low roof was extended over the front part as well. The excellence of sparingly employed details in doorways and windows lent a subtle charm to the early houses of the colonists.

The climate and the nationality of the workmen, however, were not the only governing factors. There were important questions of materials. What was available had to be used, architectural styles, personal preferences, and craftsmen's traditions notwithstanding. The houses of Pennsylvania in the neighborhood of Philadelphia bear this out. Ledgestone was very plentiful here. Naturally there evolved a square, solid house, with the emphasis upon a fitting neatness and an enduring dignity rather than on display. The Dutch settlers in northern New Jersey with the French Huguenots had a brown sandstone that was easily cut to rectangular shape with a smooth face; yet their houses are very much unlike their Quaker neighbors. Seldom did they carry their thick main walls above the first story, and frequently they used stone only for the gable end walls, filling in the front and rear with clapboards, stucco, jointed siding, or shingles. They originated a peculiarly distinctive American form — the gambrel roof — apparently in an attempt to make a one-story house afford better headroom, ventilation, and light in the attic. These Dutch builders showed an amazing knowledge of the use of materials. In addition to their cut stone, usually reserved for the front or for the sturdy quoins, they utilized the smaller pieces and off-color stone in a random rubble with wide flush mortar joints. They sometimes plastered the whole face and then whitewashed it. Brick was used only sparingly for the great chimneys and ovens. Clapboards, shingles, and flush-jointed siding were used freely.

On Long Island is found another style variation. Near the western end, in close touch with the Dutch settlers, the New Jersey type was followed to a degree, but with the difference that stone was no longer available. Here is an architecture of wood, with only enough brick for the chimneys and fireplaces. Going eastward on the island, the Dutch influence wanes and the English increases. The gambrel roof gives way to the roof of straight pitch; the wide overhang disappears; two stories and an attic become the rule, with few or no dormers to break the simple roof mass. White-painted shingles, with wide weatherage, cover the walls. In plan the house usually starts with a square — a hall and two rooms — and additions are made in a series of lessening gables running in the direction of the main ridge but of less height. Across the Sound to the north, Connecticut developed still another manner of building her settlers' homes. Curiously enough they had a plentiful supply of stone, but they seemingly preferred to use wood. Here again the house was square, but the additions were made by carrying down the north slope of the roof to shelter more space below, or by raising the roof, or by

flattening its pitch somewhat in covering the area parallel with the main ridge. Here there is a free and more skilled use of wood in the moldings, mantel, paneling, doorways, and entrance porches.

About 1739, peace and prosperity came to the colonists, and many pretentious residences were built. The early Georgian style was directly responsible for the expansion of the medieval house style. This house was so placed that its length paralleled the street, and with an entrance opening into a central hall which usually ran across the entire house. On each side of the hall were two rooms symmetrically arranged. The chimneys were placed at each end instead of at the center of the house. The entrance door was located in the center and directly off the hall, with two windows flanking each side. There were five windows in the second story, arranged on an axis with the openings of the first-floor plan. Window trim was usually simple, though fine cornices or even pediments were sometimes used over the window heads. Green blinds were an essential part of the decoration. The lintel was usually a flat arch with a keystone. The cornice was elaborate with gable returns extending a foot or more around the corner. The doorways were elaborately decorated with pilaster and pediment. Dormer windows were usually high, narrow, with a simple pediment, and ordinarily were spaced on an axis with the windows below.

The architecture of the latter part of the Georgian period in America is dominated by the brothers Adam in England, and is executed by Bullfinch of Boston and Samual McIntire of Salem, Massachusetts. The typical Salem house was certainly not beautiful in form with its cubical three-story height and its white-pine construction. Its roof was so low pitched as to appear flat, often surmounted by a cupola and captain's walk. The doorway was located in the center and facing the street.

In the post-Colonial period the Georgian

Fig. 54.   Southern Colonial.

houses of the colonists have taken their copy from the classic buildings of Greece and Rome. This influence is most strongly shown in the buildings of the South.

COLONIAL ARCHITECTURE IN THE SOUTH

In the South of those early days it is harder to pick out definite styles and label them. The plantations were far apart and self-contained. Each was in effect a community in itself; with its own grinding mill, its weavers, its tailors, its shoemakers, and blacksmiths. If there are any characteristics common to all they are very few indeed — the wide, spacious central hall running completely through the house; the high ceilings usually found in warm climates, and a distinct separation of kitchen and service quarters to another building rather than in the main house.

The earliest houses in Virginia and elsewhere were undoubtedly built of wood with chimneys of stone or brick. It was probably about 1638 when the first brick house was built in Jamestown, and it was no doubt the first house built entirely of brick in the South. Whether of brick or stone, the houses constructed in the Southern states during the seventeenth century and the forepart of the eighteenth century were simple and plain in style. The typical dwelling was oblong in plan and ordinarily a door was placed on one end of the long front. The roof was steeply pitched; a chimney was built at one end and often there was but one floor, though a second floor was sometimes provided. In the roof were long dormer windows with sharp peaked gables. Three common features were noticeable: the wide, spacious "hall," the detached kitchen, and one or more bed chambers placed on the ground floor.

The later mansions of this section more or less exemplified the Georgian style. A fertile soil and slave labor were giving wealth to the planters who, for the most part, being men of good taste and refinement, built houses which reflected evidence of their culture. The Southern mansion was usually symmetrical, consisting of a main unit, in the center of which was an entrance, and a wing on either side. (See Fig. 54.) A wide hall extended the entire width of the structure from the front entrance, and on each side of this hall, large rooms were placed symmetrically. The practice of building kitchens and offices in wings or in structures apart from the main body of the house, and of planning the central hall of such spacious proportions that it could be used as a living room, was retained when the Southern planter built the mansion. These mansions often assumed imposing proportions. Great white pillars, two stories in height, supporting a massive pediment carried forward as an integral part of the roof, were common features.

ASSIGNMENT

Domestic Architecture in Colonial America

This is an informational unit designed to explain the development of the American house. This unit may be closely correlated with the study of history of the American colonies.

PROBLEMS FOR CLASS DISCUSSION

1. Trace briefly the development of the house from the log cabin to the modern house of today.

2. What good points had the so-called Colonial houses? In what were these houses lacking?

3. In what types of shelter did the Pilgrims first live?

4. Why were the timbers of the early New England shelters placed upright rather than horizontally as in the modern log cabins?

5. What are the characteristics of Georgian houses? Are all Colonial houses Georgian style?

6. When you read your history do you have a mental picture of the kinds of houses in which its characters must have lived?

7. Why do we find so many variations of the Colonial architecture in America?

UNIT

V

European Influences in American Domestic Architecture

DUTCH COLONIAL INFLUENCE

The modern Dutch Colonial house, shown in Figure 55, is not of a true type because the design has been changed to meet present-day needs. The style called Dutch Colonial is in strong contrast to the Southern architecture. One of the distinguishing features is the gambrel roof with the short slant from the ridgepole to the shoulder, and a long sweep from the shoulder to the level of the first story, often extending over the porch. The legend goes that this long sweeping roof,

with its dormer windows, was the ingenious means by which the Dutch colonists evaded the heavy tax on two-story houses. The extraordinary flexibility of the style makes it possible for one to arrange the interior to suit his taste and still be assured of a harmonious exterior. One wing or two can be added without disturbing the general contour.

This style is admirably adapted to the small modern home because it is very informal, yet pleasing.

BUNGALOW

The houses referred to as bungalows vary from each other in several ways and there is no characteristic that is common to all. The bungalow may have any kind of roof; a large porch or no porch at all; it may be of wood, brick, or stucco; it may have one or more stories; and it may be English, Dutch, or other Colonial types. There is no such thing as a typical bungalow.

The term *bungalow* had its origin in a type of dwelling built by the English living in India. This type of dwelling was always a one-story building, with a low-pitch gable roof and overhanging eaves, and a broad

Fig. 55.   Dutch Colonial.

219

Fig. 56.   Bungalow.

veranda. It needed ample surrounding space for a proper setting and was ideally situated on a level piece of ground. (See Fig. 56.)

MEDITERRANEAN INFLUENCE

The Spanish house, as we know it, is fundamentally and basically Andalusian. This house has been modified by the designers using motifs and elements from other districts of Spain as an addition to the flat-topped pueblo architecture of our own Southwest. This in truth gives us a "Spanish" house that would not be recognized in the mother country. (See Fig. 57.)

The true Andalusian house is distinguished by its simplicity, which gives it a restful quality that fits its environment. The texture of the stuccoed walls, the roof at several levels, and the unsymmetrical arrangement of the plan all contribute to its pleasing design.

The Spanish house may be identified by the outdoor living room and the indoor garden known as the patio. This central court is formed on two or more sides by the walls of the house, often pierced with arches to form a shaded arcade. The remaining sides are enclosed by high walls to insure privacy. The interior of the house is planned so that the occupants can turn their backs upon the street and enjoy the beauty and quiet of the patio. When there are windows on the ground floor, they are either very small or entirely shut in by iron grilles. On the ground floor the master has only one room; the rest of the rooms are for servants. On the second or main floor, however, the windows are usually very large and are often made the important feature of the façade by the use of rich ornamentation on the borders or of wrought-iron balconies or grilles. Windows are usually in-swinging casements, set well in from the outside of the thick walls. Interior floors are of tile or brick, and tiles are used to form a wainscot which is carried around the openings for decoration. The ceilings are invariably of wood often with painted decorations on the beams. The doorway may be anything from a simple opening to the most elaborately decorated point of interest. On the inside it is often

Fig. 57. Adaptation of Spanish House.

decorated with tiles, cut stone, or molded plaster, but rarely of wood.

The Spanish house reflects the influence of several periods of architecture, although the natural isolation of the districts has minimized the effect of outside change since about 1500. The local craftsmen have adapted details suggestive of the Gothic, Baroque, Renaissance, and the Moorish.

In the Pacific Southwest, the architecture is still influenced by that used in the old missions established at an early date in America by the Franciscan missionaries who made their way to San Diego and established missions for many miles along the coast. Florida is also dominated by the Spanish influence in architecture.

Tiling or modeled plaster is used around the fireplace as a framing for the principal doorways and as a dado around the room. The upper chimney breast may be of the plastered hood type, sloping back to join the wall at the ceiling line. The floors usually are of red tiles, waxed, and rush mats may take the place of rugs. The stairways will probably have a simple railing of wrought iron with a walnut handrail, the stairs themselves probably repeating the brick, stone, or tile flooring.

ENGLISH COTTAGE

It is customary for styles to arise in one locality and then be adopted by others as fast as their qualities are perceived and the conditions are ripe to receive them. Thus the classic style arose in Greece, was transplanted to Rome, and spread over all the Roman empire. The Gothic was developed in northern France and conquered the whole civilized world. It, in turn, was succeeded by the Italian-born style of the Renaissance, which spreading slowly produced in England at its end the style we know as the "Georgian" and here in the United States as our "Colonial."

The English house is as different from the Colonial as possible. It is not symmetrical; it has no cornice remotely suggesting the classic; its windows are neither large nor widely spaced, but small and arranged in groups; it is rarely two full stories; its roof is steep, not flat, it has no porches; its doorway is seldom emphasized but depends for its effect upon the texture of the materials used. (See Fig. 58.)

It is easy to understand how it happened to develop if we bear in mind that the English cottage was a rural architecture. It was always the cheapest house that could be built of the required size, and its characteristic features arose from the limitations imposed by cost and by the available local materials. The small windows, for example, are reminiscent of the time when there were but holes in the wall which had to be kept small to keep out the rain and the cold. Then, when glass finally came to be made cheap enough so that it was possible for the peasant to afford it, the smallest and cheapest panes were used. Furthermore, since large sashes were hard to make weatherproof, small windows were commonly used.

The steep roof tells its own story; the original huts of the British in Roman times and of the peasants in Saxon and Norman times were for the most part of wood plastered with mud and thatched with straw. Heavy overhangs were necessary to keep the rain from washing away the mud in the walls, and thatched roofs must be steep to be weathertight. Later when the forests had been destroyed and lumber became so expensive that it was cheaper to build the walls of stone, and when slate began to be used on the roofs instead of the foul and

rotten thatch, the requirements of overhang and steepness were not changed. The stone was laid in poor and soluble mortar, hence the rough, uneven slates had to be laid on a slope steep enough to keep the water out. The tradition crystallized into an architectural form so rigid that these styles are classified as one of the types of architecture.

The materials of which these cottages were built varied with the locality, and the methods of construction were only similar in that they were primitive to a degree. The construction was often of lumber filled with masonry, that is, a heavy timber frame was erected, and the space between the uprights filled with brick or small pieces of stone laid in mortar.

The characteristics in our own so-called "English Cottage" are the groups of small windows with casement sash divided into small lights instead of large ones; the combination of several materials into a harmonious whole; and an unsymmetrical treatment of the elevation. Half timber is no longer used structurally, but as a decorative wall treatment, and the roofs of slate or tile are broken by many dormers.

Fig. 58.   English Cottage.

TYPICAL FEUDAL CASTLE

DEVELOPMENT OF THE FRENCH CHATEAU

DEVELOPMENT OF FRENCH HOUSE

CASTLE TO HOUSE

Fig. 59

FRENCH INFLUENCE

The tower or citadel is the characteristic feature of the French style of architecture used in homes. The towers, with narrow slit windows and diamond-leaded panes, remind a person of the age of chivalry and knighthood.

France was composed of several small kingdoms before the time of William the Conqueror, especially in Northern France where the population was scattered and the towns were small. As feudalism gained strength, the serfs built their huts about the manors or castles of stronger lords and the monasteries. The local jealousies and wars required that fortifications be built for the preservation of the "ville," and thus it was that the medieval fortified town came into being. Natural defenses such as rivers, and cliffs were advantageously used. The castle was surrounded by double walls with a moat between. The citadel appeared in the angles of the walls so that a cross fire of arrows and projectiles could be directed at the besiegers. The houses of the village followed the protective features of the castle, having the moat and citadel. (See Fig. 59.)

By the time of Charles VIII, a gradual political unification had made the growth of towns possible and the dwellings lost much of their military aspect. The turrets became the oriel windows. The citadel persisted as an architectural characteristic which still exists. The French manor as reflected in the modern adaptations has a dual birthplace, sometimes reflecting the elegance of the castle and sometimes the simplicity of the town house. They are obviously of the Gothic style. The second characteristic of the house is the steep roof with its dormers of varied treatment. The outside staircase might be mentioned as a third characteristic.

The interiors were very simple with rough plaster walls and the painted beams of the ceiling, masonry floors, and enormous fireplaces.

The materials used may be varied from half timber, stucco, and limestone, with slate or tile roofs.

ASSIGNMENT

European Influences in American Domestic Architecture

This is an informational unit designed to show the influence of European styles of houses upon the style of houses used in America. While it is true that the colonies were influenced primarily by the English styles of houses, still it is true that other European countries did make some contributions to our style of domestic architecture.

PROBLEMS FOR CLASS DISCUSSION

1. Why do we find such a wide variety of influences in the domestic architecture of America?
2. What are the characteristics of half-timber houses?
3. Are the European styles of houses adopted in this country always characteristic of the whole of the country from which they originated?
4. Describe some house in your neighborhood that exemplifies these European influences.
5. Where in this continent would you expect to find houses most strongly influenced by the styles of houses originating in France?
6. Why do you suppose that there are so very few copies of German houses in this country?
7. Are any attempts made to copy the oriental houses?

UNIT
VI

Architectural Revivals

What might be called the decline of the colonial syle of architecture began in the early part of the nineteenth century. The White House is among the last and best known of the houses designed after the colonial style.

CLASSIC REVIVAL (1800–1860)

So characteristic of the "Classic Style" is the portico with its four, six, or eight columns, its entablature and pediment, that this style has been called the "portico style." The siding of these houses was usually laid flush so that the wall presented a smooth surface in imitation of the cement and stucco. Often white plaster or stucco marked off to imitate stone was used. Even bricks were painted gray to give this same effect.

The distinctive doorway was arranged with pilasters on the side and a full entablature, frieze with cornice, and a couple of simple vertical panels, and a long, low, rectangular transom above. Thin vertical side lights were used on each side of the door. (See Fig. 60.)

The windows were of the double-hung type with panes of glass divided by wood muntins. The window trim was usually simple with little or no cornice.

The predominating feature was the second-story overhang. Classic gable returns were used at the ends of the house. Small gable windows were used for the attic. Cast-iron ornaments such as window grilles, balconies and balustrades were typical.

Roofs were of very low pitch adhering to the Greek temple form.

GOTHIC REVIVAL (1860–1880)

The great mansion with cupola and porches, oriels, bays, porte-cocheres with greenhouses attached are distinctive of this period. One can easily picture a smooth, broad lawn, policed by the cast-iron dog and his companion the cast-iron deer, dotted with the fashioned beds of cannas. The entrances were covered with a narrow "stoop" which had no particular use except to express the style. Bay windows projected even from the corners of the house; oriel windows were decorated with elaborately chamfered stiles. Jigsaw brackets; chimneys with buttresses, panels, and chimney pots; high narrow windows filled with diamond-shaped panes; mansard roofs; and the cupola were all features designed to display the newly acquired wealth. (See Fig. 61.)

ROMANESQUE REVIVAL (1876–1893)

The stone and brick houses for the most part of this period were entirely Romanesque, but to design a wood frame house in this style was a difficult operation, and the greater number of houses were of wood. In the plan these stone houses were irregular and rambling; stairways were broad with many landings; fireplaces were frequent with large openings for the accommodation of cordwood. Rooms were planned with lower ceilings; halls were short; bathrooms were numerous. Larger closets and better planned kitchens and pantries made this a more practical style of house than those of Gothic origin. Houses of stone were designed with high roofs, huge gables with half timbering, wide porches and porte-cocheres, and corner towers. The tower was usually circular and was always capped with a conical roof. The porte-cochere, which provided a porch-like covering over a driveway to protect people entering and leaving a carriage, was a mark of affluent respectability.

In the houses constructed of wood, shingles were often used on the upper half of the wall. These shingles were cut in various

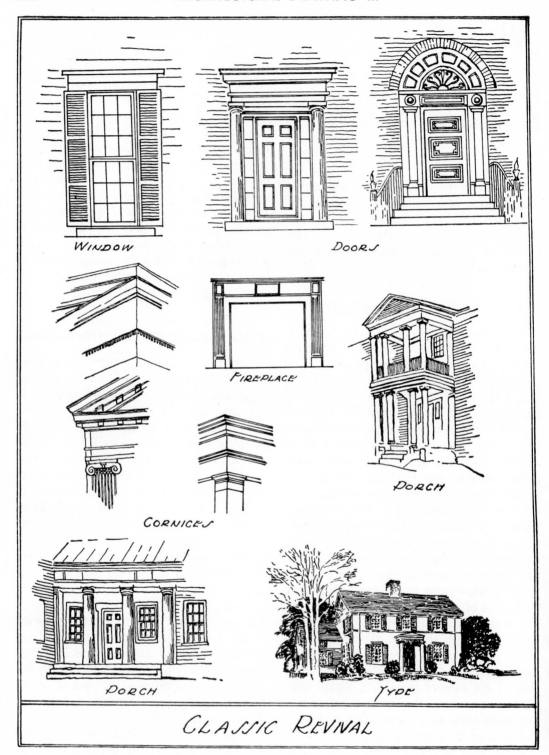

WINDOW

DOORS

CORNICES

FIREPLACE

PORCH

PORCH

TYPE

CLASSIC REVIVAL

Fig. 60

Fig. 61. American Gothic Style.

sizes and shapes, and were laid in patterns. Siding was used for the lower portion of the wall. Some gables were half timbered and decorated with stucco.

Carved capitals on columns and posts were invariably romanesque, and so were the scrolls and leaf forms of wood that appeared in the composition.

ASSIGNMENT
Architectural Revivals

This unit of work is introduced to the student because this period marks the development of the city house in America. It is closely related to the study of the "Industrial Revolution" in American History.

PROBLEMS FOR CLASS DISCUSSION

1. How many different types of architecture can be found in your city? Appoint committees to investigate different parts of town. Each committee should report to the class the result of its investigations, and if possible, should illustrate the report with photographs.

2. Study and report on the influence of Thomas Jefferson in this revival of the classical styles.

3. What were the characteristic differences between the Greek and Roman style as expressed in this revival?

4. In what other places have you seen a pediment used?

5. Choose your favorite style of domestic architecture and read as much about it as you can. Collect pictures from magazines and advertising booklets showing the influence of this type of architecture in modern homes.

Contemporary Architecture

It was possible in earlier architectural constructions for an architect to design and engineer his structures, specify the lighting, heating, and plumbing without specialized and technical assistance, and be thoroughly familiar with all building products. With the introduction of new materials, methods of construction, and items of equipment the work of the architect became increasingly difficult. Four basic structural principles have governed all buildings of permanent character — the post and lintel, the wooden truss, the masonry arch, and the modern steel skeleton. Steel quickly met all major structural requirements, and reinforced concrete has been adapted to architectural constructions (Fig. 62 and 63).

Technology in the building trades has not progressed with the accelerated growth which had taken place in development of new materials. Scientists and technicians knew the principles of central heating, electric lighting, mechanical ventilation, and sanitary plumbing long before it was generally applied to buildings. Remember that the culmination of the inventions, scientific discoveries, and actual production of sources, distribution, and application came after the turn of the century. In our earlier architectural experiments our buildings were so disguised by veneers and architectural motifs that they resembled masonry structures. There were few daring designers who frankly revealed structure and filled the openings with glass area, or began

an acceptance of larger wall spaces or openings.

One of the greatest problems that concerns the greatest number of people in America — or probably in the world — is building a home which will be permanent, convenient, attractive, and at a price the average person can afford. Everyone concerned is watching developments to see whether the many experimental building products, methods of construction, and designs will be cheaper and as adaptable as the older building practices have proved themselves to be. Once a new material has been accepted as meeting the essentials of weather resistance, good wearing qualities, permanence, ease of handling, adaptability to construction and design, along with economy of manufacture and distribution, the architects will discover ways and means of using it economically and simply. Recent improvements in construction have built the walls as units to be raised and set in position, with similar methods applied to roofs.

No builder considers labor-wasting materials, constructions, or designs as being ideal; or the assembly of individual pieces to be economical, and is searching for new solutions to his whole problem. No architect regards the resulting surfaces full of lapped edges, crevices, or joints to be ideal for appearance or construction. It must not be forgotten, however, that these familiar materials may be used in new ways and that it is possible to adapt them to meet new conditions.

The great wealth of technical knowledge shared by the inventor and manufacturer, the development of distribution and sales systems, and the increased interest in modern technology among artists and engineers, all are daily reflected in the availability of new materials, methods, and equipment.

Great progress has been accomplished in the development of wood products: such materials appeared as wood-fiber insulation; synthetic lumber made from waste wood and phenolic resin employed for building board, doors, sash, and cabinet work; plastic sur-

John Randal McDonald

Fig. 62.   Exterior and interior of a modern home.

faced plywood and structural slabs made from excelsior and wood fibers bonded together with portland cement; plywood and veneers, now increasingly used; and better adhesives, protectors, and repellents.

Carbon steels came into common use along with the use of lightweight and junior structural-steel sections. Aluminum was manufactured in many extruded shapes, corrugated sheets, tubing, and as sheeting for ducts, shingles, clapboard, and foil for reflective insulation. Steel and aluminum windows became more widely used. With the increasing demand for larger window areas, designers began using more of the possibilities of natural lighting.

The quality of sheet and plate glass improved. Heat-absorbing glass had its uses. Plate glass screened damaging ultraviolet light. Directional glass blocks were introduced, and glass fibers and cellular-glass formations were marketed for insulation. A renewed interest was given to natural lighting and many studies were made to gain maximum advantages of its effects, as well as to eliminate undesirable features. In artificial lighting, progress was made in concealed lighting, and some fixtures were introduced which advanced toward the principles of diffusion.

A tremendous use of plastics for archi-

tectural purposes was developed for table tops, counter tops, bathroom and kitchen tiles, and so on. Significant developments in acoustical correction and in sanitation resulted in many sound absorbent tiles, and increased production of acoustical plaster. The color possibilities of asphalt tile were improved upon, and rubber tile was made harder, denser, and given more elasticity. Flush doors became popular and the all-glass door found wide favor. The use of insulation, particularly in residences, spread rapidly as studies of its advantages were published. Windows were made of twin sheets of glass separated by an air space which reduced heat loss through the popular larger window areas. Kitchen and bathroom planning studies were instituted. They considered the appearance of new pieces of equipment such as: the garbage disposer, improved cabinet units, redesigned plumbing fixtures, and new methods of installation.

Advances were made in the development of forced hot-water circulation at higher temperatures and through smaller pipes. The forced circulation of hot air, with the improvement of temperature controls and regulators, gave better heating results. Radiant heating was accomplished by installing in floors, walls, or ceilings, coils which circulated hot water (Figs. 77–79). Prefabricated heating coils were introduced to help reduce the cost of installation. Warm-air radiant systems generally employed an overhead plenum; a variation carried warm-air pipes or structural clay tiles, embedded in the floor, to registers near window areas. Electric radiant heating was accomplished by conductive rubber panels, by radiant heating glass panels, and by special cables placed in walls, floors, and ceilings. Radiant baseboard heating was developed during this period, and radiation-using convectors became popular. New heating devices included the anthrative and the heat pump. There were tentative panel cooling installations. Solar heating and electronic heating, although workable, were still in the experimental stage. Materials with which to build and finish structures, and equipment with which environment could be controlled were becoming available in ever increasing quantities.

If these new ideas were used only reluctantly at first, it is understandable when one remembers that few of the products had been time-tested. In fact, since that time, many of them have been radically altered and improved. In addition to the need for absorbing an increased amount of technical knowledge and for investigating ideas, methods, and construction procedures of his own, the architect was face to face with a widened social responsibility and a field of activity potentially greater than in the past. Thus the architect's sense of responsibility, in some cases his actual participation, expanded in two directions — the building itself and beyond the

walls of the building toward individual objects which contributed to the immediate environment.

The need has long been recognized for construction through larger units of factory-fabricated material, capable of being set in place more simply and quickly, and with greater economy of labor. Prefabricated houses have been devised in units capable of being economically transported to a site and easily and rapidly erected with inexpensive labor, in a few uncomplicated operations.

Tomorrow's home — what will it be like? "With contemporary methods and materials, the architect is given the freedom of expression heretofore confined to artists, sculptors, musicians, and poets. A gifted architect becomes a 'Master of Arts,' for his building can now be shaped as sculpture, enriched with color and rhythm, and as undisciplined as free verse [Fig. 63]."* As we grow more and more accustomed to the qualities of glass, the surface of metals, the pure hues possible in plastics, a new color sense will gradually develop. We are primarily accustomed to gray architecture, but the modern trend will see a much more daring use of color as exemplified in nature.

It would appear that all new construction would be of contemporary nature because these new methods permit lower building construction costs, easier erection, a more flexible plan arrangement, and less maintenance, thereby affording more leisurely living. These advantages are accomplished not only by the omission of

* John Randal McDonald, architect.

Fig. 63.
Rendering of a
modern home.

John Randal McDonald

frills and fancy work, but in utilizing simple wall surfaces of large expanses of glass, pre-cast concrete or metal-surfaced wall panels, vaulted roofs of thin-shell concrete, steel, or laminated wood requiring no interior support, allowing movable interior partitioning of light-weight plastics.

The house plans will depart from the number-of-rooms concept. Space dividers will be movable and usually will include storage units so that room shapes and sizes can be changed as family requirements change. This simplification of surface and reduction of complexities lends itself to producing these building panels by machine. They can be mass produced in modular dimensions so that endless shapes and sizes can be achieved. This pre-fabrication of parts allows a single wall panel to include finished exterior and interior walls of epoxies, baked enamels, porcelain, anodized aluminums, stainless steel, and other factory-applied surfaces. Insulation, electrical wiring, plumbing, even heating and cooling and inter-communications can be integral parts of each panel. Shipped pre-finished to the building site, the panels are locked together with a minimum amount of field labor to produce a building in the contemporary manner. Furthermore, these panels permit easy rearrangement of space, remodeling, and, if properly engineered, moving of the entire house. These modular types of panel construction include interior and exterior wall panels, floor panels, and roof of panels since they can be solid or of transparent or translucent materials admitting light from floors and ceilings as well as walls. These panels can be fixed or sliding; roofs, walls, and even floors can slide open as desired. The advantages are only limited to architectural imagination.

Buildings of contemporary materials, machine produced, lack one element vital to their acceptance — sensitivity. A sensitive building is one that is aware of the needs of the persons within it. Shelter and convenience are not enough. The building must create a living environment of esthetic warmth, security, drama, romance, and individuality; and most important, the home must become the family as the family becomes the home (Fig. 62). A home cannot be solely a machine for living, for, as a machine, it is cold and insensitive. It remains with the architect to combine new materials and construction methods with the timeless esthetic needs of the family before contemporary homes will be accepted.*

ASSIGNMENT
Contemporary Architecture

This unit of work is designed to be of informational nature, intended to arouse interest in the development of the modern interpretation of a modern house. A number of very interesting projects can be worked out related to this unit of study.

PROBLEMS FOR CLASS DISCUSSION

1. How has the development of materials, methods of construction, transportation, and other factors influenced the evolution of residence architecture? the design of the modern house?

2. Write or give an oral report of what developments are likely to be produced for the home of the future.

3. Look up the biography of some of the better known architects and give an oral report to the class on one of them.

4. What effect will a government housing program have upon the development of modern house styles in your community?

5. What differences can be pointed out between the old and new residence areas of your city? Can you trace the historical development of your city through the evolution of its house designs?

6. Do you have a "Better Homes' Campaign" organized in your community, a building trades' fair, or a some form of a home show?

7. Develop the working drawings and a model of a conventional house; a contemporary house.

8. Discuss the reluctance to accept prefabricated houses even though they have many convincing arguments in their favor.

9. Invite an architect of the modern school to discuss contemporary architecture and the new architectural philosophies.

_____
* Ibid.

UNIT
VIII

Methods of Obtaining a House Planned to Your Taste

There are two methods of obtaining a house: (1) buy one already built which suits you as to design, size, arrangement, equipment, location, price, and so on; (2) build one which meets your requirements. If you plan to build, the problem becomes one of organizing your needs and wants so thoroughly that they can be explained clearly to the builder and his workman. If these desires are clear enough to be expressed to others they can be fulfilled. You must know how to get what you have in mind, and yet keep within your means. How much you can have for what you can afford is usually the deciding factor of the whole home building problem.

The plan for a house is determined after consideration of the following points:

1. Budget
2. Site
3. Space requirements:
   a) Type of family
   b) Activities of family
   c) Size of family
4. Types of construction

In contemplating the building of a small house, probably the first consideration is the total cost limit which must be maintained. Considered a good way to arrive at this is to multiply your year's income by one and a half. This will give you a safe cost for the house you can afford. Then multiply your yearly income by three and you have a maximum figure of cost. The final, over-all cost of your home had best be adjusted between these two amounts, just where being partly conditioned by how much cash you have available for a down payment. When this is determined a budget should be prepared which will determine the proportion of the total amount to be expended for the lot. For obvious reasons there should be a proper ratio between the value of the lot and of the house. It is evident that a small, cheaply constructed house on an expensive lot will depreciate the value of the property, and conversely a large expensive home on a small lot, or on property in a less desirable neighborhood, will never bring more than a fraction of its true value in case of sale. In this connection it is safe to say, under normal conditions, 15 to 20 per cent of the total cost should be expended for the lot.

The second point to be considered is the selection of the lot. This must be done before any plans are started. The direction which the lot faces is a very important consideration bearing on the arrangement of rooms. Consideration of sunlight and prevailing winds at the different seasons of the year are first considerations. Second, the outlook from any piece of property will invariably be more pleasing in one direction than in others. A lot which is narrow and deep will call for a different arrangement than a broader and shallower piece of property.

The next point to consider is the space requirements for the family. A house for a family of older people must be of a different type than that for a family in which there are children. The activities of the family generally determine the type of house needed. The principal activities of the family are eating, sleeping, entertainment, and work. This divides the house into three groups to accommodate the activities: (1) living rooms, which includes the living room, dining room, library, and entrance hall; (2) sleeping rooms which include bedrooms, bathroom, and sleeping porches; (3) workrooms which include kitchen, pantry, laundry, and storerooms. The living rooms are the public part of the house; the workrooms should be placed where they are the least conspicuous, and the sleeping rooms in the more secluded portions. The plan must give good proportions to each room. The living room should be the largest room in the house, and the dining room nearly square, with a slightly smaller kitchen. Hallways should meet the needs required of them.

The requirements to be met in any house are in reality the requirements of the people living in it. No two families will agree upon the number, size, and arrangement of rooms, but all will acknowledge the comfort and convenience of the household is dependent upon the proper arrangement. Economical planning reduces waste space and will provide the right size for the stairway, hallways, bathrooms, and closets in addition to the principal rooms. It also provides the proper space for the proper installation of plumbing, heating, and lighting.

While there is a definite relation between the size of a house and its cost, it is not always realized that in two houses of identical floor area, one may be built for very much less than the other. This is due to the manner in which the rooms are arranged to form the plan. In the one instance there may be extravagance in plan and construction, and in the other economy and simplicity.

Three important fundamentals must be considered in the building of a house which do not have to affect the cost of the house, namely: (1) beauty, (2) comfort, and (3) convenience. In considering beauty first, there are three dependable guides to the problem of house design. First is the work of the prominent architects of the present day. They have spent their lives in the study of architectural design and have years of experience in the supervision and planning of buildings. Even the architect, devoting a lifetime to designing buildings cannot master all the intricate knowledge that is daily accumulating in the building field. He knows where to get

the knowledge, and how to find and profit by the experience of others; and he has a vast fund of experience and information of his own. Second among the recommended guides of planning is the wealth of information to be found in the handbooks and current magazines. The study and analysis of house designs that have stood the test of practical application will afford a good perspective on modern trends and fashions. The third guide is a well-developed judgment in matters of taste. Taste in design can be acquired by familiarity with first rate design or by study of the principles of design. Appreciation of good design is an essential part of general culture, opening many areas of enjoyment and interest.

Through centuries of experience man has discovered that designs made according to certain studied principles are pleasing to the eye. These principles are orderly arrangement, unity, balance, rhythm, and proportion. Orderly arrangement implies an intentional studied arrangement in assembling the parts of the whole design and helps produce a feeling of strength and permanence. In a house design it is achieved through window arrangement, roof pitches, choice of materials of construction, pleasing decoration, and so on. Simplicity is one of the greatest aids in achieving order. Unity may be described as a feeling of relationship — all parts of the design in agreement with one another, and of the design as a whole. Consistency in the treatment of details, simple use of color, and the problem of dominance of mass contribute toward a better appearance. Prominent porches and dormers often offend unity in house design by attracting attention away from the main body of the house. Indiscriminate mixing of materials often contributes to poor design. Balance means stability and a feeling of repose. In a house it may be formal with two halves of the façade alike, or informal with the sides unlike but so arranged that they preserve the feeling of alikeness. Informal balance is more difficult to achieve for it depends upon a subtle arrangement of sizes and positions. Rhythm may be defined as an orderly repetition of similar parts. While the mass of the house should give an impression of solidity and permanence, the details of material and decoration should carry the eye over its surface in pleasing, rhythmic progress. Aids to rhythm are found in repetition of construction details and decoration, in transition found in curving lines, in radiation by the skillful handling of light and shadows, and in gradual change and blending of colors. Proportion is a matter of relative sizes. Major proportions of height, width, length, of roof and wall area should present an interesting variety in size and space divisions, rather than a monotonous repetition of the same dimensions. Thus a rectangle is better than a square for the design of the front elevation of a house, and unequal areas of roof and wall are more pleasing than equal space divisions. Scale is the proportion of minor details to the whole, meaning the proportion of the sizes of the windows, doors, porches, dormers, and other parts of the structure. The following rules generally apply:

1. A building must fit its site.

2. A building must serve its purpose.

3. A building must express its purpose.

4. A building must express the social conditions of the place and period of its construction.

5. A building should show its construction and be free from sham and pretense.

6. Ornament should be structural and not applied.

7. Every detail must be in character with the whole.

8. The plan must be as direct and simple as possible.

A home should be truly comfortable — a place to relax and refresh from the problems of everyday living. The importance of good landscaping should be a basic part of home planning. Lighting also has a lot to do with comfort, not only at night but during the day as well. Windows should be ample in size and, wherever possible, should look out on an attractive scene. Generous light should be provided at all work areas with provision for controlled ventilation. Artificial lighting should be such as to prevent glare and consequent eyestrain. Comfortable living must be designed into a home. Make every provision for the tastes and interests of each member of the family — for recreation, for hobbies, for family activities, and for privacy when desired. A cheery fireplace, built-in bookcases, a writing desk, a home workshop, a snack bar or cozy breakfast nook, all add to the comfort and contentment of the family and its guests.

Comfort and convenience are so interwoven that these two elements may almost be considered together. Convenience makes for comfort. The keynote of good planning is to arrange your equipment conveniently. To do so, everything needed for any frequently performed task should be within easy reach which minimizes the steps to be taken and makes the work more pleasant and less tiring. In planning a house the following points should be considered:

1. A square house is the most economical form in which a given amount of space may be enclosed. It requires less hall space, is cheaper to build, easier to heat, but is not as attractive in appearance.

2. Doorways connecting a series of rooms should be alike in shape and size. The doors in the same room should at least be similar in design. If possible have no more than two doors in a room, and have them at one end of the room. If privacy is desired the living room should be at the dead end of the house. Doors at each side of the fireplace make traffic lanes where there should be seclusion. Too many doors defeat privacy.

3. Window sills should be below the level of the eye of a seated person so that a full view may be obtained.

4. A large opening opposite the fireplace opens the heart of the room to callers.

5. If maximum light and air are desired,

plan the house accordingly. South and west exposures give the most sun.

6. If the room is narrow and there is a fireplace in the long wall, there should be wall space directly opposite, large enough for davenport and tables.

7. The entrance hall should be conveniently located to the living room and arrangement made for the closet space for wraps. The route from the kitchen to the front door should be as direct as possible. The main doorway should lead from the entrance hall.

8. The kitchen should be conveniently located to the dining room and to the breakfast area. The stairway to the basement should lead from the kitchen or from the hallway directly connected with the kitchen.

9. Stairways leading to the second floor should be placed directly over the stairway leading to the basement.

10. Bedrooms located on the first floor should have a passageway which isolates them from the living room.

11. The upstairs hallway should be centrally located.

12. Cross ventilation should be provided for the kitchen and bedrooms.

13. Closet and cupboard space should be provided as well as an adequate amount of built-in furniture and cabinets.

When you have selected an architectural style which assures the attractiveness of the house and pleases you, and when you have decided on a floor plan that fits the requirements of the family there remains a third and very vital consideration, the durability of your house. Here there are two factors to consider — proper construction and the selection of the right materials. Methods of construction may be applied which could scarcely be expected to give satisfactory results. Too much emphasis may be placed upon speed and cheapness, and too little on thoroughness. Economy of labor and materials can be carried so far in any construction as to impair the strength and rigidity of the structure. Bulging walls, cracked plaster, sagging floors,

creaking stairs, and the continual sticking and binding of doors and windows are all results of faulty construction, and can be avoided. By employing recent improvements in construction the house of today can be made as durable, more comfortable, more weatherproof, and more fire resistant than the houses built in the past. In building your house you will find it profitable to allow the builder sufficient scope so that it will not be necessary for him to "skimp" on the construction. The following considerations are worthwhile in getting the most for your money in planning:

1. A square house is the most economical form in which a given amount of space may be enclosed. An irregular plan can be so arranged as to make it as economical as a simpler rectangular one, if the arrangement saves in hall or other waste spaces inside the house.

2. A low pitched roof costs less than a high pitched one. A roof without a dormer window costs less than one with dormers.

3. An inside chimney costs less to build than a decorative one on the exterior. It should be unnecessary to have more than two chimneys in the well-planned house.

4. The fewer the outside corners the lower the cost of the house. A rectangular house is cheaper than an L (ell) shape.

5. An elaborate exterior cornice requires expensive material and greater labor costs.

6. A full basement adds cost to your house. For the extra amount you may build an extra room above ground. A sloping lot requires less excavation than a flat one. A tile, cinder block, or concrete block foundation is usually less expensive than a poured concrete basement wall.

7. Room sizes which conform to the standard lengths of lumber produce a house which may be built with less waste and less labor.

8. Fireplaces add to the cost of the house. A fireplace is not necessary to a comfortable and pleasant home.

9. A front hall is pleasant, but you can-

not live in it and it adds to the cost of the house.

10. Your plans should call for only "stock" sizes of doors, windows, and other millwork. Custom millwork has no place in a low-cost house.

11. Interest cost accumulates during the building process; time is money spent.

12. Lower grades of flooring look and serve as well as better grades when finished.

13. Lighting fixtures may be attached after the house is built and may be changed at any time.

14. Compare prices on doors. Some patterns or styles of doors cost more than others.

15. Stained woodwork is cheaper than painted.

16. Certain types of wood floors may be finished so that they are as easily cleaned as linoleum. Linoleum may be laid later.

17. If necessary to eliminate a room make it the dining room.

18. Galvanized half-window-length screens can make savings.

19. It is not necessary to finish off a second bathroom at the time the home is constructed. The plumbing for the second bathroom may be roughed-in and then finished later when you can afford it.

20. Plain glass is cheaper in windows than plate glass.

21. Siding for the outside of the house comes in different thicknesses and grades at various prices.

22. Plaster walls may be tinted or painted with a water soluble paint and papered later.

23. Gutters along the eaves may be omitted until later if a bed of gravel or cinders is laid to catch the drip, and plants are set beyond the line of the roof edge.

24. On the second floor insulate only the ceilings, for bedrooms require less heat than the living rooms.

25. The style of house will determine to a large degree the cost. Remember that a

two-story house requires less basement and

less roofing for the amount of living space provided.

26. Stairways are cheaper when built between partitions.

Whether you plan to buy or build, the status, sex, interests, and activities of each member of the family must be recognized in its arrangement. Two methods of approach may be followed. One method starts with a rough estimate of requirements expressed to the planner, builder, or realtor and then develops into a process of elimination. Plans are examined and those not meeting the requirements are rejected. Most people can readily express what they do not want or like, but few are able to express their positive wants or desires. A house is thus purchased or built and requires living experience in it to determine the success of the choice.

The recommended method is to plan the house from the inside out. The first step would be to make an inventory of the needs and requirements of each individual, and then of the family collectively, and finally of the social needs for the entertainment of guests. The second step is to consider the arrangement, approximate size, and the furnishings of the various parts. This requires a consideration for the planning of the separate rooms, followed by a study of the plan as a whole in terms of comfort, convenience, economy, and beauty. The third step is to study the plan for the equipment wanted and needed, and the types of construction and materials best filling the needs of the family. The fourth step is to adjust the wants and needs to the financial means.

CHECK LIST OF FAMILY NEEDS AND REQUIREMENTS

I. Personal Room Requirements

A. Profession or other work: office work at home ( ); studio ( ); work shop ( ); music room ( )

B. Hobbies, avocations, collections (list): . . . .

C. Sports (list): ....
....

D. Other activities (list): ....
....

E. Special requirements (list): ....
....

F. Sleeping: separate bedroom ( ); shared bedroom ( )
Beds: twin ( ); double ( ); single ( )
Sleeping porch ( ): early riser ( ); late riser ( )
Window ventilation: north ( ); south ( ); east ( ); west ( )
Prefer morning sun ( ); does noise bother ( )
Equipment at bedside: stand ( ); telephone ( ); radio ( )
Read in bed ( )

G. Dressing: separate dressing room ( ); shared dressing room ( ); combined dressing room with wardrobe ( ); combined dressing room with bath ( ); combination bedroom ( )
Built-in units: wardrobe ( ); dresser ( ); mirror ( ); vanity ( ); lavatory ( ); water closet ( ); safe ( )

H. Bath: private ( ); shared ( ); access from bedroom ( ); access from hallway ( ); water closet and lavatory ( ); complete bathroom with tub ( ); separate shower ( ); shower combination ( ); powder room ( )

I. Closet and storage:
In season storage: suits ( ); dresses ( ); hats ( ); coats ( ); shoes ( ); robes ( ); sport clothes ( ); nightwear ( ); hose ( ); lingerie ( ); handkerchiefs ( ); scarfs ( ); gloves ( ); blouses ( )
Out of season: suits ( ); dresses ( ); coats ( ); shoes ( ); sports clothing ( ); riding clothes ( ); hunting clothes ( ); fishing clothes ( ); work clothes ( )

J. Furniture: radio ( ); television ( ); cedar chest ( ); dresser ( ); tables ( ); chest of drawers ( ); vanity dresser ( ); bedside stands ( ); occasional chairs ( ); rocking chairs ( ); davenport ( ); coffee table ( )

K. Equipment: refrigerator ( ); stove ( ); built-in stove ( ); built-in oven ( ); built-in cabinets ( ); furnace ( ); (freezer) ( )

L. Accessories: telephone ( ); second telephone ( ); bed lamps ( ); sun lamps ( )

M. Fireplace ....

N. Unit air conditioner ....

II. Possessions and Interests of Family

A. Books: total planned for ( ); shelf heights required ( ); built-in cases ( ); movable cases ( ); location ( )

B. Musical instruments: special room ( ); combination room ( )
Piano ( ); organ ( ); harp ( ); band ( ); orchestra ( )
State rooms where radio facilities are wanted ....
Built-in hi fi ....
State room facilities for television viewing ....
Built in television ....

C. Entertainment facilities: motion pictures ( ); television ( ); radio ( ); billiards ( ); pool ( ); cards ( ); parties ( ); ping pong ( )

D. Art and treasures: antiques ( ); paintings ( ); tapestries ( ); books ( ); china ( ); stamp collection ( )

III. Types of Entertainment

	Number Monthly	Number of Guests	Time	Formal
Dinners	...	...	...	...
Clubs	...	...	...	...
Movies	...	...		...
Card parties	...	...	...	...
Television	...	...	...	...
Radio	...	...	...	...
Cocktail parties	...	...	...	...
Buffet suppers	...	...	...	...
Musicals	...	...	...	...
Luncheons	...	...	...	...
Dances	...	...	...	...
Teas	...	...	...	...
Garden parties	...	...	...	...
Children parties	...	...		...
Barbecues	...	...		...

IV. General Requirements

Living-room size ( ); ceiling height ( ).
Indoor and outdoor living space relationship ....
Dining room: separate ( ); combination ( ); size ( )
Outdoor living areas: enclosed porch ( ); screened porch ( ); terrace ( ); sun deck ( ); sun room ( ); greenhouse ( )
Library or den: size ( ); shelf space ( ); book shelves in living room ( ); fireplace ( )
Powder room: lavatory ( ); water closet ( ); mirror ( ); size ( )
Location ....

Door accessible from ....

Game room: size ( ); hobby shop ( ); work shop ( ); dining facilities ( )

Location ....

Style of house: one story ( ); two story ( ); split level ( ); basement ( )

Style of achitecture ....

Uses of basement: hobbies ( ); storage ( ); workshop ( ); heating plant ( ); fruit storage ( ); fuel storage ( ); car storage ( ); utility room ( ); laundry ( )

V. Car Storage Facilities

Carport ( ); separate garage ( ); attached garage ( ); basement garage ( ); heated ( ); number of cars ( ); screen storage ( ); storm window storage ( ); garden tool storage ( ); bicycles ( ); general storage ( ); trailer storage ( ); boat storage ( ); workbench ( )

Garage doors: overhead ( ); swinging ( ); folding ( ); sliding ( ); automatic control ( )

Entrance relative to main entrance of house ....

VI. Gardening Facilities

Tool storage: garage ( ); tool house ( ); garden house ( )

Storage for ....

....

Garden structures: pool ( ); fountain ( ); arbor ( ); terraces ( ); greenhouse ( ); hotbed ( )

Recreational areas: tennis ( ); badminton ( ); croquet ( ); basketball ( ); putting green ( )

VII. Care of Pets

Kennels ( ); enclosure ( ); runways ( )

Kinds of pets ....

VIII. Special Storage Provisions

Give space required and location:

Screens ....

Windows ....

Awnings ....

Luggage ....

Sewing equipment ....

Clothes drying equipment ....

Porch furniture ....

Lawn furniture ....

Winter sports equipment ....

Children's play equipment ....

Baby carriages, strollers, walkers, etc. .....

....

Garden tools ....

Boats, tents, etc. ....

Fishing equipment ....

Utility trailer ....

Game equipment ....

Food freezer ....

UNIT
IX

Selection of a Suitable Site

Two procedures may be followed in selecting a suitable site for your home: you may find your land before you begin designing your home or you may begin planning your home and then locate a lot to fit your needs. Either way the site and the building must be treated so that they end up in the closest possible harmony. This requires a considerable amount of time to make sure the plot is suited to your needs. Finding the right site for a house means much more than locating a piece of land at the price you can afford to pay. You must not only find a plot that has the necessary topographical requirements but it must also be located in a pleasant neighborhood with all the desired facilities. You will also want some guarantee that the land and house you build on it will not rapidly decline in value.

RESTRICTIONS

Building Codes. Most communities have various restrictive building codes designed to insure that each building will be a safe place in which to live, and eliminate the danger that a dishonest builder will use inferior materials which are unsuited for the job. The code may insist that foundations under certain soil conditions be set a certain distance below the surface (and frost level), to insure a good solid base. Some codes dictate the kind of materials as well as the quality of workmanship that goes into the house.

Before proceeding on any project, consult the local building authority or engineer as to the code requirements and strictly adhere to them since your construction will be open to inspection and approval at all times.

Zoning Regulations. Zoning has been adopted in communities to stabilize real estate values, to protect owners against drastic changes in the use of buildings and land, and to assure owners that development or occupancy of adjacent property will not be detrimental to their interests. However, the fact that the neighborhood is properly zoned does not afford definite assurance that the zoning regulations can and will be enforced, or that these regulations will not be changed. It is important to know what provisions are made for making changes in the zoning regulations. The restrictions upon the land and the type of building that can be erected will appear in the abstract and should be looked up before a purchase of the lot is made, so that restrictions will harmonize with the plans of the buyer. It is highly desirable that a lot purchased for home building purposes be in a restricted area where apartment buildings, two and three flat buildings, and business property are barred. Commercial and business properties can depreciate the value of holdings and make the location undesirable. Restrictions on adjacent property should also be considered. Property owners often look only into the restrictions on the land owned by the organization from which they purchased the property and learn to their later sorrow that adjacent property is not restricted by deed or zoning ordinance.

Deed Restrictions. Previous deeds issued for the property may restrict the type of construction, style of building, cost, location of the building, or other specific details.

Easements. An easement is the right or privilege to use the land without giving compensation. This may affect in some way your rights to build on the property you acquire.

Covenants. Covenants are agreements entered into by a group of property owners to accomplish certain restrictions to their common interest. The restrictions invoked by building codes, deeds, easements, and covenants can modify your plans, contribute to increased costs, and otherwise dictate requirements as to make a certain site undesirable for you to consider. They may also have the effect of improving the whole neighborhood.

NEIGHBORHOOD ENVIRONMENT

Community Characteristics. Communities have distinctive characteristics like people, where some are rich and others are poor, some are well groomed and others unkept. Decide whether the general character of the community will satisfy your needs and the needs of your family and will be conducive to your particular habits of living. Investigate the shopping areas as to distance, quality of products, and prices. Examine the condition of the school facilities and other civic properties and services. Determine whether the community is a safe place in which to live. Is there adequate fire and police protection? Is the traffic properly regulated? What is the general reputation for safety? The salability of property is increased by the nearness of churches of several denominations. Give attention to the transportation needs of each member of your family for business, school, church, and social activities. Determine, if possible, whether there is an efficient, fair, and honest administration on the local level, which determines the type and quality of service you get in return for your tax dollar. Theaters, movies, golf, tennis, swimming, baseball, gardening, and other individual forms of recreation tend to increase the property value by making it more attractive to those wanting the facilities. After reaching a decision on the community that appears to offer most possibilities for the satisfaction of your wants, you will next explore the various neighborhoods within the community. The selection of a neighborhood involves further investigation of a more personal nature. Is the general environment right for the needs and habits of your family?

Neighborhood Environment. In choosing a neighborhood environment, look for a high percentage of owner-occupied houses, for pride of ownership results in better care of building and grounds with a resulting safeguard against depreciated property values. Consider the people living in the community to determine whether you have common tastes and interests by visiting neighborhood schools, churches, and social centers. The houses should be similar in size and character, but should vary in exterior appearance. Houses should be gauged by the people's habits of living and fitted to the contour of the ground on which they are located. They should be adapted to the regional climate. Look for houses which are substantially constructed with materials which assure long life and low maintenance. Consider both the natural and man-made features of the community. Bodies of water may be desirable, but swamp land which might flood, or rivers that might overflow must be carefully investigated. Avoid the use of rocky or rubbish-filled land which is likely to add to the cost of building, and make it difficult to grow a lawn or garden. Learn something of the past and possible future expansion of the neighborhood. Try to determine any factors that may affect its future development. Will the trend be toward commercial invasion of the neighborhood by stores, garages, filling stations, restaurants, and so on? Will there be a trend toward industrial development of the neighborhood? Is a trend toward the expansion of adjoining neighborhoods likely to increase or decrease the value of the property. Nearby heavy industry to the windward direction will be an objectionable source of noise, smoke, dirt, and odors — both from the factories themselves and the railroads serving them. Light industry on the other hand may be an asset by providing work close to home and in pleasant surroundings. Generally where incompatible groups occupy the same neighborhood, those having the least interest in the maintenance of their property drive out the group whose interest it is to preserve the quality of the neighborhood.

IMPROVEMENTS

Residential Developments. Most building lots in the suburbs of cities and on the outskirts of towns are the result of running new streets through what was once farm land, and the dividing of such farms into small parcels of land. This is usually done by an enterprising builder or real estate developer, who maintains the development until it is taken over by the town or city. The layout, and any improvements which have been put in must be acceptable to the authorities. Paved roads, sidewalks, water, gas, sewers, electricity, etc., are known as improvements and it is important in buying a lot to investigate as to how many of these improvements are actually available; and, what is the program for their being made available; and, what guarantee there may be that they will be completed as planned. When these improvements are made the lot owner will have to pay a proportional share of their cost. The payment for improvements usually takes the form of special assessments against the property for a period of years.

Trees and Other Plantings. Trees whether along the border space between the sidewalk and curb or on the lot itself, enhance the value of the property and are reflected in the purchase price. In northern climates, if many large trees with thick foliage are too near the house they shade the house creating in some cases a damp and unhealthful condition, although in the extreme heat of the summer their shade will be appreciated. Roots of large trees rob the soil of the sustenance necessary for the growing of lawns and gardens, and will often find their way into sewers and drains. Cast iron pipes are to be used in these locations rather than clay tiles, adding to the cost of installation.

Street Lighting. Adequate lighting is a desirable adjunct to the property. Check whether the cost of the lighting installation is partially or fully paid. Lamps and stop signs may also be a nuisance if their location tends to disturb the property owner.

Fire Protection. Adequate fire protection means protection of life and property as well as reduced insurance premiums. Most established communities have a full-time fire department. Some rely on volunteers. In new developments and rural areas fire protection is not as complete as in cities and older communities.

Water Supply. Before buying any property, assure yourself that an adequate supply of safe water is available. If it is necessary to provide a well, investigate the possibilities of obtaining water, pumping equipment, and piping. The supply of water may be adequate during the spring rainy season, but the well or other source may go dry during a summer drought. Safe, drinkable water is as essential as an adequate supply. Conditions causing contamination of the water supply are dependent upon surface drainage and the subterranean formation of the locality. You should certainly investigate the cost of drilling a well in the vicinity before entering into any purchase agreement, if water is not already available. If city water service is available, is there a water main in the street in front of the property, or will the water main have to be extended? Furthermore, if a water main is in the street, has a service connection been made with a pipe leading to the lot? There may be a water main within reasonable distance, but the municipality may not have jurisdiction or authority to extend service beyond a certain boundary. The water supply should be furnished at adequate pressure at all times to reach the highest floor of the building. If the water pressure is too high, this can be easily corrected at nominal cost by the installation of a pressure-reducing valve. Water should be available in sufficient volume so that it can be used for all purposes, including sprinkling the lawn and washing the car. City water supplies are tested for safety and purity by the authorities. Chlorine or other chemicals are added to the water for health protection. Rural or private water supplies should be tested periodically to determine their purity. Water may be sufficiently pure but may be discolored, cloudy, odorous, or may contain dissolved chemicals which affect its taste. Hard water not only can make laundering or dishwashing difficult but it can lead to clogged pipes and extra plumbing expenses as well. Water softeners are an additional item of expense.

Sewer. Provision for drainage of sanitary wastes and also for the drainage of storm water must be made before the house can be occupied. Sewers that are used for the drainage of sanitary wastes from toilets and plumbing fixtures are known as *sanitary sewers*. Those used to drain away rain water, and melted snow and ice are known as *storm sewers*. It is essential to determine what facilities are available for both storm and sanitary drainage at the time of the selection of the site. For sites located where municipal sewers are not available it is necessary to provide a private disposal system. Sanitary wastes are usually drained to a septic tank that has a suitable overflow to a drainage system of tile piping or to a cesspool. Storm water is drained to a dry well, a leaching pit, or a cistern, or is discharged on the surface at some distance from the house, provided it will not interfere with the property of another owner. The depth at which the sewer is located to the lot is important. If the lot is lower than the street, the sewer may be too high to permit drainage into the sewer except by expensive pump installation. Toilets and other plumbing fixtures including floor drains in the basement are not feasible without the pumping of drainage unless the sewer is lower than the basement floor. Consequently, the level at which floors are placed often determines the entire planning arrangement of the house. Sewers should be directly accessible from the lot without crossing property owned by others to make a connection.

A main sewer under the house or through a basement should be avoided, and yet the main sewer must be near enough to permit branch connections. Sewers are not always adequate in size to carry off drainage as rapidly as is necessary for the proper operation of plumbing fixtures, floor drains, and roof drains. Investigate the capacity of the sewers by making inquiry as to whether storm water and sanitary drainage are carried off satisfactorily at all times from existing houses served by the sewer. The periodic flooding of streets caused from inadequate storm sewers should be investigated. A reversal in the flow of water of a house sewer, sometimes the result of an overloaded main sewer, can cause the sewer to flow backward into the house through the floor drains or toilet fixtures and into the basement, or if the sewer is not much lower than the first floor into the first floor. Backwater valves can be installed to avoid this reversal, but it is preferable to select a site where the possibility does not exist. The city engineer's office can tell you about the size and capacity of the sewer which serves the site you have under consideration.

Electricity. Determine whether electricity is readily available. If an extension of the electrical service to the site is necessary, is there a charge to the owner and how much should it cost? If electricity is available, is the service adequate? Overloaded electric lines mean unsatisfactory service. Find out the rates charged for the service. If an electric stove or other heavy electric appliances are desired, 220 volt current should be accessible.

Gas. What will be the cost of piping the service to the house and the rates charged for the monthly service?

Telephone Service. Check whether telephone service is readily available. If an extension of the line to the house is required, what is the charge? Check what types of service are available and the rates.

Garbage Removal. Is garbage collected at regular intervals? Is this service included by the city or is there an assessment? Are the garbage cans collected at the front or rear of the property? Unsightly garbage cans emptied at irregular intervals are not contributions to the best appearance of the neighborhood.

Ash and Trash Removal. Determine what provisions are made for regular removal and inquire as to the cost of the service.

Mail Service. Do not overlook the type of mail service available at the site.

Transportation. A most important item concerns transportation for the whole family. Ask yourself how you will get to work, or to your business, in the morning and back again at night; how far it is; how long will it take. See if there are any alternative means of arriving there if your car should break down, and also what the transportation will cost. The streets in a neighborhood should be safe, convenient, and well surfaced. They should be free from through traffic, but accessible to the main arteries. Street layouts should be attractively landscaped to take advantage of all the natural features such as hills and valleys, wooded areas, and waterways. Streets fitted to an irregular terrain can provide easier grades, thereby saving on construction costs. Curves and grades must be designed to offer desirable lot sizes and shapes. Court or "dead end" streets are sometimes used to control traffic and help subdivide properties. Such streets should provide room for firetrucks or moving vans to turn around at the closed ends. Narrower streets with gradual curves will discourage through or speeding traffic and will add interest to the usual street design. Streets should cross at right angles for better vision and safety. Blocks should be carefully planned for shape and size. Long blocks result in fewer intersections and reduce accident hazards. They also lessen paving, sidewalk, and utility costs by eliminating cross streets. They also make it possible to place houses nearer to the edges, leaving broad inside spaces devoted to play and recreation. Back alleys for utilities should be avoided. An easement is usually provided in the deed which gives permission for pipes and wires to cross your property within these defined limits.

Neighborhood Facilities. Good neighborhoods include schools, churches, parks, recreational areas, and good shopping centers within easy transportation from home. Grade schools are the natural center of a neighborhood and should be designed to serve their purpose. A good school will provide facilities for adult education and activities as well as a curriculum for children. Landscaped park areas should offer what individual homes lack in space for games and recreation. A neighborhood center should include a library, nursery school, and a meeting place for teenage groups. The shopping center should be designed to fit the surroundings and with protection against the destruction of property values. Adequate parking areas are most desirable. Active public health services and nearby hospital facilities, along with adequate fire and police protection are most important factors of consideration.

TOPOGRAPHY OF THE INDIVIDUAL SITE

Surface Conditions. The topography of the site refers to its various surface characteristics such as a slope, direction of the slope, steepness of the slope, knolls, gullies, ravines, swamps, streams, rocks and roads. Each of these has a bearing on the cost and arrangement of the completed house. A flat or nearly level site involves the least cost in its development, though it does not produce as interesting a setting as a sloping site. It is always good practice to have the grade slightly higher at the building so that drainage water will flow away from the building. A site that slopes gently upward from the street is considered most desirable by most homeowners since it places the house at a higher level than the sewers which usually are located in the street. Sites located in drainage pockets are not recommended unless some provision can be made to intercept the natural drainage. Sites having steep rather than gentle slopes require greater expense in developmnt and require retaining walls, steps, and terraces. Determine whether or not the existing grades are the established grades set by the authority of the city engineer. If there are streams located on or near the site, you should find out the highest level the stream has ever reached, and whether there is ever danger of its flooding. A site may be on a hilltop with an excellent view of the city or surrounding countryside and furnish desirable summer breezes. However, consideration should be given to the exposure of the site to harsh penetrating winds during the winter months. Steep grades often cause difficulties in icy weather. The valley site may also be subject to the difficulty of encountering slippery roads during the winter months, may give only a limited outlook, get a concentration of drainage water, but it will be protected from the winter exposures. In considering the characteristics of the site you should determine whether the surface is the natural one or whether it has been changed by excavating or filling. A building site that represents the natural surface is generally the more desirable. Remember that it costs considerably more to excavate rock than ordinary soil. Good trees are an asset to the site if they can be utilized in the final plans for the project.

Soil Conditions. You can tell a good deal about soil conditions just by close observation. For example, many large trees are a good sign that soil is natural. Outcroppings of rock are a warning that perhaps the entire site is very rocky. Soft spots on the ground, depressions, and wet spots after a rain are all indications that the fill may not be solid, and therefore not suitable for building. Nevertheless, the safest method to determine the subsurface conditions is to dig a test hole. If it is a filled site, the character of the fill is important. It may be well compacted soil or it may be ashes, tin cans, trash, or garbage. The only satisfactory way to build on filled

ground is to sink the foundations far enough down that they rest on a solid base of ground, clay, or rock. Do not make the mistake of purchasing a plot of ground on the basis of one visit. The soil at the level desired for the foundation may be one of several different types. Silt, or finely divided sedimentary soil, has questionable value for the support of a house without resulting in excessive settling, especially if there is much water in the soil. Sand, especially coarse sand is generally a desirable foundation material. Sand with excess water is quicksand, and that involves unjustified expense. Sand that is damp, well compacted, and confined laterally is found most satisfactory. Clay is the soil most generally encountered and is satisfactory for the support of small buildings. The water content affects its properties. Gravel is one of the most satisfactory materials upon which to support a building. It is not difficult to excavate, though it offers no resistance to the flow of ground water into the basement. Rock is capable of supporting a skyscraper, but is costly to excavate and has a tendency to retain ground water unless a drainage system is provided.

Ground Water. Ground water follows the path of least resistance. A basement offers a location of reduced resistance into which the water will flow. Ground water may ooze from the surface in the form of a spring; it may be only a few feet below the surface of the ground, or it may be at a depth of several feet. If ground water is near the surface, the excavation for a basement may result in the equivalent of a large well. Basement floors that are at least three feet above the highest level of ground water are generally considered safe without the installation of waterproofing. In the event that the building is on a sloping site, it is sometimes possible to install a gravity drainage system with tile drains which prevent water from entering the basement. To prevent this on a level site it may be necessary to pump the water from the underfloor drainage system. Basements can be waterproofed, but a satisfactory waterproofing job is more expensive that the average home warrants. If you can find a site to your liking that is not subject to critical ground water conditions, it is to be recommended. If the ground water level is too high on the site you have purchased and upon which you wish to build, it is preferable to design the house without a basement, or so that the basement floor will be at least 3 ft. above the highest level of ground water.

ORIENTATION OF THE SITE

Facing the House. The direction the house is to face must be considered carefully in relationship to the plan arrangement. When facing the rising sun in the east, the front porch will be shady in the afternoon. Facing the setting sun in the west results in a cool and shady back yard in the early evening. A south exposure assures more pleasant rooms in the cool months, while facing north has its advantages for the summer. A healthful site should be so located that sunlight reaches rooms each clear day. The view of the site is also an important consideration. In the city the view from the living rooms, porches, and the kitchen should be pleasing.

Prevailing Winds. The direction of the prevailing winds is very important, especially where the northwest winds in winter cause difficulty in heating the house. In locating the rooms the prevailing winds in hot weather are to be considered so that sleeping porches, bedrooms, and living rooms can be placed to receive the cooling breezes. The exposure of a house is a most disputed question. The living room and dining room are often placed on the southwest or southeast corners, and the sleeping porches away from the west side of the house. The south or east exposure for a house is usually considered best.

SIZE OF THE PLOT

It is well that the owner study his lot from the standpoint of size, exposure, and whether the home he has planned will look well on the lot he is considering to purchase. He should make certain that the size and shape of the lot in the deed of sale accurately check with the information filed in the plat in the recorder's office at the county seat. It also should be determined whether an inside lot or a corner lot is wanted with the advantage of more light and air. A corner lot costs more in original price and upkeep but a house appears to advantage. In the plans of the more modern residence developments the sections are laid out in irregularly shaped lots to give a more natural appearance.

BUYING THE PLOT

Agreement to Buy. After you are sure beyond all reasonable doubt that the site you have decided upon has fulfilled your various requirements, you are now ready to enter into an agreement for the purchase of the site. The agreement should be in writing and include what you get in return for your money. The agreement should include: (1) a description and survey of the property, (2) the purchase price, (3) methods of making other payments, (4) interest to be charged on unpaid balance, and (5) the disposition of any remaining debt or charges filed against the property. The agreement should further specify who is responsible for the payment of any expenses involved in the transfer of title. The agreement should be made conditional upon the seller's furnishing a satisfactory title and deed to the property, with provision for the return of the down payment in case the sale is not completed. It is customary to require that the seller furnish the buyer an abstract, which is a record of title of ownership of the land.

Title Search. The search should reveal any legal claims against the property in the form of mortgages, judgments, liens, taxes, assessments, rights of heirs of previous owners, and so on. The title to the property should be examined by a qualified attorney or other qualified agency performing this service.

Title Guarantee. It is possible to have a title guaranteed by insurance. If the cost of the title search to satisfy the guarantee insurance company is not too expensive to warrant the charge against the property, a guaranteed title is highly recommended. Any prudent loaning agency such as a bank will not loan money to you with your house and property as security unless the title has been searched and found satisfactory, without legal claims against the property.

Land Survey. The land should be surveyed by an engineer and the corners of the plot marked with some kind of permanent marker. This survey is a plan of the piece of land showing its exact dimensions and levels, the position of any especially good trees, the lot boundaries with relation to adjacent streets and lanes, the location and levels of existing sewers and water mains, electric service, gas service, and so on. See Figure 148, p. 426.

Location Plan. This plan is similar to the survey plan except that whereas the survey plan shows the lot as it is before the building work is started, the location plan (compare with Fig. 149, p. 427) shows the lot as it will be after the building is finished, together with any landscape work, such as walks and drives. The building plan is drawn in outline only, without any indication of interior partitions or arrangement of rooms, its purpose being to show the proposed location of the house on the lot. The distances of the sides and corners of the building to the boundary lines of the property are given so as to make it easy for the authorities having the legal right to check and approve the location, and to give the building contractor the exact information as to where to make the excavation.

Landscape Plans. This plan is developed into a much more elaborate affair which indicates not only the boundary lines of the lot

and the position of the house and garage on it, but also the proposed arrangement of trees, shrubbery, flower beds, lawns, drying yard, and garden areas. For the average home such planting plans are often made by the nursery specialist and submitted with his price for the general landscaping. See Figure 150, p. 428.

The Deed. A deed is a legal document which expresses the intention of the seller and the buyer as to the quantity and quality of the ownership that is passed between them. To be valid, a deed should meet the following requirements:

1. It should be properly prepared in writing.

2. It should be executed between the proper parties.

3. It should fully describe the property to be conveyed.

4. There should be consideration for the buyer and seller.

5. There should be a proper and sufficient execution of the document; which means that it must be signed, sealed, attested, and acknowledged.

6. There should be a delivery and acceptance. Land in its legal significance includes not only the soil but everything that is firmly attached to the land, such as buildings, fences, trees, and all other rights and easements unless the contrary is expressly written in the deed.

Warranty Deed. A warranty deed is the preferred form of deed for the buyer. The seller promises by issuing a warranty deed to guarantee and defend the title which he passes to the buyer. The usual guarantees of the warranty deed are: (1) the seller warrants that he actually owns the land, (2) there are no encumbrances, unsatisfied mortgages, easements, liens, or other claims against it, (3) the seller and his heirs will defend the title against all legal claims made by other persons, and (4) the seller warrants quiet enjoyment of the property.

Quitclaim Deed. A quitclaim deed merely

says that the seller steps out of the picture and the buyer takes the seller's rights for whatever they are worth.

Title to land may be acquired by foreclosure proceedings. The sale is conducted by public auction by the sheriff or proper authority. A purchaser, before taking title, should make the usual title search not only to determine whether the mortgage was a valid lien, but also to determine whether all proceedings have been legally taken. The title is not perfected until the buyer has it recorded with the register of deeds for the county in which the land is located.

The object of bringing these matters to the attention of the buyer is to explain correct procedures in obtaining proper and rightful protection in the transaction. Naturally you should consult some qualified, trustworthy person experienced in the more detailed aspects of the problem. For advice on site selection and building, there are available the architect and the engineer, the real estate broker, the lawyer, the banker, the builders, and the building material dealers, all of whom may be most helpful to you. Many features of these problems are peculiar to the community in which you plan to locate. Some of the consultant advice you need will be gladly furnished without charge, and as a service to you. For other professional services you may have to pay a fee, but when you consider what you save through acting on competent advice, the fee is certainly money well spent.

UNIT

X

Financial Considerations in Selecting a Home

DECIDING WHETHER TO RENT OR BUY A HOME

Man's desire to own his home has increased since feudalism's grasp on all landed property was broken in the middle ages of history. Through financial progress and improvement in legal procedures, great strides have been made in the direction of small home ownership. A fine inspirational and educational job has been made possible by the building industry, by the financial institutions, and by all related interests in pointing out the advantages of home ownership as usually given:

1. *Financial independence:* Many people have learned to save through the accumulation of an equity in their home.

2. *Security:* A home represents savings that can be drawn upon in time of need.

3. *Cash equity:* A home is similar to a savings account from which interest is paid upon the accumulated principal.

4. *Credit:* Having a home gives financial and credit rating in the business world because a house and land are recognized as fundamental principles of stability.

5. *Social background:* It is a distinct advantage to have neighbors and friends whose friendships last over a period of years.

6. *Environment for children:* Social and recreational privileges on land owned by the family and in which children have a personal interest are usually greater than in rented property.

7. *Development of responsibility:* Meeting tax payments, making financial payments, and taking care of repairs, and so on develop business judgment and skill.

8. *Expression of individuality:* Opportunity for individual expressions both in the exterior and interior give property that appearance of personality.

9. *Pride of possession:* Improvements and additions may be made giving the family greater freedom to live as it wishes, without interference from a landlord.

10. *Attitude of co-operation:* Usually inspires family co-operation in doing work around the home and in the yard.

11. *Character development:* Ownership inspires respect for property of others, a desire for betterment, habits of thrift, and so on.

12. *Spirit of independence:* No one can raise the rent, order the family to move, limit the acquisition of household pets, restrict the size of family, or comment in any way upon the development of the home.

13. *Aesthetic growth:* Better furnishings can be purchased when a home is owned since they fit into a decorative plan that will last for a period of years, rather than having to be changed frequently as the family moves from one rented house to another.

The definition of a satisfactory home is one that will not absorb too much of the family income in interest or running expenses and yet meet the family's standard of living. It is a mistake to buy a lot and contract for the building of a house beyond the ability to pay, for this may result in the loss of the home through foreclosure of the mortgage, or otherwise result in a long and discouraging struggle. On the other hand, the determination to invest in the very best quality of house which can be obtained is an incentive to economy and saving.

Naturally there are some disadvantages inherent in home ownership which may be given briefly as follows:

1. *Cost of home ownership:* It usually costs

more to own than to rent, if all costs of home ownership are accurately computed.

2. *Sacrifice of family:* The struggle to meet costs of home ownership may deprive certain members of the family of opportunities of higher education or other satisfying developments.

3. *Loss of maneuverability:* Ownership ties a family to a given location, since property often cannot be sold without a sacrifice.

4. *Burden of responsibility:* Unless the family enjoys the cares and responsibilities of home ownership, these may prove to be arduous.

5. *Loss in investment:* Property values may decline and investment in a house decrease accordingly.

6. *Encumbrance of ownership:* In case of economic stress and reduced income the family may find itself encumbered with ownership costs out of reason to its income.

For one reason or another many families find that the advantages of ownership of a home far outweigh the advantages of renting. The present and future income and probable savings of the family, however, must be carefully considered before a definite decision can be made. If the family can count on the present income over a period of years, and if the yearly costs of home ownership are only slightly more than the amount the family is paying for rent, it is reasonable to assume that they will be able to carry the financial responsibilities.

TO BUY OR TO BUILD?

The family that decides to assume home ownership has the choice between buying a used or a new house, or buying a lot and building a house.

Buying a Used Home. A used house may be bought from the owner or from a real estate firm. As a general rule the cost of such a house is less than that of a new house of the same size, or the cost of buying a lot and building a house. Before a house is pur-

chased, the advice of an architect or competent disinterested builder should be obtained on any points of construction that are difficult to judge. The prospective owner should take time to check such important items as to location, neighborhood, age of house, style of architecture, adequacy of living quarters, structural conditions, plumbing, wiring, heating, landscape of grounds, and condition of finishes.

The advantages of buying a ready-built house as compared to building one may be summarized as follows:

1. *Economy of purchase:* Generally speaking it is usually cheaper to buy an existing house than to build one, since it has decreased some in value due to deterioration. The family can move into a ready-built house without incurring additional expense for such items as landscaping, porches, weatherstripping, storm doors, and so on, which the person who builds must pay for in addition to the building cost. The used house may also have extra features and conveniences built in which might not add materially to the purchase price. The street, water, and sewer assessments may have been paid on the occupied house, and the purchase price may not be higher because of it.

2. *Purchase price is a fixed amount:* After having reached an agreement on the purchase price of a used house, the buyer knows exactly what the house will cost. The person who builds on the other hand is not certain of the final cost. Changes in the cost of materials, or the necessity of substituting for different materials may increase the estimate by an appreciable amount. The owner may also change his mind and add certain desired features, which also increase the cost. After the house is completed the owner usually finds it necessary to spend additional money on items not included in the contract.

3. *Construction faults:* A house may be constructed with green lumber, or with cheap materials, inadequate foundations, or improper drainage and some of these faults

may not show up from one to ten years after the house is completed. The presence or absence of such faults can be detected in an older house.

4. *Established neighborhood:* New houses are often built in new subdivisions where you cannot be sure of the types of neighbors. When buying a house already built, it is possible to select a desired neighborhood. The resale value of a house is also influenced by the nature of the neighborhood.

5. *Immediate occupancy:* Where immediate occupancy is essential, usually buying rather than building is the solution. The person who decides to build may have to wait some time before the house is completed. Shortages in materials or strikes may slow up construction.

A summary of the disadvantages of buying a used house as compared to building a new one follows:

1. *Lack of broad choice of location:* Naturally, the person who buys must locate where the houses are for sale. It is, of course, true also that the person who builds has a choice only to the extent of the lots available.

2. *Must accept existing design:* The buyer must accept what is for sale, even though he is not completely satisfied with the design or plan of the house. Remodeling may in part overcome some of these objections.

3. *Quality of construction not easily detected:* If the house has been built to sell by some contractor or builder, it may prove to be cheaply constructed. If the house is relatively new, it may be difficult if not impossible for the prospective buyer to determine the quality of the labor or materials which went into the construction.

4. *May not be modern:* The absence of modern improvements generally results in the price of the house being lower than if it was modern throughout. Modernization may be accomplished in the future as the money becomes available.

5. *Repairs may be needed:* The prospective buyers should have the house looked over by a competent person to determine whether extensive repairs are needed immediately or will be needed in the immediate future. Things to include in the investigation are the roof, gutters and downspouts, floors, foundations, sills, porches, furnace, driveway, and drainage. The possibility of termites should not be overlooked.

Buying a New House. A new house just completed may be bought from the owner, a building company, real estate developer, or a building contractor. When the right house can be found, this is an excellent way for those inexperienced in building to buy a new house. The materials and workmanship of the house should be carefully checked with the builders, and if there is any question the advice of an expert should be sought. When the purchase is financed through a building and loan association or through a member agent of the FHA, this advice may be obtained from one of their experts.

A new house under construction can frequently be bought from a contractor or building concern. This method gives the family an opportunity to make some of the final decisions without assuming the entire responsibility from the beginning. It must be remembered however that when changes or additions made by the family exceed the estimated price, these extra costs must be added in order to obtain the total cost of the house.

In urban residential areas which are being improved by a real estate developer, one may buy a lot and select a model house to be copied in building. Certain changes may be specified to meet the families particular needs. More and more homes are being built by large-scale operative builders who undertake a whole neighborhood at once. Under these conditions the streets and houses can be built as a unit.

Building a House to Specifications. If a family has a house built to its needs it should be able to get one meeting its specifications; but it is common for persons not used to reading blueprints to get quite a surprise to see the actual house which was built from them. As they see the house going up, it is not unusual for them to discover things that ought to be changed to make them what they were expected to be. To meet these extra costs, much more expense can be involved than can be comfortably financed. In a great many cases it is wise to secure the services of a competent architect who may charge approximately 6 per cent of the cost of construction to draw the plans that will fit the family's needs and wants, and see that the contractor is building according to specification.

Building your own house is usually a long, costly, and often unsatisfactory process; and if your funds are limited and your patience short, it is not a recommended procedure for all families.

Enough time should be taken to consider thoroughly all that is involved in buying a lot and building a home, since there are many perplexing problems to be solved before an estimate of the entire cost can be made.

WHAT CAN YOU AFFORD TO INVEST?

An inventory of the owner's net worth and annual income definitely determines how much he can safely invest in the building of a house, and how much he can safely borrow if his cash is not adequate. A basis that is often suggested by good authorities is the percentage of present income being put into rent. Some counsel prospective home owners not to exceed twice the yearly income, while others will place a base at three times the yearly income. Other advisors suggest one's budget for living should afford as cost of shelter one fifth of the monthly income, and others say one fourth. A rough estimate may be had by multiplying the monthly rent by a maximum of 150.

Before a family decides to buy or build a home, the costs involved should be fully understood. No matter which method the family chooses, the costs of home ownership include more than the cost of the house and lot. Under present purchasing procedures a home owner would have to meet the following expenses when due:

1. Preliminary Costs. These costs arise as soon as the buyer closes the deal. Some of these must be paid by the buyer; others are met by the seller. Some are covered by the loan; others are not.

When buying a home, preliminary costs usually include:

a. Appraisal fees.
b. Loan fees of loaning agency.
c. Revenue stamps and notary fees.
d. Fees for recording the mortgage and the deed to the property.
e. Legal fees for examining and transferring the title to the property.
f. Pro rata insurance and property taxes.
g. Engineer's survey of property, if needed to establish property lines.

When a house is purchased, the appraisal fees and commission of the lending group, stamps and notary fees, recording and filing fees, and insurance costs are usually paid by the buyer.

When building a home, preliminary costs include most of those for buying a house, plus such costs as:

a. Costs of plans of architectural services.
b. Interest on the loan advances to contractors.
c. Premiums for insurance — fire, theft, hazard, and liability.
d. Inspection fees.

In FHA loans there are certain additional preliminary expenses such as: (1) the first year's mortgage insurance premium; (2) an advance payment for first year's taxes; (3) the first year's premium on hazard insurance; (4) fees for photographs of the house; and, (5) FHA loan examination fee. The examination fee is paid when application for the loan is made; the other items must be paid when the loan is closed.

2. Extra Costs. Sometimes necessary costs must be met by the home builder (if not provided for in the loan), such as kitchen and laundry equipment and essential furnishings, or repair or modernization if an existing house has been purchased.

3. Loan and Interest. It is unfortunate that the average family buying a home has had so little contact with and understanding of mortgages. Loaning agency officers have had long and varied experience with these documents, and much can be learned from them. The prospective home owner should carefully seek out one who can guide him to a satisfactory decision. Lending agencies want, above everything else, to get back with interest and with as little bother as possible, the sum lent. There is, therefore, every reason for them to advise a prospective borrower to sign a mortgage whose terms he should be able to meet with no great difficulty, unless he loses his health or his job — contingencies which no one can foresee.

Down payment. The size of the mortgage loan is of great importance, since the bigger it is, the larger the interest charges must be. But it is foolish to make such a large down payment that there is little or nothing left in the bank with which to meet emergencies. Temporary unemployment, sickness, need to replace a leaking roof, sudden breakdown of the heating system, and other possibilities too numerous to mention may make it very desirable to have a reserve of a few hundred dollars in the bank. If the bank payments are not met on time, the loan becomes defaulted; after a limited number of defaults the lending institution, under the terms of the mortgage contract, has the right to begin legal proceedings (foreclosure) to sell the property and apply the proceeds from the sale to the debt. Unless one has the necessary funds to keep up the mortgage payments regularly, he may be well on the road to losing his home. If a reasonable down payment cannot be made without leaving the family stripped of adequate reserves for the

unexpected, it is doubtless better to defer acquiring a home until more money has been accumulated.

Size of mortgage loan. If a buyer can pay only an exceedingly small down payment, it may be necessary for him to get two loans against the house. The lender under the first mortgage may lend him only 60 or 70 per cent of the purchase price, and the balance might be obtained by placing a second mortgage against the property. Since the risk of the loan under the second mortgage is greater, the rate of interest charged would be much higher than for the first mortgage.

How much a financial institution will lend on the security of a certain piece of real estate will depend on the institution's opinion of the ability and desire of the borrower to repay the loan, the law of the state where the institution is chartered (or federal law, if it is a federally chartered institution), and the policies of the lending institution. He is required to fill out a mortgage loan application giving all the essential information about the property and about himself. Today it is also customary for the lender to obtain a credit report concerning the borrower; this furnishes facts enabling the lender to determine the capacity and willingness of the borrower to repay the loan. The borrower's earning capacity (his job) can tell a lot about his ability to make payments of a certain size month after month. His record as to keeping his job, paying his bills, going into bankruptcy, being sued, and so on throws light on his willingness to meet his obligations. From a study of the credit report, the lending institution can judge whether it is reasonably safe to lend a larger amount, a smaller amount, or nothing. The property serves as security for the loan (the borrower's promissory note).

Maturity of the loan. The longer the period for which the loan is written, the smaller the monthly payments must be to pay it off, other things being equal. Although longer mortgages require smaller monthly payments, they cost the borrower more in interest than those running for a shorter term.

Mortgage interest rates.   When the borrower obtains a loan from some lending agency, he obligates himself to pay interest on the loan, as well as to repay the principal. It is naturally to the advantage of the borrower to secure the loan from a source which offers the lowest rate of interest. If interest rates should decline after a loan has been obtained, the borrower should try to persuade the lending agency to lower the rate for the remaining period of the loan. If a prepayment agreement has been included in the contract, a threat to pay off the loan might persuade the officials to meet this demand. If this threat is not successful a loan might be obtained from some other source, at a lower rate, and the proceeds used to pay off the old loan.

Sometimes a lower interest rate is accompanied by objectionable features to be found only by a careful reading of small print in the mortgage agreement. One provision of this sort sometimes encountered is that the borrower may not pay off the loan in its entirety before five years have elapsed, or that the loan may be paid off completely during the first ten years of its life only if a penalty of a year's interest is paid during the first five years and a penalty of half a year's interest is paid during the last five years. Sometimes a borrower prefers to pay a higher rate to a local lender than obtain a lower rate from a lender whose place of business is at a distance.

Method of paying off the loan.   Mortgages are mainly of two types, known as a "straight mortgage" and an "amortized mortgage." These can be defined, but they cannot be compared except as they meet the needs of one individual. While the characteristics of one type may be a perfect solution to the financial problem of one family, the same mortgage might be inadvisable for another. The type of mortgage that you select should be the one which best fits your own financial situation.

(a) *Straight mortgage.*   In the past, many loans made for the acquisition of a home ran for a definite number of years, at the end of which period the entire principal amount became due. At the end of the term it really became a demand instrument, full payment of which could be demanded immediately. It is customary practice for the lending agency to renew or extend the mortgage for a period of years if desired. The mortgage may be renewed for the full amount, but more often a partial payment of the principal is required. When considering the renewal of the mortgage it is important to recognize two factors: (1) the lending agency is under no obligation to renew the mortgage at the same rate of interest; and, (2) the lending agency is not obligated to renew it at all. Business conditions may force the agency to demand full payment. If this happens and you do not have the money, and if the real estate market is so poor that no other lending agency will make the loan on your property, then ownership of the home is in jeopardy. The borrower would have to refund the loan (get a second loan to pay off the first) or run the danger of having his mortgage foreclosed (property sold to secure whatever money it would sell for, to apply on the note). In the event of foreclosure, if the note were not satisfied fully by the sale of the property, there is a good chance that the borrower could be held for a deficiency judgment, since he had not made good on his promise as evidenced in the note. It is good practice when giving a straight mortgage to reserve the right to make a payment on the principal at any interest-bearing period, which is usually every six months. You may not wish to use this privilege, but it is in your best interest to reserve the right nevertheless. To do so gives you greater financial flexibility to meet any unforeseen problems.

(b) *Amortized mortgage.*   An amortized mortgage is one wherein the value of the principal is reduced by regular payments, usually monthly, quarterly, or semi-annually. In addition to the payments repaying the principal, regular interest payments are also made. When the amortized plan is used by banks and insurance companies, the principal is usually reduced monthly.

(c) *State savings and loan share plan.* In this plan the amount of the monthly payment which is in excess of the interest due is not credited directly against the principal, but is credited to a share account in the name of the borrower. If the institution is earning profits, the directors will declare dividends on the share accounts, usually semi-annually. When the amount paid into the share account, plus the dividends credited to the account equals the principal amount of the loan, then the share account is used to pay off the entire loan. The amount of the loan remains at the original figure despite the fact that monthly payments in excess of the interest due are being made over a period of years. It amounts to borrowing in one place, saving in the same place, and finally using the savings to pay off the borrowing. Usually a higher rate of interest is charged on the loan than is earned on the savings. There is another disadvantage to this type of loan for if the lending institution should fail, the borrower would still owe the company the full amount of the loan, but the percentage on the dollar which he as a shareholder gets back from his account depends upon the amount which the institution can realize from the liquidation of its assets.

(d) *Fixed monthly payment plan.* Under this method the borrower pays a fixed amount at regular intervals, usually monthly. Part of this amount goes to pay the interest due, but the balance of the payment is credited as payment on the principal of the loan. The earlier monthly installments include primarily interest and only small amounts of principal repayment. As the principal is gradually reduced, a larger and larger percentage of the monthly payment is applied to repayment of principal, until the loan is entirely repaid. Since the amount of the monthly payment is fixed, this means that a larger part of it is applied on the principal as time goes on and the borrower knows exactly how long it will take him to pay off the loan. This method is cheaper for the borrower because the part of the monthly payment which is applied against the principal reduces the base on which the rate of interest is computed. It is advisable to reserve the privilege to make payments larger than the fixed amount, these payments usually permitted at specified periods and usually limited to sums in round numbers, such as $100.

Starting with the payment as shown herewith, an amortization schedule can be constructed showing the allocation of each payment into interest and principal; also the balance outstanding after each payment has been made. Proceed by: (1) computing the interest on the previous balance; (2) deducting this from the payment; and, (3) crediting the remainder as a repayment of principal:

AMORTIZATION OF A $3,300 LOAN AT 6% FOR 5 YEARS, BY MONTHLY PAYMENTS OF $63.80

Month	Interest	Principal	Balance
First Year			
1	$16.50	$47.30	$3,252.70
2	16.26	47.54	3,205.16
3	16.03	47.77	3,157.39
4	15.79	48.01	3,109.38
5	15.55	48.25	3,061.13
6	15.31	48.49	3,012.64
7	15.06	48.74	2,963.90
8	14.82	48.98	2,914.92
9	14.57	49.23	2,865.69
10	$14.33	$49.47	$2,816.22
11	14.08	49.72	2,766.50
12	13.83	49.97	2,716.53
Second Year			
13	13.58	50.22	2,666.31
14	13.33	50.47	2,615.84
15	13.08	50.72	2,565.12
16	12.83	50.97	2,514.15
17	12.57	51.23	2,462.92
18	12.31	51.49	2,411.43
19	12.06	51.74	2,359.69
20	11.80	52.00	2,307.69
21	11.54	52.26	2,255.43
22	11.28	52.52	2,202.91

Month	Interest	Principal	Balance	Month	Interest	Principal	Balance
23	$11.01	$52.79	$2,150.12	42	$5.77	$58.03	$1,095.53
24	10.75	53.05	2,097.07	43	5.48	58.32	1,037.21
Third Year				44	5.19	58.61	978.60
25	10.49	53.31	2,043.76	45	4.89	58.91	919.69
26	10.22	53.58	1,990.18	46	4.60	59.20	860.49
27	9.95	53.85	1,936.33	47	4.30	59.50	800.99
28	9.68	54.12	1,882.21	48	4.00	59.80	741.19
29	9.41	54.39	1,827.82	Fifth Year			
30	9.14	54.66	1,773.16	49	3.71	60.09	681.10
31	8.87	54.93	1,718.23	50	3.41	60.39	620.71
32	8.59	55.21	1,663.02	51	3.10	60.70	560.01
33	8.32	55.48	1,607.54	52	2.80	61.00	499.01
34	8.04	55.76	1,551.78	53	2.50	61.30	437.71
35	7.76	56.04	1,495.74	54	2.19	61.61	376.10
36	7.48	56.32	1,439.42	55	1.88	61.92	314.18
Fourth Year				56	1.57	62.23	251.95
37	7.20	56.60	1,382.82	57	1.26	62.54	189.41
38	6.91	56.89	1,325.93	58	.95	62.85	126.56
39	6.63	57.17	1,268.76	59	.63	63.17	63.39
40	6.34	57.46	1,211.30	60	.32	63.39	0.00
41	6.06	57.74	1,153.56	Final Payment $63.71			

The table below shows the monthly payments necessary to pay off a $1,000 monthly amortized loan in from 5 to 25 years, with interest rates of from 4 to 6 per cent.

The table at the bottom of this page shows the major home expenditures after the down payment and preliminary costs are paid. The payments on the loan and the interest charges are fixed according to the interest rate and the period of payment. They are based upon a systematic loan reduction plan. For the purpose of the chart, the expenses per year for every $1,000 loaned on the house are assumed to be $18 for taxes and assessments, $3 for insurance, and $20 for upkeep. Insurance costs will probably be the same over

MONTHLY PAYMENTS TO AMORTIZE A $1,000 LOAN IN 5 TO 25 YEARS, WITH INTEREST AT FROM 4% TO 6% PER YEAR

Interest Rates

Term of Loan	At 4% Interest Monthly Payment	Total Int'st	At 4½% Interest Monthly Payment	Total Int'st	At 5% Interest Monthly Payment	Total Int'st	At 5½% Interest Monthly Payment	Total Int'st	At 6% Interest Monthly Payment	Total Int'st
5 yr.	$18.42	$105.20	$18.53	$111.80	$18.88	$132.80	$19.11	$146.60	$19.34	$160.40
10 yr.	10.13	215.60	10.25	230.00	10.61	273.20	10.86	303.20	11.11	333.20
15 yr.	7.40	330.20	7.53	355.40	7.91	423.80	8.18	472.40	8.44	519.20
20 yr.	6.06	440.00	6.20	488.00	6.60	581.00	6.88	651.20	7.17	720.80
25 yr.	5.28	584.00	5.42	626.00	5.85	752.00	6.15	845.00	6.45	935.00

ANNUAL COSTS OF HOME OWNERSHIP PER $1,000

Interest Rate	4% Interest			5% Interest			6% Interest		
Payment Period (Years)	10 yrs.	15 yrs.	20 yrs.	10 yrs.	15 yrs.	20 yrs.	10 yrs.	15 yrs.	20 yrs.
Interest and Principal Payments	$122	$89	$73	$127	$95	$79	$133	$101	$86
Taxes and Assessments	18	18	18	18	18	18	18	18	18
Insurance	3	3	3	3	3	3	3	3	3
Upkeep	20	20	20	20	20	20	20	20	20
Total Annual Costs Per $1,000	$163	$130	$114	$168	$136	$120	$174	$142	$127

the years. Taxes and costs of upkeep will vary in different sections of the country. They have been estimated at a reasonable average here because experience has shown that many people do not allow enough for these items. The figures should be adjusted where modifications are known.

(e) *Decreasing monthly payment plan.* Although this is the cheapest way to finance the cost of a home, many people do not prefer it. For younger people there is the obvious fact that the largest payment must be made at the beginning, when because of low income they are least able to pay. In later years when their earning power has increased and they are better able to pay more, the payments are smallest. Some owners consider that the smaller payments in the beginning are worth the extra cost. If you select this type of mortgage, you will probably give it to a bank. If it is a national bank, the life of the mortgage is limited to a maximum of ten years. If the bank is state controlled, the term of years may be more generous, but in either case you should consider the renewal risk if the mortgage cannot be paid in full during the time allowed. You may have to pay a renewal charge at the end of the ten-year period, and you cannot be certain that the same interest rate will be allowed to continue at the time of renewal. Loans are not usually granted on more than 60 per cent of the appraised value of the prospective home.

(f) *F.H.A. Insured mortgages.* By providing for insurance of mortgages the National Housing Act made home ownership possible for many who could make only a small down payment in cash and small monthly payments for interest and amortization. Under an FHA-insured mortgage, you borrow from your lending agency, and the U. S. government (through the Federal Housing Administration) insures the lending agency against any loss of principal if you fail to meet the terms and conditions of your mortgage. Under the FHA plan, you pay an "insurance fee" of $\frac{1}{2}$ of 1 per cent, computed monthly, on the outstanding amount of the principal for the full term of the loan. This is in addition to the normal interest charged on the loan. You also pay an FHA "processing or application fee" when application is made for the loan. These assessed fees are used to build up a

MAXIMUM MORTGAGE AMOUNTS TABLE
Proposed Construction and Existing Construction Over One Year

FHA Val.	Mtg. Amt.	FHA Val.	Mtg. Amt.	FHA Val.	Mtg. Amt.	FHA Val.	Mtg. Amt.
To $10,000	97%	$13,450	$13,000	$16,750	$16,000	$20,650	$19,000
$10,850	$10,500	13,950	13,500	17,300	16,500	21,400	19,500
11,350	11,000	14,550	14,000	17,850	17,000	22,100	20,000
11,900	11,500	15,100	14,500	18,550	17,500	22,800	20,500
12,400	12,000	15,650	15,000	19,250	18,000	23,550	21,000
12,900	12,500	16,200	15,500	19,950	18,500	24,250	21,500

For properties completed less than 1 year, the mortgage amount may be 90% of the first $18,000 of FHA appraised value and 70% of value over $18,000.

DEBT SERVICE TABLE
(Includes Principal, Interest [5½%], and FHA Premium)

Years	$10,000	$10,500	$11,000	$11,500	$12,000	$12,500	$13,000	$13,500
20	$ 72.91	$ 76.56	$ 80.20	$ 83.85	$ 87.50	$ 91.14	$ 94.79	$ 98.43
25	65.63	68.92	72.19	75.48	78.76	82.04	85.32	88.61
30	60.94	63.99	67.04	70.08	73.13	76.18	79.22	82.27
Years	$14,000	$14,500	$15,000	$15,500	$16,000	$16,500	$17,000	$17,500
20	$102.08	$105.72	$109.37	$113.02	$116.66	$120.31	$123.95	$127.60
25	91.88	95.17	98.45	101.73	97.51	100.55	103.60	106.65
30	85.32	88.36	91.41	94.46	105.01	108.29	111.57	114.86

fund to take care of the losses of home owners who default of their mortgages, making a foreclosure necessary. In order to qualify for an FHA-insured mortgage, not only the owner, but the building, its plan, its materials, and the methods of construction are appraised. Your architect or builder will have a copy of the official circular on minimum requirements of property standards which describe the minimum requirements in detail. Other restrictions regarding the eligibility of mortgagors and properties are similar to the good business practices of the average bank or other lending agencies.

Another advantage of an FHA-insured loan is that the property is inspected carefully by an FHA appraiser; and if he thinks it is not worth what you expect to pay for it, you will learn of his judgment in time to avoid an unwise commitment. If you are building a house, or if the builder from whom you expect to buy has an FHA construction loan, the FHA will supervise each step of the building process, and the builder or contractor will have to comply with the exacting standards of the FHA. It may thus be worth the extra costs to be reassured that the house is being constructed properly and checked by an impartial outside agency. There is also a negative benefit, in that if you do not apply for FHA insurance, your lender might because of the greater risk he is assuming be forced to charge a higher rate of interest.

The tables on page 256 show the maximum FHA-insured mortgages which may be secured by houses and lots of various appraised values. The monthly repayment costs of the FHA loans described include the interest, repayment of principal, and the FHA insurance premium. The "FHA Val." represents the assessed value placed upon the property, while the "Mtg. Amt." represents the FHA loan which can be granted.

The following table will give the approximate value of mortgages granted in relation to the amount of down payment in cash. The column at the left indicates the down payment, while reading across the page you will find the approximate value of mortgage which the various lending agencies will consider.

APPROXIMATE VALUE OF MORTGAGE IN RELATION TO CASH DOWN PAYMENT

Down Payment	Straight Mortgage	Amortized National Bank	Amortized Building & Loan	Amortized Insured
$ 300	$ 300	$ 450	$ 900	$ 2,700
500	500	750	1,500	4,500
750	750	1,125	2,250	6,000
1,000	1,000	1,500	3,000	7,000
1,250	1,250	1,875	3,750	8,000
1,500	1,500	2,250	4,500	8,600
1,750	1,750	2,625	5,250	8,600
2,000	2,000	3,000	6,000	8,600
2,500	2,500	3,750	7,500	10,000
3,000	3,000	4,500	9,000	12,000
3,500	3,500	5,250	10,500	14,000
4,000	4,000	6,000	12,000	16,000

The amount you earn will determine to a great extent, the amount you can be prepared to pay for housing expenses. Housing expense includes principal and interest paid, insurance, taxes, utilities and heat, and maintenance. The net effective income is the monthly income after taxes on income.

PERCENTAGE OF EXPENSE TO INCOME TABLE WISCONSIN INSURING OFFICE

Net Effective Income	Typical to Maximum Housing Expense		Per Cent
$300	$107 to	$120	36 to 40
350	115 to	129	33 to 37
400	121 to	138	30 to 35
450	128 to	147	28 to 33
500	135 to	155	27 to 31
550	140 to	163	25 to 30
600	146 to	170	24 to 28
650	152 to	178	23 to 27
700	157 to	185	22 to 26
750	163 to	193	22 to 26
800	167 to	199	21 to 25
850	172 to	206	20 to 24

The acceptable relationships between Housing Expense and Net Effective Income on a monthly basis are based on the collective judgment of borrowers, lenders, and FHA Mortgage Credit Examiners. They are used by us as guides to judgment and are not to be regarded as arbitrary limitations.

(g) *Veterans Administration Loans.* Such loans may be guaranteed for any veteran (Male or Female) who served actively 90 days or more on or after September 16, 1940, and before the end of World War II, provided the veteran terminated service other than dishonorably. These loans are not made by the government; they are guaranteed by the government. They are made by ordinary mortgage lenders, savings and loan associations, insurance companies, and individuals. The loans can be made up to 98 per cent of the purchase price of the property, provided this does not exceed the valuation placed on the property by an appraiser approved by the Veterans Administration. The VA then guarantees the lender against loss up to 60 per cent of the loan, with a maximum guarantee of $7,500. The maximum interest charged on these loans is 4½ per cent per year. The maximum maturity depends upon the nature and purpose of the loan. Loans made with a first mortgage on residential real estate as security may be made up to 30 years.

(h) *Open end loans.* In this form of loan a clause in the mortgage gives the borrower the privilege of obtaining additional funds (for purposes such as remodeling and improvements) after the loan has been reduced, without going through the formality of rewriting the mortgage. The total loan outstanding at any time is usually restricted to the amount of the original loan.

(i) *Package loans.* Under this form of loan the buyer pays a regular amount monthly over a period of years. This includes payment on the loan principal, interest, taxes, and insurance.

4. Property Taxes. The local tax authority appraises the property for a proportional part of its true value (usually one-half to three-fourths). By inquiry as to nearby assessed valuations or appraisals for taxation, a fairly close estimate may be made as to what the authorities will say the property is worth for taxation purposes. This amount is called the "assessed valuation," and is usually less than its real value. Local tax rates are established periodically, and the taxes are figured by multiplying the assessed valuation by the "rate."

5. Water Assessment or Tax. This is a charge, collected annually, semi-annually, or quarterly to cover the expenses of the water supply. It is based upon the amount of water used as reckoned by the meter, or it may be based upon the number of water outlets supplying the household, or it may be a flat rate.

6. Maintenance. The cost of upkeep, including painting and all repairs, is included in this item, which is found to average annually from 3 to 5 per cent of the cost of the house. The type and quality of the construction will influence this figure, since the cost of maintenance is higher in frame construction than in masonry.

7. Depreciation. This charge is estimated on the average life of a house and is usually figured at about 2½ per cent per year where a good class of permanent construction materials are used.

8. Interest on the Investment. While this is not a direct payment it should be figured at the present rate on which an equal amount of money would be earning, usually about 5 per cent.

9. Insurance Costs. The annual insurance premiums, which any insurance broker will approximate, must be included.

An estimate of the costs of home ownership can be made by filling in the items in the following form:

ESTIMATING THE ANNUAL CASH COST OF HOME OWNERSHIP

	Building a House	Buying a House
Preliminary Costs:		
Survey charges	$....	
Appraisal fee of lending agency	....	$....
Revenue stamps	....	....
Notary fees	....	....
Recording and filing fees	....	....
Legal fees for obtaining clear title	....	....
Title insurance	....	
Hazards, insurance during construction	....	
Insurance, fire, and liability	....	....
Inspection fees	....	
Architect's fees for plans	....	
Others	....	....

Extra Costs:
Landscaping   . . . .
Improvement of property   . . . .
Others   . . . .

Total Initial Costs   . . . .

Lot: . . . .
House: . . . .

Total Cost   . . . .

Annual Costs:
Mortgage amortization cost . . . .
Mortgage insurance
premium on FHA   . . . .
Total amortization   . . . .

Taxes   . . . .
Insurance   . . . .
Upkeep and repairs   . . . .
Interest on money so
far invested   . . . .
Total annual costs   . . . .

Total costs   . . . .

Monthly cost   . . . .

Analyzing the Family Resources and Expenditures

ANALYSIS OF FAMILY FINANCIAL RESOURCES AND EXPENDITURES

I. **Net Worth**
   1. Cash in checking accounts   . . . .
   2. Cash in savings accounts   . . . .
   3. Long term investments (Bonds)   . . . .
   4. Stocks   . . . .
   5. Mortgages   . . . .
   6. Other resources   . . . .
   7.   Total cash resources   . . . .
                                               Line
                                               I–7

II. **Annual Income**
   1. Annual salary   . . . .

   2. Annual income from investments   . . . .
   3. Income from other sources   . . . .
   4.   Total annual income   . . . .
                                               Line
                                               II–4

III. **Yearly Expenditures**
   1. Yearly rent   . . . .
   2. Household operating expenses
      (Fuel, utilities, telephone, etc.)   . . . .
   3. Savings   . . . .
   4. Other expenses   . . . .
      a) food   . . . .
      b) clothing   . . . .
      c) automobile operation   . . . .
      d) automobile depreciation   . . . .
      e) transportation   . . . .
      f) recreation   . . . .
      g) furniture (furnishings)   . . . .
      h) gifts and donations   . . . .
      i) medical expenses   . . . .
      j) entertainment   . . . .
      k) education   . . . .
      l) insurance   . . . .
      m) incidentals   . . . .
   5.   Total expenditures
         (Should equal total income)   . . . .
                                               Line
                                               III–5

IV. **Available Investment Funds**
   1. Total investment resources
      (Line I–7 above)   . . . .
   2. Reserve for emergencies (Line II–4.
      One-sixth to one half of annual
      income)   . . . .
   3. Net amount for home investment
      (Subtract line IV–2 from line
      IV-1)   . . . .
                                               Line
                                               IV–3

V. **Amount Available for Yearly Debt Reduction and Upkeep**
   1. Yearly rent (Line III-1)   . . . .
   2. Savings (Line III–3)   . . . .
   3.   Total available amount   . . . .
                                               Line
                                               V–3

FITTING THE PLAN OF THE HOUSE TO THE BUDGET

It is one thing to know how much you can afford to invest and borrow for a home of your own, and quite another to keep your expenditures within this amount, and still a third to get what you want for what you can pay. There are four possible solutions to the problem:

1. You may build or finish only a limited portion of your house completing it at a later date when funds are available.

2. You may buy a house already built for the amount you can afford to spend.

3. You may postpone your construction until sufficient funds are available.

4. You may reduce the unit cost of the house.

To enable you to keep expenditures within the prescribed amount a budget is suggested which must be strictly followed:

VI. **Funds Available**
   1. Cash available (Line IV–3)
      (Include value of site)   . . . .
                                               Line
                                               VI–1

   2. Reserves for expenses
      a) (Special features not credited in
         appraisal for mortgage—hobby
         shops, special equipment, etc.) . . . .
      b) construction contingencies (5–

10% of contract price for forgotten items of cost)

c) public assessments
(Paving, curbs, sewers, etc.)   ....

d) cost of accessories
(furniture, drapery, shades)   ....

e) moving costs
(cleaning, moving, settling)   ....

f) incidentals   ....

3.   Total expense reserves   ....

Line VI–3

4. Available amount for owner's equity
(Line VI–3 from VI–1)   ....

5. Available mortgage loan (three to four times owner's equity)   ....

6. Total amount for land and improvements (Lines VI–4 and VI–5)   ....

Line VI–6

VII. **Cost of Building Site**

1. Total cost of lot   ....

2. Cost of utility improvements   ....
a) assessments (Line VI–2–c)   ....
b) utility connections
(water, electric, gas, sewer)   ....
c) private utility
(water, septic tank, electricity)   ....

3.   Total cost of utility   ....

4.   Total cost of site   ....

Line VII–4

VIII. **Cost of Building Construction**

1. General contract items
a) excavation, back fill, grading   ....
b) foundations, footings, drainage, waterproofing   ....
c) masonry   ....
d) lumber, millwork, and carpentry   ....
e) iron and steel   ....
f) roofing, flashings   ....
g) sheetmetal work   ....
h) insulation, weatherstripping   ....
i) interior woodwork finish   ....
j) tile work   ....
k) hardware and installation   ....

l) painting, decorating   ....
m) legal fees, permits, surveys   ....

2.   Total for general contract   ....

Line VIII–2

3. Equipment contract items
a) heating   ....
b) air conditioning   ....
c) plumbing and fixtures   ....
d) electrical and fixtures   ....
e) special equipment   ....

4.   Total for equipment   ....

Line VIII–4

5. Special items not in contracts
a) screens, storm sash   ....
b) awnings, blinds, shades   ....
c) cabinet work   ....
d) ventilating fans, and special kitchen equipment   ....

6.   Total for special items   ....

Line VIII–6

7. Fees, permits, licenses, insurance
a) architect's fee   ....
b) engineer's fee (if services required)   ....
c) legal fees (special)   ....
d) insurance carried by owner   ....
e) taxes during period of construction   ....
f) other items   ....

8.   Total of license items   ....

Line VIII–8

9.   Total building costs   ....

Line VIII–9

IX. **Summary of Budget**

1. Cost of building site (Line VII–4)   ....

2. Cost of building construction (Line VIII–9)   ....

3. Total cost of property (Compare this total with item on Line VI–6)   ....

Line IX–3

To summarize the results of your analysis in terms of what you can afford the item "Total investment resources" (Line IV-1) represents your available cash and convertible wealth. From this should be deducted an amount which represents an emergency fund for illness and other unforeseen contingencies (Line IV-2). The difference (Line IV-3) is the amount you can safely put toward your new home. The "Amount available for yearly debt reduction and upkeep" (Line V-3) is the amount you can safely spend annually to keep up your property and retire any indebtedness you may incur. You can continue to spend on your new home as much as you now pay for rent (Line III-1), and if you now pay for heat, light, water, telephone, etc., it may be assumed that these operating costs (Line III-2) will carry over to the new home without material change.

HOW TO KEEP WITHIN YOUR BUDGET

If your wants exceed your means, some method must be found to reconcile them. Obviously your wants must be revised, and your house will represent a better investment if you restudy each detail choosing between essentials and luxuries. Certain accommodations are required for your family, certain items of equipment are necessary for comfort and health; all other things are adjustable for quality, convenience, durability, and cost, and may be modified to your ability to pay the price. Plan each procedure and operation in advance of making either legal or monetary commitments, and make all necessary adjustments to bring the budget into balance.

The factors influencing cost may be placed under two classifications — general, specific. It is necessary to consider the factors of a general nature from the very beginning of the development of the planning. The following factors may be reviewed:

1. The nature of the building site influences cost.

2. The season of the year the building is erected influences cost.

3. The type and style of the building influences cost.

The dimensions of all the rooms can perhaps be made smaller. Possibly some of the rooms may be omitted entirely. Some of the rooms may be made combination rooms, such as the dining room combined with the kitchen or with the living room. It is possible to build a story-and-a-half house instead of a two story thereby saving in the height of the walls. Consider the need for space in the house for equipment frequently located in the basement and decide whether they can be more conveniently and economically located on the first floor level. If ordinary soil conditions exist, basement space can be created for less cost than similar space above ground. Halls and vestibules can be reduced to a minimum thus saving floor area.

4. Savings in cost can usually be made by a judicious selection of materials. While #1 common lumber is desirable for framing floor joists, rafters, and studs, #2 may very well be used even for such uses as roof boarding, wall sheathing, rough flooring, and so on. Some materials possess local price advan-

tages. Short shingles 16 in. and 18 in. long may be specified instead of longer ones, even though the butts will be thinner. Blinds or shutters may be omitted from those windows not prominently exposed. Window sash may be 1⅜ in. rather than 1¾ in. Dormer windows should be used sparingly since they are expensive, as are bay windows. "B" grade woodwork is good enough, and "C" and "D" grade may be used for stained or painted work. All wood trim should be stock material carried by dealers. Window sills need not be thicker than 1⅝ in., and door jambs ⅞ in. Doors may be 1½ in. or 1⅜ in. thick instead of the 1¾ in., especially for less important rooms. Wallboard may be used in place of plaster for walls and ceilings, and so on.

If there are areaways loose gravel or brick may be substituted for tile drains. It is in this matter of economy that the prospective owner will appreciate an architect's assistance.

5. Availability of labor may influence the cost, as well as the local wage scale for labor.

6. Savings in cost may be accomplished by using materials and types of construction that conform to local building practices and skill.

7. The cost of the building depends to a high degree upon the ability of the builder to organize his work efficiently.

8. The large house can usually be built at a unit cost considerably less than the smaller house. The plumbing cost may be nearly the same for each house, and a similar condition holds true for the cost of the electrical work. The number of outlets, switches, and number of fixtures might well be the same in the two houses. Other parts of the house further illustrate this point — such as stairway, chimney, fireplace, roof, dormer windows, and so on. Certain items of expense in the construction of a house are the same regardless of size such as in the excavation of a basement.

The specific cost of a house is difficult to approach by a general discussion since the planning and cost analysis of every house is more or less an itemized study for a given house, at a given location, at a given date.

UNIT
XI

Methods of Obtaining Your House

There are many ways to obtain a new home: (1) you can buy one ready made with all the headaches taken care of before you move in; (2) you can buy one partially built and finish it off yourself; (3) you can buy a prefabricated one with the erection cost included in the selling price; (4) you can buy a prefabricated or precut package of the materials and erect the house yourself; (5) you can have one built to your specifications, with your architect supervising the complete construction; (6) you can build your house from stock-plans and supervise the construction yourself; (7) you can build from stock plans and do the construction yourself.

Buying a house from a speculative builder or real estate developer is a solution when you find what you want, on a site that appeals to you, at a fair price. The builder must make a profit in the transaction for he assumes risk of its disposal and he accumulates taxes and maintenance during the time it is in his possession. He also has to pay interest on the money borrowed to finance the construction as well as salary and costs for advertising and the selling of the property.

In buying a prefabricated house the chief difference is that you see a demonstration house and order one like it to be erected on your property. It is obvious that out of each dollar you pay, a definite part of it will go for advertising and selling expense for the manufacturer, part for the dealer's commission and his selling expense, another part for building the manufacturing and fabricating plants, and lastly for the actual cost of manufacture. The cost of construction may be assumed by the buyer or included in the complete price.

It is possible to let some building contractor or real estate broker sell you a complete service of design and construction for a specified price, and under a packaged contract. You can specify in your contract the amount of money you want to spend, the kind of house, and the kind of materials to be used, but you will have to be a building expert to know whether you receive full value. The contract embodies a penalty for making any changes during construction, and you place yourself unreservedly in the hands of a business executive under an agreement which compels him to earn his profit by giving you less in value than the amount you are willing to spend.

Stock plans are plans designed to meet average requirements that may be used over and over again. Your problem is to find one which best meets your needs. Complete plans are sold with provision for making minor changes for a fee. The revisions may be made by the plan service for a fee, drawn by an architect, or drawn by the prospective owner. Since these plans must be used over a period of years to repay the cost of preparation they may lack modern innovations. Having settled on your plan the next step is to get bids on the proposed construction. Be sure to include such items of cost such as grading, sidewalks, driveways, planting, and all extra items not included in the specifications. Usually it is necessary to select the exact kind of heating plant, plumbing fixtures, lighting fixtures, hardware, and so on, because they are not included in the stock specifications. If you have previously assured yourself that you have selected competent and trustworthy bidders you can select the lowest quotation and have a lawyer draw up a contract. It will be necessary for you to supervise construction, for if questions arise the contractor will interpret the specifications to his advantage. Any interpretations or changes you make not in accord with the contract will bring about extra costs. Either you must place your trust in the contractor or be something of a building expert to judge whether he is fulfilling his contract. Here are a few examples of problems which will confront you: How deep should I have the basement dug? Will drainage be a problem if basement is dug too deep? How thick should the footing be? What is the frost level for that particular **area?** How much ceiling height should be allowed for the basement? How thick should the basement floor be? Is waterproofing necessary under the basement floor? Is drainage tile around the outside of the foundation necessary? If the house is to be built on concrete slab construction, what is the best method of insulating the slab? Should balloon or platform framing be used? If I invest in some of the highest priced materials, how soon will they save me enough on maintenance costs and conveniences to pay for the extra investment? I want brick walls or brick veneer, but cannot afford the brick now. How can I build so that brick can be added later when I can afford it? I prefer an attached garage. How will this affect my insurance? These are just a few of the numerous questions that come up in the building of a house.

Employing an architect has the definite advantage of placing your problems in the hands of a person whose life work has been to learn how to design and build houses. You have a specialist working for you who knows financing methods, materials and their proper uses, building law, and how to protect the owner's interests through every stage of the process. Financially the architect should be able to save his fee to the owner by suggesting economies in planning, in construction, and in the use of materials which will not detract from the essential requirements. From the artistic point of view, the architect should either recommend to the owner the type of design best suited to the individual and the locality, or, if the owner has already determined in his own mind the character of the house to be erected, he should be able to point out and eliminate defects and develop the individuality to be expressed. In selecting an architect, both his artistic qualifications and his business ability must be considered. The recommended way to select an architect is by the results he has obtained in planning and building houses. Once the choice has been made, the architect's position should be considered as confidential as that of any professional man. The terms of employment should be frankly discussed and the amount of the fee and services to be rendered should be agreed upon, as well as the owner's limitations of size, quality, and cost. The commission charged by the architect may vary from 6 to 10 per cent. Architects who have worked up a highly respected reputation may charge from 12 to 15 per cent as the demand for their services justifies. If unusual requirements or conditions are involved an additional fee is charged the owner. On the completion of the preliminary studies and sketches, one fifth of the total estimated fee is due the architect; on completion of the working drawings and specifications, an additional two fifths is paid; and the remaining two fifths upon completion of the house. The architect's duties, aside from being the guide, philosopher, and friend of the owner and family, are to consult with his client in preparing the preliminary studies and estimates; to make full working drawings and specifications; to obtain estimated costs; and, after passing upon the estimates, to assist in drawing up the contracts. He is at the service of the client at all convenient times for consultation. After the contract is signed he supervises the construction, and certifies to the amount and time when payments are due the contractor. Finally he passes upon the completion of the building as to whether the agreements have been properly executed.

Selecting the Style for Your House

Style is a quality, not a principle of design. When a house is descriptive of a definite conception such as dignity, elegance, simplicity, picturesqueness, homeliness, it has character; and character is style. Historic style is the expression, the characteristic manner of design, which prevails at a given time and place; is an expression of the housing needs, taste, and wealth of the community; it is not the result of accident, but rather an evolution of the intellectual, moral, social, and even political conditions of the time. Style is the result of habits in planning, use of materials, and the controlling influences of economic conditions. Style is best determined by environment, topography of the site, consideration of costs, requirements of the family, arrangement of rooms, furniture, equipment, and by the materials of construction. Since our ancestors with their available transportation could not move building materials long distances, they used locally available materials. In some districts stone was easily available and the "Cotswold Cottage" is an outgrowth of its use. During the Elizabethan era and in Norman France, heavy timbers could be had for the cutting of the oak trees, and the "half timber" common to these styles was an outgrowth of these conditions. It was simpler to fill in the spaces between the framing members with brick, stone, and plaster than it was to saw the timbers into boards. Roofs were steep pitched because the roof trusses were stronger and

easier designed than for a flat roof. Also a steep pitch would shed snow and the heavy rains easier. Low walls of mud and stone were erected as high as it was economical and feasible to build them, and they relied upon thickness and weight for stability. Roofs were often built of logs left in the round and covered with whatever available material would shed water, such as the straw used in "thatch." Building a gable is more expensive than building side walls because it requires care to form the slopes of the gable to form a weather tight joint. Houses in the warmer climates were built of masonry because the materials of stone, brick, and lime were relatively cheap. The wide overhanging eaves protected the masonry from the heavy rain besides affording shade from the hot sun. With the abundance of good clays and a background of experience in its use, a clay tile was developed for roofing which had excellent water shedding properties. The roof had a low pitch because there was no snow to fall on it in this mild climate.

Climate and custom often influenced styles. In the northern part of our early colonies, a living unit was often built by co-operative help from the neighbors, and as the family grew and prospered additions were made. Under a severe climate the extensions were all built to communicate with the main quarters so that the family could pass from one unit to another under cover. In the South, where Negro labor was employed, a segregation system was employed which brought about a manor house entirely separated from the servants' quarters and the utility buildings. Moderate climate, ample land, and cheap labor contributed to the Southern solution.

Any style is good style if it fits the site and environment as naturally as it fitted the locality and conditions from which it was evolved. Whatever the style, the essential qualities of a good house are proportion, scale, color, texture, rhythm, and repose. The taking of rooms, hall, and staircases, and arranging them in sequence according to their use and importance; the erecting of walls, floors, and roofs; the relating of planes, solids, voids, lights, shadows, textures, and colors so that each gives meaning and expression, that is, style in design of a house. Such conditions created our traditional style. Our modern style is an outgrowth of new materials of construction, practical economy, and a freedom of expression and desire to think out the solution to one's problems unhampered by tradition. In all architecture the wall, lintel, and arch form the basis of construction. Architectural styles are identified by the various treatments of these elements, each style the expression of the life of the people creating it. As travel and learning spread, ideas were carried from one country to another.

When planning to build a house there are a number of things requiring careful thought, before the work is started or even before the plans of the building are in the development stage. The plan should be considered first, and even before that, the site for which the plan is to be made should be carefully studied. The outward appearance of the house should express and serve the purpose of the inside plan, and these plans depend upon such factors as the contour of the land, natural landscaping, direction the house should face, type of neighborhood, position of the house and garage upon the lot with reference to the street and other boundary lines, relative position of the different rooms to the points of the compass, and so on.

Often the prospective builder already has a piece of land which has come into his possession in one way or another and the problem is to locate the house on the lot to the best advantage. Having the lot, the builder must choose the best plan and exterior style for that particular site. If there is a choice of locations, a lot may be purchased as a setting for one's favorite style of house. Formal houses of the classic style need to stand on a wide, level lot to show off to advantage, while a rambling, irregular plan with broken roof lines looks its best when it is placed on a lot of irregular contour. A style which calls

for height in its front elevation would be inappropriate on a high terrace.

It is necessary to give consideration not only to the arrangement of the rooms with reference to the activities of the occupants inside the building, but attention must also be given to conditions which exist outside of the building and their influences upon the comfort and happiness of the family. These outward conditions may be listed as follows:

1. The size and shape of the lot and its relation to the public streets which have a bearing on the best location for the house and garage on the lot. The natural topography of the lot may determine the location of the house by restricting the choice to a few suitable areas. Some people prefer to have the house built on the back of the lot to allow as much front lawn as possible, with perhaps a driveway from the street to the front entrance and garage. If the garage is located at the side or rear of the lot, a deep lot with considerable width will be needed. Other families prefer a house located near the front of the property with only a small front yard, a short walk from the sidewalk to the entrance, and the garage located at the front or at one side of the house, and a short driveway to the street. These decisions will affect the planning of the house, for with the house placed at the rear of the lot the living and dining rooms will probably be placed to the front of the house and the kitchen placed in back. If the outdoor living space is arranged at the back of the lot, it is probable that the kitchen will be placed at the front, and the living room and dining room in such a position that the garden is accessible to them. The arrangement of rooms is also influenced by the amount of traffic on the street. With the coming of the automobile, the garage replaced the stable, which was associated with many flies and unpleasant odors. In the early houses the stable had been placed behind the house as far as possible and garages were similarly located, while in the modern house it is usual to place the garage at the front

or side of the house. Where the contour of the lot permits, the garage is often located in the basement of the house. A considerable advantage is gained if the plan can be arranged to give access to the garage directly from the house. The shorter the driveway the easier it is to clear it of snow. A steeply sloping driveway leading to a basement garage is not good. Because of poor traction on snow or ice or other slippery conditions of the driveway.

2. The plan should be arranged with reference to the points of the compass to allow rooms to enjoy warmth and sunlight when they most require it. A house planned for a lot on the south side of a street going east and west may be poorly planned for a house to be built on the east side of a street going north and south. Some knowledge of the extent to which sunlight penetrates into windows with various exposures at different seasons of the year is desirable. In northern climates the windows of important rooms should face south, and the windows facing north should be those of minor rooms.

3. The direction of the prevailing winds and the location of adjacent structures or natural obstructions which might deprive the house of its fresh air must be studied. Location of windows necessary for cross ventilation is limited by this consideration.

4. The existence and direction of any especially fine view of the surrounding country side should be taken into account to enjoy its full benefits.

5. In addition to fitting the site, the plan should also be designed to fit the needs of the family living in the house. The size of the family, the occupations, tastes, various ages of the members of the family, and their activities should all be considered in making the plan. If there are children in the family a portion of the home should be planned to accommodate the normal activities of their respective ages. A family with social inclinations needs a large living and dining area for entertaining. Another family with artistic inclinations might prefer a smaller living and dining room with emphasis placed upon a library, music room, or work shop. Each family must decide what arrangement of space is best suited to its own needs.

No matter how you plan today to secure a home suited to your own needs, some circumstance may compel you to sell your house. Whenever you seek a buyer, your house must pass the test of its true value as a good investment. It must appeal to as many potential buyers as possible. People are not willing to buy a house that departs from the prevailing and conventional style too radically. This fear of radical departure has retarded the development of new ideas in planning but probably has also spared the world a number of eccentric houses.

STYLE AFFECTED BY FLOOR AREA

The shape of a house and the resulting style of the house have a decided influence upon the usable floor area. The greater the area of actual living space which can be obtained from a given shape the more economical and efficient the plan. There are other considerations such as the architectural effect produced and the feeling of roominess, freedom from crowding of space, and so on, which may offset some sacrifice of economy and efficiency.

A square plan containing no more than three rooms on the first floor and four rooms and a bath on the second floor may be grouped about a compact central hallway making it convenient to reach each room directly. It is seldom that a satisfactory plan can be worked out so as to be in the form of a square. Most houses of colonial or Georgian style have plans of rectangular shape because this style is economical to build, and it exhibits a simplicity of exterior treatment. Under favorable circumstances four rooms on the first floor and perhaps six rooms on the second floor are possible within the outlines of a rectangular plan, but at the sacrifice in most bedrooms of cross ventilation.

To allow more freedom in giving proper orientation to the rectangular plan, extra space may be obtained by the introduction of an "ell," or wing to the design. When the projecting ell is at the extreme end of the rectangle and one wall of the ell is in line with the end wall of the rectangle there are two additional corners. When the projecting ell extends out from the main rectangle with some distance from either end there will be four extra corners. As each additional corner requires extra construction and extra cost they should be avoided in the low price house. Ells improve the layout and appearance so much on the other hand that their costs may be justified. Ells also make it necessary to have valleys constructed in the roofs, creating a possible cause for leaks but making a more interesting roof line.

The most economical way to get satisfactory living quarters in a house is to build no more than two stories in height, with an attic area added under the sloping roof, and a basement area under the entire first floor. In some modern homes the attic and basements have been omitted or reduced in size, not so much because owners do not want them or cannot make use of them, as for the reason that the builders are trying to produce the greatest amount of living space for the least cost. Also by bringing the cornice line lower than the ceiling level of the second floor or sometimes below the level of the window heads of the second floor a reduction may be made in cost. This requires a sloping of the ceiling of the second floor rooms which gives more room height in the center of the room than on the outside walls. In the same way some houses are built with the cornice level nearly to the ceiling level of the first floor. This reduces the usable space in the rooms of the second floor so much that this

story is counted only as a "half-story." Since the roof area is required in either case but the wall height is reduced, there is a saving in cost but a loss in usable space in the plan. If dormers are required for light and ventilation there is little saving in cost.

In a one story house the cornice level is at or below the level of the first-floor ceiling. If the rooms are all on one floor they will require more roof area and more foundation walls under them than if the same number of rooms were arranged in two stories. The extra cost is partially offset by the saving in cost and space due to the omission of the stairway. There is also some saving in the piping which serves the bathroom and kitchen area.

FACTORS IN PLANNING WHICH TEND TO GOVERN STYLE

There are a number of considerations affecting style which require a lot of planning, but may be briefly listed as follows:

1. If all the residences in a community or neighborhood are well designed and pleasing to the eye, it is harmful to build in the midst of them a house of radical design, cheap construction, and otherwise out of character of the neighborhood. Simple styles affected by the shape of the plan and the number of stories can economize on cost and yet give a pleasing design. The style of house which may be built in a particular community may sometimes be determined as a result of certain building laws or restrictions enacted by the governing authorities. Such restrictions and requirements, while they do not dictate the style to which the house must be designed do have some effect upon the choice which is made.

2. Geographical location makes limitations upon the style and plan of the house.

3. Considering a future selling value of a house it is good planning to build a house in a style which will be popular at the time of

eventual selling. Age is not the determining factor in a sale if the house is of good construction, well planned, and of pleasing design.

CONSTRUCTION FEATURES WHICH AFFECT STYLE

The nearer the first-floor level of a house can be kept to the ground level the more the house will appear to be growing out of the ground and belonging to it. It is the need for light in the basement and the desire to keep the floor joists and beams out of the damp ground which fixes the level of the first floor. The employment of areaways constructed with walls of metal, masonry, or concrete will provide light into the basement. These areaways do have the disadvantage of filling with snow and should be provided with drains to remove surface water. The alternative is to keep the basement window sills above ground level.

The Federal Housing Administration recommends a minimum ceiling height of 7 ft. 6 in. on the first floor, 7 ft. 0 in. on the second floor, and 6 ft. 6 in. in the basement. The heights are considered as minimum and greater heights should be provided to fit the particular wants and needs. Rooms on the first floor should preferably have a ceiling height of at least 8 ft. 6 in., second floors at least 8 ft. 0 in., and the basement 7 ft. 0 in.

In the houses of colonial times the chimneys were usually large with several flues to accommodate the several heating units, and were often located in the center of the house. Therefore chimneys adapted to modern versions of these early styles usually present a substantial appearance even when only a few flues are actually required, and are often located on an outside wall and made a decorative feature of the elevation. Chimneys function better for draft when they are built entirely inside the walls of the house, and when they rise at least 2 ft. above the highest ridge line of the roof.

Newer homes are designed with the outdoor living space in the form of terraces, patios, and porches overlooking the gardens in the rear of the house and offering privacy to the occupants. In some styles of houses porches are to be found occasionally, but usually they are more decorative than useful, although they do afford some shelter when used at the front entrance to the house.

Choosing Your Builder

THE CONTRACTOR

The man who is paid to construct the building, whether a single carpenter or an organized company, is referred to as the contractor, and it should be obvious that the more experienced, reliable, and painstaking the builder, the more satisfactory the finished house will be. A feeling of mutual confidence between the builder and the owner is vital. Sometimes the builder acts in the capacity of the designer and builder both. Often the owner may act as the architect and hire the builder to do the construction. It is recommended that the owner select a contractor whose character and ability are known to the owner, and with whom a friendly relationship can be maintained. Where the selection must be made on competitive bids there are two procedures: (1) a limited number of reliable firms may be invited to submit estimates, (2) a competition may be held. In common fairness the bidders should know something of the basis for selection and no one should be allowed to give his time unless the owner would willingly accept him to do the work.

THE SUBCONTRACTORS

In the construction of a house many spe-cialized workmen representing the trades take part. In rural areas the local carpenter and handy man is usually competent to do the entire job, with the assistance of the plumber, electrician, mason, and so on. In metropolitan areas the situation is more complicated for each trade is highly organized and jealous of its jurisdiction, specialized labor and machines are easily obtainable, and all agreements and contracts must be carefully drawn and observed. One contractor may be hired for the general construction with delegated authority to subcontract for the heating, wiring, plumbing, masonry, roofing, plastering, painting, etc. Thus the work is co-ordinated under one authority and yet the responsibility rests with both the contractor and his subcontractors. If the owner directly employs the subcontractors, the responsibility for their co-operation is shifted to the owner or the architect in which case his fee is correspondingly increased.

RESPONSIBILITY OF SUPERVISION

The architect's duties require him to supervise the work from the excavating to the decorating, with close co-operation of the owner. The owner cannot demand changes in the construction or specifications if the contractor is complying with the terms of the contract unless an adjustment is given in cost. Further all orders for any changes must be given in writing and must come only through the person delegated with the authority in the contract. If the progress is not satisfactory, a conference between owner and the contractor in the architect's office often expedites matters. It is best to avoid discussions on the job and in the presence of workmen. Care should be exercised that instructions be given to foremen or to the contractor, rather than through individual workmen.

Arranging the House, Rooms, and Garage on Your Property

In planning your house it is necessary to think of designing your home (1) to fit the site, (2) to take advantage of the sun in the arrangement of rooms to the points of the compass, (3) to face the house properly in relation to the views and streets, and (4) to arrange the proper relation of the garage and the other features of the house. A small lot limits the possibilities of arrangements because of space, zoning laws, street setbacks, ordinances, and so on.

The first step is to consider the sunlight in relation to the various rooms. During the winter the sun is desirable for heat and light; in the summer, shade and cooling breezes are desired. During the winter the sun is low in the sky and it throws light further into the rooms, while in summer the sun is high and can be regulated by awnings, projections over windows, and shade from trees. Generally it is best to plan rooms for their winter sunlight (unless the house is to be occupied only during the summer months), and to use trees and awnings to form shade that makes it more comfortable during hot weather. The morning sun is also very low in the sky but relatively cool, while the late afternoon sun is also low and usually warm. Both extremes throw light deeper into the rooms. When a house is placed with one wall to the north, one to the south, one to the east, and one to the west, the rooms facing the south receive

direct sunlight the year around, the rooms to the east and west receive sunlight in summer but in the shorter days of the winter only the oblique rays will reach them, while the rooms on the north have no sunlight in winter, and only a little in summer. If a house can be so placed that one side is toward the southeast and one side toward the southwest, direct sunlight during a part of every day will reach more rooms than when the house faces east and west.

From these facts we can assume that in northern climates the windows of the important rooms should face south, if possible, and windows facing north should be those of minor rooms. Unless there are especially good views which determine the direction in which the rooms should face, it can be said that from the point of view of lighting, it is best for the living room to have south, southwest, west, or southeast exposure. Dining rooms should face south, southeast, or east. Kitchens should face north, northeast, or east (never to the west if it can be avoided). Libraries, studios, and hobby rooms should face north for uniform light, or toward the east if used mostly in the afternoon. Bedrooms may have almost any exposure, and in most two-story houses they must be placed on all sides. Since they are sleeping rooms primarily, orientation for sunlight is seldom the governing factor. Preferred views or exposure to prevailing winds in summer may influence the location of the master bedroom. Eastern exposure may inconvenience late sleepers. Western exposure is not advisable for children's bedrooms, but nurseries and playrooms should have direct sunlight, preferably from the south. Sun porches designed for winter use may face toward the south or southeast, but summer porches or terraces should be located where prevailing winds will cool them and where there is good shade rather than the hot sun. These principles of orientation should be given more thought than is generally accorded them, but they must be considered in relation to several other factors.

Figure 64 shows four lot-and-house plans, the houses facing north, east, south, and west

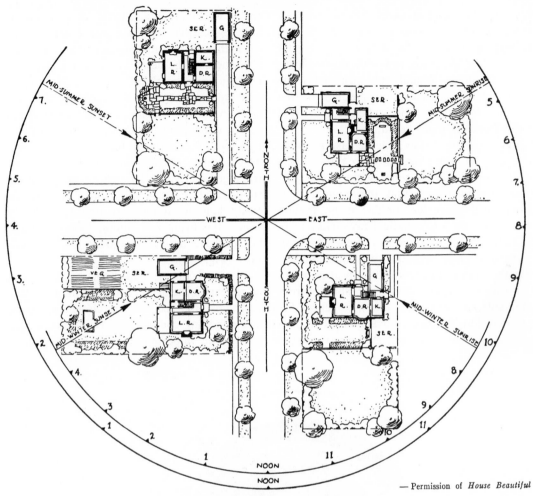

— Permission of *House Beautiful*

Fig. 64. Orientation of house.

respectively. It is assumed that it is most desirable to have the morning sun in the dining room and the benefit of the fullest amount of light at all times in the living room. The large arc represents the path of the sun in midsummer; the small arc, in midwinter. By drawing lines from the points of the arcs through the center and then parallel lines to any of the four houses, it will be seen that in midwinter the sun shines from sunrise until noon in the eastern windows, from sunrise to sunset in the southern windows, and from noon until sunset in the western windows; while in midsummer it shines from sunrise until noon in the eastern windows, from eight

until four in the southern windows, from noon until sunset in the western windows, and from four until sunset in the northern windows.

A study of the incidence of the sun's rays with the windows of the various rooms of each frontage view at different times of the day and year will show that the living room of each house is so placed that in practically every case the rays of the winter sun will enter the room from the time it appears in the east until sunset. In winter, because the sun is farther south at noon, its rays enter at a low angle and will carry their cheer well across the room. In summer, because the sun is nearly overhead at noon, its rays will not enter the living room in any annoying degree. It may be necessary for a few days to shut out the late afternoon sun with shades, awnings, or blinds. Usually at such times the shade of the terraces and porches of the east side of the house will invite the household away from the living room.

All the dining rooms face the east, allowing the early morning sun to peep through the windows at breakfast time. Some of the windows are so placed that the noon sun of winter will cheer the midday meal, though in summer the sun's vertical rays will hardly be noticed. The morning sun of early autumn and late spring will not be objectionable. Even though in the north the sun at noon on the shortest winter days may shine across the table, it need cause no annoyance, for partially lowered shades will control it.

The kitchen, because it is the service cen-ter of the household, should be as comfortable as possible for those whose work keeps them there. The morning sun will add to the cheeriness of the new day and drive away the contagious prebreakfast blues. In May, June, and July the rays of the morning sun will enter every kitchen shown, but it soon climbs out of range, and in most cases the northern light will predominate the rest of the day. The kitchens of the southeast and northeast frontages receive a few rays of the declining sun during these months, but they can be easily shut out if they are objectionable. In winter the living and dining rooms of these houses have an ideal exposure to the sun's rays (Fig. 65).

Plans of the second floor must depend largely upon the arrangement of the first floor partitions, the location of chimneys, stairs, and plumbing connections. While the second floor is an important element in the home-

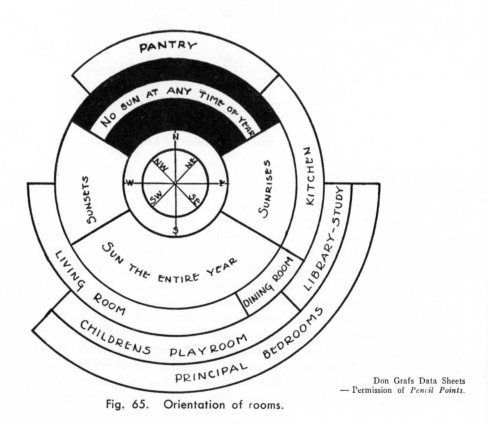

Don Grafs Data Sheets
— Permission of *Pencil Points*.

Fig. 65.   Orientation of rooms.

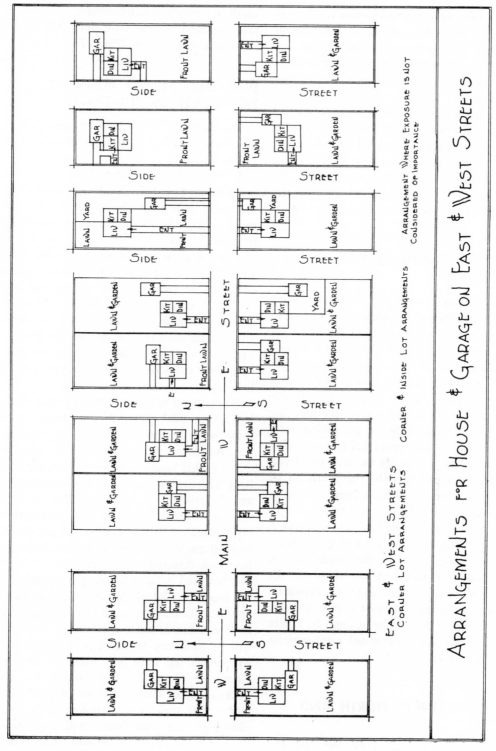

Fig. 66

ARRANGEMENTS FOR HOUSE & GARAGE ON EAST & WEST STREETS

likeness of a house, a discussion of the exposure of the rooms of the first floor will serve our present purpose. An eastern exposure is commonly preferred for bedrooms during most of the year, especially if cross ventilation can be obtained, even though the early morning sun often interrupts an invigorating morning nap. A western exposure eliminates this annoyance, but the afternoon sun or a very hot day may make the room warm; however, quite often during the night following such a day, open windows allow the west wind to create cooling breezes.

STREETS RUNNING EAST AND WEST

The common arrangement of four similar houses complete with garages are shown in Figure 66. The arrangement of the house on the northwest corner of the street intersection could well be used as an ideal arrangement for light; for the living and dining room get the southern exposure, and the dining room and kitchen receive the morning sun favorably especially for the dining area. There are those who would feel that the living room and dining room are too near the street. The houses represented to the northeast of the street intersection have been shown in two arrangements. In the preferred arrangement the living room has some southern exposure, with the kitchen facing northeast and the dining room to the southeast. An even better arrangement would place the living room with a full southern exposure, the kitchen to the northeast corner and the dining room to the northwest area. In Figure 66 are shown some suggested arrangements of houses on inside lots.

STREETS RUNNING NORTH AND SOUTH

When lots are located on the east and west sides of the streets running north and south, the conditions are different from those just described. In this case the depth of the lots run east and west (Fig. 67).

DIAGONAL STREETS RUNNING NORTHEAST OR NORTHWEST

The problems involved in the arrangement of rooms on these streets are illustrated in Figure 68.

With the discussion thus far given on the orientation of the house and the rooms within the house, it is generally agreed that the immediate grounds about the house should be planned as extensions of the indoor rooms and as such should enhance the view from within, and at the same time draw people outdoors for entertainment, dining, and recreation whenever weather permits. This requires a careful study of the lot, its views and less pleasant aspects, to the end that the living rooms and possibly the master bedroom may overlook the most pleasant part of the site.

At the point of consolidation of your thinking into a final plan for your house, each room must be considered as to its function, size, furniture arrangement, closets, relationship to other rooms, and orientation for sunlight. The site itself, its good and poor aspects, and its relation to the street and lot lines are fixed features that may predominate over other planning considerations. The garage has been given its due importance, and thought has been directed toward gardens, terraces, porches, and general landscape treatment of the property. Out of this set of requirements you may sketch a tentative plan, perhaps several; and out of these preliminary studies it will be necessary to develop elevations that will reflect the style best suited to all conditions of plan, site, and budget. Let the pattern of your house grow out of its requirements. Let logic and reasoning guide your planning, then your house will grow from the inside out. Your design will be an honest expression of your needs and environment.

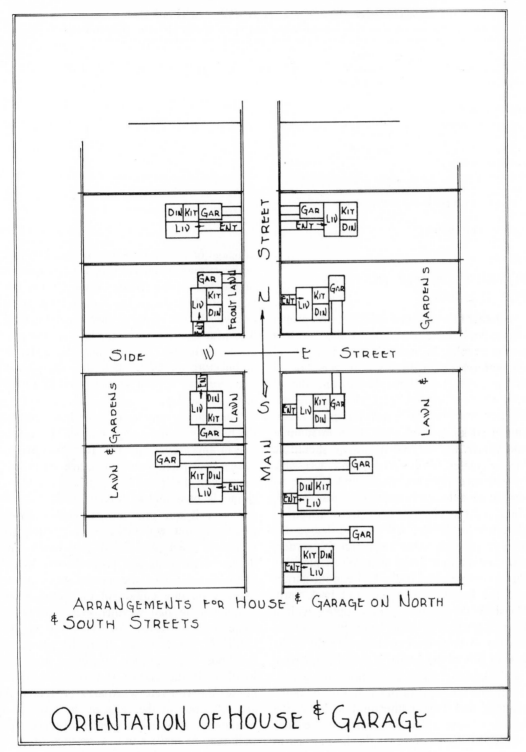

ARRANGEMENTS FOR HOUSE & GARAGE ON NORTH & SOUTH STREETS

ORIENTATION OF HOUSE & GARAGE

Fig. 67

ORIENTATION OF ROOMS IN HOME PLANNING

Place an (X) after the exposures you are determined best apply to your planning situation, and a check mark (✔) to those you would like if the final plan could be worked out to provide them:

Room or Area	Ideal Exposure	N	NE	E	SE	S	SW	W	NW
Living room	S, SE, SW, W								
Dining room	S, SE, E								
Breakfast room	E								
Den, library, studio	N, NE, E, SE								
Kitchen	N, NE, E								
Bedroom, master	Prev. wind								
Bedroom, children's	S								
Bedroom, guest	Any								
Dressing room	SE, S, W								
Sun porch or sun parlor	SW, S, SE								
Dining terrace	E, SE, S								
Screened porch, terraces	N, NE, NW								

PLANNING PROPER HOUSING FOR THE CAR

Another factor often conflicting with proper orientation unless carefully studied with a particular site in mind is the location of the garage. Originally the car was housed in the stable behind the house, and out of habit the first detached garages were similarly located. Now, however, with the car a necessity in all kinds of weather, both in summer and winter, the car and its garage should be located closer to the street, and accessible by entrance door to arrive and depart by car. Such a location saves driveway paving costs, means smaller areas from which to shovel snow in the winter, and leaves the area at the back of the house free for garden, lawn, or outdoor living area. When planning the garage, consider traffic between the garage and the house, and garage and back yard. Consider the housewife or shopper with a load of bundles to carry from the car to the kitchen. A large door opening directly to the rear or side of the garage is usually preferred.

The considerations in planning the garage begin with the study of the layout of the home grounds and the architectural style of the house. Choose a location that will be convenient to the entrance to the house. See to it that the spot is one where there is good drainage or decide on some method in which drainage may be provided in the construction of the foundation. Next, decide on the material of which the garage is to be built. Select one which will make a permanent building. The next decision to be made is on the plan of the structure. Do not mix the styles of architecture no matter how nice the plan of a garage may appear when printed in a magazine or catalog.

There are a number of materials suited to the building of the garage that will be attractive in appearance and give it lasting service. Frame construction will, of course, be in harmony with the frame house, and if the house siding is of shingles, similar siding for the garage will not only be in harmony with the house but will make a most attractive structure when considered separately. The design of the roof and proportionate height of walls will make the garage seem almost like a miniature edition of the house itself.

For use in bad weather there should be some way provided for members of the family or guests to get from the garage to the house with proper protection from the weather. If the garage is very near to the house, the concrete walk may be roofed in and left open at the sides in the form of a breezeway. If it is at greater distance, the walk may be made a more attractive addition if a pergola is built over it and shrubs

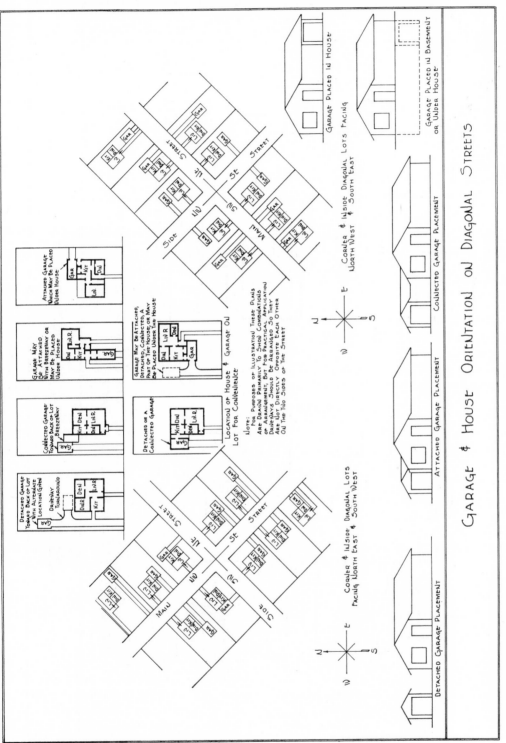

Fig. 68

GARAGE & HOUSE ORIENTATION ON DIAGONAL STREETS

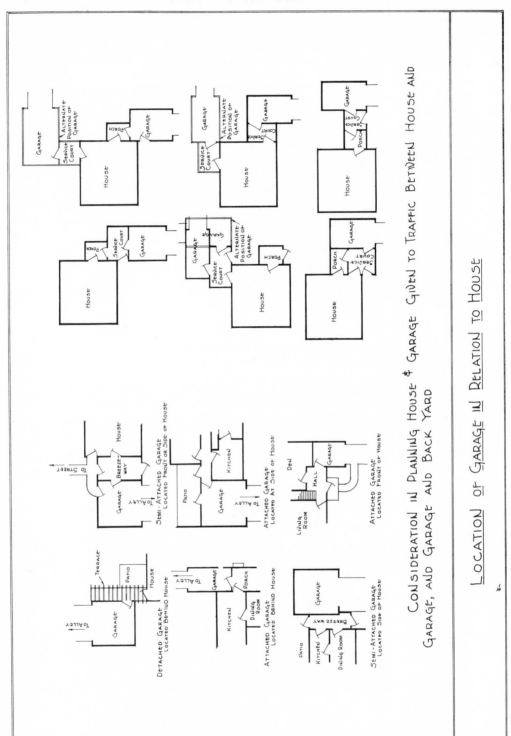

Consideration in Planning House & Garage Given to Traffic Between House and Garage, and Garage and Back Yard

LOCATION OF GARAGE IN RELATION TO HOUSE

Fig. 69

and vines are planted for accent. Many city and suburban homes are planned with the garage as a part of the house. In planning, you should keep in mind that the two structures should be considered as one building, and not have the garage appear as a second thought to the planner (Figs. 68 and 69).

The garage itself should not be slighted in the landscaping of the grounds. Plantings of shrubs or small trees will help add to its attractiveness.

When a small home has failed to provide space for a workshop, men with mechanical or hobby inclinations often use the garage as a place to work in. There, sufficient space may be allowed for a workbench and tools.

In fact, many who have ample basements tend to prefer workshop space in the garage because the light and air are better, and it seems easier to clean up the litter in a garage than in a basement.

Where play space is a problem, the garage often becomes an improvised playroom. If a recreation room is lacking, a covered breezeway or porch-type playroom at the back or side of the garage will serve as a sheltered play area for both children and adults.

These features all serve to indicate the careful thinking and wise planning involved in making garage utilization a project for the whole family.

UNIT
XV

Heating the House

The principal systems of heating in general use are hot-air, steam, and hot water heated by oil, coal, gas, or in some cases electricity. The choice of a heating plant depends upon the local climate or prevailing weather conditions, the size of the house, available fuel, cost of installation, cost of operation, and the individual taste and preference of the owner. Where the house is to be occupied only during periods of mild weather, the first consideration is the quick distribution of warmth rather than the continued maintenance of a high temperature. In a small compact residence, either the hot-air unit furnace or the small hot water heater may be placed in a small closet in a central hallway. The hot-air furnace is not as efficient in a house which covers considerable area in that the flow through the horizontal pipes is sluggish, and may be stopped entirely if there is a wind leakage in the building near the end of the pipe run. The circulation of hot water or steam is not affected in this way. Radiators can be placed more effectively, and the piping requires less space than registers in their metal ducts.

Available fuel may be the determining factor in the selection of the furnace. For a house built in a rural area and in timbered country, far from rail or other transportation, use of coal or oil would be expensive. On the other hand, a house built in the urban area where coal and oil are easily obtained without interruption from bad weather or poor transportation, wood is not desirable.

Natural gas is a very satisfactory fuel because it is clean, and in some areas very economical.

No system is absolutely foolproof, and no system will operate satisfactorily without a fair amount of attention and care. People's tastes must be considered, for some people will dislike the excessive heat contained in a steam radiator; others may fear a possibility of a freeze and the resulting pipe or radiator break in a hot water system; some hot-air furnaces spread dust; oil may clog; and ashes are dusty and a nuisance. A prospective builder should rely upon the advice of heating engineers or his architect, backed by literature and comparisons of proposed systems of heating.

Basically there are two kinds of heating systems, either of which can be employed, or which can be used in combination with each other. One of these methods distributes heated air by means of ducts. The other system circulates a heating medium, such as hot water or steam through pipes, radiators, or convectors. The second system employing pipes takes less room in the walls and floors, but the radiators occupy space in the rooms. Radiators and convectors may be recessed into the walls to overcome their use of space in the rooms. The duct system has the added advantage of accommodating an air conditioning system; the air can be heated, cooled, or humidified at a central point and circulated to the rooms. Sometimes the heating systems are classified as direct and indirect. The direct system heats the air in the room but does not introduce fresh air. The indirect system heats fresh air and distributes it into the rooms thereby forcing out an equal quantity of used air. Fireplaces are built in to modern houses to add cheer and comfort, to aid in ventilation, and to warm the room in moderate weather.

HOT-AIR FURNACES

The systems employing air ducts are of three kinds: direct-fired, indirect, and split system. In principle, the parts of a hot-air furnace are the firebox where the heat is generated; the air chamber surrounding the firebox where the air is heated; the cold air box or cold air return pipe which supplies the air for circulation; and finally, the ducts which carry the heated air to the points of delivery, called registers (Figs. 72, 73, 74, and 75). No air going to the rooms actually comes in contact with the fire or the products of combustion. Filters for cleaning the air and devices for adding moisture to it may be installed as auxiliary units to the furnace, and a blower or fan can be added to provide more positive circulation than is possible by gravity. The registers may be placed in the floor, or in the wall of the room, usually in that part of the room nearest to the furnace because of the economy of the piping. The exact location depends upon such factors as size of room, prevailing winds, window locations, and other factors. Wood, coal, oil and gas are used as fuel in the furnaces. To heat satisfactorily, the furnace must be large enough to heat the house in the most severe weather. A hot-air gravity furnace should be placed as near the center of the basement as possible and must be set low enough so that all the pipes carrying the hot air slant upwards from the furnace. Sometimes, in order to get sufficient slope for the pipes, the furnace is set in a pit below the floor level. Furnaces using oil for fuel should not be placed under the living room because of the disturbing noise. Pipes leading to the second floor run between the walls or in closet spaces.

The gravity system works on the principle that warm air is lighter than cold air. Thus the cool air at the floor level descends through the cool air duct to the bottom of the furnace. The air is heated in the air chamber between the furnace proper and the outer casing, and from there it rises through the heating ducts into the rooms through registers. The success of the warm air furnace depends upon proper installation, which in turn depends upon the size of pipe and the register area used in relation to the size of the furnace and the area of the space to be heated. Recent im-

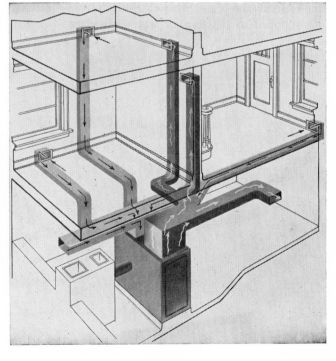

Fig. 72. Conventional forced warm air heating system.

National Warm Air Heating and
Air Conditioning Association

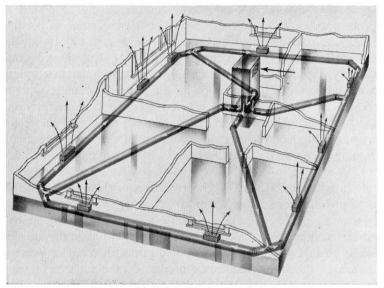

Fig. 73. Perimeter loop system used in a concrete slab floor and served by a downflow furnace.

National Warm Air Heating and Air Conditioning Association

provements in the design of hot-air furnaces have reduced to a minimum the possibility of coal gases and dirt entering the rooms through registers, and an automatic humidifier maintains a comfortable percentage of moisture in the air. Present practice provides for the recirculation of air, where formerly all the air supplied to the furnace was taken from the outside. There are extreme limits as to the location of a gravity-type furnace. It is imperative that it be below the floor level (which makes a basement or partial basement necessary) in order to obtain the proper flow of air currents, and it must be centrally placed with registers located on inside walls so that all rooms have an equal chance at the

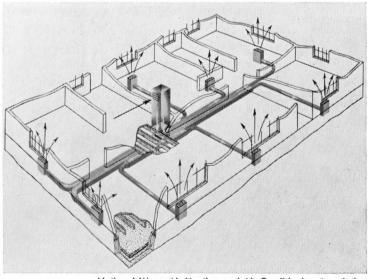

Fig. 74. Perimeter trunk and branch system.

National Warm Air Heating and Air Conditioning Association

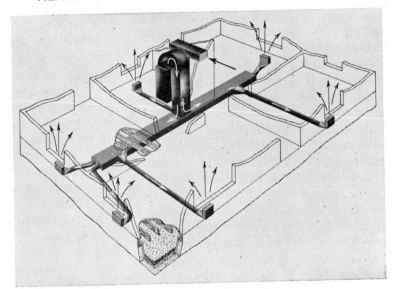

Fig. 75. Conventional up-flow furnace with perimeter system of distribution.

National Warm Air Heating and Air Conditioning Association

heat distribution. The advantages are low cost installation, simple automatic control, no danger of broken pipes from freezing when the house is not occupied, effectiveness where the area of the building is not too great, and quick firing and distribution of heat. With a gravity furnace the distribution of heat to rooms at a distance from the source of heat, or to rooms lying in the direction of strong winds is difficult, and the fuel consumption is greater than for hot water or steam. A disadvantage is the lack of uniform heat in an off-and-on source, and a lack of hot water for domestic service when the furnace is not in use. It is also difficult to prevent combustion noises in the furnace from traveling through the duct system.

The forced hot-air system does not depend upon the variation in warm and cool air weights for heat distribution, and as a result the ducts can be smaller in cross section and can be run to greater distances. A blower unit draws the cool air down into the heating chamber of the furnace and pushes the heated air up through the warm air ducts to the registers. Generally an air filter is placed in the path of the returning air, so that it is strained of dust and dirt before it reaches the heating chamber. Since the air is moving

under pressure, the warm-air-duct arrangement can be most flexible; ducts may even pass over the ceiling and down to the registers in the rooms. With a forced-warm-air-type system the furnace may be placed above or below floor level; and the size of the house, unless very large, does not appreciably hinder the distribution of heat.

Very small, compact houses can be heated without the use of ducts when the so called "pipeless furnace" is used. A recent development of this principle is the floor furnace. The principle on which this type of furnace works is very simple: the heated air rises through the central part of the large register located directly over the furnace, and the cooler air near the floor flows down into the furnace through the opening around the rim of the same floor register.

In the indirect system the air is heated by blowing it over heated coils contained in a separate chamber. The heating coils are heated by steam or hot water passing through pipe coils. The warm air is circulated through the house by means of ducts originating in the heating chamber. A fan or blower is installed in the return duct. Better control of room temperatures is possible with this system, and insulation can give better protection against sound transmission. The disadvantage of the system is the increased installation cost. One new system on the market uses warm air to heat the floor or ceiling. With this system a steam boiler supplies steam which flows into steam coils that are enclosed in an air chamber. Air passing over the hot coils is heated. The heated air is circulated between the floor and ceiling, making radiant panels of them. If it is desired to transmit the heat in one direction only, either the floor or ceiling may be insulated. Radiant baseboards for warm air are also available in place of registers. The heating duct connects directly into a metal baseboard, which is hollow and has a narrow opening in the top edge. This opening allows a thin film of warm air to travel up the wall, warming the room by convection. The base itself becomes warm and emits a portion of the heat to the room as direct radiant heat.

Conditions sometimes make it undesirable to heat all parts of a house by means of warm air conveyed through ducts. Because of odors generated in garages, kitchens, and bathrooms, air from these rooms is not desirable for recirculation. Sometimes it is not convenient to carry heating ducts to the second-story rooms through partitions. It is difficult to heat rooms by warm-air ducts if they are located a distance away from the source of heat. The solution to many of these problems may be accomplished by means of the "split system" (Fig. 76). In this method of heating, the steam or hot water is circulated through pipes to radiators in the desired rooms, and the remainder of the heat passes to a heating coil located in a heating chamber near the boiler. From this heating chamber the air is circulated through ducts as described for the indirect system. In this indirect part of the system the air can be humidified, filtered, and recirculated, and with the addition of refrigerating equipment the air can be cooled in summer. A split system is more expensive and more difficult to control automatically.

UNIT AND SPACE HEATERS

Where the heating season is mild, many homes do not require central heating systems but rely on unit or space heaters. Even in the northern climates smaller homes can be adequately heated by space heaters of the proper size. They are manufactured as units to be built into the floors, or walls, or to stand in the room. These units are available with or without circulating fans which make for more effective distribution of heat. The free standing units are available for use with coal, oil, or gas. Oil or gas is the accepted fuel with the floor or wall furnaces. Many of these units also have built in thermostatic control which automatically varies the heat output with the room need.

Smaller auxiliary heating units, usually known as unit heaters are available for use in giving extra heat to certain areas where extra heat is required at times, or in portions of the house where cold spots may develop. Unit heaters may be built into a wall or carried in a portable enclosure.

DUCTS OR PIPES

Most hot-air heating systems require pipes which may be laid out in either of two systems. In the individual duct system each room has a separate supply pipe from the furnace or air conditioner. The trunk duct system uses a large main supply and return duct which reduces in size the farther it is extended from the furnace. Branch ducts lead to the separate rooms. Round pipes occupy less actual space for a given quantity of air than do the rectangular pipes, but they do not fit as neatly into the structural spaces. Rectangular ducts must not be proportioned more than four times wider than they are deep. All bends in pipes should be of a radius not less than one-and-one-half times the diameter of the duct.

There has been some successful experi-

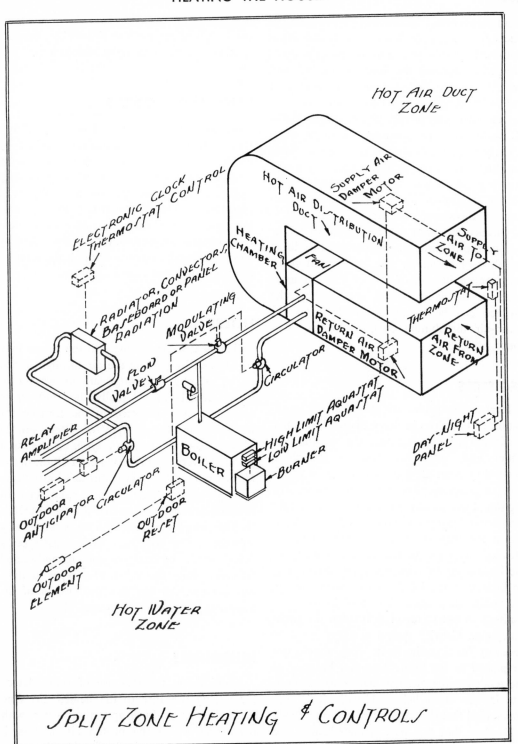

HOT AIR DUCT
ZONE

ELECTRONIC CLOCK
THERMOSTAT CONTROL

HOT AIR DISTRIBUTION DUCT

SUPPLY AIR DAMPER MOTOR

HEATING CHAMBER

FAN

SUPPLY AIR TO ZONE

RADIATOR, CONVECTORS, BASEBOARD OR PANEL RADIATION

MODULATING VALVE

THERMOSTAT

FLOW VALVE

CIRCULATOR

RETURN AIR DAMPER MOTOR

RETURN AIR FROM ZONE

RELAY AMPLIFIER

HIGH LIMIT AQUASTAT
LOW LIMIT AQUASTAT

DAY-NIGHT PANEL

OUTDOOR ANTICIPATOR

CIRCULATOR

BOILER

BURNER

OUTDOOR RESET

OUTDOOR ELEMENT

HOT WATER ZONE

SPLIT ZONE HEATING & CONTROLS

Fig. 76

mentation with "perimeter" placement of ducts for forced air heating in basementless houses. With this type of installation the ducts are placed beneath the floor, before the concrete is poured, for the entire perimeter of the walls. Registers are tapped into the duct in the outer wall of the various rooms. Since all warm air passes through a single duct, a fairly large cross section is required. Since the ducts also partially warm the slab, a certain portion of the heat is supplied to the rooms as radiant heat. Since the introduction of this forced-air system, a new style of furnace has been developed known as the "counterflow" furnace. It is designed to direct the flow of warm air out of the bottom of the furnace instead of out of the top as is done in the conventional style. Thus, the furnace can be mounted directly over the warm-air distributing chamber which saves space.

REGISTERS

Registers or grilles are placed at the termination of the pipes in the walls of the rooms. Their purpose is to make the air inlet or outlet look attractive, and to furnish a method of controlling the air stream in direction or velocity. For best appearance the register face should be placed with longer dimension horizontal. The area of the opening in the register should be more than the area of the pipe, to reduce the velocity of the heated air into the room. Registers may be located in the baseboard or higher up on the walls. They are best located in the sidewalls so as not to direct heat upon the room occupants. Gravity system registers must of necessity be near the floor. They should not be placed in the floor, however, because of the tendency for dirt and debris to accumulate in the ducts below. Usually it is recommended that they are not placed on outside walls since they lose part of their heat to the outside air. Forced air registers are placed at various heights on the walls. Return regis-

ters are often placed across the room from the supply registers, and if possible, beneath windows or near an open stairway.

FANS AND BLOWERS

Better distribution of hot air may be obtained by forcing the circulation of air by means of a fan. The fan may be kept going all of the time, but a more economical method stops and starts the fan automatically by a thermostatic control according to the need for heat. Both propeller and centrifugal types of fans are used, but if the duct capacity and filters would cause a drag on the circulation, a centrifugal type is required.

FILTERS

The heated air passing into the rooms may be cleaned by passing the air through filters, or by passing it through an air washer in larger installations. Usually the cold air is filtered as it is returned to the furnace for recirculation. Three types of filters are in common use. In the fabric type, air is passed through layers of porous paper or cloth. In the fibrous type, air is passed through loose vegetable, or mineral fibers such as spun glass. In the viscous type, air is passed through a metallic fiber which is coated with an odorless, oily substance. The advantage of the last type is that it may be washed and reconditioned for use, while the other two types require replacement. An electro-static system of filtration is now coming into use.

HUMIDIFIERS

Humidifying requires use of some device for adding moisture to the heated air. One method consists in evaporating water with pans over which the heated air is passed. The pan is automatically filled with water, with the amount regulated by a drip feeder, or by a float mechanism. Another method sprays water into the path of the air as it passes through the heating chamber or in the duct work.

SAFETY CONTROLS

Safety controls prevent overheating and explosions. Among boiler safety controls is the low-level water cutoff and water feeder. This control regulates the water level in the boiler and shuts off the fuel supply when the water level gets dangerously low. The automatic fill replenishes the water supply. The water temperature control shuts off the heat supply when the water gets too hot. In oil-fired units a combustion control prevents continuous pumping of fuel when there is no ignition spark. Required in many localities is a metal seal which snaps a valve closed and stops the oil supply when heat melts the seal. Gas furnaces have similar safety devices. A stack draft control prevents fires caused by excessive drafts.

There are several safety measures to be observed when installing a heating plan. A boiler or furnace should be kept a safe distance from wood beams, partitions, and so on. The ceiling above the plant should be surfaced with two heavy coats of cement plaster, or a 1½-ft. clearance should be allowed between the heating plant and the ceiling. No steam or hot-water pipe should be closer than 1 in. from ceilings, partitions, beams or other inflammable material. When pipes pass through partitions or floors they should be given at least 1 in. clearance all around.

HEAT REGULATION

Modern heating plants may be equipped with various valves and dampers which permit automatic control of the temperature. All types of automatic heating equipment are now provided with a thermostat which can be set for a desired temperature, and when the temperature falls below this predetermined point will start the heat source equipment. Some thermostats may be set to maintain a constant temperature, or they may be arranged to allow a low temperature for some determined time and then at a certain hour to raise the temperature to the desired degree of heat. The most complete type of automatic control provides the control of the temperature of each room, while a modification groups several rooms into a zone which is independently controlled. An important secondary feature of automatic control is to limit the boiler pressure or furnace temperature as a safety measure, and to prevent the starting of mechanical firing equipment when it may be injurious to permit its operation. A hydrostat in the hot-water system, or a pressurestat in the steam system regulates water temperature in the boiler.

Some thought must be given to the proper location of the thermostat, however, for a wrong location can decrease the efficiency of the heating system. The best place is on an inside wall, four feet or so from the floor. It should not be located near light fixtures because the resulting heat affects its proper operation. Neither should it be placed near outside doors because of the resulting cold air blast. It naturally follows that the thermostat should not be placed where it will be influenced by the direct rays of the sun or by the heat of a register or radiator, kitchen range, or fireplace. In most homes the best location is in the living room where most of the social activity is carried on. The temperature may vary in the kitchen and bathroom as a result, due to the heat from the kitchen range and the hot water from the bath or shower.

The use of a thermostat is not entirely satisfactory in radiant heat installations since the temperature of the water in the coils determines how warm the air in the room is rather than the temperature in the boiler. A better control is accomplished by wiring a circulator into the general control system. With this method, when the thermostat calls for heat, the circulator will start up to force the hot water in the boiler through the coils. If the temperature of the water is not sufficient to do the job, the mechanical firing equipment will be started to increase the temperature of the water to the proper degree.

HEAT LOSS AND HOW TO COMPUTE THE AMOUNT OF RADIATION REQUIRED

When the inside temperature to be maintained in a building is higher than that of the outside, there is a constant loss of heat from the structure. Direct transmission through the building materials accounts for the greatest loss of heat, with the remainder credited to air leakage or air infiltration through cracks and construction joints. It naturally follows that heat loss is determined by:

1. The larger the room, the greater the heat loss.

2. The poorer the wall construction, the greater the heat loss.

3. The colder the outdoor temperature, the greater the heat loss.

Basic rule for computing heat loss. Heat loss = area × wall effectiveness × degree temperature difference.

Area refers to the square feet of only that surface which is exposed to a temperature less than room temperature. *Surface* refers to wall, glass, door, floor, roof, and partition area that may be exposed to a cold temperature. It should be noted that no heat loss occurs between adjacent rooms if each room is heated to the same temperature. *Wall effectiveness* expresses the ability of a certain type of material to resist the flow of heat. A heat-flow transmission coefficient has been assigned to every type of commercially used surface. Constructions with low transmission coefficients indicate good insulators;

those with relatively high factors indicate poor insulators. These factors are variously referred to in the trade as "heat transmission coefficients," "B.T.U. Constants," "K factors," or "U factors." Reasonably accurate values showing the number of B.T.U.'s (British Thermal Units) transmitted per hour, per square foot of exposed surface, per degree of difference in temperature for various types of materials are usually used in heating computations. (See "Table of B.T.U. Constants," p. 289.) *Degrees temperature difference* represents the arithmetical difference between the inside room temperature and the coldest outside temperature likely to occur in a given locality, expressed in degrees (F.). It is common practice to use 70 deg. for the inside design temperature, with outside design temperature varying with the geographical location. The outside design temperature is not the coldest temperature ever recorded in a given locality, since extremely low temperatures usually exist for only short periods of time and it would be uneconomical to base design on that basis. The symbol for this temperature difference is T. (See "Table of B.T.U. Required for Heating Air," p. 290.) The basic rule for heat loss may now be stated thus: Heat Loss = A × U × T (Area times B.T.U. constant times temperature difference).

Time is a factor to consider. If a wall has a heat loss of 600 B.T.U., it is necessary to know whether this takes place in one minute, one hour, or one day. It is customary to express all heat losses in terms of B.T.U. per hour, written "B.T.U./hr."

Example Showing the Use of Tables

It is desired to heat a room to 70 deg. temperature with the outside temperature 10 deg. below zero. Assume that the room is of frame construction and hot-air heat is used. Assume also that the room contains 1800 cu. ft. of space, 200 sq. ft. of exposed wall, 70 sq. ft. of exposed single glass, and 180 sq. ft. of ceiling with floor above.

Solution

Referring to the table of B.T.U. for heating air we find the coefficient of 1.684 for a −10 outside temperature and a 70 deg. inside temperature.

	B.T.U.
1800 cu. ft. × 1.684	3,031

From −10 deg. to 70 deg. equals 80 deg. difference. With a wall with ¾-in. sheathing we get a heat loss of .35 from the table of B.T.U. constants.

200 sq. ft. wall × (80 deg. difference × .35)	5,600

With single windows we get a heat loss of 1.09 from the table of B.T.U. constants.

70 sq. ft. glass × (80 deg. difference × 1.09)	6,104

With a ceiling with floor above we get a heat loss of .26 from the table of B.T.U. constants.

180 sq. ft. ceiling × (80 deg. difference × .26)	3,744
B.T.U./hr.	18,479

These tables give all the information necessary to calculate the transmission losses when the size and construction of the building to be heated are known. Heat loss by infiltration is usually calculated by assuming that the entire volume of air is changed a given number of times each hour. With the total heat loss of the building thus determined it is necessary that a heating plant of sufficient capacity be provided to offset this loss.

The area and dimensions in inches of leaders (warm-air pipes in basement) and wall stacks (warm-air pipes running vertically); the gross area and dimensions of warm-air registers; the area and dimensions of outside-air ducts and the area and dimensions of outside-air registers must be calculated. On these figures are based the calculations for the size of the furnace and the capacity of its fire-pot, taking into consideration the size of the chimney and smoke pipe.

The judgment and experience of the designer may dictate allowances under special conditions such as intermittent heating, exposure factors, type of occupancy, and so on. Usually the design of the heating plant is left to the study by a specialized heating engineer since the problem involves more than elementary knowledge of air handling. Your contractor, architect, or local heating contractor can guide you in the most important selection. These experts can tell you the range within which you should make your choice, where your desires are in line with good engineering practice. Do not be too anxious to override their suggestions.

Table of B.T.U. Constants

The following constants indicate the heat loss through different materials per square foot of surface per hour per degree difference. The heat loss is expressed in B.T.U. or fractions thereof:

Walls

8″ brick	.46
12″ brick	.33
16″ brick	.27
20″ brick	.23
8″ reinforced concrete	.55
12″ reinforced concrete	.40
12″ sandstone	.44
18″ sandstone	.31
8″ concrete	.70
6″ plastered partition	.35
12″ concrete	.50
16″ concrete	.41
Corrugated iron	.85
⅞″ overlapped clapboard..................	.50
Same with paper lining.....................	.38
Same with ¾″ sheathing....................	.35
Same with ¾″ sheathing and paper...........	.32
Poor, loose construction................	.60 to .80

Openings in Walls

Single windows	1.09
Double windows	.56
Wood doors	.45

Exposed Roofs

Slate on 1″ boards....................	.50
Composition	.35
Reinforced concrete	.55
Sheet iron	1.30
Corrugated iron	1.50
4″ concrete, cinder fill..............	.65
Wood shingle	.38

Ceilings

Lath and plaster, floor above............... .26
Lath and plaster, no floor above.............. .42

Floors

¾" wood, plaster below.................... .21
¾" wood, no plaster below................. .42

TABLE OF DUCT AREA IN SQUARE INCHES

For 1st-floor rooms divide the total B.T.U. by 120
For 2nd-floor rooms divide the total B.T.U. by 150
For 3rd-floor rooms divide the total B.T.U. by 180

TABLE OF B.T.U. REQUIRED FOR HEATING AIR

External Temp.	Inside Temperatures			
	40	50	60	70
—40	1.802	2.027	2.252	2.479
—30	1.540	1.760	1.980	2.200
—20	1.290	1.505	1.720	1.935
—10	1.051	1.262	1.473	1.684
0	.822	1.028	1.234	1.439
10	.604	.805	1.007	1.208
20	.393	.590	.787	.984
30	.192	.383	.578	.770
40	. . .	.188	.376	.564
50	. . .	. . .	.184	.365
60	. . .	. . .	. . .	.179

External Temp.	Inside Temperatures			
	80	90	100	110
—40	2.703	2.928	3.154	3.379
—30	2.420	2.640	2.860	3.080
—20	2.150	2.365	2.580	2.795
—10	1.892	2.102	2.311	2.522
0	1.645	1.851	2.056	2.262
10	1.409	1.611	1.812	2.013
20	1.181	1.378	1.575	1.771
30	.963	1.155	1.345	1.540
40	.752	.940	1.128	1.316
50	.551	.735	.918	1.102
60	.359	.538	.718	.897

TABLE OF APPROXIMATE RADIATOR COEFFICIENTS

Single column 1.65
Two column 1.55
Three column 1.45
Four column 1.35
Window radiation 1.45

TABLE OF SIZES OF REGISTERS

Pipe Sizes	Size of rectangular floor register	Pipe Sizes	Size of baseboard register for 4" maximum stud	Size of baseboard register — no depth limit
6	8 x 8			7 x 10	7 x 10
7	8 x 10	8 " pipe	7 x 12	7 x 12
8	8 x 12	8 " pipe	8 x 13	8 x 13
8½	9 x 12	9½" pipe	10 x 12	10 x 12
9½	10 x 14	10½" pipe	10 x 13	10 x 13
10	10 x 16	11 " pipe	12 x 14	12 x 14
11	12 x 15	11½" pipe	12 x 15	12 x 15
11½	12 x 18	12 " pipe	12 x 18	12 x 18
12	12 x 20			
12½	14 x 16			
13	14 x 18			
13½	14 x 20			

HOT-WATER SYSTEMS

Heating with hot water (Figs. 77, 78, and 79) is very desirable and grows in favor because of its ease of automatic control, low fuel consumption, and even temperatures. Instead of the rapid heating and cooling with steam, hot water gives a steady warmth. Recent improvements on small-size hot-water boilers has brought this method of heating down to the scale of the small home.

The essentials of a hot-water-heating system are the *fire box,* surrounded by a *water jacket* with as much of its surface exposed as possible to the hot gases as they pass up the chimney. The water is heated and allowed, or forced, to circulate through a piping system to radiators or convectors, and to return to the boiler for reheating. The water gives up a part of its heat in each radiator or convector, heating the room by radiation.

There are two kinds of hot-water systems: gravity and forced circulation. Each may be either an open or closed system. The open

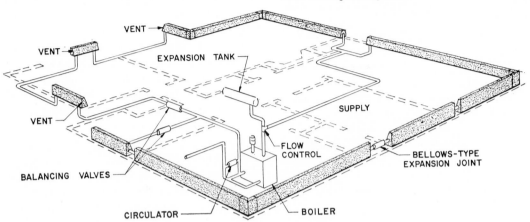

Fig. 77. Baseboard heating vent (left), circulation system (below).

Better Heating-Cooling Council

VENT
VENT
EXPANSION TANK
VENT
SUPPLY
FLOW CONTROL
BELLOWS-TYPE EXPANSION JOINT
BALANCING VALVES
CIRCULATOR
BOILER

Better Heating-Cooling Council

Fig. 78. Partially recessed convector.

temperature of the water will make it possible to use smaller radiators, and, the temperature can be raised faster. Some closed systems employ a "cushion" tank not open to the air, and containing air and water, installed near the boiler. As the water increases in temperature it expands and compresses the air which adds pressure to the water. Some systems are connected directly to the city water supply through a pressure-reducing valve combination providing constant pressure.

With the forced system, an electric pump at the boiler pushes the heated water around the piping circuit. When the rooms are at the proper temperature, the thermostat shuts off the pump. As the room temperature drops, the thermostat restarts the pump, circulating the hot water through the radiators, convectors, or heating panels. As the water gives up the heat to the rooms, a second thermostat (called an aquastat) within the boiler allows the burner to ignite where gas or oil are used as a fuel, or starts up the stoker where coal is automatically fired.

In both systems the heated water passes to the radiators through one set of piping called "supply" piping, and the cooler water

systems have a tank above the highest point in the line which is open to atmospheric pressure, and limits the heating of the water to below 212 deg. Fahrenheit, at which point the water would turn to steam. If, however, the pressure is controlled by a mercury column which adds 10 lb. to the atmospheric pressure, the water temperature can be raised to about 240 deg. without boiling; the higher

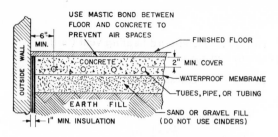

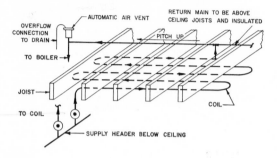

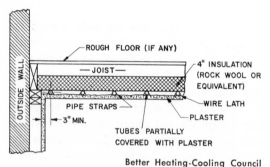

Better Heating-Cooling Council

Fig. 79. Three systems for running piping for radiant heating.

is returned to the boiler through a separate system called "return" piping. These are known as *two-pipe* systems. After the water passes through one radiator it does not pass through another radiator until it has been taken back to the boiler and reheated. Another system called the *one-pipe* forced circulation system is applicable to small homes. In this system there is only one main line of piping which starts at the boiler, and returns. At each radiator location water is taken from the main and is returned. At the end of the main the water is pumped into the boiler and is reheated.

Steam Heating. Steam has been used to a limited extent for heating houses, but is

less popular than warm air or hot water, partly because it requires more expert, and closer supervision than is possible in the average home. The steam-heating systems most frequently employed may be classified as: steam or vapor-vacuum; one-pipe or two-pipe; and direct or semi-indirect (split system). With direct steam the radiators are either very hot or cold, the valves cannot be adjusted for moderate temperatures, and the fire has to be hot enough to keep up a good steam pressure if steam is to circulate through the piping and give warmth.

The one-pipe steam heating and the equipment required for it consists of a steam boiler, piping to convey the steam to radiators or convectors and at the same time permit the water of condensation to return from the radiators to the boiler through the same pipes carrying the steam. All this is accomplished by having one or more mains starting from a point above the boiler and circling around the basement ceiling on a continuous downward pitch until they arrive back at a low point near the boiler, to which they are connected through a return header. Each radiator is connected at the bottom to one of the steam mains by a single pipe pitched downward from the radiator so that even though steam is rising through the pipe, the condensed steam which has turned to water can still flow through it back to the basement main and to the boiler. Each radiator must have a steam valve on the supply line and an air vent to allow the air trapped in the radiator to escape, or be pushed out by the steam.

When there is a supply line to piping with branches to each radiator and a return line with branches from the bottom of each radiator, it is known as a two-pipe system. This system insures ready circulation, but the installation requires more labor and material than the one-pipe system.

With the vapor-vacuum system a valve is installed which allows the air to escape from the piping and radiators as the steam advances, but which does not allow the steam to escape nor the air to return. When, therefore, the steam gives off its heat and condenses into water, a partial vacuum is created. This vacuum draws the water vapor from the boiler and maintains a circulation of vapor through the system, even though there are only a few ounces of pressure at the boiler. The condensed steam returns as water to the boiler, by gravity in the simpler systems and by pump where the boiler cannot be placed well below every part of the radiation.

The semi-indirect (or split system) is distinguished by a change in the location of the radiators rather than in the method of circulating the steam. To eliminate the unsightly appearance of radiators in the rooms and to insure fresh, warm air rather than a dead, dry heat, specially designed radiators are placed in a sheet metal enclosure or heating chamber, having intakes through the walls for the fresh or recirculated air. Each indirect radiator or pipe coil acts as a separate small hot-air furnace. This type of installation is quite expensive.

Radiant Heating. The oldest way of transmitting heat to the room from a hot-water heating plant is by means of radiators, groups of cast iron tubes through which the hot water passes. These tubes radiate a certain amount of heat to the room and give up the remainder of their heat by convection, by heating the moving air of the room as it passes over the tubing. Radiators can be "free standing" or "recessed." Recessed radiators, built into the walls, require insulation behind them to prevent the loss of heat through the wall. Radiators can be covered in either type of installation, in which even a greater proportion of the heat is transmitted as convected heat since the radiation is diminished by the radiator cover. Convectors which may also be free standing or recessed are always enclosed, and achieve a greater proportion of heat transfer by means of thin fins on the water tube within the enclosure. The heat of the water is absorbed by the fins, which in turn give up the heat rapidly to the air passing over them. It is customary to place radiators or convectors on outside walls, usually under windows, to form as effectively as possible a film of warm air over the coldest walls of the room.

Actually there is no such thing as strictly radiant heat in home heating, since all methods are a combination of convection and radiation. The costs of installation of radiant baseboards are higher than radiators or convectors but is no more complicated, and the advantages of more even heat distribution are usually considered more than worth the difference. There are two types of cast iron radiant baseboard: the strictly radiant type and the radiant convector type. The convector baseboard is recommended for installations where wall space for the regular radiant type is not adequate. The convector units can transmit more heat per running foot than any other type. Radiant and convector baseboards are made to fit harmoniously into the room design. Special corner sections and end pieces are used where the heating baseboard does not extend the full length of a wall to make the radiators inconspicuous. Some designs can be installed in conjunction with regular wood baseboards so that the heating baseboards are not noticeable. Baseboard radiators are particularly adaptable to basementless houses, since the heat rays given off at ankle height contribute to much greater comfort at the floor level than where conventional radiators are used.

The most popular type of large panel radiant heating makes use of coils installed in the floors. The greatest use of floor coils is made in basementless houses where the coils are set in a concrete floor slab, but many radiant floor-panel installations place the coils under wood floors. About an equal number of installations are made in the walls and ceilings, with the coils embedded in the plaster. Metal lath or wood lath, with the coils either behind or on the plastered side of the lath, seem to offer equally effective means of getting the heat into the room. It is important

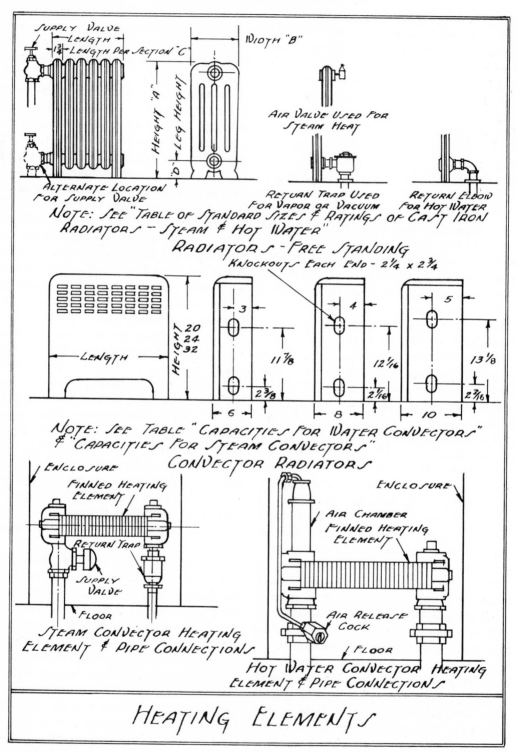

Fig. 80

that adequate insulation be placed behind the panels, so that the heat from the coils will be directed into the room to be heated, with a minimum of heat going to waste.

Radiators and Convectors. Radiators have undergone considerable change in design, and efficiency during the past years. The old-fashioned cast-iron column-type radiators have given way to the tube type, formerly built-in sections 2½ in. on center but now available in narrow slender-tube sections spaced 1¾ in. on centers (Fig. 80). The following table gives the standard sizes, and the ratings of cast-iron radiators for water and steam heat. The second column of the table gives the heat output per section in square feet of equivalent direct radiation (E.D.R.). One square foot of E.D.R. gives off 240 B.T.U.'s per hour (when the radiator is filled with steam at 215 deg. and when the room temperature is at 70 deg. Fahrenheit). To use the table, divide the B.T.U.'s per hour heat loss by 240 to arrive at the number of equivalent square feet of radiator surface required. Then select the height and width desired (columns A and B). Divide the rating per section into the E. D. R. required to give the number of sections.

Example

A certain room has a heat loss of 18,479 B.T.U./hr. What size of steam radiator would be selected?

Solution

$$\text{Required E.D.R.} = \frac{18{,}479}{240} = 77 \text{ sq. ft. of radiator}$$

surface. Assume a height of 25 in. which will be accommodated with a width of 4⁷⁄₁₆ in. A radiator with these dimensions has a rating of 3.0 sq. ft. per section of 6 tubes.

$$\text{Number of sections} = \frac{77}{3.0} = 26 \text{ sections}$$

The over-all dimensions are as follows:

Length = 26 × 1¾″ = 45½″
Width = 4⁷⁄₁₆″
Height = 22″

When radiators are to be used for hot-water systems the B.T.U. per hour heat loss (E.D.R.) of the room will be divided by the factors given in the following table which depend upon the average water temperature in the radiator.

E.D.R. PER SQUARE FOOT FOR HOT-WATER RADIATORS

Method of Firing	Average Water Temperature in Radiator	E.D.R. per Square Foot
Hand fired	180 degrees	165
Stoker fired	190 degrees	180
Oil or Gas fired	200 degrees	200

TABLE OF STANDARD SIZES AND RATINGS OF CAST IRON RADIATORS STEAM AND HOT WATER

Number of tubes per section	Sq. ft. rating per section	Height A	Width B Minimum	Width B Maximum	Thickness C	Leg Height D
		Section Dimensions — Measurements given in inches				
3	1.6	25	3¼	3¼	1¾	2½
	1.6	19	4⁷⁄₁₆	4¹³⁄₁₆	1¾	2½
4	1.8	22	4⁷⁄₁₆	4¹³⁄₁₆	1¾	2½
	2.0	25	4⁷⁄₁₆	4¹³⁄₁₆	1¾	2½
5	2.1	22	5⅝	6⁵⁄₁₆	1¾	2½
	2.4	25	5⅝	6⁵⁄₁₆	1¾	2½
	1.6	14	6¹³⁄₁₆	8	1¾	2½
6	2.3	19	6¹³⁄₁₆	8	1¾	2½
	3.0	25	6¹³⁄₁₆	8	1¾	2½
	3.7	32	6¹³⁄₁₆	8	1¾	2½

CAPACITIES FOR HOT-WATER CONVECTORS EXPRESSED IN MBH
(Thousand B.T.U. per hour) BASED ON AVERAGE WATER TEMPERATURES

6" Depth

Length given in inches:

Height	Av. Water Temp.	20"	24"	28"	32"	36"	40"	44"	48"	56"
	215	3.6	4.4	5.2	6.0	6.8	7.5	8.3	9.1	10.7
	210	3.4	4.2	4.9	5.7	6.5	7.2	8.0	8.7	10.2
	205	3.3	4.0	4.7	5.4	6.2	6.9	7.6	8.3	9.7
20	200	3.1	3.8	4.5	5.1	5.8	6.5	7.2	7.9	9.2
	195	2.9	3.6	4.2	4.8	5.5	6.1	6.8	7.4	8.7
	190	2.8	3.4	4.0	4.6	5.2	5.8	6.4	7.0	8.2
	185	2.6	3.2	3.7	4.3	4.9	5.4	6.0	6.6	7.7
	215	4.2	5.1	6.0	6.9	7.8	8.7	9.6	10.5	12.4
	210	4.0	4.8	5.7	6.6	7.4	8.3	9.1	10.0	11.8
	205	3.8	4.6	5.4	6.3	7.1	7.9	8.7	9.5	11.3
24	200	3.6	4.4	5.1	5.9	6.7	7.5	8.2	9.0	10.7
	195	3.4	4.1	4.8	5.6	6.3	7.0	7.8	8.5	10.1
	190	3.2	3.9	4.6	5.3	6.0	6.7	7.4	8.0	9.5
	185	3.0	3.4	4.3	4.9	5.6	6.2	6.9	7.5	8.9
	215	4.5	5.4	6.4	7.4	8.4	9.5	10.4	11.5	13.4
	210	4.3	5.2	6.1	7.1	8.1	9.0	9.9	11.0	12.8
	205	4.1	4.9	5.8	6.8	7.7	8.6	9.4	10.5	12.2
32	200	3.9	4.7	5.5	6.4	7.3	8.1	8.9	9.9	11.5
	195	3.7	4.4	5.2	6.0	6.9	7.7	8.4	9.3	10.9
	190	3.4	4.2	4.9	5.7	6.5	7.3	8.0	8.8	10.3
	185	3.2	3.9	4.6	5.3	6.1	6.8	7.5	8.3	9.6

		8" Depth				**10" Depth**		
		Length given in inches				Length given in inches		
Height	Av. Water Temp.	32"	40"	48"	56"	40"	48"	56"
	215	8.0	10.2	12.4	14.5	11.3	13.6	16.0
	210	7.6	9.8	11.8	13.9	10.8	13.0	15.3
	205	7.3	9.3	11.3	13.2	10.3	12.4	14.6
20	200	6.9	8.8	10.7	12.5	9.7	11.7	13.8
	195	6.5	8.3	10.1	11.8	9.2	11.1	13.0
	190	6.1	7.9	9.5	11.2	8.7	10.5	12.3
	185	5.8	7.4	8.9	10.4	8.1	9.8	11.5
	215	8.7	11.0	13.3	15.6	12.8	15.5	18.2
	210	8.3	10.5	12.7	14.9	12.3	14.8	17.4
24	205	7.9	10.0	12.1	14.2	11.7	14.1	16.6
	200	7.5	9.5	11.4	13.5	11.1	13.4	15.7
	195	7.0	9.0	10.8	12.7	10.4	12.6	14.8
	190	6.7	8.5	10.2	12.0	9.9	11.9	14.0
	185	6.2	7.9	9.6	11.3	9.2	11.2	13.1
	215	9.2	11.7	14.2	16.7	14.0	16.9	19.8
	210	8.8	11.2	13.6	15.9	13.3	16.1	18.9
	205	8.4	10.7	12.9	15.2	12.7	15.4	18.0
32	200	8.0	10.1	12.2	14.4	12.0	14.6	17.1
	195	7.5	9.5	11.5	13.5	11.3	13.7	16.1
	190	7.1	9.0	10.9	12.8	10.7	13.0	15.2
	185	6.6	8.4	10.2	12.0	10.0	12.2	14.3

Convectors are radiators consisting of non-ferrous or cast-iron heating element, which is usually finned to increase the heat-transfer rate. The element is placed in a decorative metal enclosure, which may be recessed in the wall, be semirecessed, or left free-standing against the wall. The table on page 296 gives the capacity for hot-water convectors expressed in MBH (Thousand B.T.U. per Hour) based on average water temperatures.

Insulation of Piping and Boilers. To maintain the temperature in the pipes, and to prevent water pipes from freezing in exposed positions in winter they are covered or insulated. Insulation of asbestos paper is placed around hot-water pipes to insulate against heat loss. Hot-water and steam pipes are covered with asbestos paper or corrugated asbestos paper wrapped with a cloth covering. Sometimes this insulation covering is held in place with metal bands. Boilers and water tanks may be covered with magnesia plaster, one or more inches thick, containing enough Portland cement to give a hard, glossy surface. A less expensive method is to place pipes inside walls or in floors, and insulating between studs or floor joists with mineral wool or other vermin and fireproof materials manufactured for the purpose.

Zone Control of Residential Heating. One thermostat cannot estimate the heating requirements for today's modern home. One section of the house may face the sun while another is sheltered. There may be wide dif-

CAPACITIES FOR STEAM CONVECTORS E.D.R. PER SQUARE FOOT WITH 215° STEAM AND 65° ENTERING TEMPERATURE OF AIR

6" Depth
Length given in inches

Height	Av. Steam Temp.	20"	24"	28"	32"	36"	40"	44"	48"	56"
20"	215	16.1	19.5	23.0	26.5	30.0	33.4	37.0	40.5	47.5
24"	215	18.5	22.5	26.5	30.5	34.5	38.5	42.5	46.5	55.0
32"	215	20.0	24.0	28.5	33.0	37.5	42.0	46.0	51.0	59.5

8" Depth
Length given in inches

		32"	40"	48"	56"
20"	215	35.5	45.5	55.0	64.5
24"	215	38.5	49.0	59.0	69.5
32"	215	41.0	52.0	63.0	74.0

10" Depth
Length given in inches

		40"	48"	56"
20"	215	50.0	60.5	71.0
24"	215	57.0	69.0	81.0
32"	215	62.0	75.0	88.0

Example

A certain room has a heat loss of 8,479 B.T.U./hr. The hot-water boiler is gas fired. Height of convector to be not over 24 in. and not deeper than 8 in. Probable average water temperature 200 deg.

Solution

$$1000 \text{ B.T.U./hr. (MBH)} = \frac{8,479}{1,000} = 8.479$$

Referring to Table **Capacities for Hot Water Convectors Expressed in M.B.H.** (Thousand B.T.U. per hour), for 8 in. depth and 24 in. height, we find 8.479 lies between 7.5 (32") and 9.5 (40"). The larger length should be selected so the room will not be underheated. Therefore the following specifications of convector would be used:

Height = 24"
Length = 40"
Depth = 8"

Example

Working the above problem out for a steam convector we would arrive at the following solution:

$$\text{E.D.R.} = \frac{8,479}{240} = 35.3$$

Referring to the Table **Capacities for Steam Convectors E.D.R. Per Square Foot**, for 8-in. depth and 24-in. height, we find the nearest factor to be 38.5 E.D.R. for 32-in. length. Therefore the following specifications of convector would be used:

Height = 24"
Length = 32"
Depth = 8"

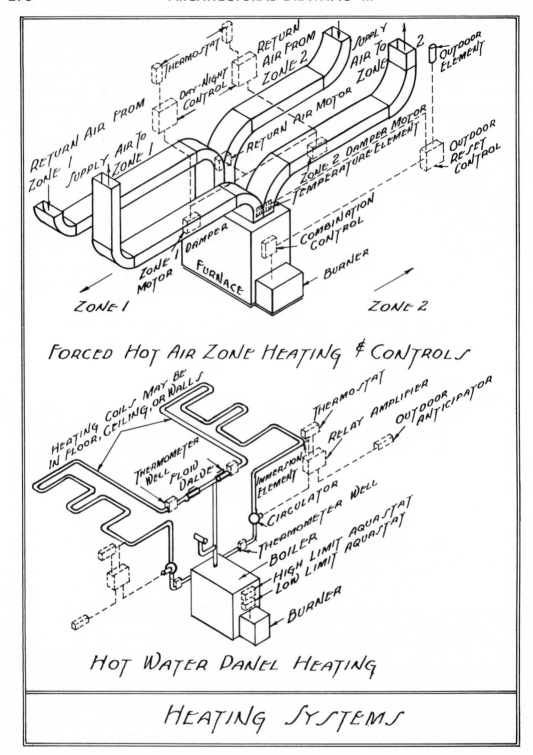

FORCED HOT AIR ZONE HEATING & CONTROLS

HOT WATER PANEL HEATING

HEATING SYSTEMS

Fig. 81

ferences in glass area, exposure, and occupancy. Heating requirements may vary from one group of rooms to another. Changes in weather or occupancy may cause some rooms to be colder than others. Any thermostat, no matter how good it may be, can only measure the temperature in the room in which it is located.

The best solution is to design the heating system to fit the home's natural heating areas and to provide thermostatic control for each zone (Fig. 81). The problem of determining the number of zones varies with the type of heating system, the design of the home, and the living habits of the occupants. One home may require a separate zone for the recreation room in addition to a zone for the balance of the house. Another may require a zone for sleeping quarters in addition to the recreation room and living quarters. Still another may need additional zones for service quarters, and so on. Finally, large homes may require individual room control as the best solution to the heating problem. Completely automatic, the temperatures in each of these zones can be maintained at the various selected levels throughout the heating system, for example, the sleeping zone can be held around 70 deg. during the early morning hours and be permitted to drop to 65 to 60 deg. during the rest of the day when it is unoccupied and return to the desired temperature for sleeping. Temperatures in the service portion can be held around 65 deg., because the physical activity usually associated with the kitchen or laundry makes a higher temperature both uncomfortable and unhealthful. The dining and living rooms can be warm during the waking hours and cool during the night. Temperatures in all zones can be lowered at night when occupants are asleep.

Another refinement in the control of home heating is modulation. This system provides a continuous flow of the heat medium, with just the right amount of heat constantly delivered to replace the amount being lost. In other words, your radiators are kept just warm enough at all times, or enough warm air is always being delivered through the grilles to make up the total lost through ceiling, walls, windows, and so on, instead of an intermittent supply of heat as with the "on and off" system. This operation can be used with zone heating so that it is now possible to have each of the principal parts of the home kept at the most desirable temperature, and at the same time have this particular temperature evenly maintained.

PRACTICAL CONSIDERATIONS IN PLANNING THE HEATING SYSTEM

1. The modern heating plant can be made a part of the space planned for recreation or other open area, since the modern units are designed as basement furniture. When the unit is placed in an open area, it can more efficiently heat the basement level of the house.

2. The unit should be placed as near the chimney as possible, since long smoke pipes reduce the heating efficiency. Gravity systems should be centrally located in the area to obtain an equal distribution of heat.

3. Place radiators beneath windows or against cold walls wherever possible because the cold air leaking in through the window is warmed before it reaches the interior of the room. Where large picture windows extend nearly to the floor a forced warm-air system or some form of radiant heat, such as the radiant baseboard, might be advisable. Double-glazed windows at these locations may help solve the problem.

4. In a warm-air system always arrange the ductwork so that the warm air is blown toward the colder outside walls.

5. Second floor partitions directly over those of the first floor are ideal for carrying the vertical risers of the heating ducts.

The heating system must be made an important consideration in the planning of the home since it directly influences the following:

1. The shape, size, and location of windows if radiators are to be used;

2. The arrangement of the basement area if the basement is to be heated, or if the heating unit is located in the recreational area;

3. The location of the chimney for efficiency of the heating unit;

4. The thickness of walls, spacing of the studs, and location of the partition walls if warm-air ducts are to be placed in them;

5. The construction of floors and ceilings where radiant heat is desired;

6. The location of room openings and wall spaces to provide for proper installation of registers and radiators, as well as for the warm-air return registers;

7. The construction of the house to achieve maximum heat insulation;

8. The shape of the house, and planned room arrangement to contribute toward compactness and consequent economy in heating.

DESIGN PROCEDURES IN PLANNING HEATING SYSTEMS

This chapter has been written specifically to enable a student in architectural drawing to study some of the information regarding heating systems for residential work. Sufficient technical data cannot be included in a general text, nor is a beginning student properly prepared to design heating systems which require specialized knowledge and wide practical experience. The following information is necessary for a complete set of heating plans:

1. Compute the B.T.U. heat loss per hour for each room to be heated.

2. Select registers, radiators, or convectors from manufacturer's data according to their rated output.

3. Determine the size of boiler necessary to give the necessary output. This may be found in the manufacturer's catalogs or other data sheets.

4. Make a sketch of the proposed piping or duct layout consisting of the supply and return lines and their branches, register or radiator locations, and risers to the second-floor level.

5. Prepare the finished layout drawing showing the following:

a) Locate boiler or furnace, water heater, storage tank, expansion tank, and oil burner tank where oil is to be the fuel. If the boiler or furnace is to be coal fired, plan the location of the coal storage bin. Check local codes for restrictions. Show all supply and return mains, and indicate the location of branches and risers giving all necessary size information. Be sure to show the smoke pipe from the boiler or furnace to the chimney flue, keeping this as short as possible.

b) Show the location of all registers, radiators, or convectors, and give their size and capacity on the first-floor plans. Show a schedule of manufacturer's sizes and catalog numbers. Show all risers to upper floors.

NOTE: It is not necessary to show every valve and fitting, since it is only necessary to give the size and location of the main pipes or ducts. If convectors or radiators are to be recessed, be sure to show a detail of the recess and also indicate the framing details on the framing plans.

6. To locate the thermostat properly, follow these rules:

a) Locate the thermostat in the room that is most frequently occupied by the family. This is usually a living room, dining room, or den.

b) Put it where there is reasonable air motion over it. Do not hide it in an alcove or corner of the room.

c) Use an inside wall to avoid the chance of a cold wall affecting its operation.

d) Avoid that part of the wall that has a warm-air duct, chimney flue, or perhaps a kitchen range behind it.

e) Avoid a location where warm air from the furnace, register, or radiator will affect its operation.

f) Place it so that heat given off from lamps, radios, television sets, and so on will not affect its operation.

g) It is usually desirable that the thermostat be located from 30 to 39 in. above the floor.

HEATING SCHEDULE

Space Heated	Iden.	Convector	Flow Tee	Depth	Recess Length	Height
Laundry	R1	FK- 5C-36" x 30"	¾" x #2	None		
Shop	R2	FK- 5C-42" x 30"	¾" x #2	None		
Living Room	R3	SG- 5C-36" x 18"	¾" x #2	3¾"	36½"	18¼"
Living Room	R4	SG- 5C-36" x 18"	¾" x #2	3¾"	36½"	18¼"
Living Room	R5	SG- 5C-36" x 18"	¾" x #2	3¾"	36½"	18¼"
Ent. Hall	R6	SG- 5C-30" x 24"	½" x #2	3¾"	30½"	24¼"
Dining Room	R7	SG- 5C-30" x 18"	¾" x #2	3¾"	30½"	18¼"
Dining Room	R7A	SG- 5C-30" x 18"	¾" x #2	3¾"	30½"	18¼"
Study	R8	SG- 7C-42" x 18"	¾" x #2	3¾"	42½"	18¼"
Lavatory	R9	RG- 3C-22" x 18"	½" x #1	3¾"	22½"	18¼"
Kitchen	R10	SG- 5C-48" x 30"	¾" x #2	3¾"	48½"	30¼"
Bedroom #1	R11	RG- 5C-30" x 24"	¾" x #2	3¾"	30½"	24¼"
	R12	"	"	"	"	"
Bedroom #2	R14	RG-10C-36" x 18"	¾" x #2	11"	36½"	18¼"
Bedroom #3	R15	SG- 7C-36" x 18"	¾" x #2	3¾"	36½"	18¼"
Closet #1	R13	RG- 5C-22" x 24"	½" x #2	5¾"	22½"	24½"
Closet #2	R17	RG- 3C-26" x 26"	½" x #2	3¾"	26½"	26½"
Bathroom	R16	SG- 5C-30" x 24"	½" x #2	3¾"	30½"	24¼"

ONE PIPE CIRCULATED HOT-WATER HEATING SYSTEM

Example Showing the Use of Tables: It is desired to heat a room to 70 degrees temperature with the outside temperature 10 degrees below zero, steam at 220 degrees. Assume that the room is of frame construction and that two-column radiators are used. Assume also that the room contains 1800 cu. ft. of space, 200 sq. ft. of exposed wall, 70 sq. ft. of exposed single glass, and 180 sq. ft. of ceiling, with floor above.

Solution: From −10 degrees to +70 degrees equals 80 degrees difference. Subtracting the room temperature from the temperature of the steam = 220 − 70 = 150 degrees. Since a two-column radiator is used, this 150 must be multiplied by 1.55 (see Table of Radiator Coefficients) which equals 232 B.T.U. per sq. ft. of heating surface per hour.

Referring to the constants for 80 degrees temperature difference we have the following losses through the various materials:

	B.T.U.
1800 cu. ft. × 1.684	3031
200 sq. ft. wall × (80 degrees difference × .35)	5600
70 sq. ft. glass × (80 degrees × 1.09)	6104
180 sq. ft. ceiling × (80 degrees × .26)	3744
	18,479

18479 divided by 232 equals 79 sq. ft. of two-column radiation.

Ten per cent should be added to the above for northern climates and windy exposures.

The length of each section of radiator is 2 in. and the width is 8 in. for all heights. The heating surface per section of radiator is as follows:

42"	5 sq. ft.
27"	3 sq. ft.
34½"	4 sq. ft.
31"	3½ sq. ft.
38"	4½ sq. ft.
23"	2½ sq. ft.
19½"	2 sq. ft.

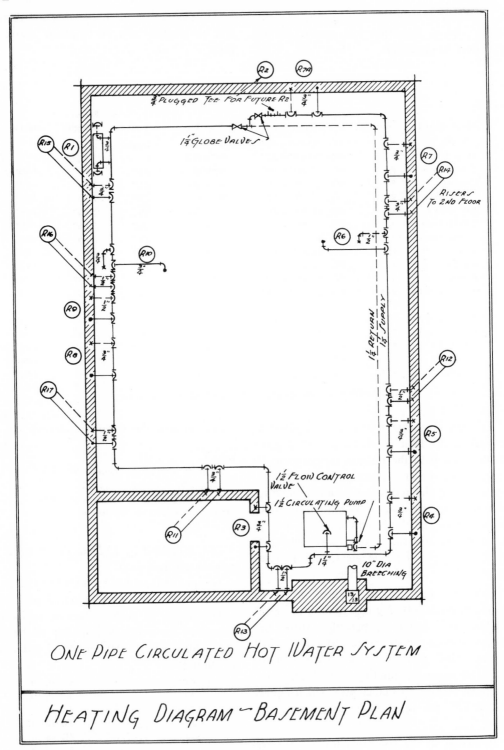

ONE PIPE CIRCULATED HOT WATER SYSTEM

HEATING DIAGRAM — BASEMENT PLAN

Fig. 82

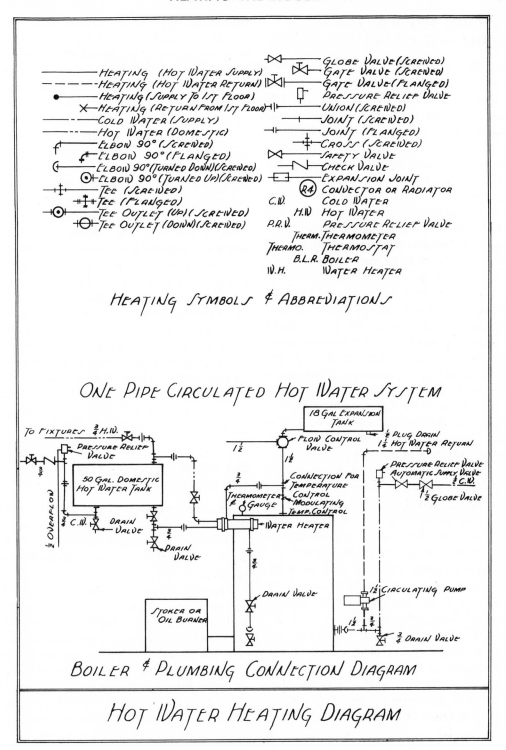

HEATING SYMBOLS & ABBREVIATIONS

ONE PIPE CIRCULATED HOT WATER SYSTEM

BOILER & PLUMBING CONNECTION DIAGRAM

HOT WATER HEATING DIAGRAM

Fig. 83

DRAWINGS REQUIRED FOR INSTALLATION OF HEATING SYSTEM

For large buildings, special heating plans are made by heating engineers from the set of drawings prepared by the architect. For small residential work, the location of the radiators or registers as well as for the heating plant itself are indicated on the floor plans, or on a specially prepared plan of the heating system as the requirements may indicate. From these indications the heating contractor makes a diagram drawing of the entire heating system for the use of the workmen installing the system. This procedure is used since the architect or planner writes a clause into the heating specification which states that the contractor must guarantee to heat the building to 70 deg. F. at −10 deg. F. outside temperature. This places the responsibility for successful operation of the heating system upon the contractor, therefore it is proper that he should do the necessary computation of the sizes of radiators, pipes, boilers, and so on. If the sizes were specified by the planner, the contractor would not be able to assume the necessary responsibility for the efficient operation of the system.

For the draftsman, the indications needed on the plans consist of showing a chimney, radiators, registers, boiler, furnace, hot-water heater and so on (Fig. 82). Pipe and duct indications are outlined in diagram on the plan for the circulation of the heated air. The types of insulation to be used for walls, windows, doors, ceilings, and roofs are shown in the detail and section drawings and by means of notes and specifications.

For residential work a 8½ by 13-in. flue lining is almost always used, except in gas-fired systems an 8-in. round is recommended to stop the condensation. For other size flues consult the recommendations of the manufacturer as found in catalogs.

The proper sizes of radiators should be obtained from the heating engineer. The radiators are indicated on the drawing by the appropriate symbol and specifications (Fig. 82). If the symbols cannot be drawn exactly to scale, they may be shown to an approximate size as a means of indicating locations. No attempt has been made in the treatment of this subject to give methods for finding the proper sizes for heating furnaces and boilers or the sizes for warm-air ducts and registers or radiators and convectors which would override the advice of a good heating engineer and later suggested practices. To do this properly would require an entire study by itself, and these methods have been set forth in textbooks on heating, ventilation, and air-conditioning as well as in publications issued by such specialized organizations as the National Warm-Air Heating Association and the American Society of Heating and Ventilating Engineers. For the draftsman or student interested in specializing in electrical, plumbing, or heating layout, the elements given here will serve as a brief introduction. Since each of these specialties is an independent phase of construction, study must be taken in the field of the student's choice.

AIR CONDITIONING FOR THE HOME

An air-conditioning system should do four things: keep the air in the house in motion, hold the air at the right humidity, clean the air, and keep the air at a comfortable temperature.

Air-conditioning apparatus is placed in the basement, attic, or out of doors with ducts leading from it to the registers in the rooms (Fig. 84). The ducts are the same as those of a hot-air heating system, except that the registers are placed high on the walls instead of down low near the floor. Incoming air, cleaned, moistened, and warmed in winter, cleaned and cooled in summer, streams in horizontally, to stir up and mix with the air ahead of it. From each room there is a duct to carry the cooled air back to the condition-

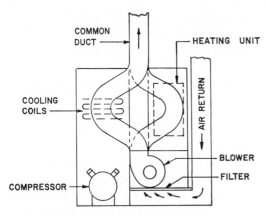

Fig. 84. Air conditioning unit.

of 71 degrees F., provided that the humidity conditions are right in the two cases to do so. An air conditioner is provided with a regulator to control the water supply, just as a thermostat controls the temperature of the air.

Another purpose of air conditioning is air cleaning. Moved by a blower, all of the air in a house passes through the conditioning machine two or three times to be filtered.

If cooling is not to be used, its future installation in most cases should be provided for by installing apparatus which can be so utilized if desired in connection with the possible later arrangement. The final touch in cooling a house or part of it is by mechanical refrigeration. Sometimes the machine is placed in the basement and is connected to coils in a cabinet in the room upstairs. Room air is circulated by a built-in fan. Sometimes the refrigerating machine is built into a cabinet. The cabinet must be equipped with a drain connection to carry off the water condensed from the air. A refrigerating machine must be used with care for there will be trouble should it produce too low a temperature. The temperature in a cooled room should be about 15 degrees F. below that of the outdoors. A lower temperature may shock one who comes in from outdoors.

Put in while a house is under construction,

ers, the registers for these being at the bottom of the wall or in the floor.

One function of air conditioning is keeping the air properly moist. Each pound of air is capable of carrying a certain amount of water vapor at any given temperature and no more. If this amount of vapor is exceeded, there is condensation. Where comfort is concerned, there is a close relationship between temperature of the air and humidification. The quicker the evaporation of perspiration, the cooler the skin feels. Consequently, the fact that a thermometer hanging on the wall says 68 degrees F. does not prove that the room may be producing comfort conditions equal to one having a similar thermometer reading

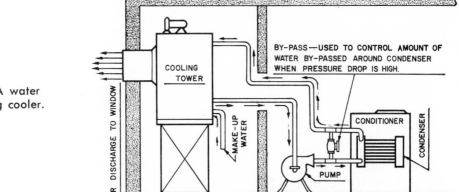

Fig. 85. A water evaporating cooler.

an air-conditioning system should cost no more than a steam or hot-water plant. The boiler is the same, with a saving on radiators and fuel costs. A house already equipped for hot air can be air conditioned, but not so effectively as when a system is built in. Conditioned air can be brought to the rooms through the same registers.

In localities with very low humidity, like the American Southwest, good results may be obtained by the evaporation of water. Air is forced over the evaporating water, and the air is cooled (Fig. 85). In areas of higher humidity, this system does not work well.

Often a unit or cabinet type of air conditioner designed to condition one room or, possibly, two small rooms is used in residences. In most of these units the parts are enclosed in a furniture steel cabinet, furnished to suit the color scheme of the room, and closely resembling the cabinet radiator. To accomplish all of the work which is ordinarily performed in the large central plants, air-conditioning units must contain fans to produce the air movement, heat-transfer surface to heat or cool the air, some means of humidifying for winter use, a deep tray to collect condensation when dehumidifying, and a small refrigerating machine which usually is located at some other point where it can be accommodated and where its operation does not offer objections. A refrigeration machine often resembles the machines used in apartment multiple-unit refrigerator installations, and is connected to the heat-transfer surface in the unit, either circulating the refrigerant directly or by the use of water between the machine and the unit.

Owing to the restricted space in which most of these units must be set, it is of considerable advantage to omit all unessential services, even though these services may be furnished and are desirable in large central plants. Since nearly all of such units recirculate 100 per cent and without the introduction of any fresh air from the outside, the matter of filtering the air becomes of secondary importance in residence work; hence, the omission of an air filter should not be regarded as too serious a matter in cabinet units. Also, in residences, it is perhaps not entirely essential to have humidification during the winter — although it undoubtedly would be desirable. Cooling during the summer is the real purpose of the unit air conditioner and without this feature there seems little to justify this type of equipment.

Plumbing System and Fixtures in a House

The plumbing system is roughed in after the shell of the house is completed. This consists of installing all the pipes through the walls and ceiling for the fresh water and the sanitary system, as well as installing the various outlets for the fixtures. The fixtures themselves are installed after the interior walls have been finished.

Plumbing for residential work is often regulated by local building codes, which vary considerably. In city areas, the plumbing codes may insist that the entire plumbing system be installed by a master plumber. Other codes may demand only that the installation meet the approval of the local health and building inspectors. In rural areas there may not be any uniformity required except that of the standards of the individual plumber. Because the comfort and health of the family members depends upon an adequate plumbing system, it is advisable to depend upon the work and judgment of one familiar with the requirements. The problems which have been solved by plumbers and sanitation engineers are of many kinds, but they all have to do with the problem of getting a supply of water into the house and the various fixtures, and getting the used water drained out and properly disposed of.

In improved city water supply systems, water is supplied under pressure to the branch piping underground to the house, which insures a constant supply available at the opening of a valve. In some localities the water is so hard that it is suitable only for drinking and sanitary purposes. For a supply of soft water, rain water stored in cisterns is distributed to the various fixtures through an entirely separate system of water supply piping. Usually this water is piped into the kitchen and laundry, and pressure is maintained by an electric motor or gasoline engine operated pump and tank. Pumps may be of the hand-operated type drawing water directly from the cistern to the sink. When the water is artificially softened, a branch line is taken off from some point in the water supply line and carried through a water softener. Some cities maintain a central water softener in connection with their water supply system.

Water is brought into the house from the street mains through pipes of lead, copper, brass, or galvanized iron (Fig. 86). The size of pipe will depend not only on the type of pipe but also on the pressure of the supply. If the water pressure is not very high, the distribution pipes should be 1 in. or 1¼ in. If the supply pressure is high, these mains can be reduced to ¾ in., but this may not always be sufficient to take care of any future expansion of the plumbing system. Short branch lines to the lavatories, toilets, etc., may be ½-in. pipe, and the kitchen sink and laundry should have ¾-in. lines. If brass or copper tubing is used, a smaller size may be substituted. It is better to use wrought iron, brass, or copper piping inside the house to carry the soft and hot water because of the chemical action of the water. Extra large pipe sizes should be used for hot water, since a lime deposit forms on the inside of the pipe. In choosing a material for piping, consideration should be given to the length of life as well as to low initial cost. The pipes supplying water to a bathroom containing bathtub, shower, lavatory, and water closet should be ¾ in. for both hot and cold water. If the water closet uses a flush valve instead of the usual flush tank, the cold water branch needs to be 1¼ in. It is convenient to have circulation pipes of ½ in. which will bring the hot water from the near end of each run of hot water supply back to the heater.

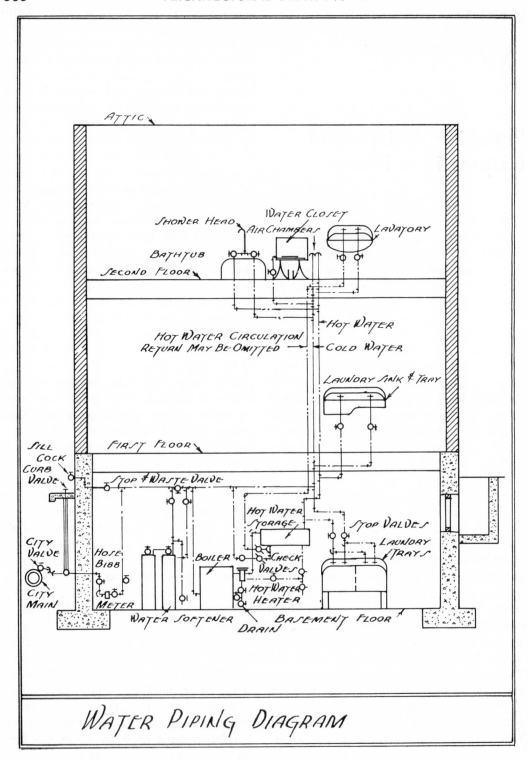

Fig. 86

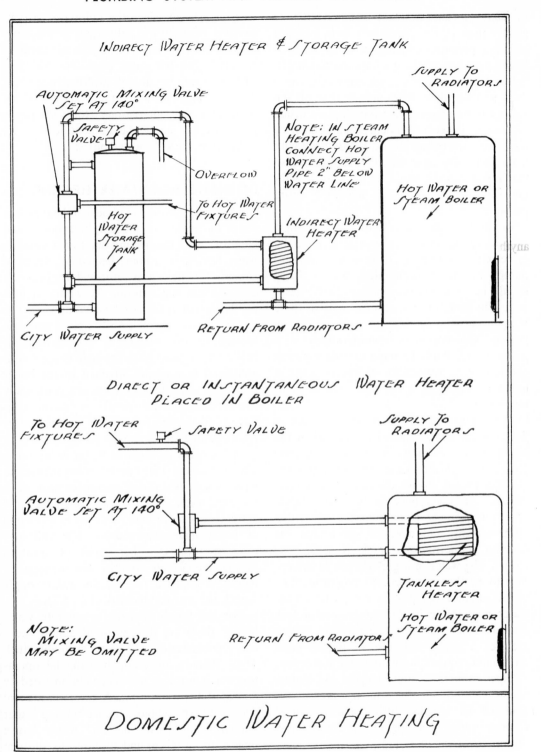

INDIRECT WATER HEATER & STORAGE TANK

AUTOMATIC MIXING VALVE
SET AT 140°

SAFETY VALVE

OVERFLOW

TO HOT WATER FIXTURES

HOT WATER STORAGE TANK

CITY WATER SUPPLY

NOTE: IN STEAM HEATING BOILER CONNECT HOT WATER SUPPLY PIPE 2" BELOW WATER LINE

INDIRECT WATER HEATER

SUPPLY TO RADIATORS

HOT WATER OR STEAM BOILER

RETURN FROM RADIATORS

DIRECT OR INSTANTANEOUS WATER HEATER PLACED IN BOILER

TO HOT WATER FIXTURES

SAFETY VALVE

SUPPLY TO RADIATORS

AUTOMATIC MIXING VALVE SET AT 140°

CITY WATER SUPPLY

NOTE: MIXING VALVE MAY BE OMITTED

RETURN FROM RADIATORS

TANKLESS HEATER

HOT WATER OR STEAM BOILER

DOMESTIC WATER HEATING

Fig. 87

In some localities where the pressure is greater than 70 lbs. per square inch, a device called a pressure-reducing valve is installed in the pipe line where it enters the basement. A main shut-off valve with provision for a drip, so that when the supply is shut off the water can be drained out from all pipes inside the house, is recommended. Each branch or riser and each fixture should be provided with a shut-off valve near the main supply line so that repair may be made to any branch without shutting off the water from the entire house.

In rural areas, if a gravity system from a hillside spring can be installed, it is to be preferred to pumping. If it is necessary to pump, the most economical motive force should be used and may be electricity, gasoline, windmill, or a hydraulic ram if there is sufficient gravity drop to generate steady power. The important considerations in a pump are its ability to stand up under almost constant use, availability of repair parts if anything should go wrong, and ease of making repairs.

If a pump is required, it needs a tank in which water can be stored for use when the pump is not running. An open or gravity tank can be placed in the attic, or a pressure tank is placed in the basement or underground. An open tank in the attic should have an overflow leading to the water-disposal system, and attention given that the framing supporting the tank is sufficiently strong. The water in a gravity tank is susceptible to weather extremes and may taste "flat" in the summer, if pipes are not protected the water may freeze in the winter, and a leak may do much damage. The pressure system requires a pump with reserve power, costs more, and requires more attention and repair.

Pipes come in standard lengths and require screwed fittings for the ordinary sizes at the ends of all lengths, turns, and branches. Copper tubing requires either compression fittings or soldered fittings.

Pipes should be insulated with wool felt, hair, or asbestos since the difference in temperature between the cold water in the pipes and the surrounding air may cause them to "sweat." The hot-water pipes are insulated with magnesia or air-cell covering to prevent their cooling. Hot-water tanks should be insulated for the same reasons. Hot-water pipes, if uncovered, should be kept at least 6 in. away from the cold-water pipes.

DOMESTIC HOT-WATER HEATING

There are several methods of heating the water for use in the kitchen, bathrooms, and laundry, using the heating plant or a separate water heater. In a home heated by means of a central boiler, it is practical to heat the domestic hot water during the winter months by the insertion of a water-heating coil. The water may be circulated through a pipe coil located in the firebox of the furnace or boiler, or it may pass through copper coils contained in a casing attached to the boiler in such a way that the coils are continually surrounded by hot water or steam contained in the boiler. Boiler manufacturers recommend that the boiler be operated year round in order to keep the boiler in top operating condition. This operational cost is somewhat higher than the operation cost of a separate water heater, but it is claimed the extra cost is more than made up in reduction of boiler maintenance costs. The coil may also be used in other types of furnaces during the winter months but a separate heater is required for the hot-water supply during the warmer months (Fig. 87).

For the family desiring a separate water heater, there are designs to fit almost every taste, pocketbook, and every available fuel. These heaters are made for manual operation and control, or automatically operated by an adjustable thermostat. A common manual controlled type employs a coal burning heater known as a "jacket heater," which has a hollow space all around the fire-box through which water is circulated and heated. The old range boiler and side-arm heater have virtually passed out of consideration as far as modern new homes are concerned. The modern designs need not be placed in the basement because of their appearance. They are completely automatic in operation, and most of them are adjustable for the desired water temperature.

Flat-top water heaters, counter-top height, have become popular where space is not at a premium. They are frequently installed in the kitchen or in a laundry room adjacent to the kitchen, making possible a very short run of piping between the heater and the point of maximum use. Counter-height heaters are available in sizes up to 40 gallon capacity.

Hot-water heaters are of two types: instantaneous and storage. The instantaneous requires no tank and automatically regulates the gas flame, or other source of heat to the amount of water required. The storage type has a storage tank of a size suitable to the demand for hot water, and the water is heated by its passing through a copper tubing which is in contact with the heat source (Fig. 88). Automatic water heaters are available for use with gas, oil, or electricity. There is a slight difference in burners for natural gas, manufactured gas, and bottled gas but they may be adapted with the insertion of new size tips. Gas can be turned on and ignited either manually or by a thermostat controlled by the temperature of the water in the tank. It is necessary for gas and oil heaters to have a chimney flue for the escape of fumes. Oil heaters require some attention from time to time to see that the burner equipment is clean. The gas and electric heaters require no attention, except with bottle gas the burner must be relighted after the gas tank has been changed.

Where electric rates are sufficiently low, electric submersion heaters are located in the storage tank and designed to use the electricity "off peak." If you are planning to use an electric hot-water heater, check with your utility company to see how much of the day is available for heating water. Usually water heaters are provided with separate meters that permit operation at a lower price than regular rates, but only at off-peak periods, that is, during the times when there is little other drain on the power supply. Since this is usually at night and sometimes only for a short period or not at all during the day, it is essential to have a heater with large enough capacity to carry the family through its hot water needs during the day.

The water heater has so much to do with kitchen and laundry efficiency today that consideration must be given to its capacity requirements. Modern households are using more hot water than ever before, because automatic washing of dishes and clothes calls for more hot water, and for hotter water than hand washing. Dish washers require up to 9 gallons for one load of dishes. Automatic clothes washers need up to 30 gallons for one 9–10-lb. load of clothes, and the average family has five such loads in the regular weekly wash. The make-up of the family counts too in the use of water — babies and

MINIMUM RECOMMENDATIONS FOR AVERAGE HOT WATER REQUIREMENTS
Oil Water Heaters

Number of Bathrooms	Number of Bedrooms	Storage Capacity
1	1–2	30
1	3–4	50
2	2–3	50
2	4–5	50

Gas Water Heaters

1	1–2	30
1	3–4	40
2	2–3	40
2	4–5	50

Electric Water Heaters

Number in Family	One Bathroom	Two Bathrooms
1	52	52
2	52	66
3	52	66
4	66	82
5	66	82
6	66	82
7	66	82

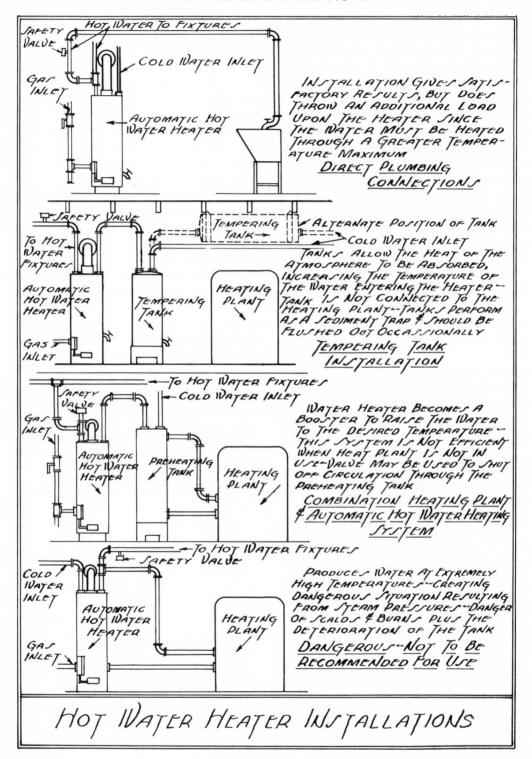

Fig. 88

very young children often requiring twice as much as an adult. Prospective customers of automatic washing machines should know that these devices will not perform satisfactorily without an adequate hot water supply. For economy it pays to buy one larger than 50 gallons in capacity, even for the smallest family. For a family of four, 60 to 80 gallons in capacity is not too large.

The table on page 311 gives the minimum recommendations for average hot water requirements. The chart is based upon the capacity of the house rather than on the number of persons who may be occupying the house at any given time.

The following table gives the average consumption of water in gallons per hour according to the fixture requirements. These figures will vary considerably according to the temperature of the water, habits of the individual user, and even to weather conditions.

AVERAGE HOT WATER CONSUMPTION
(In Gallons Per Hour)

Domestic Fixture	Gallons Per Hour
Bathtub	15–20
Shower bath	10–25
Baby bath	3–5
Lavatory (per person)	3–5
Tank closet	5
Valve closet	10–30
Kitchen sink	10
Laundry tub	20
Clothes washer — automatic	13–20 per cycle
Clothes washer — hand	12
Laundry rinse	6
Dishwasher — automatic	4–8
Dishwasher — hand	2–4

The following considerations should be given to the proper installation of a domestic hot-water heater:

1. Install the heater as close as possible to the most frequently used fixture, usually the kitchen sink.

2. If a range boiler is available, use it as a tempering or preheating tank, piping from the hot water outlet of the range boiler to the cold water of the inlet of the heater.

3. Always use as small a diameter hot-

water pipe as existing water pressures will permit.

4. Avoid long and circuitous hot-water piping.

5. Never connect the automatic storage hot-water heater to a circulating hot-water system.

6. Do not run piping so as to interfere with the servicing of the parts.

7. Install a shutoff on the cold water supply pipe to the heater.

8. Install a reliable relief valve or over-temperature shut-off valve in the system.

9. Never connect a furnace coil directly to the automatic water heater, as excessive temperatures may result.

10. Insulate all hot water piping if it may be exposed to low temperatures.

DISPOSAL OF WASTE MATERIAL AND GASES

Within city limits there are state, county, or municipal plumbing ordinances which must be followed. If there are no plumbing codes, the specifications must be carefully written to avoid unsanitary or defective installations. Thrift should be exercised through economical design rather than through cheap work and materials. Savings may be accomplished through the placing of all fixtures (including water closets, sinks, lavatories, etc.) as close together as possible, not only on each floor but one above another vertically on different floors as well.

In order to understand a typical plumbing system, it is necessary to know the function of each pipe and fitting. The essential equipment of a typical plumbing system consists of the following:

1. House sewer   5. Soil and waste stacks
2. House trap   6. Vent stacks
3. Fresh air inlet   7. Fixture branches
4. House drain   8. Traps

Drainage pipes outside of the house itself, that is between the house and the street sewer, or between the house and the septic

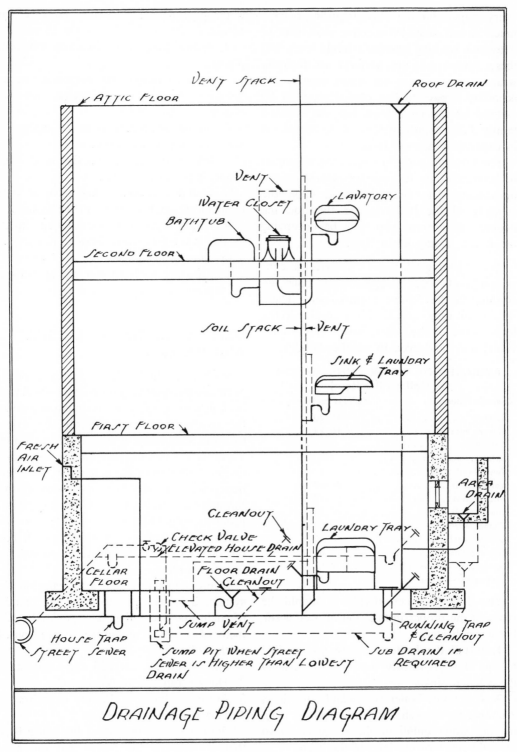

Fig. 89

tank, are called the "house sewer." They are usually of 6-in. vitrified tile, but when there are many trees at hand they should be of cast-iron since the roots will seek the moisture and grow into the tile joints. The main soil pipe placed under the basement floor, should be at least 4 in. in diameter and laid to a pitch of ¼ in. to the foot.

Directly inside the wall of the house and connected to the house sewer is the "house trap" (Fig. 89). The trap is intended to furnish a water seal against the entrance of gases from the public sewer to the piping inside the building. House traps are generally "U" shaped with cleanouts at the top of one or both outlets. Although the house trap serves an important function, occasionally it interferes with the flow of sewage and requires cleaning out. There is a difference of opinion among experts as to whether this trap is necessary or desirable, and while they are required by some building codes, in others they may actually be forbidden.

The house trap acting as a water seal will cause compression of air or gases in the stacks and house drain if air is driven ahead of a heavy discharge of water. To prevent compression which might force gases through the traps and into the fixtures an inlet is provided on the house side for fresh air to enter the system. This "fresh air inlet" should be half the diameter of the house drain, although many plumbers prefer to keep it the same diameter as the drain. This pipe should be furnished with a perforated brass grill at its outer end, and this outlet should be a minimum of 6 in. above grade.

The "house drain" is the horizontal drain inside the house into which the vertical soil and waste stacks discharge (Fig. 90). It must have a minimum diameter of 4 in. and a pitch of at least ⅛ in. to the foot. The location of the house drain depends upon the depth of the public sewer below grade. The house drain may be embedded in the cement floor, suspended by metal straps from the floor joists above, or it may be fastened along the foundation wall by metal straps. To prevent clogging, cleanouts (C.O.) should be provided at intervals not more than 50 ft. apart and at the end of the house drain beyond the last vertical stack, and at each change of direction of horizontal run.

To receive the waste water from the various fixtures in the bathroom, kitchen, laundry, and so on, vertical lines of pipe called "soil" and "waste stacks" are provided, which connect at the bottom to the house drains in the basement. To prevent decomposition of the waste matter, a circulation of air throughout the stacks and drains must be provided. The air circulation dilutes poisonous gases, retards pipe corrosion, and maintains balanced atmospheric pressures in the various parts of the system.

"Vent stacks" in the plumbing system are intended to provide the air circulation to the soil lines. They should be at least one half the diameter of the soil or waste stack. Vents for fixtures and branch connections should be at least 1½ in. in diameter.

"Fixture branches" are the horizontal pipes running from the fixture traps to the soil stacks and must have a pitch of ⅛ to ½ in. per ft. If this pitch is to be maintained, the branches must be kept short, especially if they are to be laid between the joists of a floor and ceiling below. "Branch vents" are to the horizontal fixture branches as the vertical vent stacks are to the vertical soil stacks. They should be pitched so that any moisture that may collect in them can flow back to the branches, and so arranged that waste matter flowing through the fixture branches cannot clog and foul the vents.

The house drain, soil line, and waste line are made of extra heavy cast-iron; the joints are packed with oakum and then sealed with soft pig lead hammered into the hub of the joint. Branches are of galvanized wrought iron, or sometimes of lead. The exposed portions of pipe are made of brass and are nickel plated, especially in bathrooms. The ordinary "wiped" joint may be made by soldering,

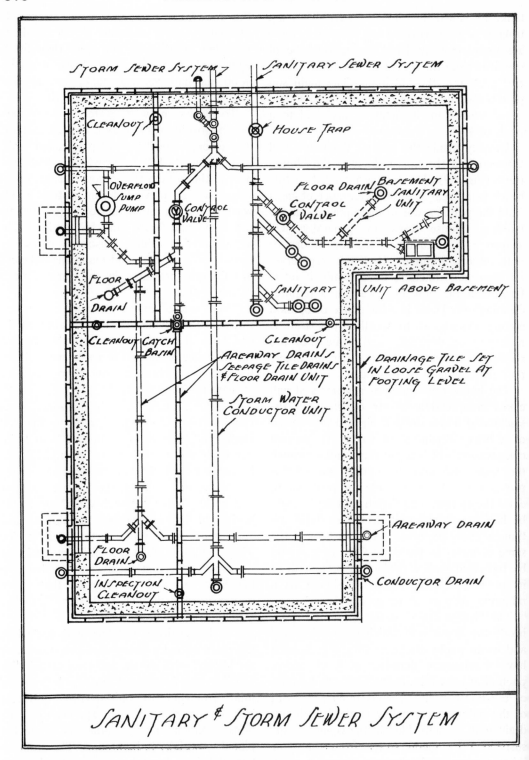

Fig. 90

out where lead and cast-iron pipe are to be connected, a brass ferrule must be used to make the junction. The joints on the ordinary wrought iron pipe are screwed.

The branch waste lines for water closets should be a 3-in. diameter minimum with 4-in. diameter recommended. For bathtubs and laundry tubs a 2-in. diameter minimum, with a 3-in. diameter worth the additional expense. Wherever possible the pipes in the floors should run parallel with the joists, which avoids cutting and weakening the members. Vertical 4-in. pipes are too large to be enclosed in ordinary partitions, so that either the partition must be thickened or the pipes must be run in out-of-the-way corners of closets. The soil pipes running from water closets may be packed with pipe covering, or in mineral wool to deaden the noise of the flow of water. The fixtures in each case must have a water-filled trap either as a part of the fixture itself, or inserted in the waste pipe line at the fixture. One trap may be used to serve several fixtures depending upon their character and how close they are together. Every trap must have a pipe connecting to the soil pipe near it so that air can pass freely through these pipes to the waste pipes at each fixture. If these branch vents were not used, a tendency for air to be drawn from the rooms through the fixtures and into the waste pipes would exist; this air would push the water out of the traps into the waste pipes. If sinks, laundry tubs, or lavatories because of their location cannot be connected to this single stack, then a 2-in. waste pipe is sufficient for them provided it is carried above the roof and at the roof line increased to 4 in. in cold climates to prevent its becoming clogged with frost.

PLUMBING FIXTURES

The selection of fixtures for the house is largely a matter of preference and price. Inexpensive fixtures by a reliable manufacturer are quite as sanitary as expensive ones. Five general materials have been used for plumbing fixtures: porcelain, enameled iron, vitreous ware, marble, and soapstone. Porcelain is the most expensive and is suitable for all fixtures. Enameled iron fixtures are lighter and less liable to break and are taking precedence over the porcelain models because of improved manufacture and lower cost. Vitreous ware is not unlike porcelain, though it is more like "crockery." Sometimes this grade goes under the name of "vitreous earthenware." Marble was formerly used but is now being crowded out by other materials. Soapstone at present is used chiefly for laundry tubs. Modern plumbing systems have been in common use with little change except for the introduction of new materials, methods of manufacture, and design of fixture for improved appearance.

Bathtubs and Showers. Modern bathtubs are of the built-in type where the back and one or both ends are placed flush with the wall, and the front extends down to the floor leaving no space under the tub for an accumulation of dirt. Brackets or hangers can be obtained so that the rim of the tub can be supported on the wall studs and the remainder of the weight carried by the floor joists. All enameled iron tubs have roll rims varying in width from 1½ to 5 in., the 3 or 3½ in. being the popular size. Tubs are 30 or 36 in. wide and from 4 ft. 6 in. to 5 ft. 6 in. long, with the 4 ft. 6 in. commonly used. The height of a bathtub is usually 14 to 20 in. from the floor to the top of the rim. Recently a square tub has been designed to give a diagonal bathing space of 5 ft. 6 in. which can be used in bathrooms of unusual shape, or set into a 4 ft. 0 in. square recess (Fig. 91).

Bathtubs can be used as a shower-bath receptor and enclosed with a curtain. The trend, where cost permits, is toward a separate compartment which may be built in or bought as a separate unit. The door opening may be closed with a curtain or fitted with a metal or glass door. These showers

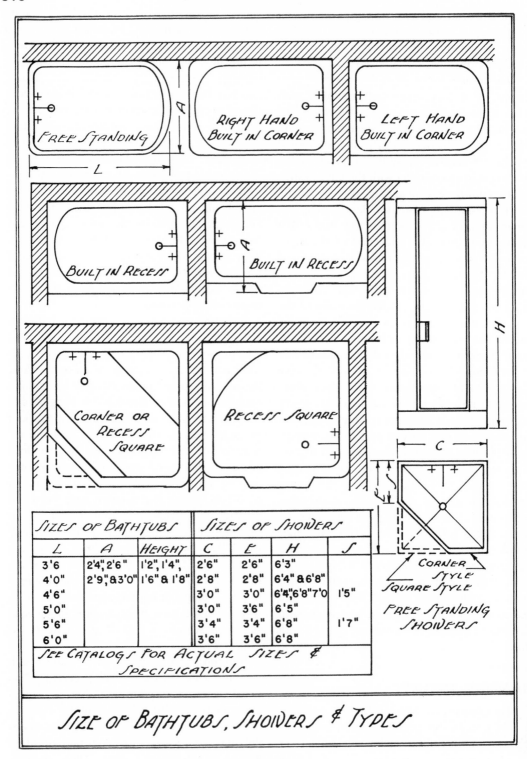

SIZES OF BATHTUBS			SIZES OF SHOWERS			
L	A	HEIGHT	C	E	H	S
3'6	2'4", 2'6"	1'2", 1'4",	2'6"	2'6"	6'3"	
4'0"	2'9", & 3'0"	1'6" & 1'8"	2'8"	2'8"	6'4" & 6'8"	
4'6"			3'0"	3'0"	6'4", 6'8" 7'0	1'5"
5'0"			3'0"	3'6"	6'5"	
5'6"			3'4"	3'4"	6'8"	1'7"
6'0"			3'6"	3'6"	6'8"	
SEE CATALOGS FOR ACTUAL SIZES & SPECIFICATIONS						

SIZE OF BATHTUBS, SHOWERS & TYPES

Fig. 91

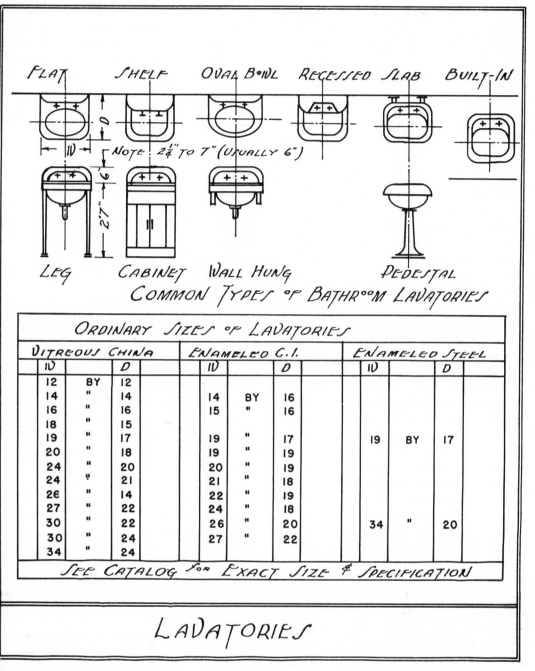

Common Types of Bathroom Lavatories

ORDINARY SIZES OF LAVATORIES								
VITREOUS CHINA				ENAMELED C.I.			ENAMELED STEEL	
W		D		W		D	W	D
12	BY	12						
14	"	14		14	BY	16		
16	"	16		15	"	16		
18	"	15						
19	"	17		19	"	17	19 BY	17
20	"	18		19	"	19		
24	"	20		20	"	19		
24	"	21		21	"	18		
26	"	14		22	"	19		
27	"	22		24	"	18		
30	"	22		26	"	20	34 "	20
30	"	24		27	"	22		
34	"	24						

SEE CATALOG FOR EXACT SIZE & SPECIFICATION

LAVATORIES

Fig. 92

can be installed in tiled wall recesses, or the prefabricated compartments may have sheet-steel walls. If a tile floor is used a lead pan should be used under it to prevent leakage, or a receptor of precast stone, porcelain, or enameled cast iron, or stamped steel may be used. The shower head may be of the pierced type, which requires cleaning, or of the self-cleaning type. The valves for controlling the water supply to the shower may be separate and adjusted by the bather, or a more expensive mixing valve may be used to obtain the desired temperature. Mixing valves are of three types: (1) hand-operated, which does not maintain the water at a constant temperature automatically; (2) pressure-regulating type, which takes care of any sudden changes of pressure in the hot-water line; and (3) the thermostatic type which automatically provides for any changes in temperature or pressure.

Modern fittings are chromium-plated brass because the plating is hard and will not tarnish. The overrim nozzle located in the wall at the end of the tub is preferred to the bell type of supply fitting attached to the inside of the tub. The bathtub valves may be combination hot and cold, or separate faucets. Instead of the rubber plug with chain, a pop-up waste fitting controlled by a lever may be used.

Lavatories. Hand bowls or lavatories are of three types distinguished by the manner in which they are supported: (1) wall-hung, which rests on brackets supported from the wall; (2) pedestal, which is supported from the floor on a central pedestal of the same material as the lavatory itself; and (3) leg, which is partly supported by brackets on the wall and partly on two chromium-plated metal legs at the two front corners of the fixture. Lavatories may have round bowls, oval, half-round, and corner shapes, as well as fittings such as metal towel bars, and so on. A 13 by 17-in. bowl is very convenient, though some run as large as 15 by 21 in. The area of the entire lavatory is from 24 in. wide and 36 in. long down to 21 by 26 in. A good average size is 20 by 24 in., containing a bowl 12 in. by 15 in. See Fig. 92.

Water Closets. There are two main types of water closets: (1) the siphon-jet, which is preferable, and (2) the washdown bowl, which is cheaper. See Fig. 93. There are two methods of operation: (1) flush

tank with an accumulation or storage of water in a flush tank holding from 3½ to 8 gallons or (2) flush valve, with water pressure in the supply pipe operating through a direct valve. For the flush-valve type there must be sufficient pressure in the supply pipes at all times, and the supply pipe usually must be a minimum of 1¼-in. diameter. Since this type is sometimes considered noisy it is not generally used in homes. However, some flush valves are noiseless and do not require large-diameter piping. The modern fixtures have shown a preference toward the low flush tank and in some styles are made all in one piece with the closet bowl (Fig. 94). Recent years have seen an acceptance of colored fixtures rather than white porcelain.

Sinks. Sinks come in many types and materials (see Figs. 115, 116, pp. 373 and 375). The material may be either enameled cast iron or enameled pressed steel, and for a little additional cost they may be made acid-resisting. Porcelain and vitreous china sinks may be purchased but are not generally used because of their cost. A more expensive type of sink may now be purchased in monel metal or stainless steel. Sinks may be purchased with one or two drainboards, and for either hand in the single board. They are also purchased in the single bowl, or may be had in the double bowl, which is most convenient for dishwashing. Sinks may have an integral splashboard back on which the fittings are placed, or without a splashboard in which case this feature becomes a part of the wall. At the waste outlet a large strainer may

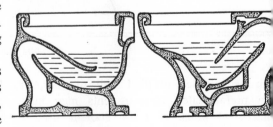

Fig. 93.   Siphon (left), siphon jet (right).

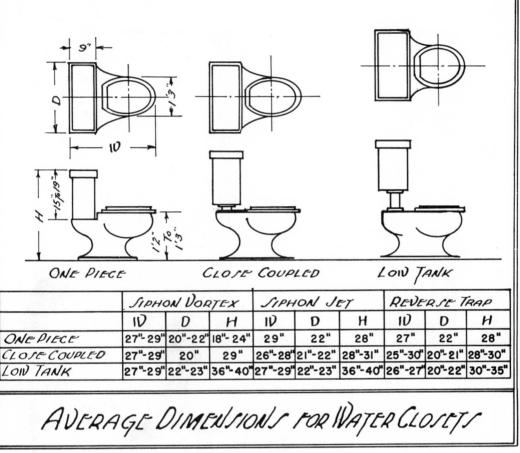

	SIPHON VORTEX			SIPHON JET			REVERSE TRAP		
	W	D	H	W	D	H	W	D	H
ONE PIECE	27"-29"	20"-22"	18"-24"	29"	22"	28"	27"	22"	28"
CLOSE COUPLED	27"-29"	20"	29"	26"-28"	21"-22"	28"-31"	25"-30"	20"-21"	28"-30"
LOW TANK	27"-29"	22"-23"	36"-40"	27"-29"	22"-23"	36"-40"	26"-27"	20"-22"	30"-35"

AVERAGE DIMENSIONS FOR WATER CLOSETS

Fig. 94

be provided which simplifies the removal of waste. Sinks may also be of the cabinet type with storage space provided below the sink, wall-hung and open below, or wall-hung and leg-supported.

The kitchen sink should be placed so that the height of the sink from the floor to the top of rim of the sink will be from 36 to 38 in., or so that the height is comfortable for the person using it. The size of sink commonly used is 22 by 42 in., though there are many other sizes available. A double bowl with a single drainboard usually is about 22 by 60 in. while a double bowl with two drainboards would be about 22 by 79 in.

An excellent location for the sink is on the outside wall and under a window, but this requires placing the supply and waste pipes where they will not freeze in extreme weather or protecting them by sufficient insulation. In some modern arrangements the sink is located in the center of the room or other convenient location to the work space. Windows over a sink must be placed high enough to allow the splashboard to fit under the window sill. Since most sink backs are about 9 in. high, the bottom of the window must be placed above the splashboard. A new corner sink is now on the market.

Faucets and Fittings. There are several varieties of faucets on the market, and one of the most satisfactory is the swivel-nozzle type which delivers hot or cold water, or water mixed to any desired temperature.

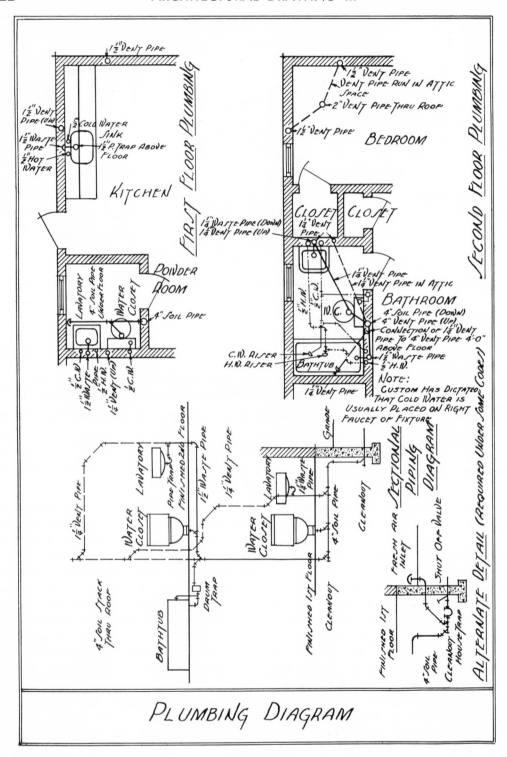

Fig. 95

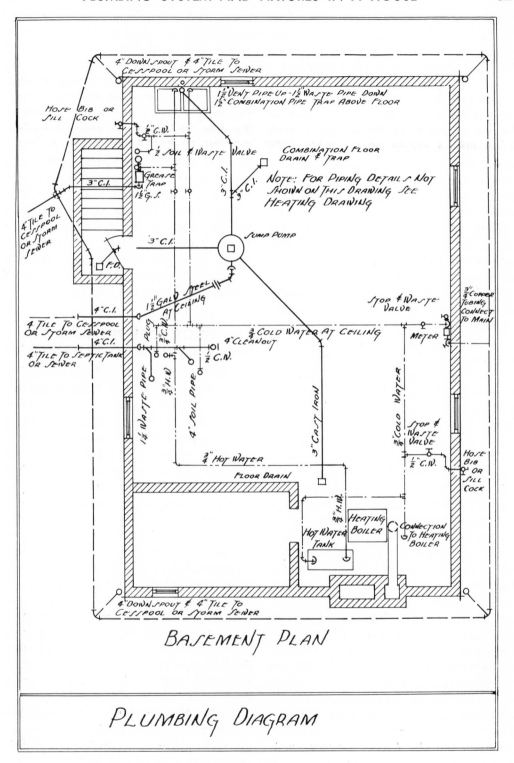

BASEMENT PLAN

PLUMBING DIAGRAM

Fig. 96

Often a spraying attachment with a short hose is included, and in some a brush with a spray in one unit. Most fittings are chromium-plated brass; some faucets are bronze with a chromium-plated brass housing.

Laundry Tubs. Laundry tubs may be of porcelain, enameled iron, aluminum, slate, or soapstone: the last named being the cheapest and durable but not as sightly or as easily cleaned. Usually they are mounted on a metal stand with legs often adjustable for height. The two tubs are usually built into one unit and are about 54 by 26 in.

Sewage Disposal. Disposal of sewage and waste water outside the house is a simple problem if there is a municipal sewer system and disposal plant. The plumber installs his iron pipe or tile through or under the foundation wall and 4'0" or 5'0" beyond the foundation wall. It is the responsibility of the contractor to extend the sewer pipe or tile from this point to the city sewer. Care must be taken that there is no possibility of the settling of the foundation or wall to break the piping. A cleanout plug is installed just inside the foundation wall. The connections to the city sewer may be done by the plumber and supervised by the city, or in some localities only the city may do it.

Septic Tanks and Cesspools. The cesspool is merely a hole in the ground about 10 ft. 0 in. deep and 8 ft. 0 in. in diameter and lined at its circumference with bricks, loose stones, or cement blocks. The sewage is drained into the hole and the liquid gradually seeps into the soil. This method, however, may pollute wells in the area.

The better and more modern system is the installation of a septic tank. The operating principle of the system is based upon the fact that the upper layer of soil contains air, and when dead organic matter comes in contact with air, the oxygen and nitrogen convert the matter into harmless mineral form. The most efficient form of septic tank is one which consists of two chambers — a settling tank, into which the sewage flows directly from the

house, and a treatment chamber, which is emptied by an overflow or syphon action into a system of drain tiles in which the purification of the sewage is completed. The settling tank consists of a hermetically sealed concrete box where bacteriological action is constantly taking place, breaking down and dissolving the solid matters and rendering them harmless to health. When the settling chamber is filled the liquid overflows into the treatment chamber where bacterial action continues. The overflow from this chamber is discharged into one or more series of radiating lines of tiled drain pipe set 12 to 18 in. below the surface, with open joints which allow the liquids to be distributed under a wide expanse of soil. The sun and air rapidly disinfect and dry up the liquids.

DRAWINGS REQUIRED TO INDICATE PLUMBING INSTALLATION

The floor plans will indicate the location of the bathroom, kitchen, laundry, and toilet rooms, giving the location and size of the various fixtures. This is all that is ordinarily necessary since an experienced and competent plumbing contractor, guided by these plan locations and the plumbing codes in force, can install the system properly. Some sets of working drawings may include drawings of the plumbing installation represented by a section with a single line representation of the pipes, fittings, and an elevation symbol representation of the fixtures (Fig. 95). On these drawings the lines are coded for the representation of hot-water lines, cold-water lines, soft-water lines, steam, and the single line representations of the fittings. A similar line representation is made of the piping on the floor plan (Fig. 96). Such representations are usually made of the storm-sewer system, the sanitary system, drainage tiles, etc.

The architectural draftsman should refer to a plumbing fixture catalog for the sizes of the various fixtures to avoid poor planning factors before actual work begins.

Modern Lighting and Electrical Installations

Progress made in the use of electricity in recent years affects almost every phase of our living, and has changed the ideas of house planning, principally in lighting but also in the use of various pieces of electrical equipment. It is necessary, as a result, when planning a house, to have sufficient knowledge of recent studies in methods of lighting, number and location of electrical outlets, adequate wiring for present and future use, suitable electrical fixtures, and so on.

INTERIOR HOUSE WIRING

There are two general classes of wiring, one in buildings under construction, and the other in buildings already constructed. The first type represents less difficulty in wiring and is less expensive for the same general class of electrical service. The wiring of finished buildings requires the tearing up of floors and additional labor difficulties.

The wires are laid in a building by several different types of installation. These may be enumerated as follows: (1) rigid conduit; (2) flexible conduit; (3) armored cable; (4) metal and wood molding; and (5) the knob-and-tube. The type of building construction and the available funds for the work, as well as the state and city electrical codes in force, dictate which system is most applicable.

Consider first the installation of the rigid-conduit type. The conduit consists of soft steel pipe cut in standard 10-ft. lengths, quite similar to the ordinary gas and water pipe, and has the standard pipe threads. It is made in the nominal pipe sizes. Conduit couplings and standard bends may be obtained for joining the lengths and forming the curves. The best method of obtaining the proper bends, however, is to bend the pipe as desired, since the soft steel pipe readily permits of such treatment. Where several parallel circuits are run, and where the sizes of conduit vary, the only way to produce angle bends of the same concentric amount is by bending the conduit according to requirements. The conduit must run in rigid continuity from one outlet to another. These outlets occur wherever a switch, light, or other device is to be located. The conduit terminates in an outlet box of metal construction to which it is made rigid by means of lock nuts. These outlet boxes afford a space for the wires to be tapped for the branch circuit. Such construction when completed is continuous from the supply end throughout the building to every outlet connection (Fig. 97). This conduit system may be put in while the building is under construction. Then, after the building construction has been completed, the wiring may be pulled through from outlet to outlet and the fixtures and attachments then connected so that the system is elecrically complete. This type of construction represents the best practice. If, at later periods, the wires become damaged, they may be pulled out and other wire introduced without disturbing the building construction at all. This represents a very desirable asset. This system is more expensive than the others in first cost, but it is most highly recommended and has the minimum of fire hazard.

The next type of installation is that of the flexible conduit. This also is a highly approved type of construction, although not quite of the high standard of the rigid conduit. It is made of steel strips wound spirally to form a tube with the edges of the strips so interlocked that considerable flexibility of the tubing is permitted. It comes in coil lengths ranging from 50 to 250 ft., depending

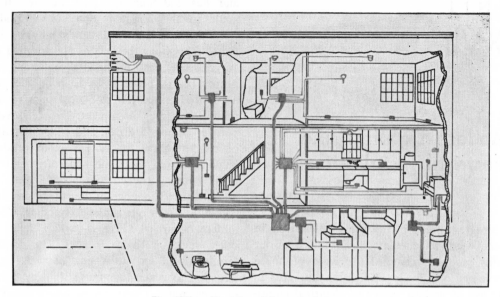

Fig. 97.   Electric wiring service.

upon the size, and is made from ⁵⁄₁₆ to 2½ in. inside dimension. The flexible conduit must be continuous from outlet to outlet and is attached to the outlet boxes by means of a collar that clamps a threaded end. This end may be held to the outlet box by lock nuts. This type of wiring may be used for concealed work in either finished or unfinished buildings. Of course, the installation of a rigid system in a finished building means a difficult and expensive undertaking; but the flexible conduit may be fished around through the partitions and under the floors with a minimum of removal of floor boards.

The third system which is often used, is the so-called armored cable. It is a flexible conduit, constructed directly over the wire with its insulation. Lead-covered cable is often used in damp locations, and is also directly installed in a concrete setting. These types of cable cannot be joined by couplings because of the wire connections and, therefore, the cable must be continuous from outlet box to outlet box. It may be held into the outlet boxes by means of clamps. Such construction is readily fished through the finished building.

Molding is a form of construction which is used entirely for exposed wiring. It is unsightly but does render a cheap construction that is often necessary where economy is of first importance. There are two forms of molding; one is metal and the other is wood. The metal molding is permitted in most places, but wooden molding is not in good repute in general and many city ordinances prohibit its use at all, although the underwriters do sanction its use for certain places. The metal molding consists of a backing in the form of a sheet-metal trough over which a cover of the same material may be snapped into place after the wires are installed in position. There are fittings for angles, receptacles and "T" connections in order to make possible a continuous metal covering. The metal may be cut in any desired lengths by a hacksaw or be bent if the cover is on. The molding backing is fastened into place by means of screws. Wherever the molding passes through a ceiling, it must be protected by first installing pipe through which it may be passed. If the molding is to be put through a wall, no pipe is required provided the wall is not subjected to moisture and that the molding is continuous through the partition without any joints. Wood molding may be used only for exposed work and is not allowed in damp places or for circuits having higher than 300 volts.

The cheapest form of electric wiring that is used for concealed work is called the knob-and-tube system. It has been used to a great extent in wiring moderate-priced houses. In the more progressive communities, it is becoming an obsolete form, however. The porcelain knobs are employed to support the wire from contact with the surface over which it is wired. Tubes are used for general protection and wherever the wires pass through the walls or any other obstruction. There is also a tubing of flexible nature called "circular loom." It is used for protection to the wire and serves as additional insulation, being used especially where taps are taken to an outlet to protect the wires as they pass into the outlet box.

Obviously, the wiring of a building under construction is relatively simple. The circuits may be located as desired without constructional difficulty and regardless of the system employed. When wiring old or finished buildings, however, ingenuity is required as well as a general knowledge of types of architecture and construction. The service will lead into the house by a bracket support and glass insulator where the wires will enter a conduit and drop down for entrance into the basement. A drip loop is always allowed just where the wire enters the post head of the conduit, in order to permit moisture to collect and drop off rather than run down the wire inside of the conduit. Conduit fittings are employed at the angles so that a continuous protected circuit may lead directly into the basement. Sometimes the wires are led from the bracket supports directly into the attic. In any event, however, the service board is placed as near as possible to the entrance point and the wires are run directly into a fuse block and main switch. The meter is next connected in to record the consumption of electricity. From the meter the live wires are run into distribution blocks from which the individual circuits radiate through the house, each being protected by a set of fuses. A branch circuit should not be over one hundred feet in length and not more than 660 watts per circuit is permitted.

In the wiring of a house of finished construction an analysis of a complete system throughout the house is described. The number of watts to be located on each circuit must be calculated to determine the number of circuits to radiate from the service board. The armored cable is by all means advisable and would, therefore, be used for wiring in the average installation. One circuit would be carried across the basement to the nearest point to that section of the house to be covered. Suppose the rooms to be lighted by this circuit are the kitchen, pantry, back porch, and the dining room, and that three wall lights are required in the kitchen, one in the pantry, one on the porch, and a three-light chandelier over the dining-room table, to be operated by an electrolier switch at the entrance from the kitchen, and four wall-bracket lamps. The circuit would be run up through the wall separating the kitchen and dining room to the floor above. A junction box would be placed there and would permit a tap to be made for a circuit to the kitchen, the pantry, and the porch lights. The porch light would in this case be controlled by a switch placed near the kitchen door. This circuit can readily be fished around. When a central or ceiling fixture is to be installed, the wire may be run out to the proper position by simply removing a couple of boards in the floor above. The wall switch for the control of such a center fixture must be connected in series with the lights of the fixture. The electrolier switch is so devised that, by successively snapping the switch, one, two, three, or more lamps may be lighted as desired. For the dining room and for the central fixture in a large living room or library such electrolier switches are more convenient.

The drawing room and living room should have portable units, such as floor or table lamps so that the arrangements may be flexible. The use of wall brackets judiciously placed in conjunction with the portable lamps produces a system whose flexibility permits of any degree of variation. The lighting of any room may be studied from three viewpoints, each a consideration of the use to be made of the light at that particular point. The first consideration is the general flood of light used to illuminate the room. This can best be obtained by a ceiling fixture. Second is the low level of general illumination around the outside of the room, useful for auxiliary lighting but not intended for practical lighting sufficient for the activities carried out in the home. These local highlights are furnished by bracket lights 5 ft. 6 in. to 6 ft. above the floor. The last consideration is of the direct lighting designed to accommodate the family in its natural activities. For this lighting shaded lamps of many descriptions are used.

Closely related to the lighting outlet is the switch with which these lights are controlled. No longer do pull chains and cords dangle from the ceiling fixtures of the modern home. The clumsy snap switch was closely followed by the more efficient push button, and this is now superseded by the tumbler switch. Three-way switches make it possible to light up a room as you enter it from one side, and to switch off the light when you leave through a door at the opposite side. These have long been in use at the head and foot of the stairway. Pilot lights, which warn by a brilliant bull's eye on the switch plate when a distant light has been left burning, reduce the chance that a lamp in the attic, basement, or garage may not be turned off.

A sufficient number of convenience outlets should be located on the wall surfaces where electric current might be required in the future. The cost of installing these outlets at the time of building is very small in comparison to special installations after necessity requires them. Convenience outlets of the duplex type, providing opportunity for plugging two appliances into the same outlet, are in general use. All outlets should be located after consideration of the particular function which they are intended to perform. Most of these outlets belong on the baseboard near the floor where they will be inconspicuous and yet accessible. Floor lamps, television, and similar furnishings are seldom moved and may be considered semipermanently located.

Equipment of the nature of a vacuum cleaner requires plugging in the appliance cord every time it is used. Locating outlets for these at waist height will eliminate the necessity for continual stooping to the baseboard.

The general room illumination of the dining room should be relatively low, whereas the localized lighting, by means of a central fixture over the table, should be more brilliant to display the center of attraction and to cause the important details, such as walls and pictures, to form a shadowy background for the table proper. An inverted bowl may be employed having a system of droplights around its edge. The inverted bowl diffuses the light generally about the room, whereas the drop lights directly illuminate the table. The shade holders for the drops should be sufficiently deep to screen any glare from direct rays. In large rooms, in addition to such a central fixture, the general illumination may be supplemented by well-placed wall brackets having units of small candle power and protected by silk screens or shades.

The illumination of the hallway and vestibule should be controlled from one downstairs position near the street entrance and one position at the head of the stairs.

The lighting requirement of kitchens, closets, pantries, piazzas, and basements are so general that it is necessary only to remind one that an adequate amount of light is essential and that the location of the units should be well chosen so that their purpose will be fully accomplished.

In the bedrooms, wall brackets with appropriate shades form a very attractive lighting arrangement. More elaborate requirements may demand reading lamps from floor plugs and small table lamps for use at the bedside.

The bathroom should have a light unit placed at both sides of the mirror over the lavatory. Such light shines into and illuminates the face directly.

There is another important unit of the electric wiring installation to which more consideration should be given than is usually the case. This is the fuse box, where the various wiring circuits are protected against any overload which might result in serious damage. Only in recent years has it become customary to locate this unit where it could readily be found. In the past this important unit was located in the basement where it could only be reached by the man of the house. The modern preference is to place this box in the wall of some part of the service quarters of the house. It is logical that this unit be placed near the load center which is the kitchen. Circuit breakers are replacing the customary fuse boxes in the more recently built homes.

LIGHTING THE HOME

The newer concept of lighting a home is to plan the lighting that we may see the things we want to see, clearly and comfortably. Lighting should be conditioned to our needs, making it serve our comfort, convenience, health, and visual tasks. Illumination engineers have defined the rules of good lighting as follows: (1) artificial illumination should not be exposed to direct vision, and glare should be eliminated by shielding, shading, or placing it out of line of vision; (2) general illumination of the room should not be less than one tenth of the brightest areas of local lighting, to avoid sharp contrasts; (3) each area of the room should be lighted according to the activity it is designed for, and accomplishes; (4) all lighting in areas where activities vary should be subject to control according to the various needs of changing occupancies and activities.

Two factors must always be considered in planning the lighting of your home: the practical and the decorative. First to be considered is the necessity of providing adequate amounts and conditions of lighting for the various tasks and occupations carried on in the home, many of which are extremely demanding visually. Reading, sewing, food preparation, and ironing are at the top of the list of jobs requiring plenty of light. Also on the practical side is the location of lights and switches for handy and instantaneous service whenever and wherever needed, in basement, attic, closets, garages, and entrances.

The decorative aspect is no less important. Its first principle is to furnish an over-all level of illumination intense enough to form a cheerful background for living, yet not so intense as to be distracting or disturbing. It is practically impossible to have too much light indoors, provided sharp contrast and glare are eliminated. The amount of light in a given area or surface can be measured with a light meter, which measures units called "foot-candles." One foot-candle is the amount of light on an object or surface 1 ft. away from a standard candle. Lighting recommended for some of the household activities are given as follows:

Five foot-candles are the suggested minimum for general lighting of the garage, bedroom, basement, bathroom, hallway, stairway, dining room, living room, sun room, utility room, and library. The kitchen should have a minimum of 10 foot-candles.

More light than this is needed for some activities such as reading and sewing, and provision must be made to supply this additional light. Suggested illumination for specific areas where these light demanding activities are carried on are:

40 foot-candles for bathroom mirror, laundry, range, sink, study table for children, desks, and work counters in the kitchen, basement, and garage.

20 foot-candles for dressing table mirror and writing table.

10–40 foot-candles for game tables.

20–40 foot-candles for reading areas.

20–100 foot-candles for sewing areas.

Proper distribution of light is as important as sufficient quantity. Sharp contrasts in lighting should be avoided. A bright reading light in an otherwise dark room is hard on the eyes. In a well-designed fixture, the bulb cannot normally be seen from any part of the room.

Secondary to the general intensity of illumination is the use of lighting to enhance the significant architectural and decorative features of a room. This is one function table lamps perform; other examples are concealed lighting in bookshelves, niches, and mantels, and the use of spot or flood lights to highlight pictures, statuary, or other decorative accessories.

Methods of Lighting. Light distribution from any artificial source may be direct, indirect, semi-indirect, or a combination of these. Where the light is directed downward with little or no attempt to conceal the source, the most light is given for the least cost. The disadvantage is that this type of lighting produces strong contrasts with objectionable glare, and the light is not uniformly distributed over the room. To get uniform distribution, the ceiling lights should be spaced apart one-and-one-half times the vertical distance between the surface illumination level and the lights. This form of lighting is classified as "direct lighting." When indirect lighting is used all the light is directed upward to the ceiling by means of inverted reflectors, and the source of light is hidden. The ceiling is brightly lighted and reflects the light, which requires more electrical current to give the required amount of light but it does give a softer and more uniformly distributed light than does direct lighting. Semi-indirect lighting directs most of the light to the ceiling, but allows some of it to be projected downward. Some of the softness and diffusion is sacrificed, while the cost is re-duced for a given amount of light from that of the indirect type. Fixtures with shallow bowls distribute light better than do deep ones. Two feet below the ceiling is the most efficient position for the bowl; however, for appearance' sake since homes have low ceilings, bowls can be placed 4 to 6 in. below the ceiling. The closer the fixture is mounted, the lower the number of foot-candles obtained. Lighting recessed in the ceiling is also used.

In almost all planning there are some local areas where special activities are carried on, which require an intensity of light much greater than provided by general lighting. All lighting will consist of a combination of general and localized types. The largest group includes lighting units suspended from the ceiling, whose function is to light areas at a distance from the walls and to unify all lighting. They also keep the floor plan from being cluttered up with too many tables and portable lights. Wall lights which include brackets, urns, and cove lights are used for wall illumination and to light the ceiling areas above. Cove lights are designed to cast the light out on the ceiling from a point above the eye level and thereby conceal the glare. In cove lighting the light source is recessed behind a setback of the walls of the room or above a projecting ledge, and usually is installed along the two facing long walls of a room. The greater the width of the room, the lower the cove must be to allow the light rays to fan out and avoid a dark area in the center of the ceiling; it is impractical for ceiling heights of less than 9 ft. and room widths greater than 18 ft. The height from the floor, the distance of the light from the wall, and the light wattage all must be carefully calculated — a job requiring some expert help. Special construction also helps make cove lighting the most expensive, but also one of the most attractive and satisfactory lighting applications. Panel and soffit lights are built flush into a surface and have a reflecting box containing the light source. The front may be enclosed by lenses or prismatic glass arranged to distort the light beams in the desired directions. The box may be built into the ceiling or be suspended below it, and has the light shielded and reflected by a series of vertical cubicles. In cornice lighting, fluorescent tubes are installed close to the ceiling behind a cornice board set a few inches out from the wall. Distances, tube wattages, and so on, need not be so carefully figured, since it is not essential to light the entire wall evenly. In fact this effect might be undesirably flat and monotonous. Valance lighting involves no special construction and is the most easily installed of the three built-in types. Lights are installed behind a window valance to shine down on the draperies, up on the ceiling, or both. One of the most appealing aspects of valance lighting is the way it approximates the effect of sunlight flooding the draperies, giving the room somewhat the same appearance at night as during the day. Two minor cautions to observe with valance lighting: (1) to place the light source far enough out from the draperies to keep the ruffled headings and deep folds from casting shadows, and (2) to select the fabric under the same lighting conditions. Spotlights may project lights on points of interest such as side walls, niches, mantels, dining tables, and so on. All of these forms of lighting may be cleverly designed to fit any decorative scheme or style. Old-fashioned fixtures may be used for their association and decorative value rather than for practical use. It is just as practical to conceal the light source as it is to hide the laundry or heating plant.

Lighting Needs in the Individual Rooms. Since the living room is one of the most important all-purpose rooms of a house, a study of its complex lighting may serve to exemplify the problem of lighting in the simpler rooms. If the room is planned around the furniture to be used, at least a rough draft of the floor plan with the furniture grouping should be available. Circles large enough to embrace the area of light cast should be drawn to mark the area served by local lighting of high intensity. These circles represent the light cast by portable lights such as floor lamps, table lamps, and so on. Dotted circles for lamps not frequently used will help in your study. These circles indicate two things: (1) where the light is concentrated if there is no general illumination, and (2) where the areas of light will strike the ceiling if the shades are open at the top. Perhaps the local lighting will be scattered around the perimeter of the room leaving the center dark to suggest general illumination from a center ceiling fixture. If the lighting is concentrated near the center it would suggest lighting concealed around the walls in troughs or coves. If the lighting is grouped near one end it would suggest cove lighting at the other end, or a torchère lamp or wall lights of indirect type which will serve the same purpose. The areas in the plan that are not well served by the circles representing portable reading lamps in general use will become the centers of much larger circles indicating general light sources. Next it must be decided where emphasis is needed in the general lighting scheme and adding the extra light sources needed on the dominant parts of the lighting composition. These portions of lighting may be indicated by some symbol such as half circles or whatever form shows where the light will fall, and where it comes from. The final step is to locate special types of lighting that are only used upon occasion and do not contribute to the general illumination of the room. From this study it is immediately possible to locate convenience outlets for all portable lamps to be spaced at 6 to 10-ft. intervals around the walls or baseboard areas. Convenience outlets will also be needed for fans, electric clocks, radios, television sets, vacuum cleaners, and so on.

Lighting in the dining room should be directly down from over the center of the table, from a source that is shielded from the eyes under normal conditions, and yet spread enough to highlight the head and faces of the persons at the table. It should be bright enough to make the table the brightest spot in the room, but glare must be eliminated by general illumination. Diffusion of the light from the linen and table service will serve to light the lower part of the faces, and prevent distorting shadows. One method employs a spotlight concealed in the ceiling directly over the table, and soft cove lighting for general illumination. The same effect can be produced by a fixture in which the direct down light is incorporated in a combination with bowl-type indirect general lighting. The candle-type chandelier is often used with shades around the lamps but is not as efficient, for most of the lighting must be reflected from the ceiling.

At the front entrance, lighting that will serve four purposes is needed: (1) identification of the house by illumination of the house number, (2) expression of hospitality to the visitor, (3) identify the visitor, and (4) reveal the beauty of the entrance. If the entrance has any sort of porch or canopy, a concealed ceiling light near its forward edge may serve the purpose of a floodlight, and in such a situation if the doorway is painted a light color enough reflection may be had to identify the visitor. If the doorway lacks such a porch, ornamental bracket lights will serve the purpose. Inside the door there must be a balance between the brightness of the outside lighting, and the better lighting immediately inside. Indirect lighting, or diffused lighting, or a combination of both is used.

Stairway and hallway lighting should be designed to develop soft but clear contrasts between stair treads. Bright lights at the head or foot of the stairway causing glare should be avoided.

Side-wall lights spaced well away from the mirror but bright enough to light up the whole body are recommended for dressing purposes in a bedroom. Indirect lighting of the whole ceiling should be projected horizontally and be diffused to approximate conditions of natural lighting. For reading in bed two methods are suggested: (1) use a semi-indirect type of light at the head of the bed, (2) use indirect lighting off the wall at the head of the bed. It is recommended that for bedrooms and hallways emergency lights be provided. A light may be placed in the baseboard and controlled by a switch within easy reach of the sleeper. Some hall lights are provided with a dimmer for night lighting.

In the kitchen and bathrooms, laundries and closets, in the basement and the garage, place lights where they will illuminate the things you want to see. Fluorescent lighting is coming more and more into favor for these types of places, for about three times the number of foot-candles are produced without glare by a fluorescent tube than by a tungsten bulb from the same amount of current. The fluorescent tube gives off less heat but is not as desirable from a decorative point of view, unless it can be recessed.

Wiring and Convenience Outlets. Because the electrical system in a house plays such an important role in modern living in such things as physical comfort, health, household work, and leisure activities, the installation should be carefully planned for the convenient use of every piece of electrical equipment. This planning should begin with a list of: (1) the number of lights needed and their location; (2) the kind and number of major and portable electrical appliances to be used and the rooms in which they will be located; and (3) the convenience outlets which will be required for the portable appliances and lamps, and their best placement (see outline following). With this detailed information the electrical system of your house can be laid out so that it will be efficient, convenient, and adequate to carry safely the electrical load to be required of it. Future needs should be considered as well as immediate ones, since it is expensive and sometimes impractical to change the wiring after the house is built. The electrical wiring system must follow local building codes and requirements of the utility furnishing the power. It should also follow

ELECTRICAL EQUIPMENT THAT CAN BE USED IN THE HOME

Check list of the large variety of items requiring electric power in a home. While most homes will not carry all of these, this list gives an idea of the potential wiring facilities needed:

Living Room:

1. Convenience outlets for:
   a) Vacuum cleaner
   b) Clock
   c) Electric toys
   d) Portable fans
   e) Humidifier
   f) Floor lamps
   g) Table lamps
   h) Movie projector
   i) Phonograph
   j) Floor polisher
   k) Radio
   l) Television

2. Switch controls for:
   a) Ceiling light
   b) Bookcase lighting
   c) Cove lighting
   d) Cornice lighting
   e) Valance lighting
   f) Convenience outlets

3. Lighting outlets for:
   a) Ceiling light
   b) Bookcase lighting
   c) Valance lighting
   d) Cornice lighting
   e) Cove lighting

4. Special outlets for:
   a) Door chimes
   b) Air conditioner
   c) Thermostat

Halls and Stairways:

1. Convenience outlets for:
   a) Floor lamps
   b) Floor polisher
   c) Radio
   d) Table lamps
   e) Vacuum cleaner

2. Switch controls for:
   a) Ceiling or wall lights
   b) Front hall
   c) Rear hall
   d) Bedroom hall
   e) Other halls
   f) Attic stairs
   g) Basement stairs
   h) Second-floor stairs
   i) Closet lights

3. Lighting outlets for:
   a) Ceiling lights
   b) Closet lights
   c) Wall lights

4. Special outlets for:
   a) Door chimes
   b) Telephone
   c) Intercommunication system

Bedrooms and Bathrooms:

1. Convenience outlets for:
   a) Electric blankets
   b) Floor polisher
   c) Portable fans
   d) Dressing-table lamps
   e) Ultraviolet lamp
   f) Table lamps
   g) Sewing machine
   h) Vacuum cleaner
   i) Bed lamps
   j) Clock
   k) Curling irons
   l) Hand iron
   m) Floor lamps
   n) Heating pads
   o) Bottle warmer
   p) Room warmer
   q) Radio
   r) Hair dryer
   s) Humidifier
   t) Heat lamp
   u) Vibrator
   v) Shaver

2. Switch controls for:
   a) Convenience outlets
   b) Master control
   c) Valance lights
   d) Ceiling light
   e) Night light
   f) Cornice lights
   g) Closet lights
   h) Cove lights

3. Lighting outlets for:
   a) Bathroom mirror
   b) Valance lights
   c) Cornice lights
   d) Ceiling lights
   e) Cove lights
   f) Closet lights
   g) Night light

4. Special outlets for:
   a) Intercommunication system
   b) Built-in room heater
   c) Room cooler
   d) Thermostat

Kitchen:

1. Convenience outlets for:
   a) Portable broiler
   b) Ice-cream freezer
   c) Coffee grinder
   d) Floor polisher
   e) Knife sharpener
   f) Bottle sterilizer
   g) Waffle grill
   h) Portable fans
   i) Hand iron
   j) Coffee maker
   k) Refrigerator
   l) Liquidizer
   m) Food mixer
   n) Percolator
   o) Grill
   p) Hot plate
   q) Juicer
   r) Radio
   s) Roaster
   t) Toaster
   u) Can opener

2. Switch controls for:
   a) Cabinet lights
   b) Ceiling light
   c) Sink light
   d) Pantry light
   e) Entry light

3. Lighting outlets for:
   a) Cabinet lights
   b) Work-counter light
   c) Ceiling light
   d) Pantry light
   e) Sink light

4. Special outlets for:
   a) Towel-drying cabinet
   b) Ventilating fan
   c) Intercommunication system
   d) Dishwasher
   e) Garbage disposer
   f) Home freezer
   g) Chimes
   h) Clock
   i) Range

Laundry and Utility Rooms

1. Convenience outlets for:
   a) Hot plate
   b) Washing machine
   c) Floor polisher
   d) Hand iron
   e) Portable fans
   f) Portable cord light
   g) Ironer
   h) Radio

2. Switch controls for:
   a) Light over washer
   b) Light over ironer
   c) Ceiling lights
   d) Light over workbench
   e) Light near furnace

3. Lighting outlets for:
   a) Light over washer
   b) Light over ironer
   c) Ceiling lights
   d) Light over workbench
   e) Light near furnace

4. Special outlets for:
   a) Air-conditioning system
   b) Intercommunication system
   c) Home freezer
   d) Water heater
   e) Ventilating fan
   f) Electrostatic cleaner
   g) Clothes drier
   h) Washing machine
   i) Home-workshop machines

Outdoors, Garage, Attic

1. Convenience outlets for:
   a) Small cooking appliances
   b) Floor polisher
   c) Portable cord lamp
   d) Hedge clippers
   e) Vacuum cleaner
   f) Lawn mower
   g) Decorative lights
   h) Radio
   i) Charcoal lighter for outdoor grill

2. Switch controls for:
   a) Porch lights
   b) Garage lights
   c) Outdoor floodlights
   d) Decorative lighting
   e) Terrace lights
   f) Attic lights
   g) Entrance lights
   h) Garage door opener

3. Lighting outlets for:
   a) Ceiling lights
   b) Wall lights
   c) Outdoor floodlights

4. Special outlets for:
   a) Attic fan
   b) Intercommunication system
   c) Lighted house number

the recommendations of the National Board of Fire Underwriters, which determines standards for insurance purposes. Materials used in the installation should be new and suitable for the purpose, and bear the approval of the Underwriter's Laboratories, Inc. Electrical wiring should be concealed. It should be protected against overload and mechanical injury. Every house should have at least the minimum number of circuits, outlets, and equipment recommended by the National Electrical Code.

The recommendations of adequate home wiring are briefly described as follows:

1. The wiring between the meter and the point of connection to the power company's lines should be sufficient to provide for all electrical uses anticipated. Wires of a certain size will carry safely and economically only a given amount of electric current. A heavier current load forced through them results in slower operation of the appliances causing them to consume more expensive wattage necessary to do the job, dimming the lights because of reduced voltage, fading of the radio, and danger of fire from overloaded and overheated wires. See the accompanying tables.

TABLE OF ELECTRICAL CURRENT CONSUMED IN WATTS

(Average)

Appliance	Current Consumed
Air conditioner	700–1200–3100
Broiler	660
Dish washer	200–500
Egg cooker	660
Furnace motor	400–550
Table grill	1000
Room warmer	1000–1320
Home freezer	300–350
Heat lamp	500
Ironer	1275–1620
Mixer	125–150
Oil burner	300–550
Radio	50–200
Razor sharpener	60
Roaster	1150–1350
Sun lamp	250
Toaster	600–1350
Vacuum cleaner	300
Water heater	750–3000

Kitchen clock	2
Attic fan	500–1500
Clothes drier	Up to 4500
Garbage disposer	250–500
Electric fan	50–300
Furnace blower	300
Hair drier	350
Heating pad	65
Hot plate	600–1000
Iron (hand)	660–1000
Juice extractor	60–100
Motor, ¼ h.p.	530
Coffee maker	400–600
Range	7000–14000
Refrigerator	200–300
Stoker	400–1250
Television	200–400
Towel drier	100–500
Waffle iron	660–1000
Kitchen vent fan	90–110
Washing machines:	
Wringer type	375–450
Spinner type	375–1600
Automatic	350–1600

TABLE OF WIRE SIZES

Sizes of wire providing for normal lighting, portable appliance load, range, water heater, and a possible increase thereof:

Watts Consumed	Floor Space in Square Feet	Wire Size
3500	1000	#6
4200	1500	#4
5300	2000	#4
8800	3000	#2
9500	4000	#1

TABLE OF RATINGS OF MAIN SWITCH OR CIRCUIT BREAKER

May be subdivided into not more than six fused switches or six circuit breakers:

SWITCHES		CIRCUIT BREAKERS	
	Floor Space		Floor Space
Amperes	in Square Feet	Amperes	in Square Feet
50	1000	50	1000
60	1500	60	1500
70	2000	70	2000
80	2500	80	2500
90	3000	90	3000
100	4000	100	4000

TABLE OF BRANCH CIRCUIT PROTECTION

Purpose	Fuse Rating	Wire Size	Fuse Rating
Lighting	15 Amps	#12	20 Amps
Appliances	20	10	30
Range	50	8	40
		6	60

RECOMMENDED NUMBER OF BRANCH CIRCUITS

General Purpose (15 amp.):

1. One circuit is recommended for each 500 sq. ft. of floor area for lights and occasional appliance use. Avoid overlong circuits in large houses by use of feeders and branch distribution panels. Total load should be evenly proportioned among the branch circuits according to their capacity.

   These circuits operate on 115 volts with circuit conductors of #14 (minimum) wire (for runs not exceeding 30 ft.), protected by 15-amp. circuit breakers.

Appliance Circuits (20 amp.):

1. Serving all convenience outlets (other than clock outlets) in kitchen, laundry, pantry, dining room, breakfast room:

   These circuits operate on 115 volts with circuit conductors of #12 (minimum) wire (for runs not exceeding 45 ft.), protected by 20-amp. circuit breakers.

Floor Area of House (square feet)	Number of Circuits Kitchen and Dining	Laundry	Utility and Garage
Up to 800	1	2	*
Up to 1500	2	2	*
Above 1500	2 or more	2	1

* May be served by general purpose circuits up to 1500 sq. ft.

Individual Equipment Circuits:

1. Serving single appliances and equipment units:
   These circuits operate on 115, 220 volts.
   It is desirable to provide not less than four individual equipment circuits in even the smallest size home.

Floor Area of House (square feet)	Number of Circuits	Equipment Installation
Minimum	1	Electric range*
	1	Water heater*
	1	Heating unit
	1	Laundry equipment
1000	1	Bathroom heater
1500	1	Clothes drier
	1	Garbage disposer
2500 or more	1	Air conditioning

* Gas units may be preferred.

EQUIPMENT AND ROOMS SERVED BY CIRCUITS

Circuit	Equipment	Rooms Served	Remarks
General purpose 15 amp.	Lighting Small Portable Appliance	All Rooms Living Bed Bath	Arrange circuits so that an interruption of one circuit will not interfere with the service of a whole floor or portion of house. Fixed clocks and small ventilating fans in kitchen and laundry may be connected to these circuits.
Appliance	Refrigerator, dishwasher, fan, mixer Waffle grill, toaster, etc. Ironer, hot plate, hand iron Freezer, workshop	Kitchen Kitchen Dining Laundry Utility Garage	Two circuits to serve kitchen and dining space, two circuits to serve the laundry, and one circuit to serve the utility room and attached garage.
Individual equipment	Range, 110/220 volts, 3 wire, 35 amps, 9000 watt Water heater, 220 volts, 2 wire, 20 amps, 3000 watt Heating unit, 110 volts, 2 wire, 20 amps, 800 watt Laundry equipment, 110 volt, 2 wire, 20 amps, 350 watt Bathroom heater, 110 volts, 2 wire, 20 amps, 1000 watt	Kitchen Basement Utility Basement Utility Basement Laundry Utility Bath	Each appliance served by an individual circuit.

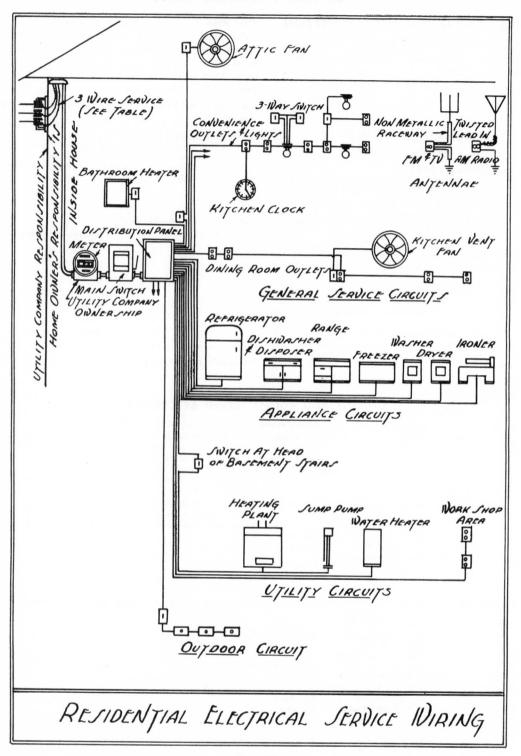

Fig. 98

2. There should be a sufficient number of branch circuits of large enough wire size to serve adequately all lights and appliances plus the provisions for future additions. An overloaded circuit causes:

(*a*) fuses to blow often or frequent resetting of the circuit breakers; (*b*) light bulbs to burn dim; (*c*) lights to flicker each time an appliance motor starts; (*d*) motors to run more slowly and hotter; and, (*e*) toasters, irons, and so on, to heat slowly (see Table of Branch Circuit Protection).

There are three main types of branch circuits (Fig. 98) — general purpose, appliance, and individual. General-purpose circuits are for lights and such items as radios and lamps. One such circuit will serve up to 10 light and convenience outlets. The minimum recommendations for a home installation is one 15-ampere circuit for each 500 sq. ft. of floor area. When there is more than one circuit, outlets should be divided evenly among the circuits. Appliance circuits are for portable appliances. To avoid flickering of lights and low voltage, appliances and lights should be supplied from separate circuits where possible. At least two 20-ampere circuits are usually required. For homes over 1500 sq. ft. of floor space, three such circuits are desirable. Individual branch circuits are intended for one piece of equipment. Each of the following should have an individual circuit — range, dishwasher, garbage disposal, water heater, automatic clothes washer, clothes drier, attic fan, air-conditioning unit, refrigeration unit, water pump, bathroom heater, furnace, and so on.

3. There should be an ample number of outlets, both light and convenience. Light outlets are necessary for all basic lighting receptacles for fixtures and switches. The outlets should be located so that the fixtures provide sufficient light where needed. A receptacle outlet should be provided for each 20 lineal feet, or major fraction of the circumference of a room. Some standards recommend a receptacle for each 12 lineal feet

of wall. Ceiling outlets for lights should be installed in the kitchen, dining room, bedrooms, and halls. Wall outlets may be used for the bathroom. Wall outlets may be used at the entrances where the entrance light is located on the exterior of the house (see Table of Equipment and Rooms Served by Circuits).

Enough convenience outlets should be equally distributed along the walls so that extension cords are unnecessary. They should be placed so that no point along the floor line is more than 6 ft. from an outlet. All outlets should be set flush with the wall. Even with ceiling lights, convenience outlets for lighting should be provided to give local lighting. Whenever practical, half of the outlets in a room should be wired on one circuit, and the other half on another. In this way, only half of the outlets will be affected if trouble occurs on one circuit.

4. Wall switches should be conveniently located for the basic utility and security of all rooms. All frequently used lights should be controlled by switches. The light in each room having more than 30 sq. ft. of floor area should be controlled by a wall switch located near the entrance and at a convenient height. If there is to be no ceiling or wall fixture in the living room, at least one lamp should be controlled by a switch located near the entrance to the room so that it will not be necessary to cross the room in the dark to turn on a light. A great convenience is to have every portable lamp on a switch-controlled circuit, so that as you leave the room one switch will put out all the lights. This calls for convenience outlets of the duplex-circuit type. One outlet of the pair is on a circuit controlled by the wall switch and is used to connect lamps only. The other one is on a separate circuit not governed by the switch and may be used for devices which run continuously such as clocks, or by such devices as radios, television, and phonographs which are used during the day when lights are not needed. Switches should be located on the

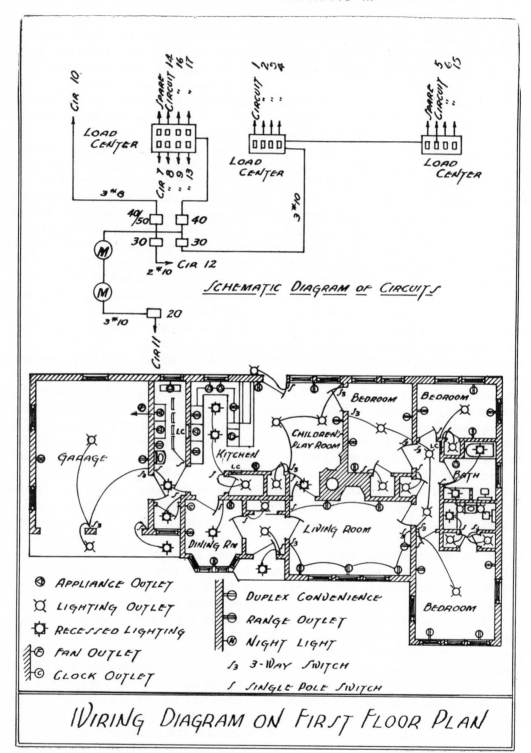

SCHEMATIC DIAGRAM OF CIRCUITS

CIR 10

LOAD CENTER

SPARE CIRCUIT 14
16
17

CIR 7
8
9
13

3"8

40/50   40

30   30

2"10   CIR 12

CIR 11   20

3"10

CIRCUIT 1234

LOAD CENTER

3"10

SPARE CIRCUIT 56
65

LOAD CENTER

GARAGE

KITCHEN   LC

DINING RM

CHILDREN'S PLAY ROOM

LIVING ROOM

BEDROOM

BEDROOM

BATH

BEDROOM

LC

Ⓐ APPLIANCE OUTLET

☼ LIGHTING OUTLET

✪ RECESSED LIGHTING

Ⓕ FAN OUTLET

Ⓒ CLOCK OUTLET

DUPLEX CONVENIENCE

RANGE OUTLET

Ⓝ NIGHT LIGHT

S_3 3-WAY SWITCH

S SINGLE POLE SWITCH

WIRING DIAGRAM ON FIRST FLOOR PLAN

Fig. 99

knob side of a doorway, and arranged to control lights so that a person can pass from room to room, turning on lights ahead of him and turning off those behind without retracing his steps. Three-way switches should control stairway and hall lights, as well as lights in the garage or any other outbuilding, and large rooms with two entrances more than 10 ft. apart (Fig. 99).

With careful planning a master switch may be used to turn on all unlighted lamps in the house, or one or more in each room as burglar protection. Flipping a switch at your bedside or in the first floor hallway will light up every part of the house (and the grounds if desired). Sometimes lights are placed on the corners of the house just under the eaves for outdoor lighting of small lots.

There are many types of switches to choose from and as many as three switches may be placed in a single box and plate. Silent mercury switches are used wherever the noise of the usual snap switch is objectionable. Time switches are available which turn lights on or off upon a predetermined time setting of the switch, and are convenient for entrance lights, attic lights, basement lights, and other lights apt to be left on by oversight. The electrolier switch is so devised that by successively snapping the switch, one, two, three, or more lamps in a fixture may be lighted as desired, or the one lamp in a floor lamp may be turned on to varying degrees of brightness. In this field of wiring devices it is almost literally true that you may obtain any kind of control desired, from stock supply or upon special order.

Low-Voltage Wiring. Low-voltage control in home wiring is a method that permits lighting fixtures, lamps, and appliances to be switched on or off from any number of locations without the bulky wiring circuits required for conventional wiring. A low-voltage switch can be installed in this lighting circuit simply by making a fine wire connection between the extra switch and the original switch. This type of wiring makes feasible the control of all lighting in the house from a single point, such as the garage or master bedroom, and many home owners are making this remote-control addition to their wiring systems by calling for extra switches or "master control panels" at desired points. Low-voltage wiring can be used with all the lighting circuits in the house, or with only a few selected circuits as desired. Circuits connected for low-voltage switching can have extra switches installed at any time. The installation of extra switches in a conventional switch circuit cannot be done unless the entire circuit is revised and rewired.

MINIMUM WIRING INDICATIONS ON FLOOR PLANS

Living Room (Den, Library, Reception Hall, Sunroom, Recreation Room)

1. Lighting outlets:
   a) Ceiling outlet — more than one needed in large rooms (over 400 sq. ft. in area) or rooms with extremely low ceilings. Rooms twice as long as wide may require more than one outlet. Fixed lighting outlets in rooms may be omitted, provided:
      1) Wall cove or valance lighting outlets are substituted;
      2) Switches are provided for one or more convenience outlets;
      3) The outlet is controlled by switch.
   b) Bracket outlet — according to needs for decorative or supplementary lighting.
2. Switch controls:
   a) A single-pole switch at the entrance door to control general illumination. One at the same point for outside wall brackets, if installed. One at the same point for group of outlets to permit convenience in use.
   b) Multiple control by three-way switches wherever commonly used doors are 10 ft. or more apart.
3. Duplex-convenience outlets:
   a) One in each usable wall space 3 ft. or more in length at the floor line. Other convenience outlets located so that no point in any wall space, unbroken by a doorway, is more than 6 ft. from an outlet.
   b) An outlet flush in the top of the mantel shelf of fireplace or adjacent to it.
   c) Outlets should be placed so that their centers are a minimum of 4 in. above the floor level which allows for cleaning under a plug connected to the outlet. For convenience and in consideration of their particular use, some of the outlets may be placed in the wall about 18 in. above the level of the floor, some are

recommended to be placed at waist height to eliminate the necessity for continual stooping to the baseboard level.

Dining Room (Dinette, Breakfast Nook)

1. Lighting outlets:
   a) Ceiling outlet — over table space or cove lighting.
   b) Bracket outlet — for decorative or supplementary lighting, according to the style of the interior.
2. Switch controls:
   a) One on latch side of door nearest kitchen.
   b) Multiple control if commonly used doors are 10 ft. or more apart.
3. Duplex-convenience outlets:
   a) Place one on each wall space where a buffet or serving table may stand.
   b) Minimum of two outlets, one of which may be a floor outlet for a table top.
   c) Outlet in each wall space of 3 ft. or more in length at floor line.
   d) Place outlets so that no point along floor line or any usable wall space, unbroken by a doorway, is more than 10 ft. from an outlet.

Kitchen (Kitchenette, Pantry)

1. Lighting outlets:
   a) Ceiling outlet — centrally located for general illumination.
   b) Supplementary outlets — supplementary lighting units for each important work area (to eliminate shadows on range, sink, counters, and so on).
2. Switch controls:
   a) Single switch on the latch side of the principal door to control central lighting.
   b) Multiple control of central light wherever commonly used doors are 10 ft., or more, apart.
   c) Single-pole switch for group of outlets to permit convenience in use.
3. Convenience outlets — at elbow height, one at each work area plus outlets for such special purposes as clock, refrigerator, ventilator fan (with wall switch), water heater, range, garbage disposal, dishwasher, and so on.

Laundry (Laundry Space)

1. Lighting outlets:
   a) Ceiling outlet — one at each work center (tubs, sorting and washing center, ironing board, and so on).
2. Switch controls:
   a) Single-pole switch at principal door.
   b) Three-way switches if commonly used doorways are more than 10 ft. apart.
3. Convenience outlets:
   a) For washer. An outlet box at the ceiling and about 3 ft. in front of the laundry tubs, with the cord extended within 6 ft. from the floor.
   b) For ironer.
4. Other types of service outlets:
   a) For hand ironer.
   b) For water heater.
   c) For ventilating fan.

Basement

1. Ceiling outlet — one near foot of stairs. Also one in each enclosed space. Additional lighting in front of furnace and at workbench, if needed.
2. Switch controls — switch and pilot near the head of the stairs to control the light at the foot of the stairs.
3. Convenience outlets — one or more near the workbench for electric tools. One may be needed for furnace.

Attic

1. Ceiling outlet — one at the top of the stairway. Also one unit in each enclosed space.
2. Switch controls — Switch and pilot light at the foot of the stairs to control the stairway light and the chief attic light.
3. Convenience outlets — one for general use.

Entrances

1. Ceiling or bracket outlet — one or more to conform with the style of architecture at front entrance. One or more at other commonly used entrances, side and rear.
2. Switch controls — one located just inside the door of each entrance.
3. Convenience outlets — one at the front entrance for decorative lighting. Other outlets at the front and rear of the house for lawn mower, hedge trimmer, and so on.
4. Illuminated house number.

Covered Porches (Terraces, Patios)

1. Ceiling or bracket outlet — one per 100 sq. ft., or major fraction of floor area.
2. Switch controls — one located within the house, multiple control if needed.
3. Convenience outlets — one per 15 ft., or major fraction of wall.

Bedrooms

1. Lighting outlets:
   a) Ceiling outlet — rooms twice as long as wide may require more than one outlet. Cove lighting or wall brackets (at least two) may be used in place of the ceiling outlet.
   b) Outlets at vanity table, bed recesses, window valances, and other points where useful.
   c) Pull-chain light in each closet off the bedroom having a floor area of 6 sq. ft. or greater.
2. Switch controls:
   a) Single-pole switch at entrance door.
   b) Three-way switches if commonly used doorways are more than 10 ft. apart.
   c) Single-pole switch for group of outlets to permit convenience in use.
3. Duplex-convenience outlets:
   a) Place outlets so that no point along floor line on any usable wall space, unbroken by doorways, is more than 6 ft. from an outlet.
   b) Outlet in each wall space 3 ft. or more in length in the floor line.
4. Other types of service outlets — radio outlet (aerial and ground) may be combined with convenience outlet.

Bathrooms

1. Lighting outlets:
   a) Ceiling outlets for bathrooms greater than 60 sq. ft. in area.
   b) Two outlets, one on each side of mirror.
2. Switch controls — single-pole switch on latch side of door to control ceiling light if installed, otherwise to control bracket outlets.
3. Convenience outlets — duplex type, near lavatory mirror but well away from faucets.
4. Service outlets — for built-in heater unit and drying fan.

Basement (Utility Room)

1. Lighting outlets:
   a) Ceiling outlet for every 150 sq. ft. of floor area, as equally spaced as practical.
   b) Outlets at utility equipment such as furnace, cooling unit, home freezer, workbench, and so on; also for each separately enclosed space.

2. Switch control:
   a) Single-pole switch for each outlet or group of outlets to permit convenience in use.
   b) Single-pole switch at entrance door. Three-way switches if commonly used doorways are more than 10 ft. apart.
3. Duplex-convenience outlets:
   a) For home freezer.
   b) At workbench for tool motors, soldering iron, and so on.
4. Service outlets:
   a) Heating unit, composed of burner motor, blower motor, and control devices (generally wired complete terminating in a junction box provided with a disconnect).
   b) For water heater. This unit may be located in the utility room, kitchen, or laundry, depending upon plan.

Closets
1. Lighting outlet — one, if floor area is 6 sq. ft. or more (pull switch).
2. Switch control — automatic door switch for added convenience (particularly useful for coat closets).

Hallways (Entrance Hallway)
1. Lighting outlets:
   a) Outlet for each 15 linear feet (or major fraction) of the hall, if the hall is not illuminated by the stairway light. Lights at the head and foot of the stairway included.
   b) In closet off the entrance hall (outlets should be provided in closets 30 in. and over in depth, or having a floor area of 6 sq. ft. or greater).
   c) Exterior outlet over the entrance door servicing garage.
2. Switch control:
   a) Single-pole switch at entrance door.
   b) Three-way switches if commonly used doorways are more than 10 ft. apart.
   c) Pull-chain switches in closets of entrance hall.
3. Duplex-convenience outlets — outlet for each 15 linear feet of hall.

Stairway
1. Lighting outlets — one outlet at head and one at foot of each stairway.
2. Switch controls — separate three-way switches at the head and foot of the stairs, for controlling each of the two outlets.

Garage
1. Lighting outlets:
   a) Outlets on both sides of the car hood (three outlets for a two-car garage).
   b) One for lighting path to house.
2. Switch controls:
   a) Single-pole switch at entrance door. In multiple-car garages, no more than two interior outlets should be controlled by the same switch.
   b) Three-way switches to control light from both garage and house.

Drawings Required for Electric Layout Plans. Apart from the technical side of electric wiring, the home builder should familiarize himself with the way the layout is to be indicated on the drawings. He should try to visualize the plans as though he were viewing the completed house. He should sketch out how the furniture will be arranged, and determine the location of the light outlets so they will be convenient for the dressing tables and beds, for lighting stairways and closets, for bathroom mirrors and kitchen sinks, and as decorative features over mantels and sideboards. In addition, the portable lamps, more and more used in living rooms and bedrooms, must have ample convenience outlets allotted for them. Duplex receptacles permitting the use of two cords from one receptacle are to be recommended. Switches must be conveniently located and yet be inconspicuous, placed near the wood trim — not in the center of large plastered areas.

For small home installations it is usually sufficient to indicate by a dotted line the relation of the outlet and its controlling switch; but where special care is taken with the working drawings, all the runs of wires and the location of the cabinets and distributing points are drawn in as well. From the architectural set of drawings for a building, the outline of walls, partitions, door and window openings are traced by the electrical engineer, and all of the electrical outlets are spotted. The engineer then proceeds to show the layout of all conduit and to indicate the number and size of wire to be contained in each. The number of watts to be allocated to each circuit must be calculated to determine the number of circuits to radiate from the service board. His design observes regulations of the building code; the work is planned with a consideration of usefulness and decoration, as well as with a regard for economy of materials and labor.

Planning the Individual Rooms of the House

The house is designed as a "machine for living," consisting of a number of elements each one of which has its particular use and each of which must be carefully planned to take care of its particular function. The activities of the family generally determine the kind of house needed. This divides the house into groups to accommodate the activities: (1) living rooms, which include the living room, dining room, library, and entrance hall; (2) sleeping rooms, which include bedrooms, bathrooms, and sleeping porches; (3) workrooms which include kitchen, laundry, and storerooms. The living rooms are the public part of the house, the workrooms are often placed where they are least conspicuous, and the sleeping rooms in the more secluded portions of the house. A garage must be considered an essential part of the modern house. A recreation room may be desired along with a den or study. Ample closet and storage space are essential, and additional bathrooms or a powder room desirable. Often a powder room containing a lavatory and toilet on the first floor are indispensable.

PLANNING FOR GOOD TRAFFIC CIRCULATION

In the planning of a house, whether it be large or small, the living room is the principal area of social contact between the different members of the family, and between the family and its visitors. As such it should be kept in order at all times, and should include these characteristics: (1) it should be located near the front entrance but should not lead directly into it; (2) it should not serve as a passage to other rooms; (3) if it must allow access directly to bedrooms, then an alternate way should be provided to reach the kitchen and dining area (Fig. 100).

By good traffic circulation is meant the ease with which the occupants of a house and their guests can move about from one room to another without having to use one of the main rooms (usually the living room) as a traffic artery (Fig. 101).

When size was a minor consideration in cost, and families required larger homes, then space was allowed for halls and passages and the achievement of a functional traffic pattern was not so difficult. In the modern home the living area has been constantly diminishing for economic reasons because of the high cost of building and the need to produce maximum space for the money.

With the increase in the size of the nation's families, the need for three-bedroom houses is being recognized. This need is too often being met by reducing the living area in order to obtain the third bedroom, without any apparent increase in the total square-foot area of the house. Hallways and passageways, the logical traffic directors, have been sacrificed. The living room now does the job, and this arrangement has become almost standard practice. The need for properly sized living areas and good circulation to and from the rooms remains constant and must be observed if our houses are to offer the livability for which they are supposedly built.

PLANNING ROOMS TO ACCOMMODATE FURNITURE

Each room should be planned to accommodate the pieces of furniture that are ordinarily used in connection with it. Thought must be given in the design so that the important groupings and such special pieces

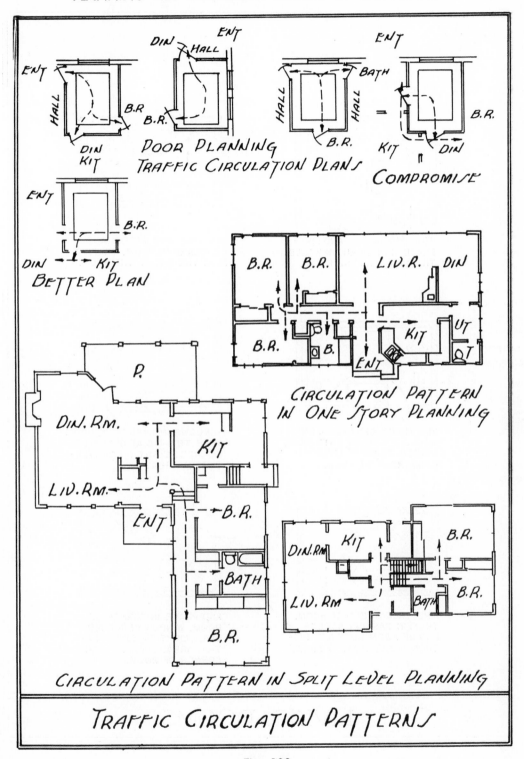

Fig. 100

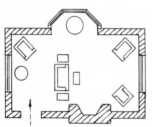

WINDOWS, DOORS, AND FIRE-
PLACE CENTERED ON WALLS.
THIS IS A DEAD END ROOM.

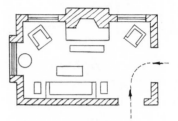

WINDOWS AND FIREPLACE
CENTERED IN ROOM. TRAFFIC
IS AT THE END OF THE ROOM.

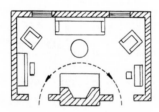

FIREPLACE CENTERED ON
WALL. DOORS ON BOTH SIDES
BRINGS TRAFFIC THROUGH
CONVERSATION AREA.

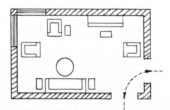

WINDOWS IN CORNER OF ROOM
WITH TRAFFIC AT OPPOSITE
CORNER. LIGHT ON CONVER-
SATION AREA.

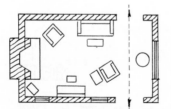

FIREPLACE AT END OF ROOM.
TRAFFIC PASSING ACROSS
END OF ROOM DOES NOT DIS-
TURB CONVERSATION AREA.

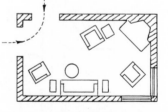

FIREPLACE IN CORNER OF
ROOM. WINDOW IN CORNER
GIVES LIGHT ON CONVERSA-
TION AREA. TRAFFIC THRU
CORNER OF ROOM.

LIVING ROOMS

Fig. 101

ways to aid in the final planning (Fig. 102).

The desired result should furnish a place for each member of the family to sit and should provide the comfort needed for relaxation, adequate light for reading, and a location which permits participation in a conversation group or an isolation for some other activity. Davenports, sofas, and other group accommodations are essentially conversation furniture, and are used to provide the extra seating space for guests as well as to serve the family generally. There is a place for formal chairs in the living room, for an alert mind and body are better obtained in an upright posture required in conversation, games, hobbies, and so on. Your need for entertaining, the number of people included, the frequency of your entertainment, and the kind of entertaining will determine the number of places you need (Fig. 103). Other equipment may then be added as necessary. A piano, radio, phonograph, television for music and entertainment; a table for games, hobbies, study; bookcases for the volumes needed for study and reading; magazine racks; occasional tables for lamps; and the incidentals for personal comfort such as smoking sundries, sewing boxes, and so on. Around this analysis a study of the furniture arrangement can be made and from this the size and proportions of a room can be determined.

This may give the impression that the living room must be big, but furniture groupings can be used for more than one purpose. Small pieces of furniture will help to consolidate space. Orderly arrangement is the answer to getting a lot of living room for every square foot of space. It can be arrived at only by the most careful planning. A room rectangular in shape is better than a square one because the furniture can be arranged to advantage more easily. A room whose width is to its length as 3:4, or 4:5 is in good proportion. Living rooms should be planned to such proportions that standard-sized rugs will fit them. Room sizes, 12 by 16 ft., 14 by 18 ft., 14 by 20 ft., and 18 by 24 ft. are considered well proportioned.

The living room should not be a traffic lane from one part of the house to another, but should open from an entrance hall or main hallway, and because of seclusion should be a dead-end room (Fig. 104). The entrance hall is convenient because it keeps the cold draft from the room, affords a place to hang wraps, shuts off the view of people coming to the main entrance, and saves a lot of dirt from being tracked over the living-room rug. If the living room must communicate with the dining room, the traffic lanes should not pass through the more intimate groups of furniture. Usually an entrance from a hall and one to a study, den, or porch are enough to take care of the average requirements. The custom of centering an entrance upon the long side of a rectangular room has a tendency to force the furniture to be arranged in two groups in order to provide a passage space at the door. This arrangement forces a person entering the room to pass in front of people to reach the further exit. For this reason it is better to plan the doors near together and at one end of the room. Too many doors give a feeling of "leaking out" in all directions, especially if they are distributed to all four walls. If there is a study it is usually better if the study and the living room can be entered only through separate entrances from the hall.

If there is a fireplace, it almost automatically becomes the focal point for the main group of furniture devoted to conversation and relaxation (Fig. 105). From one point of view, the fireplace in a modern home is obsolete and a throwback to tradition; from another, it is the essence of hospitality, the symbol of a home; from another, it may be the reserve heating system that will save the family from entire dependence upon electricity. The fireplace gives more privacy if it can be located at one end of the room (Fig. 102). On the other hand, more people can gather around if it is in the center of

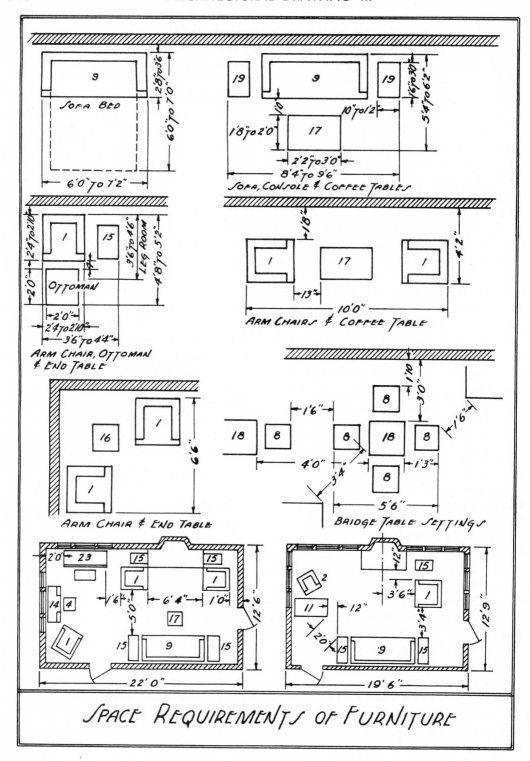

SPACE REQUIREMENTS OF FURNITURE

Fig. 103

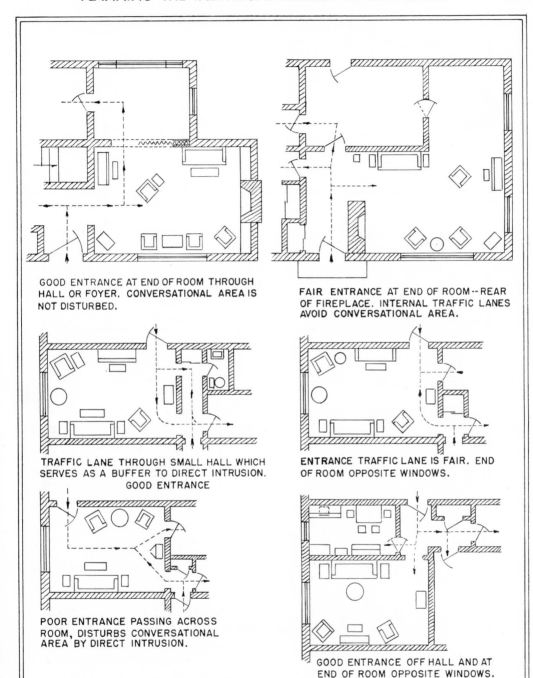

GOOD ENTRANCE AT END OF ROOM THROUGH HALL OR FOYER. CONVERSATIONAL AREA IS NOT DISTURBED.

FAIR ENTRANCE AT END OF ROOM -- REAR OF FIREPLACE. INTERNAL TRAFFIC LANES AVOID CONVERSATIONAL AREA.

TRAFFIC LANE THROUGH SMALL HALL WHICH SERVES AS A BUFFER TO DIRECT INTRUSION. GOOD ENTRANCE

ENTRANCE TRAFFIC LANE IS FAIR. END OF ROOM OPPOSITE WINDOWS.

POOR ENTRANCE PASSING ACROSS ROOM, DISTURBS CONVERSATIONAL AREA BY DIRECT INTRUSION.

GOOD ENTRANCE OFF HALL AND AT END OF ROOM OPPOSITE WINDOWS.

LIVING ROOMS

Fig. 104

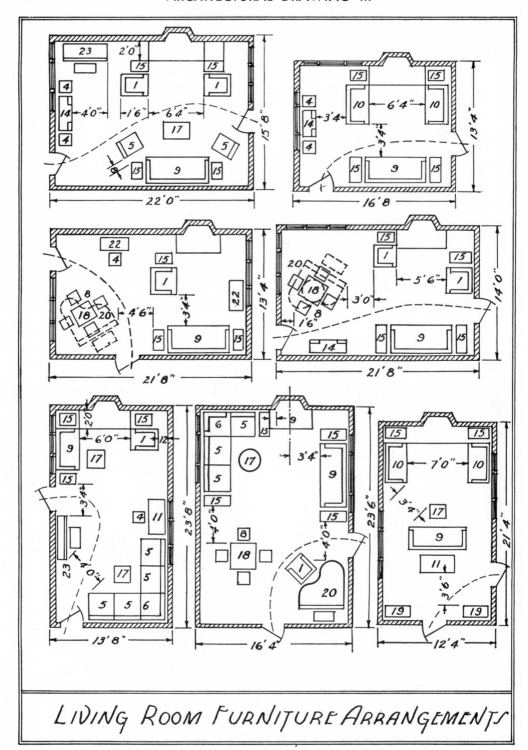

Fig. 105

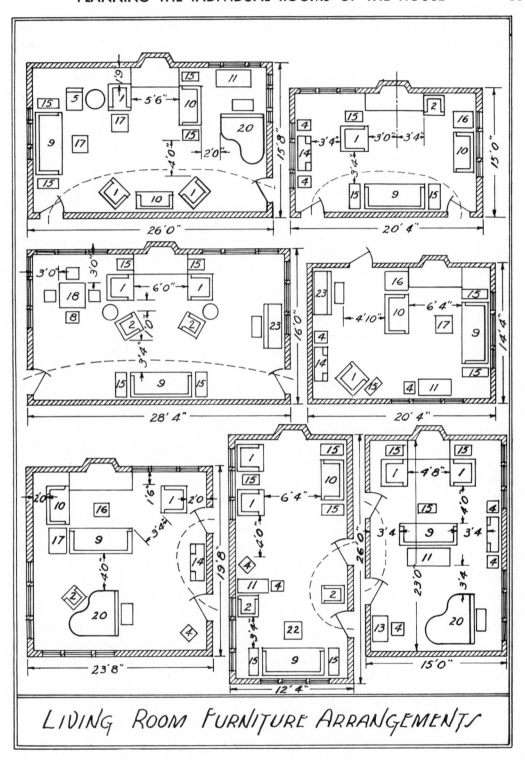

Fig. 106

a long wall (Fig. 106). A sound rule is to keep the fireplace remote from any doors since the traffic will disturb a conversation group, and there will be an awkward arrangement of the furniture.

The fireplace may often serve as a primary or an auxiliary heating system. Summer homes can be made comfortable on chilly days. In year-round homes, a fireplace can be used in spring and autumn on chilly days instead of the central heating system. Also a fireplace can be very handy in case the main heating system happens to break down. The fireplace, therefore, should be designed for efficiency as well as for good appearance. In an ordinary fireplace an enormous percentage of available heat is wasted by going up the chimney. There are many ways of conserving this heat and putting it to use. Certain sizes and proportions in fireplace construction have been found more efficient as was explained more fully in Unit XI of *Architectural Drawing II*. The width and height of the opening are related to each other, to the size, shape, and position of the throat and smoke shelf, and to the size of the flue. The angle of the splay of the sidewalls and back have a direct bearing on the way the heat is reflected. Another method to obtain more heat from the fireplace is to use a patented metal hood forming the front of the overhearth and stack. This hood is warmed by the flue gases and radiates heat through the room to supplement the radiant heat of the fire itself. Another method is to build air ducts around the hearth and lower part of the flue through which air can circulate, gather heat, and deliver it to the room.

A wide fireplace in which logs may be burned is a thing dear to the heart of interior decorators. In front and at the sides of the fireplace may be grouped the most comfortable of the room's furnishings, and the effect always is a homelike picture of comfort. The fireplace should be designed to harmonize with the style of the room. Fireplaces may project into the room, or may be built into

the wall so that only the decoration of the opening protrudes beyond the wall surface (Fig. 124). Mantels, hoods, or a flat decoration applied around the opening may be used to finish the fireplace. Ready-made mantels are not recommended. The mantel should match the woodwork in the room, and should be decorated in the same manner.

Of course, instead of privacy the living room may express sociability. More desired than seclusion may be the open areas for entertaining which may be obtained by room opening into room so that there is no separation between the hall and the living room and the dining room. The fact that our houses have been shrinking in size has brought about the combination living and dining room. This planning has several advantages for it gives the feeling of size to a very small house, with a fairly large room instead of two boxlike ones; it permits the living area to be more easily used for other purposes; and it allows for additional dining space when the owner entertains on a large scale. Its disadvantages are that it is not always easy to plan the room to give the desired privacy; it often makes the living room harder to furnish, especially if the dining space is an alcove at right angles to the long axis of the room.

If the house is planned from the inside out, as is done in good planning, then the windows are placed where you most want the light and view; they are also planned for a pleasing rhythm of opening and wall space inside; and to provide wall spaces large enough to take the desired furniture comfortably. Unbroken wall areas are of value for two reasons; they are restful in contrast to the more exciting windows, and they are necessary for the placement of the larger pieces of furniture (Fig. 107). From one third to one half the length of the outside walls should be allowed for window openings, and there should be as few doors as possible. Two outside walls are desirable for a living room so that there may be plenty of window space. Often the living room is placed across one

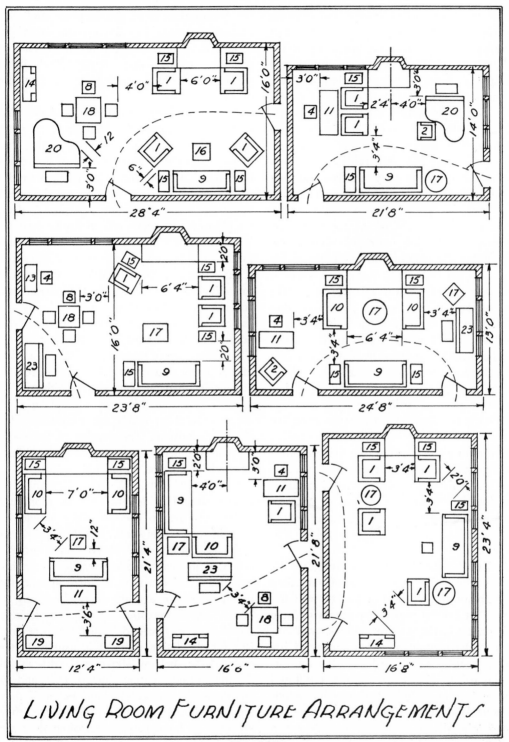

LIVING ROOM FURNITURE ARRANGEMENTS

Fig. 107

end of the house so there may be windows on three sides. The proportions and types of windows will definitely be based upon the architectural style of the house, but if the planner has fixed ideas about windows these will undoubtedly influence the style of house. If he likes large window areas, he will prefer a modern style over a colonial. On the other hand small panes of glass have a domestic scale and are still favorably considered despite the fact that they are not the best means of lighting a room or bringing in the most sunlight. The placing of the windows in the extreme corners of the room has the advantage of leaving unbroken wall space, and putting the windows in the parts of the room that are difficult to furnish. A room is pleasanter if the window sills are below the level of the eye of a seated person, so that a full view of the out-of-doors is obtained. Windows should be arranged so that chairs may be placed near them in such a way that the light will come over the left side of the person occupying the chairs. A pleasant view should be planned to be seen from the windows such as a flower garden or an attractive lawn.

Except in warm climates, the living room is usually given a southwest exposure so that it will have the maximum of sun. Sometimes a position giving greater privacy or a closer relation to the garden may be more desired and necessitate a less favorable relation to the sun.

Artificial light is being introduced by sources which give larger areas of light than do lamps or the old-type ceiling or wall fixtures. This lighting may be by means of large flush panels in the wall or ceilings, wall columns, or by continuous lights concealed behind a cornice or along a beam. It may thus be planned to give both a general diffused light and a local light and yet be inconspicuous. With such lighting sources, light becomes primarily a means of seeing, not a decorative piece. Light should pervade the room as heat now does, as compared with the localized heat of the fireplace and old-fashioned stoves. The living room especially should have provision for an abundance of general lighting, and ample local lights planned in definite relation to the grouping of furniture.

So far we have thought only of the plan of the living room: the relation of its parts to use. The next step is to think of the kind of room desired. Whatever style of house has been decided upon, the living room naturally will conform to it. If it is to be a modern home and one built within a limited budget, the decorative effects will probably have to be obtained by means of color and texture rather than by any architectural elaboration. If the house is to be of traditional architecture the detail of mantel, trim, bookcases, and cornice will follow more or less closely the established precedent, but even in these homes the trend is toward simpler woodwork. The elimination of moldings wherever feasible means fewer places for dust to collect. A narrow, inconspicuous baseboard with beveled edges 3 to 6 in. wide, and a simple trim of 4- or even 3-in. width are satisfactory for the average room. The cornice of the room may be trimmed with a very simple molding, or the trim may be eliminated entirely.

Built-in cabinets, wherever they may be placed, should be designed for the room and space they are to occupy. They should be thought of as an architectural feature as much as a useful one. Shelves built into the depth of the wall, made possible by furring out, usually give a more finished appearance to the room. In a room devoted entirely to books, where maximum shelving is desired, the shelves may extend from floor to ceiling. But for the living room it is usually better to build the shelving above cupboards useful for the storage of magazines, games, and so on. Generally bookcases look better if they are carried to the ceiling, especially when they are built in large panels, but often they are aligned with the tops of doors and windows. Books keep in better condition when the air circulates freely around them; furthermore, books on an open shelf are a decorative feature to the room. Bookshelves should not be wider than is necessary for the widest book, for the additional width only serves as a dust collector. The shelves should be spaced to accommodate the type of books desired, or made so that they are adjustable. A fireplace may range from one with simple enframement for the inexpensive small house, to a more elaborate treatment which may include an entire paneled wall, or a group of enclosed bookcases. Panel treatment may be sparingly used in the moderately priced home.

The actual character of furnishings selected depends upon the way the room is to be used — that is, the type of room it is to be. This, in turn, depends upon the type of house. If the room is to receive primarily daytime use, and sunlight and a feeling of outdoor freedom are desired, the windows will be lightly curtained. For such a room heavy draperies may reduce the light by as much as 50 per cent. For a room used chiefly at night the hangings that give a feeling of warmth and enclosure are desirable. But even in the modern house with large expanses of glass, the windows appear better if they are entirely blocked out at night by hangings continuing to the floor and preferably the color of the walls — or not too different in tone — so that the walls will seem continuous. Uncurtained windows after dark are black holes and give the feeling of a room leaking out into the night.

Whether the woodwork is stained or painted depends upon the character of the house. It is impossible to evade the conclusion that a room paneled in wood, stained or naturally weathered has a warm, friendly, inviting appearance. At the other extreme is the room with plain plastered walls and the minimum of woodwork, and furniture simple but comfortable, and in which color, sunlight, and texture of hangings and rugs play the chief roles. Such a room is inviting because of its oversimplicity, its clean-cut lines and freshness. The important thing is to know in the

beginning the character desired, and then to make every detail contribute to it. The character of the room will be worked out before the plan is finally finished. After a decision is reached, the plan, background, and furnishings will be interwoven into a consistent whole. Because this integration is so essential one should not attempt to change the character of an important room at the last minute; to try to make it modern, for instance, when colonial or Georgian is plainly indicated, or to decide upon a pine-paneled room when the rest is developed along modern lines. The successful house is one that has been clearly visualized at the outset, with every detail worked out to make a consistent whole, before actual construction begins.

REVIEW OF PRINCIPLES INVOLVED IN PLANNING A LIVING ROOM

1. The living room should be well proportioned, length to width. A long narrow room is hard to furnish and appears to be a corridor.

2. Wall areas should be large enough to accommodate large pieces of furniture.

3. Windows should be well placed for ventilation, reading, writing, or conversation. A window and an electrical outlet should be located near every probable reading spot. If maximum light and air are desired, plan accordingly. South and west exposures receive the most sun.

4. Furniture should be carefully planned and arranged so that the important pieces are related to each other, and to the whole plan.

5. Wall areas should not be cut up by too many openings. Doors are best placed near corners, so that they do not destroy wall areas useful for furniture.

6. Heating registers, radiators, and electrical outlets should be located where they will not interfere with furniture. These utilities are best located near the ends of large wall areas or under windows; not behind chairs, sofa, chests, or other furniture.

7. If the room is narrow and there is a fireplace in the long wall, there should be a

wall space directly opposite large enough to take a group of conversational furniture.

8. The fireplace must be carefully located, and be out of the normal traffic lanes.

9. Window sills should be below the eye level of a seated person, so that a full view can be obtained through the windows.

10. An ash dump should be provided in the fireplace. Ashes should drop from the fireplace to a cleanout in the basement.

11. Circulation through the living room should be direct, to take up as little floor space as possible. Circulation is the amount of space needed to go from one part of the house to another.

12. A large opening in the wall opposite the fireplace opens the heart of the room to guests.

13. Coat closet should be included. The stairway should be conveniently arranged in relation to the second-floor plan. It is better not to have to cross the entire living room from the front door to reach the coat closet or the stairway to the second floor.

14. The front door should be well located. The housewife should not have to cross the entire living room to answer the doorbell.

15. The necessary furniture groups should not block traffic. Normal circulation (or traffic) through the living room should be easy and unobstructed.

16. Privacy should be provided. Neighbors should not be able to look directly into the living room. The entire room should not be visible from the front door. If privacy is most highly desired the living room should be a dead-end room.

17. Noise must be considered. The living room should be separated from the bathroom and kitchen noises.

18. The living room should be planned to accommodate the furniture and rugs.

CHECK LIST

General Plan

1. General exposure of room: north ( ); south ( ); east ( ); west ( )
2. Principal view toward: garden ( ); street ( )

3. Entrance to room from: hall ( ); street ( ); terrace ( ); porch ( )
4. Windows: casement ( ); double-hung ( ); picture ( ); glass block ( ); awnings ( )
5. Doors: paneled ( ); flush ( ); glazed ( )
6. Lighting: cove ( ); spotlight ( ); floor lamps ( ); table lamps ( ); wall brackets ( )
7. Electrical outlets: radio ( ); lamps ( ); clock ( ); telephone ( ); television ( )
8. Fireplace: stone ( ); brick ( ); ash dump ( ); mantel ( ); fuel storage ( ); spark screen ( ); natural radiation ( ); circulating unit ( ); andirons ( ); grate ( ); fire basket ( );
9. Built-in features: bookshelves ( ); storage cabinets ( ); cupboards ( ); paneling ( )
10. Adequate space for furniture: occasional chairs ( ); club chairs ( ); wing chairs ( ); straight chairs ( ); davenport ( ); sofa ( ); love seat ( ); desk ( ); secretary ( ); bookcases ( ); coffee tables ( ); end tables ( ); occasional tables ( )
11. Space required for additional furniture: television ( ); grand piano ( ); radio ( ); upright piano ( )
12. Carpeting: standard-size rugs ( ); wall-to-wall carpeting ( )

KITCHENS — THE HOME WORK CENTER

When the kitchen was the busiest, largest, and most important room in the house the family carried on its living here because it was the warmest room in the house, and the housewife of necessity did her work in this area. The modern tendency to make the kitchen more efficient was started by the necessity of reducing the amount of space because of the cost of modern housing and the smaller living quarters of city living. To save space, cabinets and equipment were given a lot of study and standardized, making kitchens comfortable and attractive as well as convenient. Recent studies have revealed much about the pattern of kitchen work in the average home, spaces needed for the different types of work, supplies and utensils used in the average kitchen, and the most convenient storage for them. Kitchen experts have studied not only arrangements for saving steps and time but also for avoiding stooping, stretching, and lifting (Fig. 108). The modern kitchen recognizes that fewer families can afford servants and that the housewife does more work and yet has more outside interests than ever before. As the house becomes more compact it seems in-

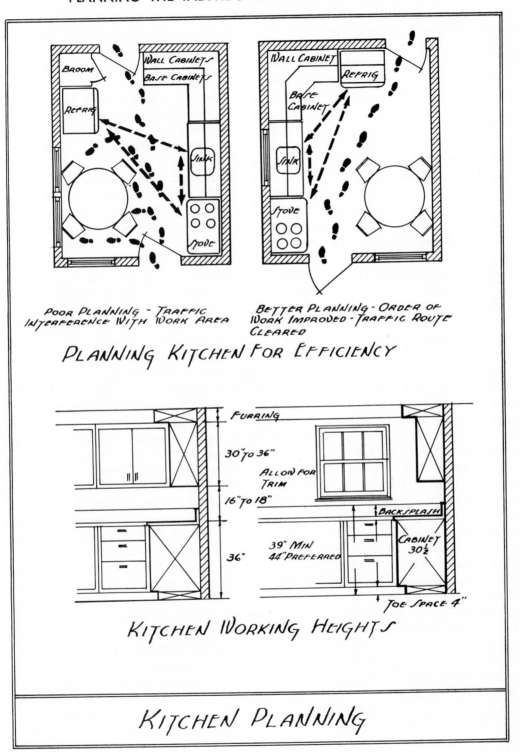

POOR PLANNING - TRAFFIC
INTERFERENCE WITH WORK AREA

BETTER PLANNING - ORDER OF
WORK IMPROVED - TRAFFIC ROUTE
CLEARED

PLANNING KITCHEN FOR EFFICIENCY

KITCHEN WORKING HEIGHTS

KITCHEN PLANNING

Fig. 108

creasingly convenient to include space for informal dining in the kitchen. This also provides more serving space for the meals in a dining or living room. Another trend is the interest in utility rooms planned into the kitchen areas to contain laundry facilities, sewing machine, workshop, home freezer, heating plant, and so on. A well-planned kitchen may be a separate room in the house, or may be combined with other areas without having its efficiency decreased.

The two most common combinations are the kitchen-dining room and the combination kitchen-laundry, and some kitchens combine all three functions, at least to the extent of having a snack bar or small table for breakfast and odd-hour snacks. The combination kitchen and dining room holds great appeal for families who like the opportunity it offers for the whole family to visit together while dinner is being prepared; and for the family to assist when needed. A play area for the children while the mother works is a great asset. Even minimum eating space in the kitchen makes it possible to feed the children with greater speed and convenience, and without mishap to the carpet. For special parties and guest dinners there are talking points for the living-dining-room combination. Some housewives prefer to serve light meals in the kitchen, but at times want to get out of the work area to enjoy their meals more. A combination kitchen and laundry can be efficient and attractive with the modern equipment now made available. The kitchen-utility room of a basementless house, which takes in the heating plant and water heater as well as the laundry equipment is often desired. A rectangular room works well for this combination, with the kitchen and laundry at opposite ends, and perhaps additional partial separation in the form of cabinets or equipment to isolate the areas.

It is never too early to start planning the kitchen, whether you are building soon or just beginning to consider the house you would like to have. Any modern kitchen is a sizable investment, often the most expensive room in the house, and once built it is difficult to change without considerable added expense. After plumbing and wiring are installed, you cannot shift the sink or range to a more convenient location as families do with furniture in other rooms. Once walls and cabinets are in, you cannot stretch counters or cupboards that are too small, or change the location of doors and windows. The time to do all this planning is before the house is built — in your mind's eye and on paper. You can get excellent help from many places — magazines, pamphlets put out by equipment manufacturers, the extension home agent in your county, or your state college or university. Often gas and electric utility companies offer free kitchen-planning service. Draw up a tentative floor plan and place the equipment symbols in their locations. It is better to make these plans to scale. The wall elevations may be arranged around the floor plan showing the elevations of the arrangement by lowering the walls into the same plane as the floor plan. It is suggested that a scale model be worked out of the room and its equipment, making the models of the equipment so they may be moved around to study the problem better.

The kitchen should be scaled in size and layout to the individual requirements of the family. Certain essential equipment is needed in every household, but as the food-service load increases, the need for utensils or storage space is not proportionally increased. Also kitchens should be planned for normal rather than special needs, so that the house will be readily salable at any time. To determine kitchen capacity, allow two persons to the master bedroom, one person to each additional bedroom, and add two extra persons to represent requirements for guests. This sum represents the number of persons for whom food service is required. Some authorities use the formula of the number of bedrooms plus three, and the capacities of the major elements are thus found in

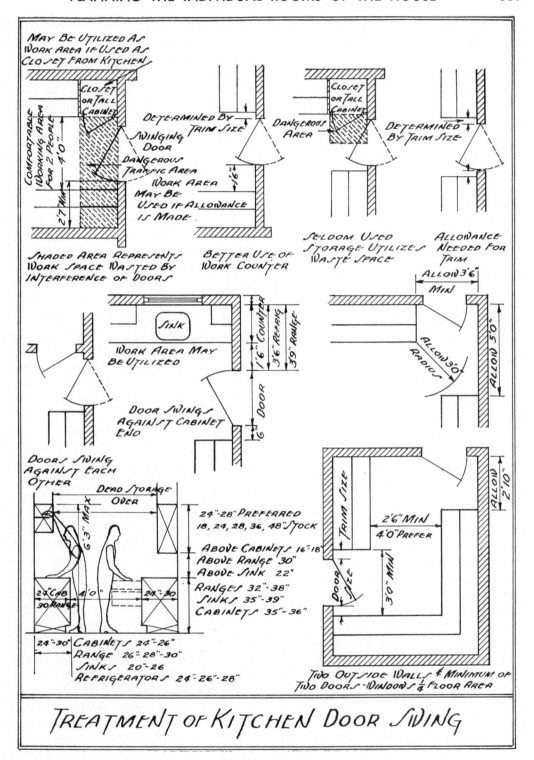

TREATMENT OF KITCHEN DOOR SWING

Fig. 109

accordance with the following considerations: (1) allow 1 cu. ft. per person plus 1 extra cu. ft. for normal refrigerator capacity; (2) allow 6 sq. ft. of shelf area in wall cabinets per person, or 2 lineal feet of shelf space per person for 30-in.-high cabinets, 12-in.-deep inside measurement; (3) allow approximately 12 to 16 cu. ft. of shelf and counter space in base cabinets per person; (4) capacity of cooking and baking areas are adapted to individual needs; and (5) sizes of sinks or dishwashers, or a combination of both vary widely. It is generally agreed that 4 or 5 lineal feet of sink space including the work top is to be recommended, and up to 8 to 10 ft. may be preferred.

In planning the space provided for a kitchen, the following factors are essential to maximum convenience and efficiency:

1. Avoid miscellaneous traffic through the kitchen work areas. Kitchen traffic should be only that which is needed to receive supplies, store and prepare them, serve food, and clean and put away dishes and utensils. There must be access to the service entrance and the dining room, but all other traffic should be routed around the kitchen rather than through it. A hallway should be provided which leads both to the kitchen, and to the front hall, cellar stairs, and storage rooms.

2. Well-located doors and windows increase the efficiency of the complete plan. When doors swing into a kitchen they create a congestion that partially destroys effective use of adjacent work tops or space for desired equipment and cabinets. As a result it is desirable to arrange cabinets so that the door swing will come against the end of the cabinet and not obstruct the work area, allowing the door to extend not less than 18 to 20 in. beyond the face of any cabinet, range, refrigerator, or sink (Fig. 109). If practical, a door space should be near the center of a wall to permit a cabinet or counter surface to be installed in the corner. Whenever possible danger-zone areas should be minimized by use of one of the following alternatives:

a) Swinging doors may be divided into two vertical halves, each with half the swing of a normal opening.

b) Storage cabinets for cleaning utensils, brooms, vacuum cleaners, and so on should be placed at either side of the door and at right angles to normal work areas to act as a buffer zone.

c) Arrange the doors so that they do not swing into the kitchen.

3. There should be as many windows as possible without reducing the required amount of cabinet space, with this window area equal to 15 to 25 per cent of the kitchen floor area. Kitchen windows should be so arranged that the kitchen will get the benefit of sunshine in winter and the prevailing breeze in summer. It is advantageous to have windows in two walls to get the best light and ventilation. Cross ventilation, most desirable in summer, may be achieved by placing the two windows opposite each other. If there is only one window, the room will have cross ventilation if the window is placed opposite the door leading out of the house. Windows placed 42 to 46 in. from the floor and reaching to within a foot or less of the ceiling give convenient wall space below the window for work tables. They also provide ventilation to the upper and warmer portions of the room. Double-hung windows are recommended for the kitchen. Windows are usually best located above the sink or other work areas, although they may be located near the preparation and cleaning center on either side, depending upon the working habits of the housewife, the location of the mechanical equipment, and the orientation of the kitchen. Windows may be located in the corner of the room; however this cuts out wall space ordinarily available for cabinets and is usually undesirable. When a window is located near a corner, the trim should be set at least 13 in. from the inside of the corner to permit installation of wall cabinets. An allowance of 16 in. to the jamb should be used as a minimum (Fig. 110).

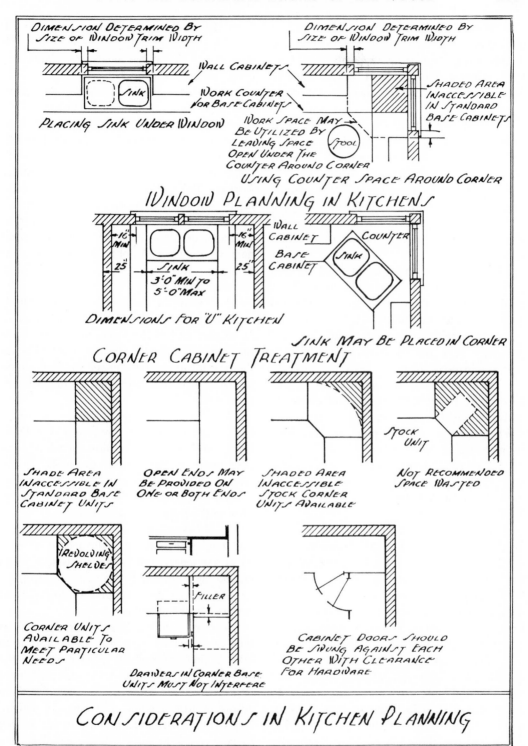

Fig. 110

4. If possible, have only two doors, one to the outside, and locate both at the same end of the room, away from the work line. One large window plus a glass in the outside door should give enough daylight for comfortable work.

5. Nonworking areas should be segregated from the working areas. The objective is to keep work areas closely related to each other to save steps between them.

6. When the kitchen plan develops corners formed by adjacent cabinets, the corner space is comparatively useless because of its lack of accessibility. The following alternatives are suggested:

a) Corner areas may be blocked off and the cabinets joined at corners with fillers used to enclose these dead spaces. Modern corner cabinets may be obtained with revolving shelves making the space useful. The corner may also be enclosed from floor to ceiling and used for ducts, riser pipes, structural members, and so on. Sometimes this space may be utilized by a small closet or shelves accessible from another room.

b) Work-top spaces may be provided through use of fillers to adjust cabinet units to existing room dimensions. When base cabinets meet at corners, necessary clearance must be provided for interfering drawers, doors, and hardware.

7. Provision should be made for replacement of old equipment with sufficient space for larger sizes. As a family grows in size the needs increase. Adequate space should be allowed for additional equipment such as disposal units and automatic dishwashers. Be sure that the water heater is adequate not only for present needs but anticipated needs.

8. Try to arrange the working centers in a triangle — with refrigerator, sink, and range at the points of the triangle and no more than 6 ft. 0 in. between each of these units. Recent studies show the heaviest traffic between the table, sink, and range so that it may make for greater convenience if the refrigerator takes a position farther away from the table or the dining-room door. If possible, have the refrigerator near the outside door, the range near the dining-area door, and the sink in between.

9. Arrange a continuous line of appliances with working counters and cupboards between so that work moves smoothly from one work center to another. Usually it is best that work moves from left to right — the direction most convenient for a right-handed worker. The arrangement may be around three adjoining walls to form a U-shaped kitchen, around two adjoining walls for an L shape, or along opposite walls in a small narrow kitchen with doors at either end. The last arrangement saves space but is the least convenient for work.

10. Locate the meal table, planning desk, and other extras outside the line of work — at another end of the room, in another wing, or along a fourth wall. In a U-shaped kitchen the best location is at one end; in an L shape, in the free corner provided by the two unused walls.

11. Provide generous counter space at each work center for comfort and convenience, but also as a provision for adding new equipment in the future. Generally if the work counters are adequate in size, the cupboards above and below will hold the supplies and equipment used there.

12. Have at least one double-convenience outlet at each counter to take care of electrical appliances. For safety it is best to avoid outlets near the sink so that no electrical appliance will be grounded through a wet surface or the plumbing system.

13. Plan your cupboards for the articles they are to store. One way to do this is to take an inventory of all articles used in the average home kitchen and add any extra items which are often used. Then list them according to frequency of use, weight, height, and whether they must be easy to see as well as convenient to reach. With these lists you can plan the cupboards so that the most frequently used items are within easiest reach;

those used least are on higher or lower shelves. Store heavy utensils on or just below the counter tops — electric mixer on the counter, heavy pans or kettles below. Narrow shelves are best for packaged and canned goods, cups, and glasses. Vertical files are convenient for platters, trays, baking dishes, pans, and covers. Supplies and equipment are handiest when kept near the center where they are used — flour and sugar in bins or drawers at the mixing center near the stove; soap, brushes, and other dishwashing supplies at the cleaning center, and so on. Arrange shelves, files, or other partitions so they can be moved to adapt the cupboard as future needs require.

14. When planning the over-all size of the room, be sure there is space for two people to work together without crowding.

15. For jobs that are done most comfortably at levels lower than the 36-in. standard counter height, plan pull-out boards in the base cabinets.

16. A table on wheels is essential for saving space and labor for rolling dishes and food to and from the table, and providing extra work space wherever it may be needed — at range, refrigerator, mixing center, or sink.

17. The kitchen window should face the play yard of young children.

18. If you like outdoor meals, you will want the kitchen where you can have an adjoining patio, porch, or attractive yard. It is understood that you cannot have everything in an inexpensve home design, but it is worthwhile considering all these features and trying to include as many as you can.

As a food-preparation center, the kitchen must be designed for sanitation. Crevices and corners which collect dirt and are hard to clean must be eliminated. Materials for work surfaces and storage spaces must be durable and washable. Refrigeration of perishable food is essential, and closed cabinets for utensils and staple foods are desirable. Facilities for the sanitary disposal of garbage and waste products are necessary. Storage for cleaning equipment must be provided.

One of the basic needs in the kitchen is clean, fresh air. Most compact kitchens do not provide the benefit of cross ventilation. Windows alone are not adequate for ideal ventilation nor will an exhaust fan placed on the opposite wall from the range prove satisfactory because the greasy vapors from the range will be pulled across the room and be deposited on the walls and ceiling before they can be exhausted. A small exhaust fan placed in the cabinet over the range and piped to the outdoors will provide the cooking area with ample fresh air and exhaust heat, odors, and vapors before they can be spread into the room. This exhaust fan is often built into a metal hood located above the range. The hood should be designed to include removable filters to remove the greasy particles which tend to gum up the efficiency of the exhaust system.

The recommended exposure for the kitchen is toward the northeast or northwest, or where there is an outer wall toward the north. This provides a cooler kitchen, with less glare from the sun. Ideally, this room should be placed near the garage entrance for the convenience of carrying in the groceries and taking out trash and garbage. A kitchen location next to the garage allows for a trash bin with an opening on both sides of the wall so that papers, cans, and bottles can be disposed of easily and neatly in the kitchen and carried away from the garage. A kitchen on the corner of a house allows for cross ventilation with the minimum of windows. On a corner the kitchen can have a large window on one wall and a door with a glass in it on another wall. One large-size window costs less and gives more light than two small windows.

Artificial lighting in the kitchen should be so placed that it does not create a glare, and care should be taken that it does not cast a shadow at any of the work centers. Light from fluorescent tubes or filament-bulb fix-

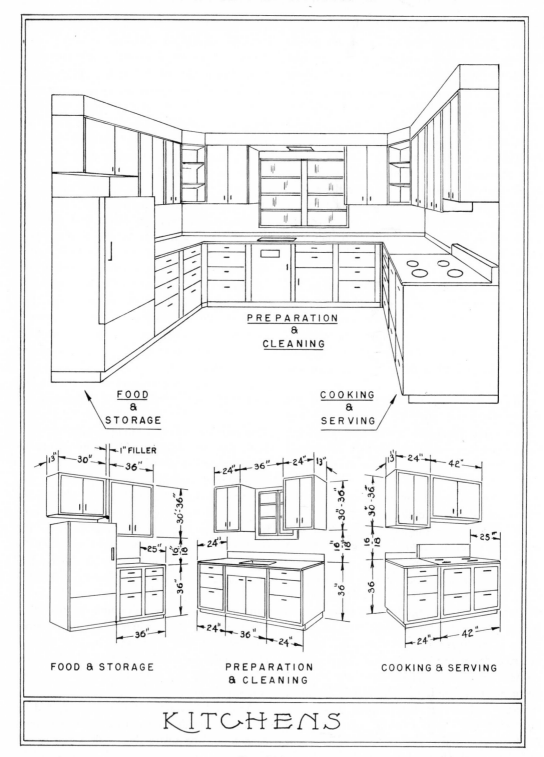

FOOD & STORAGE

PREPARATION & CLEANING

COOKING & SERVING

KITCHENS

Fig. 111

tures should be provided by central ceiling fixtures for general illumination, plus local lighting on the wall or in the ceiling directly above each work center such as the sink, range, counters, or other work areas. Recommended values of kitchen illumination are as follows:

1. General illumination, 10 foot-candles;
2. Supplementary illumination, 40 foot-candles.

The central lighting fixture should be multiple-controlled by conveniently placed switches where important entrances are more than 10 ft. apart. For the work centers, switches can be located at or near the fixtures. Electric appliances used in the kitchen require adequate wiring on a separate circuit for safety and efficient operation. There should be at least one duplex-convenience outlet for each 4 ft. of work counter, and one provided at the location of the refrigerator. An electric range would require heavy-duty wiring. Convenience outlets should be provided for an electric clock, fan, dishwasher, disposal unit, and so on.

The most important factor in planning the kitchen area is the basic arrangement of the three major work centers — storage and preparation center, washing and cleaning center, and the cooking and serving center (Fig. 111). These three units properly arranged and outfitted with utensils, dishes, equipment, and so on, should be related to each other so that the work flows conveniently from one center to the other. The basic plan of the kitchen is arranged around these three centers, but in actual practice they will overlap functions. The organization of each center is just as important as its relationship to the whole plan. Unless the food supplies, utensils, dishes, equipment, and so on, are grouped and arranged conveniently in each center, the kitchen will lose much of its step-saving efficiency.

The *food-storage center* is the place where most of the bulky and perishable foods are stored. The flow of food starts from the serv-

ice entrance to the refrigerator, which implies that this appliance should be located convenient to the service entrance. Adequate counter space in combination with base and wall cabinets should be provided for storing supplies used in mixing foods. Either a large drawer or cabinet at counter level should be provided for the electric mixer. Cabinet space above the refrigerator provides additional storage space. Ideally the storage center should include a work top where supplies can be placed upon delivery, sorted, cleaned at the sink if necessary, and then be put away. Practically all refrigerators are equipped with doors hinged at the right, although left-hinged doors may be obtained if desired. If a standard right-hinged refrigerator door is to be used, it is desirable to arrange the remainder of the work center to the left of the refrigerator. If the sequence of operations from food storage through preparation, cleaning, cooking, and serving is planned to be from left to right, the refrigerator should be supplied with a left-hand door. This storage center should be convenient to the sink and range (Fig. 112).

Since the sink is needed in food preparation, the *cleaning center* is logically developed nearby. Here the dishwasher should be located. All the soaps, scrubbing brushes, and cleaning utensils for the kitchen should be stored within easy reach of the sink. If a garbage-disposal unit is provided it is placed beneath the sink bowl and connected into the drain line. The hopper or chute for a built-in incinerator should be conveniently placed; or a garbage receptacle should be placed underneath the sink. Often the space under the sink is the only available space for placing the radiator. In such a situation a vent should be brought up behind the sink for the distribution of heat. Towel racks may be placed in front of the heat source in such a position that the circulation of air will dry the towels. Organization for efficient work at the sink requires that dirty dishes are placed to the right of the sink for right-handed per-

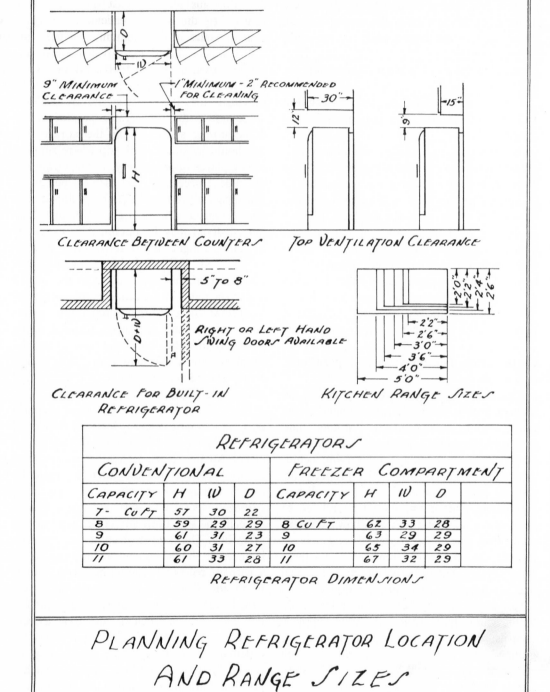

CLEARANCE BETWEEN COUNTERS

TOP VENTILATION CLEARANCE

CLEARANCE FOR BUILT-IN REFRIGERATOR

KITCHEN RANGE SIZES

RIGHT OR LEFT HAND SWING DOORS AVAILABLE

REFRIGERATORS							
CONVENTIONAL				FREEZER COMPARTMENT			
CAPACITY	H	W	D	CAPACITY	H	W	D
7- Cu Ft	57	30	22				
8	59	29	29	8 Cu Ft	62	33	28
9	61	31	23	9	63	29	29
10	60	31	27	10	65	34	29
11	61	33	28	11	67	32	29

REFRIGERATOR DIMENSIONS

PLANNING REFRIGERATOR LOCATION AND RANGE SIZES

Fig 112

sons, and clean dishes for drying are placed to the left of the sink. The cabinet for storing dishes should also be to the left (always on the same side as the drainboard). A left-handed person will find it desirable to reverse the procedure. The washing and cleaning center should be located centrally, both to the storage and preparation center and to the cooking and serving center.

The *cooking center* consists of the range and space for storing utensils and materials used in the cooking process. Work counters should be placed on either or both sides of the range for placing food when it is removed from the oven or surface burners, and for serving the food while it is hot. Ideally no space should be left between the range and work centers since such spaces only contribute to more work in cleaning, but such spaces are necessary for fire safety unless the cabinets are fireproofed and the range is insulated. It is recommended that ranges that are not insulated should be spaced 6 in. from the walls and adjacent cabinets, and 3 in. from insulated ranges and fireproof cabinets. Flue connections are not necessary for gas or electric ranges, but required for wood or coal ranges. No kitchen is well equipped that does not have effective ventilation for removing cooking odors and smoke.

In larger homes there may be a fourth work center, called the *planning center*. This requires space for a small desk with drawers for recipe files, books, grocery accounts, and records relating to kitchen management. A telephone and a radio are desirable additions. In small homes, small cabinets may be placed near the preparation center for storing recipe books, and the kitchen table may be used for planning.

These principles of planning refer primarily to new construction where the problem can be solved without interference from existing construction. In remodeling or modernization work it is often impractical to perfect such ideal arrangements because of the expenses incurred in relocation of doors, windows, partitions, and so on. In principle, any plan which interrupts a continuation of the three major work centers by a door opening, closet space, or any other element not constantly used in the work area is faulty to the extent that it requires extra steps, reducing the working efficiency of the kitchen.

Obviously it is desirable to work toward an ideal in planning a kitchen. Thus, if work centers must be physically separated, their *relative* location should be such as to allow a natural sequence of activity *from* storage and preparation, *through* washing and cleaning, *to* the cooking and serving center. Each work center combines a major item of mechanical equipment with storage and working facilities necessary for its most efficient use. Each work center should be equipped for the storage of utensils, supplies, and dishes, according to the point where each is *first used*.

Besides being efficiently organized in themselves, the work centers should be arranged in logical sequence so far as the conditions of the plan permit, from the point where the supplies enter the kitchen progressing along its walls to the point nearest the dining area. There are six basic organization plans of these work centers (Fig. 113):

1. The U-shaped kitchen is an ideal arrangement from the standpoint of food preparation because the work surface is continuous around three sides of the room, and because the major units (plus a great many cabinets) can be fitted into a very small space. In such a plan the sink is usually placed at the base of the U, with the range on one stem and the refrigerator on the other.

2. The L-shaped plan has a continuous work surface along two sides of the room, with the refrigerator, range, and sink grouped together as compactly as possible. The remaining two walls may be used for door opening and additional windows, and this plan allows for a convenient location of a dining space.

3. The two-wall or corridor-type kitchen contains two long walls given over to coun-

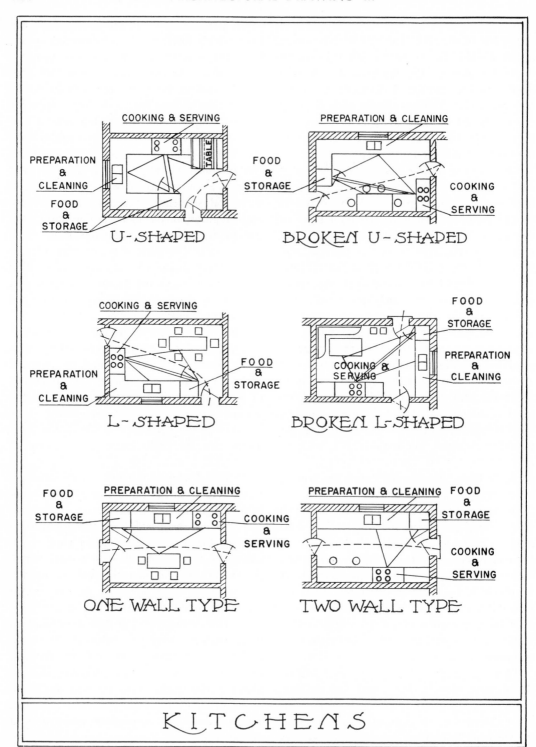

Fig. 113

ters and the mechanical equipment. The cleaning center should be located on the outside wall, with the cooking center on the opposite side. The refrigerator may be satisfactorily placed on either side. The plan is often used for small homes and apartment kitchens adaptable to long, narrow rooms. The only objection to this plan is that it usually leads to placing a door at each end; and this inevitably means the kitchen becomes a traffic corridor.

4. One-wall kitchens are adaptable to living room-kitchen combinations where there is a minimum of wall space. The plan may be located in an alcove off the living room, separated by a folding screen. A continuous work surface may be obtained by locating the refrigerator and range at opposite ends of the wall arrangement.

5. Combinations or variations may often be made of Nos. 1 and 2. There is the broken U, the broken L, and the "individual center" in which three doors are located on different sides of the room, and the work centers are separated to conform to the plan. These eliminate costly structural changes and are therefore especially suitable for modernization of existing kitchens.

Correct apportionment of needed wall and base cabinet storage facilities to the work centers has only recently been given serious consideration. Wall cabinet capacity is based upon the square feet of shelf space, with an allowance of 6 sq. ft. per adult in the family. Base cabinet capacity is based upon linear front feet of the cabinet, not including the range or refrigerator. The following size relationships are used by some authorities:

No. of Bedrooms	No. of Persons	Shelf Space in Wall Cabinets	Shelf Space in Base Cabinets
1	2	24 sq. ft.	3–4½ lin. ft.
2	3	30 sq. ft.	4½–6 lin. ft.
3	4	36 sq. ft.	6–7½ lin. ft.
4	5	42 sq. ft.	7½–9 lin. ft.

Base cabinets are made in three principal types (Fig. 114):

1. All-drawer unit;

2. Drawer and/or cupboard type, having a drawer with shelf space beneath enclosed by doors;

3. All cupboard, containing adjustable shelves, towel rack, or other special accessories enclosed by doors.

The capacity of base cabinets is approximately 6 cu. ft. per lineal foot for cabinets with a normal counter height of 36 in. and a work top 25 in. wide. The height of 36 in. from the floor was not arrived at arbitrarily. Manufacturers took into account that some women are short, some tall, and decided upon this medium standard. It is a simple matter to have a higher counter level by blocking up the base as the equipment is installed. This standardization of height eliminates the cost of building special cabinets, thereby making mass production possible. These base cabinets are normally built with a toe space — approximately 4 in. high and 3 in. deep — so that one can stand closer to the counter and work in greater comfort.

Wall-cabinet space is normally made up of standard cabinets approximately 13 in. deep and 30 or 36 in. tall. The over-all height from floor to cabinet top varies from 7 ft. slightly upward. Between the top of the base cabinet and the bottom of the wall cabinets is a space which allows for full use of the counters. This usually varies between 16 to 18 in., depending upon the height of the wall cabinets, and the over-all height from the floor to the top of the wall cabinet.

Both base and wall cabinets come in a great many standard widths. They start at 15 in. and increase by 3-in. multiples up to 30 in., with larger sizes showing width increases to 36, 42, 45, and 54 in.

It may be noted that cabinets above refrigerators are relatively inaccessible and should usually be counted as surplus storage space for extra quantities of staple foods to which constant access is not needed. Cabinet space above the range is often necessary but if used should be protected from possible heat damage by a sheet of asbestos attached

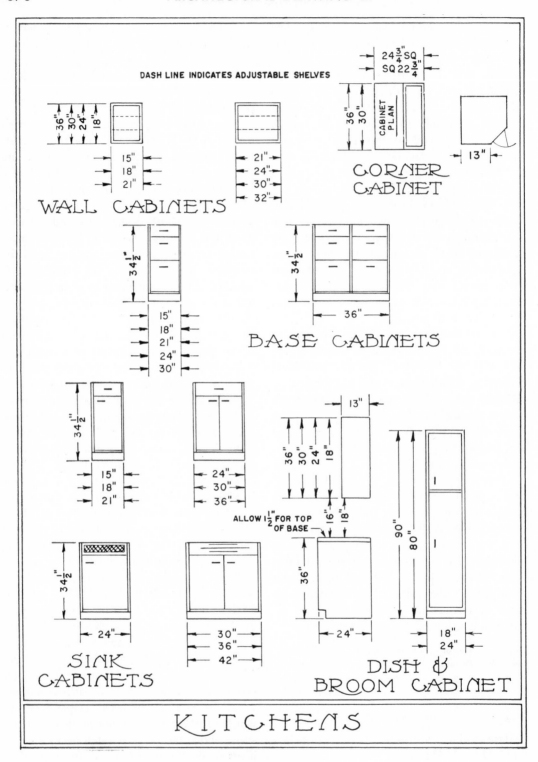

Fig. 114

to the underside. Cabinet space over a sink must provide adequate headroom of at least 5 ft. 6 in.

Corner cabinets to co-ordinate with wall cabinets are available, however their shelf capacity cannot be counted as fully effective.

The real job in designing a kitchen is the selection of cabinets which fit the available space and fulfill the function required. Naturally this depends upon the size of the room and its layout, and the size of the mechanical appliances. If it is a new kitchen being planned, you can design it to fit your needs and taste. But if you are remodeling, you may have to fit your plan to existing conditions. It is a case of trial and error until you obtain the satisfactory combination. Where two walls meet at right angles a 2-in. space is required on the cabinets for the clearance of the drawers and doors in opposing cabinets. Wood or metal fillers may be supplied by the manufacturers of the cabinets, to give the cabinet wall an unbroken, finished appearance.

There are many variations in standardized cabinet fittings and designs. They may be stock cabinets with one, two, three, or more shelves closed by swinging or sliding doors. The shelves may be stationary, or adjustable. There may be an attached flour bin arranged so that, by pulling out the shelf and turning the sifter crank, the flour can be sifted into a bowl underneath.

Under the sink you may install cabinets in which to keep dish mops, cleaning powders, and other equipment and supplies. To the door may be fastened a small garbage can or towel rack.

You may have cabinets with drawers of varying size, fitted with work-saving devices, such as a wire rack for dishes or pan covers. Other conveniences built into cabinets are bins for the storage of flour, sugar, and so on, a wooden bread board, a bread box with sliding cover, and wire cake shelf, also a sliding knife, fork, and spoon box. There is not much to choose between wood and metal

cabinets for each fulfills its purpose. They are attractive and built to last for years. The wood is thoroughly seasoned and accurately sized; the steel is carefully designed, and cleanly fabricated. The only real difference you may notice between the wood and metal cabinets is the finish. Metal cabinets are finished in baked enamel or porcelain, while the wood cabinets do not have as hard and wear-resistant a finish. The metal cabinets tend to be noisier in operation.

Coverings and finishes should all be durable, nonabsorbent, stain-resistant, and easily cleaned. The work-center tops should be covered with heat-resistant material. Metal tops are shiny and durable, and unaffected by stains; they are also chip and crack proof. Compressed wood is chemically treated to resist grease, moisture, and acids; it is also resilient and quiet. Plastics are beginning to occupy a more important place in modern living, and they are tough and wearable. Moldings for facing counter edges should not discolor the worker's clothing. Since most tasks are done while the worker is in a standing position, a resilient floor will reduce fatigue.

The exterior design of the cabinets may vary. Usually the doors are built of plywood and flush, without dust-catching moldings, but they may be latticed or louvered for ventilation.

Needless to say, a kitchen is not a kitchen unless it contains more than cabinets. You must have a sink, range, and refrigerator. And a really modern kitchen will have several other major appliances — a dishwasher, garbage waste-disposal unit, ventilating fan, and so on. The installation of special features is part of the basic arrangement of the kitchen. These features are designed with both practical and ornamental functions; thus ornamental shelving over the range, with curving valance, may also be practical with concealed lighting and space for seldom used utensils. In many modern kitchens the distance between the work-counter top and the underside of wall-hung cabinets has been increased. This reduces head bumping and permits installation of small intermediate shelves for condiments and small articles. Some kitchens feature a built-in desk; knee space may be provided under a section of counter top to permit a person to sit there conveniently while planning menus, writing letters, or using the telephone. Window sills may be extended beyond normal depth to provide room for potted plants, and glass shelving may be built into windows for the same purpose.

Ranges and sinks planned to project into the room frequently have built-in cabinets, or counters in back of them with shelves facing a dining or living area immediately adjacent to the kitchen. Special treatment may be given a back splashboard around work areas. Covering this area of the wall to a height of 12 in. or more with tile or a sheet plastic is very effective. Sliding-door cabinets with vertical storage compartments for trays and pot lids are other desirable features of cabinet construction. These call for special planning in advance of construction.

The snack bar and breakfast nook have established themselves as almost standard items. The choice of a snack bar and a built-in nook will be dictated by the amount of space allotted to the kitchen, the owner's preference, the size of family, and the types of family activities. The snack bar may be combined with ceiling-hung cabinets to form a pass counter between the kitchen and dining room, giving an illusion of more space. It is usually more economical than the built-in nook. Although there are some ready-built units available, it is more common to have the breakfast nook built to order.

The present trend is for the sink to be built as an integral part of the kitchen-cabinet work. Cabinet sinks are made in a full range of sizes and styles, and sink bowl units are also available in a complete range of sizes and styles for installation into built-in cabi-

nets. Faucets are of the mixing type, having a swinging spout for directing the water for washing or rinsing (double-compartment sinks may require a longer than standard spout). In all except the most economical installations, a spray for rinsing is a part of the faucet assembly, having a diverter valve supplying water to the spray whenever desired. A faucet having provision for introducing a detergent into the spray for dishwashing has met with some popularity.

Both electric and gas ranges have kept step with the advances in design and construction of kitchen fixtures and appliances. Finishes are heat-resistant and easily cleaned. Improved insulating materials make cooking cool work on even the hottest days. In many sections of the country the kitchen range is considered as built-in equipment, which permits its inclusion in the mortgage. Range sizes vary from small four-burner units with the oven placed in the space below for minimum cost and inclusive space, up to six and eight burner models with two ovens and broilers. A built-in-the-top griddle for frying eggs, bacon, pancakes, and so on, is often provided. Built-in lights are often desirable and many units feature timing devices that turn the heat off at the lapse of a given time, or even start and stop the procedure at specified times. A new design feature is the construction of both electric and gas stove in "modular" units which may be arranged in any desired combination of units. Burner units may be installed in counter tops. Oven units may be combined with drawers to set the oven at any desired height. Greater freedom in kitchen planning is thus possible, since designers are no longer limited by the package size of the conventional range.

More efficient insulating materials and smaller power packages have increased capacities of refrigerators without adding to over-all dimensions. Freezer compartments are now standard. It is sound practice to provide as large a refrigerator as space and

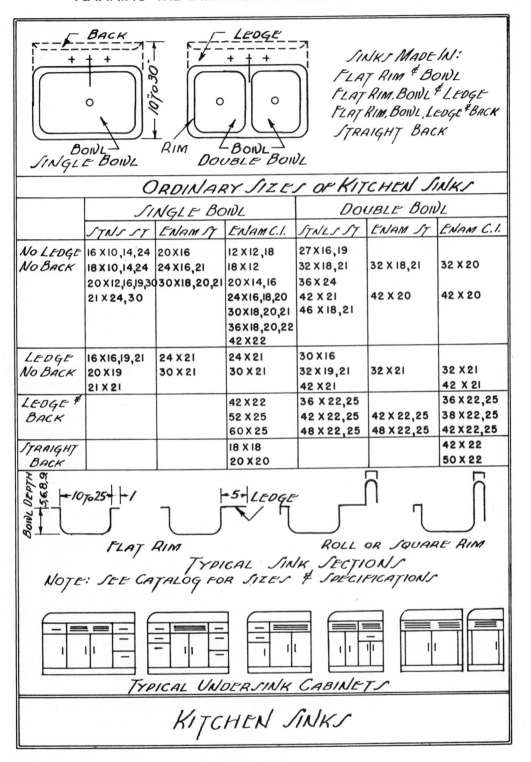

SINKS MADE IN:
FLAT RIM & BOWL
FLAT RIM, BOWL & LEDGE
FLAT RIM, BOWL, LEDGE & BACK
STRAIGHT BACK

ORDINARY SIZES OF KITCHEN SINKS

	SINGLE BOWL			DOUBLE BOWL		
	STNS ST	ENAM ST	ENAM C.I.	STNLS ST	ENAM ST	ENAM C.I.
No LEDGE No BACK	16 X 10,14,24 18 X 10,14,24 20 X 12,16,19,30 21 X 24,30	20 X 16 24 X 16,21 30 X 18,20,21	12 X 12,18 18 X 12 20 X 14,16 24 X 16,18,20 30 X 18,20,21 36 X 18,20,22 42 X 22	27 X 16,19 32 X 18,21 36 X 24 42 X 21 46 X 18,21	32 X 18,21 42 X 20	32 X 20 42 X 20
LEDGE No BACK	16 X 16,19,21 20 X 19 21 X 21	24 X 21 30 X 21	24 X 21 30 X 21	30 X 16 32 X 19,21 42 X 21	32 X 21	32 X 21 42 X 21
LEDGE & BACK			42 X 22 52 X 25 60 X 25	36 X 22,25 42 X 22,25 48 X 22,25	42 X 22,25 48 X 22,25	36 X 22,25 38 X 22,25 42 X 22,25
STRAIGHT BACK			18 X 18 20 X 20			42 X 22 50 X 22

TYPICAL SINK SECTIONS

NOTE: SEE CATALOG FOR SIZES & SPECIFICATIONS

FLAT RIM   ROLL OR SQUARE RIM

TYPICAL UNDERSINK CABINETS

KITCHEN SINKS

Fig. 115

costs permit. Freezers for kitchen installation may be obtained in either upright or counter styles.

Dishwashers either are built in as part of the sink cabinet by the manufacturer or may be obtained as separate units. They may also be obtained without cabinets for custom installation. Top and front loading models perform with equal efficiency and ease in loading, and the selection may be made on the basis of space needs. Where dishwashers are installed the builder will have to make provision for the necessary hot-water requirements. For proper sterilization of dishes a temperature of 180 deg. is necessary. Most hot-water heaters are not designed to supply water at this temperature, and there is danger of scalding if the water in the hot-water pipes throughout the house is of this temperature. Many units have booster heaters to raise the temperature of the water for dishwashing. Dishwashers are usually motor-driven, and provision for electrical connection should be made if a dishwasher installation is contemplated at a later date.

Waste-disposal units, electrically operated grinders, shredders, or pulverizers mounted in the sink drain, are the modern method of handling food wastes. The unsightly garbage can, greatest single factor of rat infestation in cities is eliminated by the use of a garbage-disposal unit. Table scraps, food wastes, even bones are all shredded by hardened steel grinders in the unit and flushed down the drain. Modern units are quiet, dependable, and safe in operation. Interlock devices prevent operation unless water for carrying away the wastes is flowing. These units may be obtained to mount on any modern sink already in place. Local codes should be checked for installation requirements. Some require a minimum of a 2-in. waste line; others permit disposal units in combination with a grease trap.

The individual incinerator type of disposal unit may be used in locations having plumbing-code restrictions. Waste material is placed in a metal container which is fired by gas. The residual ash is removed at periodic intervals, and safe, odor-free operation is assured.

Builders of minimum-space units such as motels and kitchenette apartments have prompted the development of unit kitchens in which range, oven, sink, and refrigerator are assembled into one or two compact units taking as little as 48 in. of floor space. While such compactness is not advisable for general use, these units sometimes solve problems in creating attic or basement flats, making conversions, and so on.

Modern kitchen sinks range in size from 42 to 96 in. in length and have more than ample workroom if their size is chosen according to the family's needs (Fig. 115). It is desirable to install the two-drainboard sink if space permits. The double-bowl sink having separate compartments for dishwashing and rinsing is preferred by housewives. Sinks are typically of porcelain enameled steel or cast iron, but may also be of stainless steel. Stainless steel is subject to scratching by abrasive cleaners but makes a beautiful appearance if properly cared for and will not chip. Drainboards may be obtained in widths of 42, 48, 54, 60, and 66 in. For sinks built into a corner counter top, a 24 by 21-in. bowl is about minimum, while a 30 by 21-in. bowl size gives better workroom. Double-compartment sinks for counter-top installation are 32 by 21 in. and 42 by 21 in. Cabinet bases of wood or metal can be had for sink installations in lengths of from 42 up to 144 in. Longer units include cupboards or drawers in addition to the undersink compartments. Special brackets and moldings are available for mounting sink-bowl units into any type of custom-built counter top. Individual sink cabinets are supplied by manufacturers in both single and double drainboard, single and double bowl to match and harmonize with other cabinet and counter installations (Fig. 116). Sinks not having garbage-disposal units built in should have

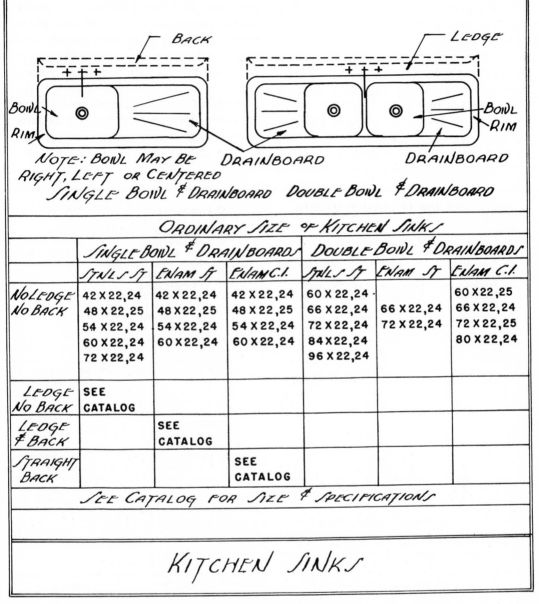

ORDINARY SIZE OF KITCHEN SINKS						
	SINGLE BOWL & DRAINBOARDS			DOUBLE BOWL & DRAINBOARDS		
	STNLS ST	ENAM ST	ENAM C.I.	STNLS ST	ENAM ST	ENAM C.I.
NO LEDGE NO BACK	42 X 22,24 48 X 22,25 54 X 22,24 60 X 22,24 72 X 22,24	42 X 22,24 48 X 22,25 54 X 22,24 60 X 22,24	42 X 22,24 48 X 22,25 54 X 22,24 60 X 22,24	60 X 22,24 66 X 22,24 72 X 22,24 84 X 22,24 96 X 22,24	66 X 22,24 72 X 22,24	60 X 22,25 66 X 22,24 72 X 22,25 80 X 22,24
LEDGE NO BACK	SEE CATALOG					
LEDGE & BACK		SEE CATALOG				
STRAIGHT BACK			SEE CATALOG			
SEE CATALOG FOR SIZE & SPECIFICATIONS						

KITCHEN SINKS

Fig. 116

drain openings of a size which will permit later installation of the unit. Minimum opening is 3½ in., with a 4-in. opening generally used. Some disposal units require a 5½-in. opening. Electrical roughing-in should be provided at the time of construction for a future garbage disposal and dishwasher.

In discussing the problems of modern kitchen planning it is assumed that a completely equipped culinary center of the very latest type with continuous work tops, built-in cabinets, ranges, and all the other elements so attractively presented in most model kitchens are to be provided. However, if your budget does not permit this concentration of expense in the kitchen at first, it is better to arrange the units you must have in such a manner that later on you can fill in the gaps and complete the ideal kitchen you prefer. Until cabinets can be purchased, ordinary kitchen tables may serve as work areas. A modern kitchen need not be all electric or all gas or be equipped with any particular manufacturer's equipment. It need not be all metal with stainless steel, or monel-metal work tops and trim, or all enamel, or all aluminum, or modernistic in style; for these are all external factors. A "modern" kitchen means that it is an efficient, pleasant work area for the housewife's culinary duties. It should be attractive and colorful to offset the drudgery and monotony that characterized the early kitchens. A little thought given to details of design, a careful choice of cheerful colors, and your kitchen will become a place to impress your guests with your housekeeping abilities and your good taste.

CHECK LIST FOR KITCHEN PLANNING

I. General

1. Number of persons regularly served ( ); number served in entertaining ( )
2. Food prepared and served by members of family ( ); by servants ( )
3. Provision for pantry ( ); breakfast nook ( ); breakfast bar ( ); planning center ( ); telephone ( ); electric clock ( ); radio ( )
4. Preferred shape of work center: U shape ( ); L shape ( ); one wall ( ); two parallel walls ( )
5. Equipment type: individual units ( ); continuous work tops ( )
6. Kitchen exposure: north ( ); south ( ); east ( ); west ( )
7. Access from kitchen to: backstairs ( ); main-entrance hallway ( ); service entrance ( ); garage ( ); dining area ( ); basement ( ); living room ( ); patio ( ); pantry ( ); laundry ( ); servant's area ( )
8. Electrical lighting outlets for: ceiling fixture ( ); lights under wall cabinets ( ); over sink ( ); over range ( ); planning center ( )
9. Electrical service outlets for: range ( ); refrigerator ( ); freezer ( ); toaster ( ); mixer ( ); coffee maker ( ); waffle iron ( ); plate warmer ( ); clock ( ); radio ( ); door bell ( ); pilot switch to basement ( )
10. Windows: casement ( ); double hung ( ); fixed sash ( ); sliding ( ); awning ( ); glass block ( )
11. Mechanical and electrical equipment: dishwasher ( ); garbage disposal ( ); incinerator ( ); range: electric ( ), gas ( ), oil ( ), coal ( ); water heater: electric ( ), gas ( ), oil ( ), coal ( ); ventilating fan ( ); refrigerator: electric ( ), gas ( ); food freezer: electric ( ), gas ( )
12. Kitchen units: sink: double bowl ( ), single bowl ( ), counter top ( ), closed cabinet ( ), open ( ), splash board ( ); wall cabinets ( ); base cabinets ( ); work counters ( ); work table ( ); ironing board ( ); cleaning closet ( ); storage space ( )

II. Equipment at Work Centers

1. Food storage:
   a) Supplies bought daily ( ); weekly ( ); quantities ( )
   b) Refrigerator: cu.-ft. capacity ( ); width ( ); depth ( ); height ( ); doors swing left ( ); swing right ( )
   c) Work top for sorting supplies ( )
   d) Area for nonrefrigerated foods and supplies ( )
2. Food preparation and cleaning center:
   a) Work top for mixer ( ); flour bin ( )
   b) Sink type: single bowl ( ); double bowl ( ); single drainboard ( ); double drainboard ( ); cabinet style ( ); counter style ( ); size ( )
   c) Garbage-disposal unit ( ); dishwasher ( ); incinerator ( )
   d) Towel drier ( ); other accessories ( )
   e) Wall cabinets ( ); base cabinets ( ); revolving shelf corner cabinets ( ); corner fillers ( )
3. Cooking center:
   a) Range: coal ( ); wood ( ); oil ( ); electric ( ); gas ( ); size: height over-all ( ), height to burners ( ), width ( ), depth ( ); insulated ( ); no. of burners ( ); no. of ovens ( ); broiler ( ); warming oven ( ); range hood with exhaust fan ( ); cabinet style ( ); leg style ( )
   b) Ventilating fan ( ); natural draft flue ( )
   c) Work top for hot dishes ( ); left side ( ); right side ( )
   d) Separate serving center ( )
4. Pantry:
   a) Use: dish storage ( ); cold foods preparation ( ); tableware cleaning ( ); beverage bar ( ); pass pantry ( ); breakfast-nook combination ( )
   b) Equipment: sink type ( ); sink size ( ); dishwasher type ( ); dishwasher size ( )
   c) Refrigerator: type ( ); height ( ); width ( ); depth ( ); cu.-ft. capacity ( ); door swing ( )
   d) Work space for serving ( ); preparation ( ); soiled dishes ( )
   e) Cabinet storage space ( )
5. Tableware storage (kitchen-pantry or dining room)
   a) Service plate ( ); dinner plates ( ); salad plates ( ); soup plates ( )
   b) Cereal bowls ( ); soup bowls ( ); service bowls ( )
   c) Cups and saucers ( )
   d) Butter dishes ( ); side dishes ( ); casseroles ( )
   e) Glassware: tumblers ( ); goblets ( ); sherbets ( ); beverage ( )
   f) Platters ( )   g) Covered dishes ( )
   h) Compotes ( ) i) Pitchers ( ); decanters ( )
   j) Trays ( )   k) Silver service for ( ) persons
   l) Carving sets ( ); ladles ( ); serving implements ( )
   m) Silver hollow ware ( )
   n) Linens: tablecloths ( ); napkins ( ); mats ( ); doilies ( ); towels ( )

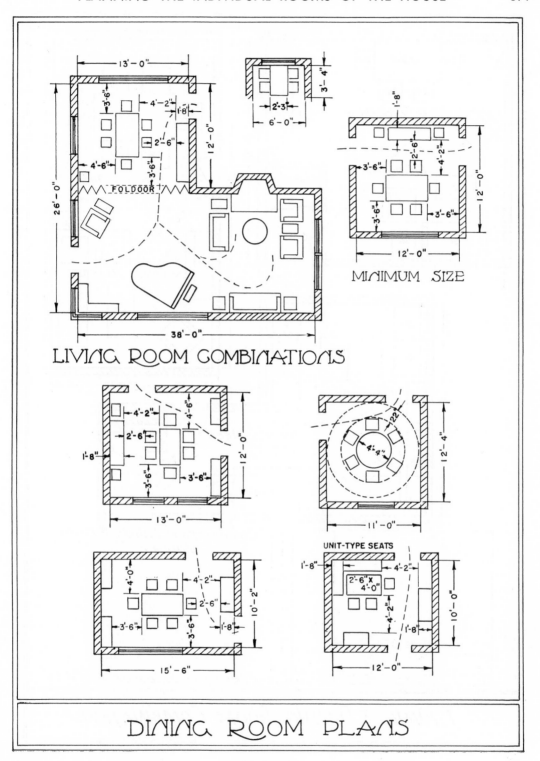

LIVING ROOM COMBINATIONS

MINIMUM SIZE

UNIT-TYPE SEATS

DINING ROOM PLANS

Fig. 117

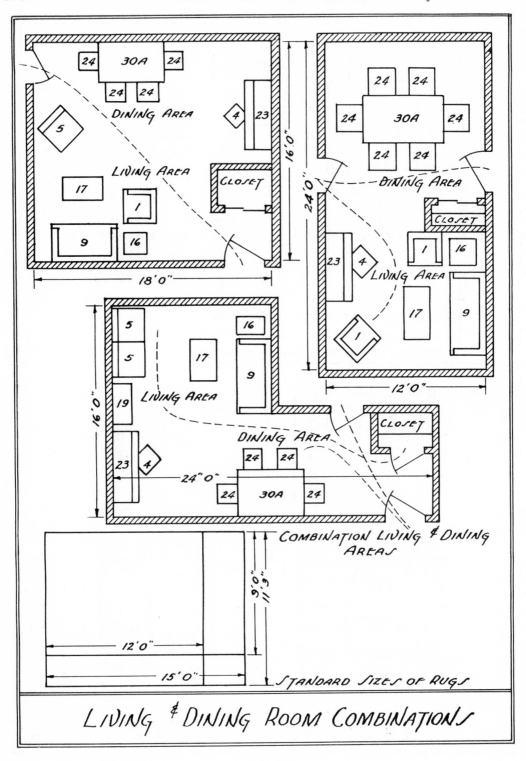

Fig. 118

DINING ROOM, DINING ALCOVE, OR DINETTE

A most important function of the house is to provide space in which the family may enjoy its meals. The formality of entertaining is passing and formal dining is becoming less frequent because of the high cost of living space. The need for complete segregation and enclosure of the dining room, and the dignity and formality of its furnishings is giving way to a combination living and dining area or a kitchen-and-dining-area combination. Home planners have learned to devise ways of making the dining area connected with the living area, or a part of it. Seldom today will you find the traditional special room set aside for the sole purpose of serving and eating meals.

In today's scheme of living, the dining area can range anywhere from the minimum of a double-duty table-and-chest arrangement (placed anywhere in the living room proper), to a permanent grouping of furniture located in a special place at the end of the living room; a special dining alcove with definite separation from the living room; or the separate room for dining (Fig. 117). Each situation has its purpose and its advocates. The first situation requires extra dining service space, taking area from the living room. It presupposes a minimum of mealtime use for the family and emphasizes the buffet style of entertaining. For the dining-room grouping that has a permanent place in one end of the living room there are two approaches to consider: (1) to make the division of uses as inconspicuous as possible; and (2) to emphasize the division, creating the effect of two separate rooms (Fig. 118).

In the first instance, the only problem involved is the selection and arrangement of the furniture — table, chairs, buffet, or cabinet. The table and two chairs can be placed flat against the wall when not in use, with the other chairs and chest pieces arranged to appear like living-room furniture. In the second approach, the buffet or chest or cabinet serves as a partial divider between the living-room proper and the dining end. Screens or accordion wall dividers can also be used to good advantage.

Certainly if your budget permits and your needs require both living and dining rooms of adequate size, and furniture for both rooms in keeping with your taste, this new trend has no significance. Wherever you plan to eat you will need: (a) adequate lanes of traffic for serving, (b) provision for serving, (c) good close-at-hand storage space for linens, silver, glassware, and china, and (d) comfortable space for social entertainment of guests (Fig. 119).

The dining room must be comfortable regardless of its size or other merits. There must be warmth in winter and plenty of air to make the room cool in summer. Next to this insistence on comfort, the dining room demands every convenience which will save steps and labor for the family which is without servants. Make sure that plenty of electrical outlets for toaster, coffee maker, and other appliances are provided. Place these outlets convenient to counter, serving table, or sideboard where there is room to operate them efficiently. You must think ahead to provide furniture like buffets, cabinets, and so on, and allow enough wall space so that they will fit into the room. Consider having a "pass counter" opening from kitchen or pantry into the dining area, through which dishes and trays may be passed. This counter may serve as a breakfast or snack bar, saving much work. Work and step-saving features are important and should be kept in mind in planning.

The size of the dining room depends upon the size of the family and the amount of entertaining done in the home. A rectangular-shaped dining room is preferable to one square in shape, because it is more convenient when the dining table is extended. A dining room 11 by 12 ft. and preferably 12 by 15 ft. is in good proportion (Figs. 120 and 121).

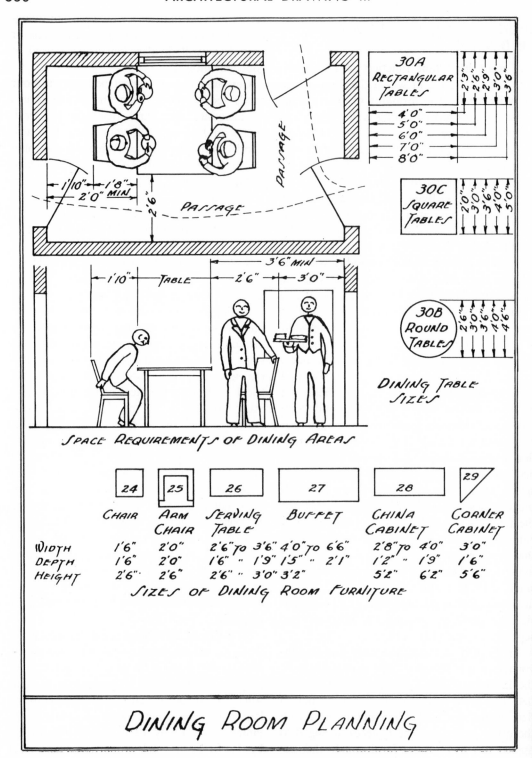

SPACE REQUIREMENTS OF DINING AREAS

DINING TABLE SIZES

SIZES OF DINING ROOM FURNITURE

DINING ROOM PLANNING

Fig. 119

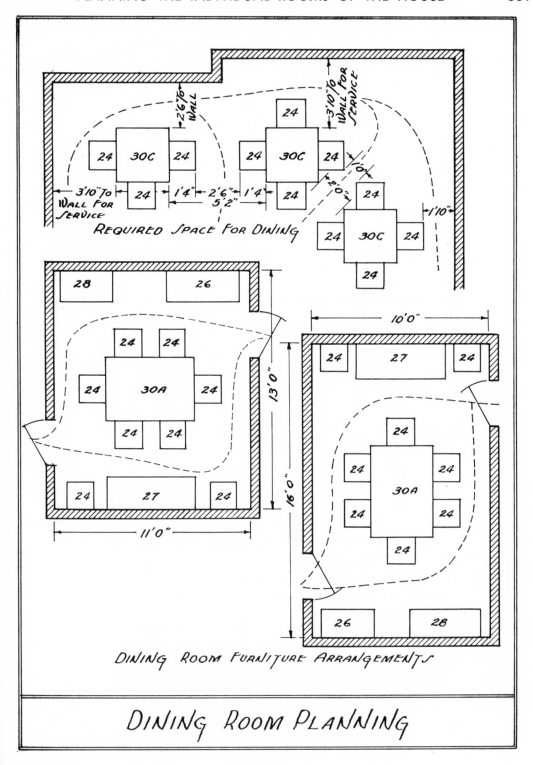

REQUIRED SPACE FOR DINING

DINING ROOM FURNITURE ARRANGEMENTS

DINING ROOM PLANNING

Fig. 120

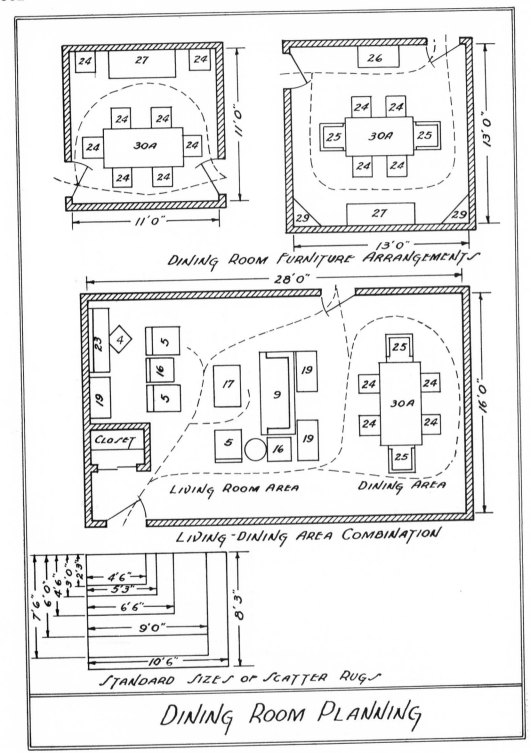

DINING ROOM FURNITURE ARRANGEMENTS

LIVING-DINING AREA COMBINATION

STANDARD SIZES OF SCATTER RUGS

DINING ROOM PLANNING

Fig. 121

A southern or southeastern exposure is ideal. The windows should be placed in groups and centered in the wall space. A pleasant view is desirable. Double-hung windows are usually chosen but casement windows may often be used to good advantage.

China closets are convenient and may be made with glass doors to display the china. They are more serviceable when built in straight rather than diagonally across the corner of the room.

If the dining room is to reflect its festive character perfectly, a good deal of attention must be given to the kind and position of its lighting fixtures. The preference for subdued lighting must be given as much thought and attention to detail as is the choice for a flood of lighting focused upon the table. Artistic effects are achieved by both forms of illumination. If full lighting is preferred some form of fixture in the center of the room, like the old dome shade, to direct illumination upon silver, glass, and linen on the table and on the faces of the diners serves best. It should be suspended in the average room about 4 ft. from the ceiling. It may be as ornate and elaborate as harmony with the furnishings and decorations will permit. Side lighting of the room to supplement the light given by such a fixture will be necessary if full illumination is desired. In the modern home the most interesting and effective of all lighting effects may be installed, such as indirect lighting from the juncture of the ceiling and walls, which will provide soft light for the entire room with no concentration at any point and no shadows. This type of lighting is called cove lighting.

Breakfast Nook and Dining Alcove. In small families of not more than four people, a dining alcove in or adjacent to the kitchen can be made to serve in place of the dining room. Sufficient space should be allowed to accommodate four people at a table. Provision should be made for easy cleaning of this area, by making the table movable for sweeping and washing the floor. This is especially important if fixed benches are used at the table. One problem involved in an alcove is to arrange seating so that each individual may be called away from the table without disturbing other members of the family seated at the table. A desirable minimum size of this alcove should be about 7 by 9 ft.

Dinette. The dining alcove is not intended as a suitable space for entertaining anyone except close friends, and for this reason a dining space is often provided as a part of the living room in cases where a separate dining room is not desired. The two most common schemes used are (1) to make the dining area an extension of the living room without any separation except by a sliding curtain with tracks across the ceiling, accordion-pleated folding curtain, sliding doors or partitions, folding doors, or screens; or (2) to make two rooms in the form of an "L" with the dining area appearing like a large alcove or continuation of the living room around a corner. This way, the area may be closed off while the table is being set and cleared, and then may be made part of the living room between meals. In some cases a small dining space of this kind is separated from either the kitchen or living room only by low partitions formed by a "pass counter," bookcases, or china cabinets. Sometimes the tops of these cabinets are made wide enough to serve as long, built-in tables, and are called breakfast bars or snack bars with lunch, tea, or breakfast being served on them from the kitchen side.

Outdoor Dining Area. In moderate and warm climates plans are often so arranged that a patio or other portions of the garden area are extensions of the living and dining areas of the house. Accommodation must be made for the serving of the food directly from the kitchen, from an outdoor fireplace or grill, or in picnic style. Provision must be made for outdoor privacy, and for some shading from the sun, as well as for protection from insects and pests.

REVIEW OF PRINCIPLES INVOLVED IN PLANNING DINING ROOM OR DINING AREA

1. Access from the kitchen serving area to the dining table should be short and direct.

2. The size must be adequate for the furniture intended. Adequate space must be provided around table and chairs for traffic necessary in serving.

3. Wall areas must be large enough to accommodate furniture.

4. Windows must be well arranged for view, light, and ventilation. Windows must be placed where they do not cut up wall areas needed for furniture.

5. The door from the kitchen must be placed where it does not interfere with guests seated at table, and arranged in such manner that those seated at table do not have a view of the entire kitchen working area.

CHECK LIST

1. General exposure: north ( ); south ( ); east ( ); west ( )
2. Doors open into it from: living room ( ); kitchen ( ); hallway ( )
3. Type of area: separate dining room ( ); dining area part of living room ( ); dining area part of kitchen ( ); separate breakfast or luncheon alcove ( ); dining terrace ( )
4. Combination rooms separated by: folding partition ( ); sliding doors ( ); folding screens ( ); drapery ( ); folding doors ( )
5. Type of table: extension ( ); drop leaf ( )
6. Shape of table: round ( ); rectangular ( )
7. Unit type of furniture: china cabinets ( ); food bar ( ); sideboard ( )
8. Type of entertaining: buffet ( ); formal ( )
9. Furniture: table ( ); chairs ( ); buffet ( ); china closet ( ); server ( ); tea cart ( )
10. Storage for: linen ( ); table pads ( ); table leafs ( ); silver ( ); table decorations ( ); glassware ( ); china ( )
11. Windows: casement ( ); double hung ( ); fixed sash ( ); sliding ( ); French doors ( ); glass block ( ); picture ( )
12. Lighting: cove ( ); drop fixture ( ); ceiling spot ( ); wall bracket ( )
13. Electrical outlets for: coffee maker ( ); grill ( ); toaster ( ); illuminated table decoration ( ); radio ( ); telephone ( ); dinner chimes ( )

BEDROOMS

Bedrooms are usually multipurpose rooms since they are used for sleeping, dressing, and privacy. They are personal rooms for each member of the family. To attempt to accomplish their purpose they should be dark and quiet by night, but be bright and cheery by day; small for sleeping, but large enough for dressing and daytime living; they should have an outlook by day, but care should be taken in locating the windows that the same outlook at night does not admit unpleasant noises from the street and neighborhood and disturbing sounds of wind and rain; windows open for fresh air in winter chill the room below the point of comfort in dressing but are necessary in the summer for ventilation; windows open in summer add to the physical suffering of hay fever and asthma victims, yet windowless rooms would be unwelcome during the daylight hours. Individuals are required to share the same room because separate rooms are too expensive for most families to afford, yet one person may snore, one may prefer a cool room for sleeping, one may like to read in bed, one may need to rise early, and so on.

It is rather shortsighted to provide four walls, a few windows, and a door or two, and then, when the house is finished, to struggle over the task of placing furniture where it can be used comfortably (Fig. 122). In planning a bedroom, the articles of furniture should be drawn in the plan, or the furniture should be drawn to scale on stiff cardboard, and each article of furniture cut out. These cutout pieces can then be laid on the room plan and moved about to indicate the effect of placing the furniture in different arrangements. When arranging the furniture cutouts on the plan of the room it is advisable to remember that the placement of mirrors used for dressing introduces some very interesting considerations. If you want to see your complexion or other coloring, the subject must be lighted rather than lighting the mirror. Locate mirrors so that light is directed away from the glass and toward the object to be seen. This principle is recognized by the frequent use of side lights at shaving and dress-

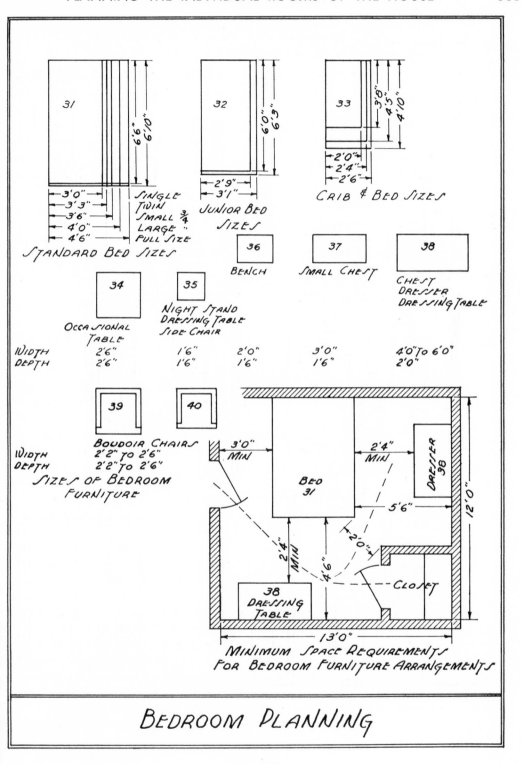

Fig. 122

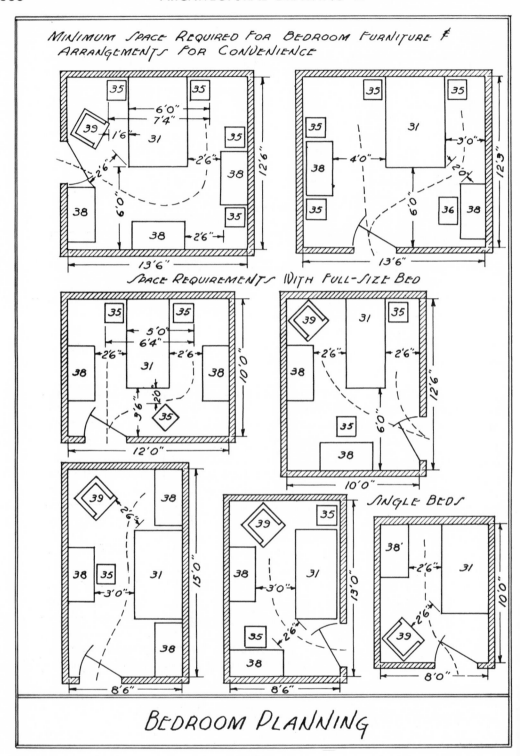

Fig. 123

ing mirrors, but this use of light violates another equally important principle: never direct glaring light toward the eyes. Provision must be made for artificial lighting from substantially the same direction at night as that supplied by natural lighting during the day. These principles should help in the placement of furniture usually associated with the dressing function of the bedroom.

The amount of space needed for any room depends on its furniture, which in turn is dependent upon the measurements of the human body (Fig. 123). To the actual size of a piece of furniture, a nominal amount of floor space must be added to provide for its proper function and use. There must be about 2 ft. of space added to the front of a chair to accommodate the occupant's feet and legs. The area for making a bed would be a strip about 2 ft. wide across the foot and both sides. To pull out the bottom drawer of a dresser requires about 4 ft. A 2-ft. space is needed between the nearest corners of two pieces, so that a person may comfortably pass between them. Therefore the minimum size of a bedroom may be found by combining the pieces of furniture to be accommodated with their areas of use.

Bedrooms should be arranged in the house plan to get the benefit of cross ventilation in the summer, that is, so the fresh air can enter the room through one window, circulate through the room, and escape through another window. This should be accomplished in such a way that the air will not blow directly over the bed. To meet this requirement it is necessary that at least two walls of each bedroom be outside walls containing windows. This means that each bedroom must be a corner room, and in a simple rectangular plan there cannot be more than four bedrooms on the second floor. If more than four are required some must do without cross ventilation, or the simple plan must be abandoned in favor of a plan with one or more projecting ells. If the bedrooms are fully air conditioned all of the advantages of an especially good sleep-

ing room may be had by effectively shielding the windows with heavy drapes to cut off the outside light and noise.

A bedroom door should always open out of the hallway — never out of another bedroom (Fig. 124). Two bedrooms may be interconnected with an intervening bathroom, to form a sick bay in emergencies. One bedroom can then be used by the patient and the other by the nurse or attendant. This plan is also desirable for use by parents, and a very young child. A bedroom door should be located and hung so that when it is partly open it will hide, rather than expose the bed. The master bedroom should be located so as to command the approach to the children's rooms. For economy in heating there should be some means of shutting off the bedrooms from the living area of the house without disturbing the cross ventilation of the areas. The sleeping areas may be separated from the living areas by a door which may be closed in cold weather so that the thermostat will properly control the heat for the living rooms. Usually it is desirable to have the sleeping areas at a cooler temperature. Sleeping rooms should be located as far as possible from the living areas so that children may be undisturbed by entertaining. Soundproofing between adjacent bedrooms, between bedrooms and bathrooms, and between bedrooms and living areas may be accomplished by placing the closets between rooms, using the double walls as sound barriers. Emergency sleeping facilities should be provided for unexpected guests or for convenience during sickness by using a study, den, or other seclusion room and installing a door bed or davenport-bed combination.

The average home should provide a minimum of three bedrooms, one for the parents and one for children or adults of each sex. A two-bedroom house can be justified only by the fact that there are some newly married couples who want a small house they can afford, and older couples who have already raised their family and now require

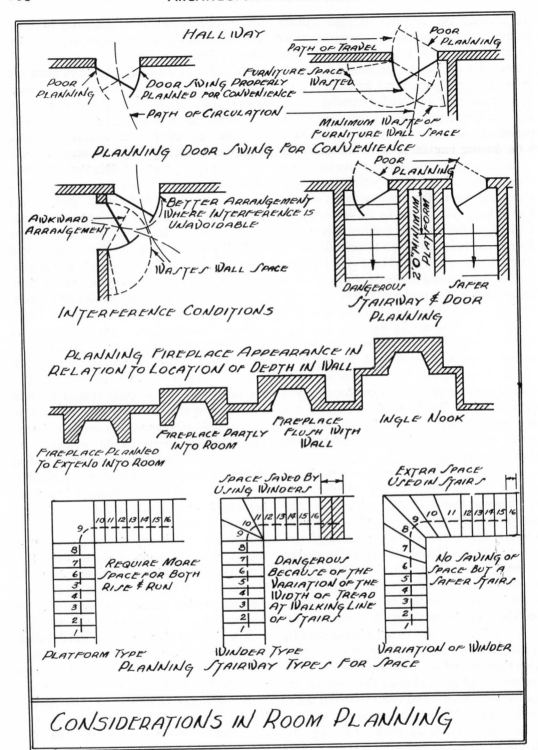

Fig. 124

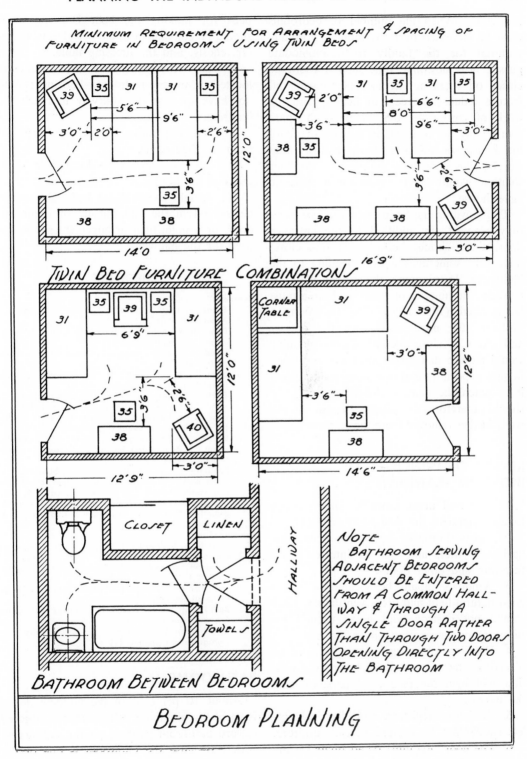

Fig. 125

less room. When the number of bedrooms must be increased over the number normally required for the family to accommodate guests, it is desirable that such a room be closed off when not in use. This closing-off feature reduces the cost of heating and the work of caring for the room. Such spare rooms may be arranged in a wing or ell of the house, or off a separate hallway that can be closed from ordinary use. Another solution would be to maintain a separate "guesthouse."

Traffic within the bedroom should be carefully planned. In addition to the entrance door, there should be at least one closet door, and sometimes a door leading to the bathroom. In planning the traffic patterns, consider the number of times each area must be reached (Fig. 125). The bathroom is probably the most used with the dresser and closet a close second. Good planning would require that a bed must not be placed in such a position that one must walk around it to reach the clothes closet or dresser; it should, therefore, be placed on one of the walls further removed from the entrance door.

REVIEW OF PRINCIPLES OF BEDROOM PLANNING

1. The wall areas must be large enough to accommodate the desired furnishings.

2. Doors should be located to open back against a wall, and not to interfere with furniture and other doors.

3. Windows should be located to afford good natural light and cross ventilation. They should not destroy wall areas needed for furniture or cause drafts over the bed.

4. Dressing tables and mirrors should be placed so that natural daylight from a window will light the face of a person facing the mirror.

5. Radiators, registers, and electrical outlets should not be located behind furniture.

6. The floor area must be adequate for the furniture. Space should be allowed around

beds for making the bed. Dressing areas should be convenient to clothes closets, dressers, chests, and the dressing table.

7. The bathroom should be conveniently located near the bedroom. Persons should not have to pass the stairway to reach the bathroom.

8. Bathroom noises should be insulated from the bedrooms.

9. Bedrooms should be located in quiet areas of the house.

10. A light switch for a hall light should be located in the hall outside the bedroom door, or a night-light arrangement should be used for the hallway.

CHECK LIST

Bedrooms
1. Exposure; north ( ); south ( ); east ( ); west ( )
2. Approximate size ( )
3. Doors from: hallway ( ); private bath ( ); bathroom ( ); sleeping porch ( )
4. Windows: double hung ( ); casement ( ); cross ventilation ( )
5. Lighting: ceiling light ( ); floor lamps ( ); table lamps ( ); wall brackets ( )
6. Electrical outlets: bed light ( ); electric clock ( ); night light ( ); call bell ( ); dresser lights ( ); door switch for closets ( ); closet lights ( ); switch for hall light ( ); radio ( ); telephone ( )
7. Built-in equipment: bed ( ); bunk ( ); wardrobe closet ( ); double-deck bunks ( ); dresser ( ); mirror ( ); shoe racks ( )
8. Furniture: bed ( ); bedside table ( ); bookcase ( ); cedar chest ( ); chaise longue ( ); highboy dresser ( ); vanity dresser ( ); dresser ( ); crib ( ); play pen ( ); davenport ( ); desk and chair ( ); boudoir chair ( ); floor lamp ( ); radio ( ); study table ( ); lounging chair ( )

Dressing Room
1. Door from: bedroom ( ); bathroom ( ); hallway ( )
2. Approximate size ( )
3. Windows: casement ( ); double hung ( ); glass block ( )
4. Lighting: ceiling light ( ); closet light ( ); lamps ( ); wall brackets ( )
5. Built-in equipment: closets ( ); dresser ( ); vanity ( ); wardrobe ( ); mirror ( )
6. Combination use: boudoir ( ); sewing room ( ); storage room ( ); study ( )

BATHROOMS

About 10 per cent of the building dollar is spent for plumbing, a large part of it going toward bathroom fixtures, piping, and accessories. Because the bathroom is one of the most used rooms in the house and one of the

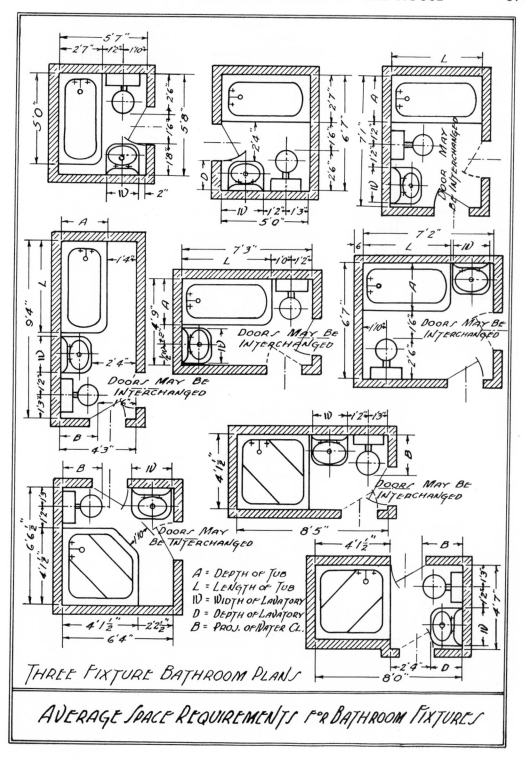

A = DEPTH OF TUB
L = LENGTH OF TUB
W = WIDTH OF LAVATORY
D = DEPTH OF LAVATORY
B = PROJ. OF WATER CL.

THREE FIXTURE BATHROOM PLANS

AVERAGE SPACE REQUIREMENTS FOR BATHROOM FIXTURES

Fig. 126

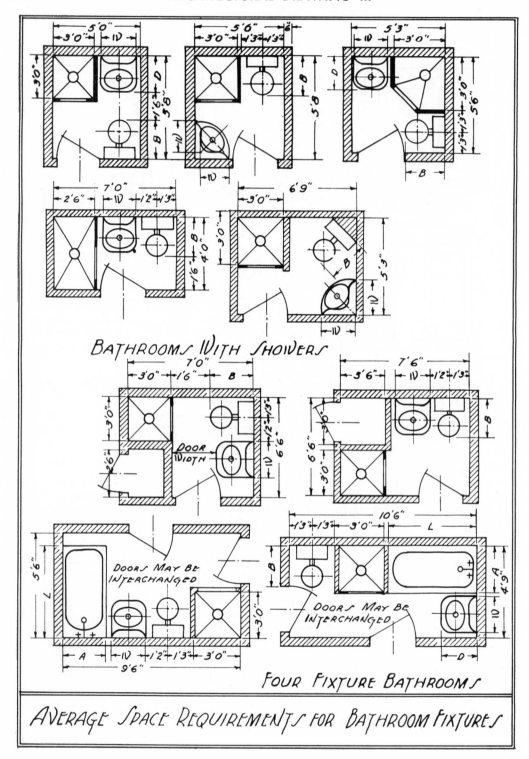

Fig. 127

most expensive for its size, one needs to be certain to get the most value for the money spent. There was a time when the bathroom was placed in whatever space was left over after the remainder of the house planning was completed; little care was taken as to its location, size, or to placement of the fixtures within the room. No matter what type or price home you plan to build you will want a bathroom that will consider the needs of each family member.

The ideal number of bathrooms for your particular plan will depend upon the number of persons in your family, the amount of entertaining you do, and the size of your budget. If you can afford it, by all means have more than one bathroom. Any modern home requires at least one bathroom, and if it contains six or seven rooms probably a bath and powder room combination is to be recommended. Some authorities give as minimum toilet requirements for a house accommodating three persons or more to include two water closets, one shower, and one bathtub; the latter two may be combined if desired (Fig. 126). These fixtures may be arranged to form two separate units: (1) a main bathroom near the bedrooms and (2) a powder room accessible to the living areas. This minimum must be increased when the sleeping rooms are placed on two floors or more, and to provide one additional bathroom for each additional two bedrooms above the usual three bedrooms. Instead of two separate bathrooms a double-duty room may be provided by adding a few feet of room area to provide for an additional lavatory or toilet. One double-duty plan features two lavatories on the outside wall with the tub on the inside wall; all fixtures can be installed in a 7 ft. 6 in. by 10 ft. 0 in. space (Fig. 127). The ranch type of house usually calls for two bathrooms — one at each end of the rambling series of rooms. If the bedrooms are located in one wing and the kitchen and utility room in another wing, one or more bathrooms will be required for the sleeping area, and a powder room or half bath can serve the kitchen and utility room. If the ranch-house bedrooms are to be served by two bathrooms, these should be arranged back-to-back for economy in piping. In any bathroom arrangement the closets and other fixtures should be located as near as possible to the soil stack (Fig. 128). It may be practical to back the powder room against the kitchen or utility room so that the two groupings of fixtures will each be served by one soil stack. If the kitchen sink is placed under a window, the sink should be as near the bathroom as possible for economy of installation.

Two-story houses should have the master bedroom on the second floor. The best location for a single second-floor bath is at the end of a hallway so that no one need go through a bedroom to reach it. Again, to save money on piping, the second-floor bathroom, should be located above the kitchen sink or downstairs bathroom, if possible. In a country home you would probably want to locate a bathroom, half bath, or shower room close to the back door for clean-up convenience, because that is the most frequently used entrance. Consider the basement of your home as still another location for plumbing facilities. A basement shower or lavatory and toilet provide an excellent clean-up location. Then, too, if you are providing a basement recreation room the convenience of a half bath will be well worth the additional cost.

Privacy may be obtained by careful location and arrangement of doors, walls, and fixtures (Fig. 129). Locating the water closet in a separate compartment in the bathroom will allow it to be ventilated properly without cooling the larger unit; it may be better soundproofed; and it assures privacy without excluding others who may share the room. The following principles are further suggested: (1) the door should be arranged to screen the water closet from sight when the door is open or being opened; (2) bathrooms serving two adjoining rooms should

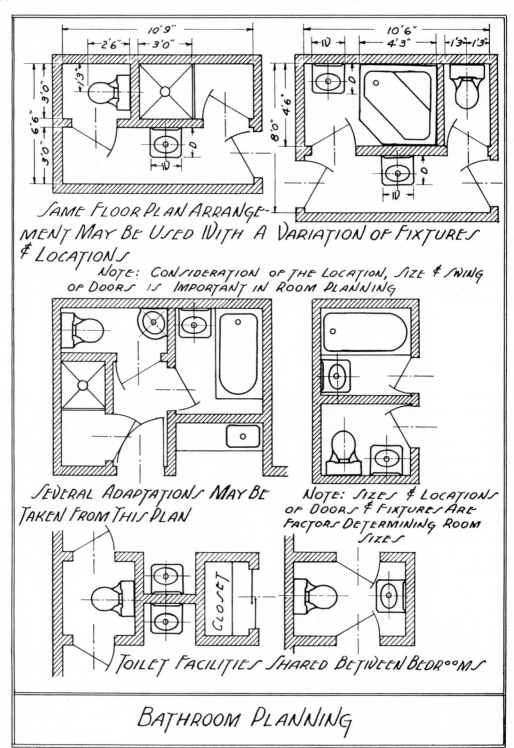

SAME FLOOR PLAN ARRANGE-
MENT MAY BE USED WITH A VARIATION OF FIXTURES
& LOCATIONS

NOTE: CONSIDERATION OF THE LOCATION, SIZE & SWING
OF DOORS IS IMPORTANT IN ROOM PLANNING

SEVERAL ADAPTATIONS MAY BE
TAKEN FROM THIS PLAN

NOTE: SIZES & LOCATIONS
OF DOORS & FIXTURES ARE
FACTORS DETERMINING ROOM
SIZES

TOILET FACILITIES SHARED BETWEEN BEDROOMS

BATHROOM PLANNING

Fig. 128

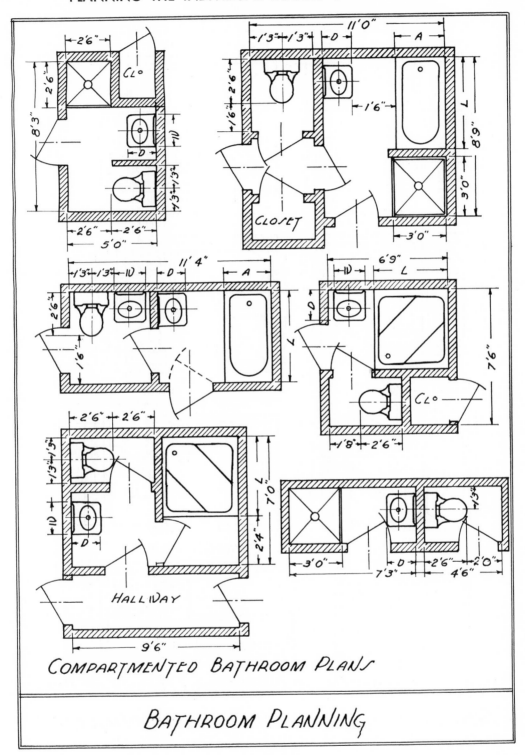

COMPARTMENTED BATHROOM PLANS

BATHROOM PLANNING

Fig. 129

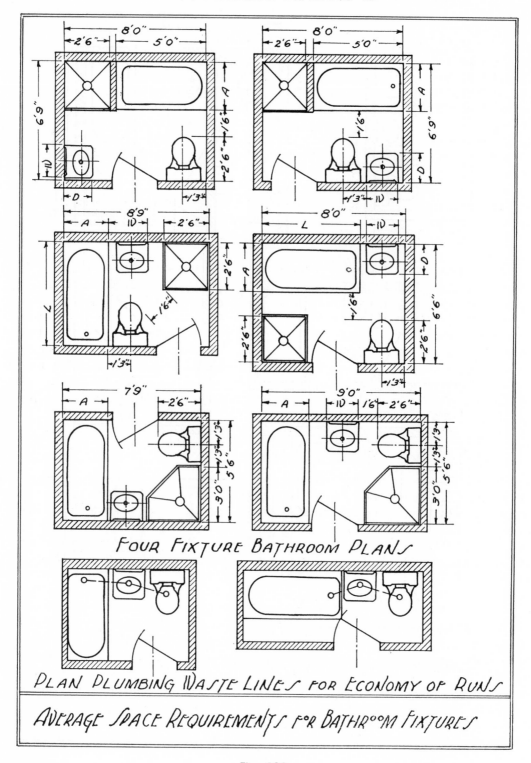

FOUR FIXTURE BATHROOM PLANS

PLAN PLUMBING WASTE LINES FOR ECONOMY OF RUNS

AVERAGE SPACE REQUIREMENTS FOR BATHROOM FIXTURES

Fig. 130

be entered from the hallway; (3) bathrooms should not be located directly at the head of the stairs; and (4) bathroom doors should be isolated as far as possible from the bedroom doors. Bedrooms and toilets should be separated from adjoining bedrooms by closets, and all piping should be heavily wrapped to prevent the transmission of noise.

The size of the bathroom will depend to some extent on the total number of bathroom facilities in your home and the size of the family. Special storage space should be provided in or near the bathroom. Shelves can be arranged above the toilet for towels, washcloths, soap, and cleaning equipment, or an 18-in.-deep floor-to-ceiling cabinet could be built in, containing drawers for towels and supplies and a pull-out shelf for sorting linens. A clothes chute to the basement is desirable. Drawers may be built under the lavatory. The recommended size for the family bathroom is 6 ft. 0 in. by 8 ft. 0 in., with a 28-in.-width door opening into the room. However, a minimum-size bathroom with an area of 5 ft. 0 in. by 5 ft. 0 in. can be planned for a smaller home with a 24-in.-width door opening. A small bathtub, triangular shower cabinet, and small-size lavatory will contribute a great deal to efficient space saving in a minimum area.

Proper placement of fixtures is perhaps the most important factor of good bathroom planning (Fig. 130). There are really only about six basic bathroom plans and although fixture arrangements can be varied, most of them are related to these basic arrangements. Remember to keep the following principles in mind when planning the fixture arrangement:

1. Windows over the bathtub are drafty for the bather; are hard to open and close because of the influence of moisture; water from an overhead shower will spray on the window and sill; the tub may be easily damaged when washing windows or putting up storm windows or screens. This arrangement is often used because of its economy from a spacing and piping standpoint. Better locations are at either side of the lavatory, over a dressing table, or in an open wall where incidental equipment may be placed.

2. Doors should be arranged to screen and conceal the water closet; they should be arranged so that they may be left open for ventilation. Doors should be so arranged that opening the door will not interfere with any person using any fixture. Usually the doors are arranged to swing into the room so that it may be readily closed from within by the person using the room, but bathrooms may be made more compact when economy of space is desired by swinging the doors outward.

3. The view into the bathroom should be of the lavatory or tub, not the toilet.

4. The lavatory should be placed between the tub and the water closet where the three major fixtures are arranged on one wall, because this arrangement provides space for the mirror and lights as well as elbow room for the person using the lavatory. In this arrangement the closet is placed near an end wall to provide a convenient location for the toilet-paper holder.

5. The fixtures should be arranged to provide maximum free wall space for the portable accessories.

6. Storage cabinets should be provided for storing supplies close to the place where they are used. Such cabinets are required for towels, washcloths, soap, toilet paper, toiletries, medicines, and cleaning supplies.

7. Accessories in the form of holders and racks should be conveniently placed for soap, toothbrushes, tumblers, bath sponges, washcloths, towels, and so on (Fig. 131).

8. Lighting should be supplied by a diffusing fixture which is centrally located to supply light for the whole room. Local lighting should be provided for the shaving mirror, dressing table, and enclosed compartments.

It is always less costly to place all the fixtures on one wall; a plan calling for a fixture on each wall greatly increases the cost of the room. Three fixtures on one wall with

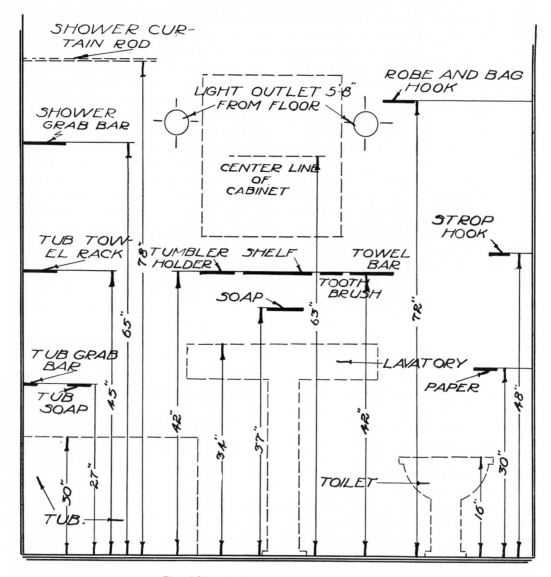

Fig. 131.   Bathroom accessory heights.

at least 6 in. of space between each fixture is the ideal arrangement for a 6 ft. 0 in. by 6 ft. 0 in. bathroom.

Some families may be interested in the compartment-type bathroom in which half partitions or floor-to-ceiling cupboards separate the bathing, washing, toilet, and dressing areas; separate or connecting entries to each compartment are left to the planner's choice (Fig. 132). The compartment idea is especially suited to irregularly shaped rooms (Figs. 133, 134 and 135). The cost of such multiple-use rooms is usually about the same as that of two separate bathrooms, or one bath and a powder room, because the cost of the partitions balances with the additional doors and windows.

Careful consideration should be given to the floor and wall coverings of the bathroom. Easily laid waterproof tile in a variety of

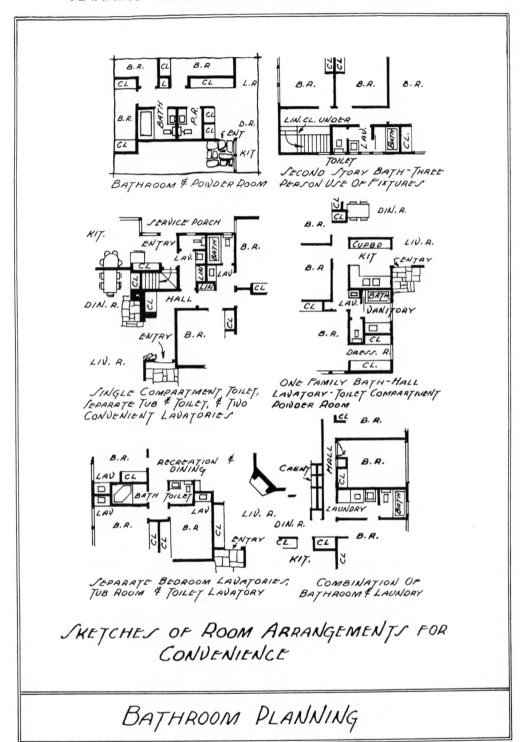

SKETCHES OF ROOM ARRANGEMENTS FOR CONVENIENCE

BATHROOM PLANNING

Fig. 132

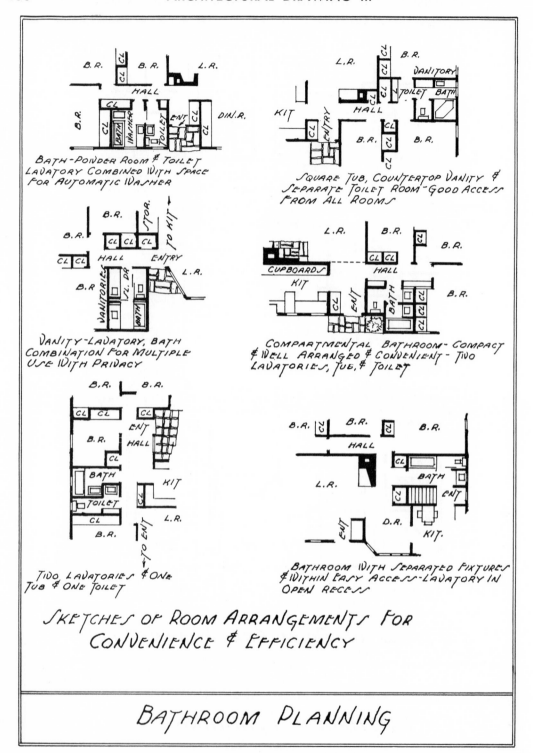

BATH-POWDER ROOM & TOILET
LAVATORY COMBINED WITH SPACE
FOR AUTOMATIC WASHER

SQUARE TUB, COUNTERTOP VANITY &
SEPARATE TOILET ROOM-GOOD ACCESS
FROM ALL ROOMS

VANITY-LAVATORY, BATH
COMBINATION FOR MULTIPLE
USE WITH PRIVACY

COMPARTMENTAL BATHROOM- COMPACT
& WELL ARRANGED & CONVENIENT - TWO
LAVATORIES, TUB, & TOILET

TWO LAVATORIES & ONE
TUB & ONE TOILET

BATHROOM WITH SEPARATED FIXTURES
& WITHIN EASY ACCESS-LAVATORY IN
OPEN RECESS

SKETCHES OF ROOM ARRANGEMENTS FOR
CONVENIENCE & EFFICIENCY

BATHROOM PLANNING

Fig. 133

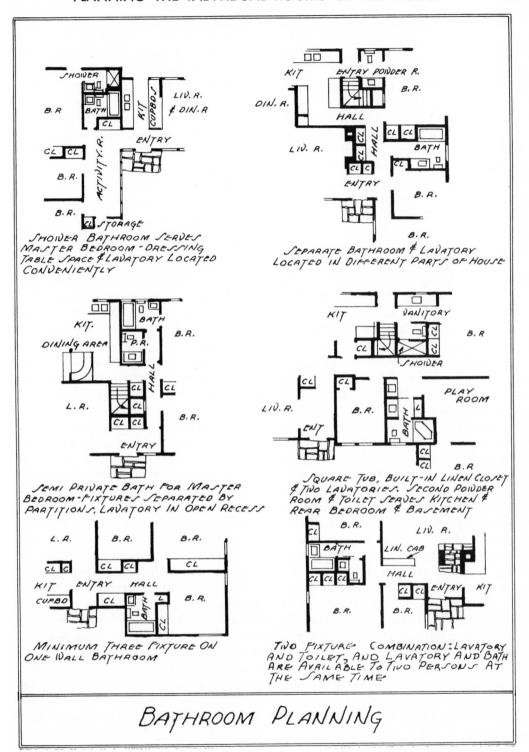

SHOWER BATHROOM SERVES MASTER BEDROOM-DRESSING TABLE SPACE & LAVATORY LOCATED CONVENIENTLY

SEPARATE BATHROOM & LAVATORY LOCATED IN DIFFERENT PARTS OF HOUSE

SEMI PRIVATE BATH FOR MASTER BEDROOM-FIXTURES SEPARATED BY PARTITIONS, LAVATORY IN OPEN RECESS

SQUARE TUB, BUILT-IN LINEN CLOSET & TWO LAVATORIES. SECOND POWDER ROOM & TOILET SERVES KITCHEN & REAR BEDROOM & BASEMENT

MINIMUM THREE FIXTURE ON ONE WALL BATHROOM

TWO FIXTURE COMBINATION: LAVATORY AND TOILET, AND LAVATORY AND BATH ARE AVAILABLE TO TWO PERSONS AT THE SAME TIME

BATHROOM PLANNING

Fig. 134

materials and wallboards are available in various colors as a permanent finish; waterproof wall coverings, glass bricks, and plaster are all good wall finishes. Linoleum and the various tiles (asphalt, vinyl, rubber, cork, cement, and clay) are ideal floor coverings for the modern bathroom because they combine practicality with good design and interesting color. Furthermore, they are waterproof and safe to walk on. Enameled and printed floor coverings are also good, and less expensive than tile. The initial costs of the floor and wall coverings should be compared on the basis of ease of cleaning, installation expense, and durability.

The bathroom accessories can add much to the safety, beauty, and convenience of the bathroom. The built-in accessories should be planned and included in the construction. Among the desirable features you may wish to include are a dressing table, mirror, recessed medicine cabinet, bookshelves, linen closet concealed by full-length mirrored doors, a hair drier, health lamp, and wall heater. There should be a towel rack for each member of the family, and an extra one for guests. Chromium-plated brass towel bars which fit on either side of the lavatory are space savers. Consider the children when planning the bathroom by installing towel holders, a low mirror, cabinets, and hooks for their convenience. Since the bathroom is often used for washing out hose, lingerie, etc., by the ladies, it is a good idea to provide simple drying facilities, such as hooks over the tub to hold a clothes line or a simple clothes reel, a folding rack, or a decorative plastic shell for the wall. Drawers at the end of a recessed tub, a side-wall mirror, a fluted glass panel at the end of the tub for bathing privacy, and a glass-block window which will act as a screen and yet admit light are ideas you may want to include in your plan.

Plenty of good light is as essential in the bathroom as it is in every other room of the home; and safety is far more important than convenience, as far as placement of light switches is concerned. All switches and outlets should be located out of reach of the tub and shower to guard against bathers being electrocuted; such outlets should also be placed away from faucets and pipes and other similar metal grounds to prevent possible shock. For general bathroom lighting 5 footcandles is the minimum, while 40 foot-candles is the recommended amount of light. Most of the light should be concentrated toward the mirror above the lavatory or dressing table. Because the light should shine on the face for clear reflection and not on the glass, shaded light at the top or on either side of the mirror does the best job of illumination. Standard frosted fluorescent tubes are excellent for this purpose for they not only provide good light but are decorative as well. If the bathroom is over 60 sq. ft. in size, a center fixture is advisable in addition to the mirror light. You may wish to include an infrared lamp in a recessed holder to remove the chill from the bathroom on cool mornings, and a low-current night light for the safety and convenience of the guests. In the family bathroom, plan for two double outlets for much-used items as electric shavers and room heaters.

The central heating system will determine the method by which the bathroom is to be heated. If you are planning a hot-water heating system you can use either a radiator or radiant ceiling, or floor or baseboard panels as a means of heating the bathroom. In a minimum-size bathroom, do not plan on a radiant baseboard for there will not be enough baseboard to give sufficient heat. Radiators and convectors may be either free-standing or recessed, the latter type allowing more space in the room. It is recommended that radiators, convectors, and radiant baseboards be installed on the outside wall of the bathroom so that the coldest wall will be enveloped with a film of convected heat. Unit or space heaters are small auxiliary heating units which provide extra heat in areas where it is needed. Such units may be built into the wall, floor,

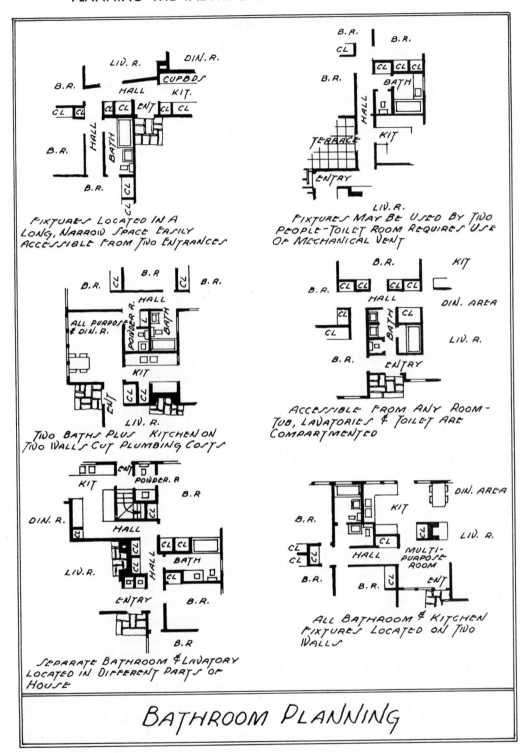

FIXTURES LOCATED IN A
LONG, NARROW SPACE EASILY
ACCESSIBLE FROM TWO ENTRANCES

FIXTURES MAY BE USED BY TWO
PEOPLE-TOILET ROOM REQUIRES USE
OF MECHANICAL VENT

TWO BATHS PLUS KITCHEN ON
TWO WALLS CUT PLUMBING COSTS

ACCESSIBLE FROM ANY ROOM-
TUB, LAVATORIES & TOILET ARE
COMPARTMENTED

SEPARATE BATHROOM & LAVATORY
LOCATED IN DIFFERENT PARTS OF
HOUSE

ALL BATHROOM & KITCHEN
FIXTURES LOCATED ON TWO
WALLS

BATHROOM PLANNING

Fig. 135

or carried in a portable enclosure, in which case they should be placed on a level surface and away from inflammable materials. Be sure that gas unit heaters are properly vented, and that electric heaters are shielded and grounded and placed where water will not splash onto them.

The bathroom window should be set high in the outside wall, since better lighting is possible when the window is located higher up. Casement windows are to be preferred for the reason that the room may be better ventilated during the hours when it is not being used, and after the floor has been cleaned. In locations where houses are set very closely together, a translucent but not transparent glass may be used to obtain privacy. At night, shadowproof shades must be used.

CHECK LIST FOR BATHROOMS, POWDER ROOMS, AND TOILETS

Main Bathroom

1. Entrance from: bedroom ( ); hall ( ); between bed-rooms ( )
2. Fixtures:
   a) Water closet: washdown ( ); washout ( ); siphon jet ( ); separate compartment ( ); in bathroom ( )
   b) Lavatory: pedestal ( ); wall bracket ( ); cabinet size . . . .
   c) Bathtub: shower combination ( ); separate shower ( ); bathtub size . . . .; type of shower enclosure . . . .; overhead spray ( ); body spray ( )
   d) Built-in fixtures: medicine cabinet ( ); clothes chute ( ); clothes hamper ( ); drying rack ( ); linen closet ( ); towel closet ( ); mirror ( ); other cabinets . . . .
3. Accessories: soap holder ( ); toothbrush holder ( ); tumbler holder ( ); toilet-paper holder ( ); towel bars ( ); other accessories . . . .
4. Lighting: ceiling fixture ( ); medicine closet ( ); shower compartment ( ); wall brackets ( ); fluorescent lighting ( ); water-closet compartment ( )
5. Electrical outlets: hair drier ( ); electric heater ( ); electric razor ( ); health lamp ( ); ventilator fan ( ); vibrator ( )
6. Windows: casement ( ); double hung ( ); sliding ( ); glass block ( ); awning ( )

Powder Rooms and Toilets

1. Preferred location . . . .
2. Water-closet type . . . .
3. Lavatory type . . . .
4. Preferred decorative treatment . . . .

SUN PARLOR, LIBRARY, STUDY, HOBBY ROOM, OR DEN

Some provision for a room which offers complete privacy for study, reading, writing, or conversation is needed in the average family. This need becomes greater with the trend of opening up the living areas into more or less continuous space, and the combining of rooms found in the modern homes. The room for study, reading, writing, and so on, should be planned small enough to accommodate a desk and chair for writing and study; one comfortable reading and relaxation chair with good light; a davenport large enough to relax upon. Bookshelves are desirable, and any other accommodations for the incidentals that add to convenience and satisfaction should be provided. If its furnishings are arranged to satisfy larger groups, the room is liable to become a popular gathering place which destroys its original purpose. The principal purpose of the room is seclusion and comfort, while location is less important. Usually this type of room should be kept near the living area, yet sufficiently removed so that the family activities will not interfere. It must be adaptable to various needs without losing its detachment advantages.

Such a room may be a library, study, guest room, or if a separate room cannot be provided, the necessary furnishings may find space in some bedroom. Some people would prefer a sun parlor or living porch which opens from the living room. A southern exposure is recommended for a sunroom, but it may be placed upon either the east or west side of the house. Many people prefer the morning sun in the sun parlor, but not the afternoon sun. It is often pleasant to be able to go from the sunroom directly to the rear lawn and garden. In a library plenty of space should be allowed for books in the form of open shelves. Good lighting is important to the planning of these types of rooms.

Each family requires a different combination of rooms and a different character to each room. Generally this discussed room is not considered the private sanctum of any particular member of the family but planned for the use of all members. Other specialized rooms may be desirable and found in the form of recreation rooms, playrooms, rumpus rooms, workshops, hobby rooms, and so on. These rooms are often found in combinations and often find place in unused portions of the house plan such as in attics or basements. In modern homes they may be planned as parts of the house and are often characterized as activity rooms. Because of the numerous specialized interests, different hobbies and the combinations that may be required for a family's wants, it is impossible to do more than generalize in the planning of these rooms. Usually these rooms are custom-planned to fit an individual's need and develop gradually as the need grows.

CHECK LIST

1. Location: ground floor ( ); basement ( ); attic ( ); bedroom ( ); separate room ( ); combination room ( )
2. Access: from hall ( ); from living room ( ); from bedroom ( )
3. Provision for toilet: private ( ); guest ( ); powder room ( ); water closet ( ); lavatory ( ); mirror ( )
4. Furnishings desired: desk ( ); table ( ); upholstered chairs ( ); straight chairs ( ); davenport ( ); file cabinet ( ); radio ( ); telephone ( ); television ( ); bookcases ( ); bookshelves ( ); fireplace ( ); safe or vault ( )
5. Character of room: seclusion ( ); study ( ); recreation room ( ); rumpus room ( ); sunroom ( ); living porch ( ); workshop ( ); hobby room ( )

ENTRANCES AND HALLWAYS

The entrance hall of a home gives an invaluable first impression of cordial hospitality, courtesy with reserve, or cold refusal of admittance. The first essential is privacy from the living rooms. Some attempts have been made to combine the living room and entrance area as one unit on the theory of space saving, and the number of times the space is put to use during the day. It is not a waste of space to segregate an area that performs such distinctive services to family life. It is a discourtesy to admit guests into the midst of family or social activities, and embarrassing to the caller, to interrupt conversation or amusement of the group without invitation. It may also be dangerous to admit strangers to the living area of the family.

The second requisite is that the entrance should be directly accessible to all active parts of the house (Fig. 136). One difficulty in planning a successful hall is that its walls must be broken by so many doors. Save at least one length of wall for seating anyone who must wait. Reserve space for a small table, for door chimes, and possibly a telephone stand. Circuitous routes from any point to the entrance invariably proves to be unsatisfactory planning. If it is possible, plan the placing of the garage so that a direct entrance leads into the house, so that entrance can be made to the kitchen without going outdoors. Consider the advantages of an outside exit to the basement.

A third requisite is a closet to accommodate all the coats, hats, umbrellas, rubbers, overshoes, raincoats, and outdoor apparel of the members of the household; each hung or supported to preserve its shape (Fig. 137). Only clothing adapted to the season should be kept in the entrance closet, and out-of-season clothing should be stored elsewhere. This entrance closet should also be planned to accommodate the hats, coats, and overshoes of a normal number of guests. Thus the size and shape of the entrance closet may be determined by the size and habits of the family and the amount of their entertaining.

A "powder room" providing a toilet and lavatory with room for a dressing table and a full-length mirror is probably one of the essentials of a modern home. It should be planned for the convenience of family and guests (Fig. 138).

The service entrance must be considered too; it should be placed where it will be convenient for deliveries to be made, but not so conspicuous that it will detract from the appearance of the house. It is usually placed at the side or back with provision in plan-

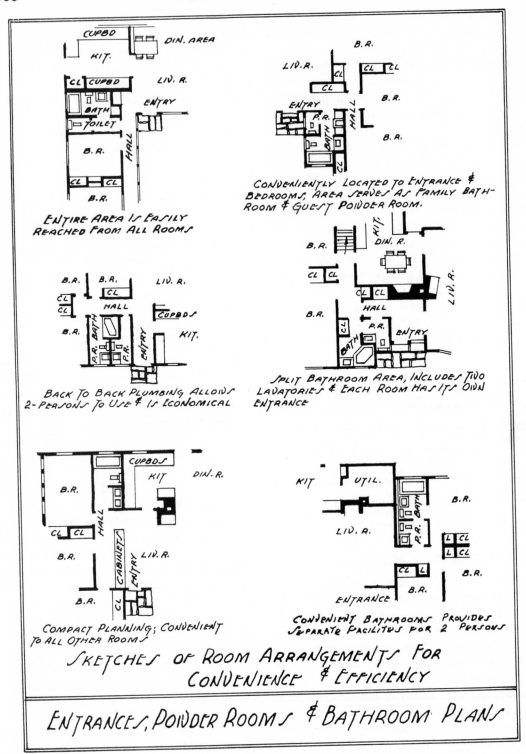

ENTIRE AREA IS EASILY
REACHED FROM ALL ROOMS

CONVENIENTLY LOCATED TO ENTRANCE &
BEDROOMS, AREA SERVES AS FAMILY BATH-
ROOM & GUEST POWDER ROOM.

BACK TO BACK PLUMBING ALLOWS
2-PERSONS TO USE & IS ECONOMICAL

SPLIT BATHROOM AREA, INCLUDES TWO
LAVATORIES & EACH ROOM HAS ITS OWN
ENTRANCE

COMPACT PLANNING; CONVENIENT
TO ALL OTHER ROOMS

CONVENIENT BATHROOMS PROVIDES
SEPARATE FACILITIES FOR 2 PERSONS

SKETCHES OF ROOM ARRANGEMENTS FOR
CONVENIENCE & EFFICIENCY

ENTRANCES, POWDER ROOMS & BATHROOM PLANS

Fig. 136

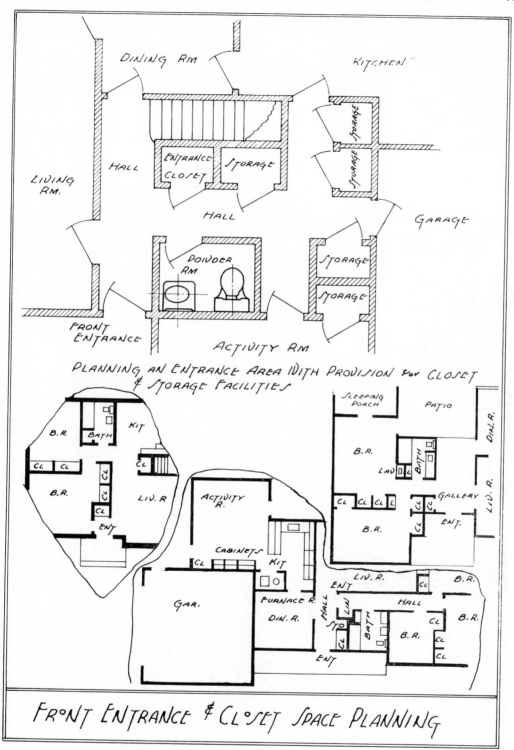

PLANNING AN ENTRANCE AREA WITH PROVISION FOR CLOSET & STORAGE FACILITIES

FRONT ENTRANCE & CLOSET SPACE PLANNING

Fig. 137

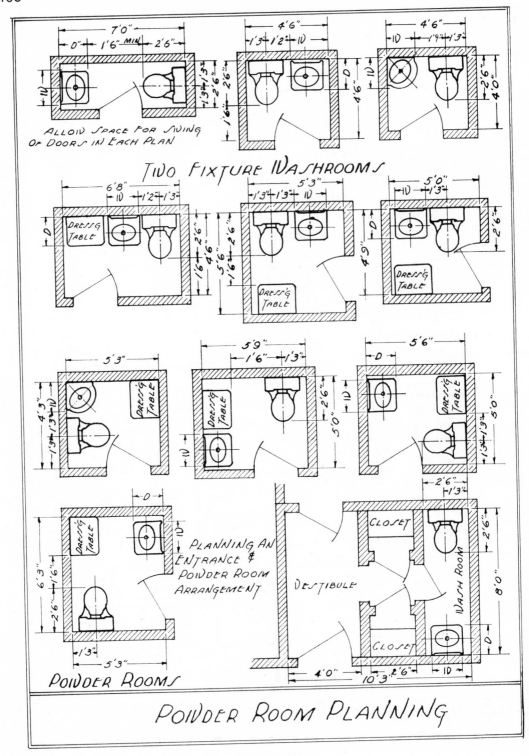

Fig. 138

ning made for disposal of waste and garbage.

Since these entrances and hallways take hard wear, a floor must be planned which will take the wear and abuse. An entrance hall should be well heated, and the lighting must be carefully planned.

CHECK LIST

Entrance Hall

1. Main entrance: north ( ); south ( ); east ( ); west ( )
2. Opening into a: hallway ( ); living room ( )
3. Door to clothes closet from: living room ( ); study ( ); dining room ( ); bedrooms ( ); kitchen ( ); powder room ( )
4. Windows to be: casement ( ); double hung ( ); glass block ( );
5. Lighting to include: ceiling fixture ( ); wall bracket ( ); floor lamp ( ); table lamp ( )
6. Electrical outlets to include: base plugs ( ); doorbell or chimes ( ); telephone ( ); switch for entrance light ( ); illuminated house number ( )
7. Hanger space for: overcoats ( ); raincoats ( ); jackets ( ); topcoats ( ); sport clothes ( )
8. Racks for: rubbers ( ); overshoes ( ); umbrellas ( ); canes ( )
9. Hat stands or racks for: men's hats ( ); caps ( ); women's hats ( )

Powder Room

1. Entered from: entrance hall ( ); living room ( ); seclusion room ( )
2. Windows to be: double hung ( ); casement ( ); glass block ( )
3. Lighting to include: ceiling fixture ( ); wall brackets ( ); switch-controlled fixtures ( )
4. Furnishings to include: lavatory ( ); water closet ( ); dressing table ( ); mirror ( ); medicine cabinet ( ); linen storage ( )

BASEMENT, OR UTILITY ROOMS

To meet the living requirements in a home, a volume of space is divided into areas to serve particular purposes. If this space can be developed below ground at less cost than above, a basement may be considered desirable. With the exception of outlook from windows, the modern home can offer as much healthfulness, comfort, and pleasing appearance to rooms below ground as those above ground. A basement provides a house of smaller area, with more lawn and garden space, and the excavation may provide the soil needed for grading. In areas where deep frost requires foundations to be carried several feet below ground a basement may be cheaper than building the equivalent space above ground.

If a basement is only going to be used to house the heating plant and its fuel, full development of the basement would be too expensive; of course, a developed basement does minimize dry rot of wooden structural members and protects the floor above from cold and dampness. But the basement area can be utilized for a comfortable recreation room and be worth the added cost of development. If the site is rocky, however, or on damp ground where the cost of excavation or waterproofing and drainage might be excessive, a basement should not be considered. Thus the size of the house, the soil it is built on, the drainage of the land, and the zone of climate will affect costs and influence your decision. The kind of heating plant and fuel used, the need of specialized storage space, and the necessity of space economy to fit the budget will have a bearing on the problem.

Heating systems operating on the gravity principle including the warm-air, hot-water, steam, and vapor systems require the heat to be generated at a low level to have it rise to the higher level with natural circulation. A partial basement accommodating a heating system and its fuel storage may be used. A forced circulation heating system with blowers or pumps may eliminate the need of a basement. Neither excavation costs alone nor heating plant costs alone should govern the decision, for there is a wide enough choice in heating systems to meet any need.

Basements offer ideal storage space for solid fuels for they can be delivered into below-grade-level bins by gravity. Basements are also well suited for storing certain foods and clothing because of the cool earth temperature. Ventilation is usually needed to dry out moisture and keep the air fresh.

It normally takes less hall space to reach all rooms if they are arranged in stories than if they are spread out on a one-floor plan. This is particularly true if the stairways are placed one above the other. Piping and duct work for heating and air conditioning cost less usually in a house provided with a basement. If a large part of the basement can be used for necessary accommodations, a basement can reduce the cost of home construction. There is less roof area to construct and maintain, less exposure to the elements giving less construction and operating cost to the compact multistory house.

Basement foundation walls and floors must be built to be waterproof and protected against internal dampness caused by condensation. To prevent condensation all cold surfaces must be insulated from moisture-laden air. An inner wall of wallboard or rustproof metal lath and plaster may be furred away from a masonry wall thus forming an air space, which is good insulation. Other methods include the use of insulation materials as part of this inner wall. Such materials include rigid fiberboards. blanket insulations, or reflective foils.

Basement floors are limited to: asphalt tile, cork tile, ceramic tile, slate, stone, concrete, and so on, which have no insulating value but do make an attractive floor. Neither linoleum nor rubber tile should be used. Hardwood flooring should not be laid unless the concrete has a membrane waterproofing course beneath it, and the surface has become thoroughly and permanently dried out. Wood floors will rot out, and linoleum or rubber tile do not cement permanently to the concrete surface.

Basement windows must be selected with as much care as any window in the upper floor levels, and should be equipped with screens to keep out field mice and insects. Areaways must be provided for windows placed below grade level. These areaways may be planned to provide more than light by using them as hotbeds if they face south. They may also be planned to serve as aquariums by using special watertight construction for a most decorative addition to a recreation room.

REVIEW OF PRINCIPLES IN PLANNING A BASEMENT

Utility or Furnace Room
A. Location and size:
1. Near to the chimney stack so that a long run of chimney pipe is unnecessary; usually less than 12 ft. is recommended.
2. Near the center of heat pipe runs for balanced distribution of heat.
3. One wall should be an outside wall for natural lighting, ventilation, and fuel delivery.
4. Near basement stairway to grade level.
5. Accessible to service stairway.

B. Equipment:
1. Heating and air-conditioning equipment, domestic hot-water heater, incinerator, refrigeration compressors.
2. Gas, electric, and water meters, electric-service panel board, oil-tank gauge.
3. Water pump and supply tank if required.
4. Sump pump if required.

C. General suggestions:
1. Walls preferably solid masonry for fireproofing and soundproofing values.
2. Ceiling plastered or finished with other fire-retardent construction for soundproofing and fireproofing.
3. Floor well drained and easily cleaned surface.
4. Ventilation for combustion with a fixed opening equal to total chimney flue area

Fuel Storage
A. Location and size:
1. Solid fuels in closed bin adjacent to furnace room.
2. Oil preferably stored underground and outside of the basement.

B. Equipment:
1. Bin or hopper-fed stoker for automatic heat with coal.
2. Coal and wood chute opening from driveway.

C. General suggestions:
1. Walls, partitions, and ceiling fireproof and dust-proof, preferably of solid masonry.
2. Floors should be sloped to feed toward access door.

Basement Garage
A. Location and size:
1. Large enough to accommodate car with necessary work space.
2. Located conveniently in relation to main stairway and hall.
3. May be arranged to serve as convenient entrance to house.

B. Equipment:
1. Floor drain to be desired.
2. Tap with hose connection.
3. Provision for heat.
4. Workbench and storage space.

C. General suggestions:
1. Windows for light and ventilation.
2. Floor pitched to drain.
3. Walls, partitions, and ceiling fireproof, sound-proof, fumeproof, and dustproof, and preferably of solid masonry.

Basement Laundry
A. Location and size:
    1. Provision for laundry chute from hallway or bathroom.
    2. Near outside entrance door, and drying yard.
    3. Near service stairs.
    4. Near plumbing of upstairs kitchen or bathroom.
B. Equipment:
    Clothes chute, laundry tubs, washing machine, clothes drier, ironing board or ironer, hot plate, work table or cabinet top for sorting.
C. General suggestions:
    1. Floor drain provided.
    2. Sanitary walls, floors, and ceilings.
    3. Provision for natural lighting.
    4. Provision for artificial lighting.
    5. Good ventilation.
    6. Work areas well organized for sequence of work.

Toilets and Shower
A. Location and size:
    Near garage or outside entrance, near service entrance, or near recreation room.
B. Equipment:
    Showers, toilets, and lavatories.
C. General suggestions:
    1. Sanitary walls, floors, ceilings.
    2. Adequate ventilation.
    3. Provision for natural light.
    4. Soundproof walls if near recreation room.

Fruit and Vegetable Storage
A. Location and size:
    1. Preferably in a recess off from basement.
    2. Room should be insulated from heated area.
    3. Room should be accessible to stairway near to kitchen.
B. Equipment:
    Ventilated bins, open shelves, provision for bags, provision for crocks, and so on.
C. General suggestions:
    1. Provide for good circulation of air in ventilation.
    2. Provide against freezing but avoid heat pipes.

Storage Areas
A. Location and size:
    1. Storm windows and screens:
    Near the outside door entrance.
    2. Luggage:
    Near the outside door entrance.
    3. Garden tools:
    Near the outside door entrance or garage.
    4. Clothing and furs:
    In an enclosure of a dry corner or recess of basement or accessible attic space.
B. Equipment:
    1. Storm windows and screens:
    Racks, preferably suspended from ceiling for easy cleaning, or patented holders hung from ceiling.
    2. Luggage:
    Racks and shelves raised above the floor for trunks, suitcases, and bags.

    3. Garden tools:
    Racks and floor space.
    4. Clothing and furs.
    Enclosed racks for hanging clothing free of walls.
C. General suggestions:
    1. Storm windows and screens:
    Walls and floors protected from moisture and condensation to avoid mildew and rot.
    2. Luggage:
    Walls and floors protected from moisture and condensation.
    3. Garden tools:
    Easy access to grade level.
    4. Clothing and furs:
    a) Fireproof construction.
    b) Sanitary walls, floors, and ceilings.
    c) Mothproof, verminproof, dustproof, and free from moisture.

Recreation Rooms
A. Location and size:
    1. Adult recreation room:
    Accessible from first floor and outside.
    2. Children's playroom:
    Outside entrance independent from first floor.
    3. Hobby rooms:
    Accessible from first floor and grade level.
B. Equipment:
    1. Adult recreation room:
    a) Billiards, bookcases, card tables, dartball, table tennis, quoits, shuffleboard, table games, dancing, movies, radio, television.
    b) Provision for preparation of refreshments for family and guests.
    c) Racks, shelves, storage cabinets for equipment.
    2. Children's playroom:
    Games, blackboard, bookcases, sandbox, boxing, wrestling, miniature stage, puppet stage, movies, radio, television.
    3. Hobby rooms:
    Woodwork machines and tools, drawing tools and equipment, photography, stamps, gardening, and so on.
C. General suggestions:
    1. Adult recreation room:
    a) The room may open to the terrace or garden.
    b) Special attention should be paid to lighting and decoration.
    c) The floor should be suitable for dancing.
    d) Ventilation should be provided, air dehumidified.
    e) Consideration should be given to heating.
    2. Children's playroom:
    a) Provide for soundproofing.
    b) Other conditions similar to those for an adult room.
    3. Hobby rooms:
    Areas developed by experiment and the particular hobbies of the family.

LAURLDRY

   House designs which brought the laundry up from the basement to a first-floor location have been largely responsible for improving the home laundry. Such a location is particularly desirable for automatic laundry equipment, for it eliminates trips to the basement every few minutes to put another load of clothes into the washer, makes it easier to keep an eye on the children or perform

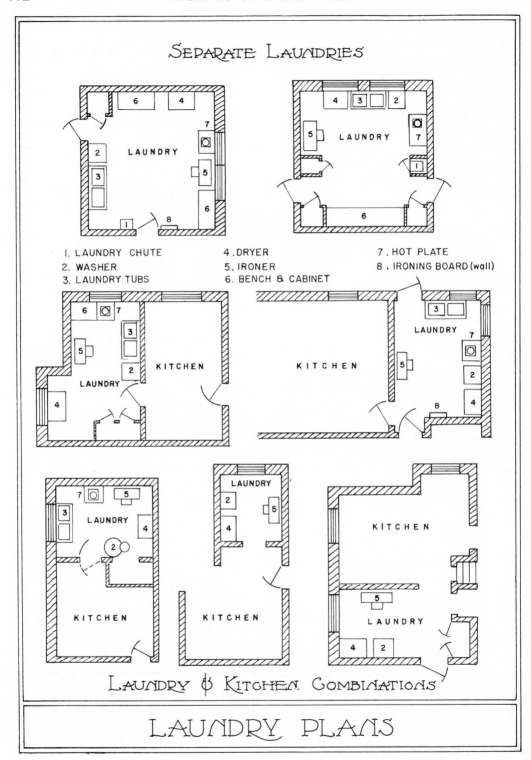

Fig. 139

other household tasks while doing the laundry, and is a more cheerful place to work. Ideally the laundry should be a separate room large enough so that the necessary washing and ironing equipment can be placed in a proper work sequence. Soiled and unironed clothes may accumulate here lessening the clutter in the remainder of the house, and if you do not have an automatic drier the room will serve as an indoor drying area. A utility room off the kitchen is the ideal place for a laundry.

In many cases, where it is not possible to include a separate laundry room, the laundry is combined with some other first-floor room: a laundry-utility room is a satisfactory arrangement for a basementless house; a combination recreation room-laundry is another solution. A kitchen-laundry is a popular combination, particularly since modern laundry equipment conforms with kitchen equipment in appearance. If you do plan a combination room, be sure there is enough space to separate the areas with either a half partition or a back-to-back equipment arrangement, for a single undivided room is inefficient when used for too many purposes. Arrange the sorting table, washer, drier, and possibly the water heater along one of the narrower walls. Opposite these have the ironer and base cabinets, which may be backed up by a snack bar. This serves to divide the kitchen from the laundry. Have open shelves, or cabinets to match those in the kitchen, above the ironer to accommodate readily the finished clothes. Near the ironer have the ironing board, which may fold into the wall.

The chief argument against joining kitchen and laundry is that soiled clothing and food do not make a sanitary combination (Fig. 139). Health standards condemn using a sink for washing clothes, dishes, and food. There is far less objection in locating an automatic washer in the kitchen. Even so, the heat and steam of washing and ironing add to the discomfort of the room in hot weather. Any automatic drier throws off a great deal of heat because of the high temperature needed for drying. Then, too, clean, freshly ironed clothes may suffer from cooking odors or food stains in the kitchen.

Nevertheless, many small home plans are showing kitchen laundries. Kitchen counters and tables can do double duty for sorting, sprinkling, and laying out ironed clothes. The stove is handy for making starch or sterilizing clothes. There is a saving in plumbing and wiring by having the centers close. A combination sink and laundry tray, or separate trays beside the sink which may be covered by a removable top are used where sacrifices of space and equipment are necessary. The ironing board and iron may be placed in a wall cabinet, the washing machine stored under a work-top space, and the mangle fitted into a closet where it is out of the way until needed. The objection to this type of planning is that neither laundry nor cooking can be efficiently accomplished if the equipment is to be so combined. Also the resale value of the house will be greater if a separate laundry is provided. A sewing room may be combined with the laundry so that clothes may be mended before ironing.

The laundry may be designed adjacent to the recreation room with its sink and work tops available for use as a bar, and its hot plate for preparing food (Fig. 140).

The laundry is combined with the bathroom in some new homes, especially if the house has two bathrooms; actually the bathroom is quite a logical place for automatic laundry equipment, for it is the room where soiled clothes normally accumulate, it has plenty of idle time during the day, and has sometimes been used for small washings anyway (Fig. 141). Of course, the bathroom is not a practical location for ironing equipment but the latter can be kept in the kitchen. In some minimum homes, a deep-bowl sink is replacing the usual shallow lavatory and an automatic washing machine is placed beside it. Ceiling space over the tub is used for clotheslines or drying racks.

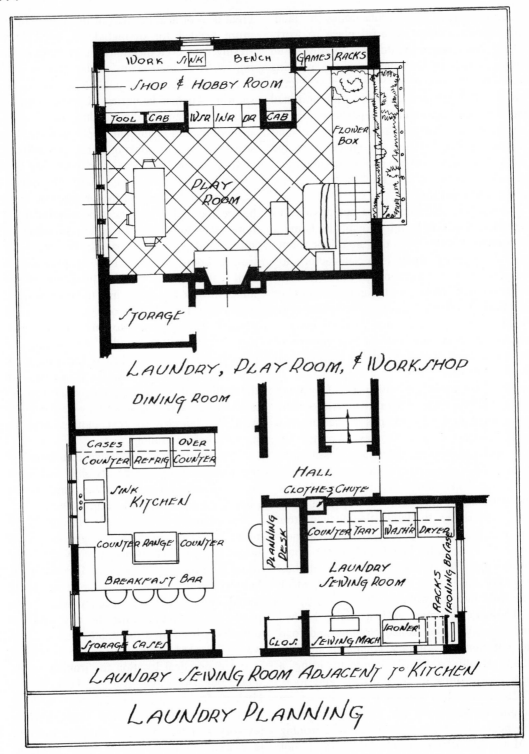

Work Sink Bench Games Racks

Shop & Hobby Room

Tool Cab Wsr Wr Dr Cab

Flower Box

Play Room

Storage

LAUNDRY, PLAY ROOM, & WORKSHOP

DINING ROOM

Cases Over
Counter Refrig Counter

Sink KITCHEN

Counter Range Counter

Breakfast Bar

Storage Cases

Hall
Clothes Chute

Planning Desk

Counter Tray Wash'r Dryer

Laundry Sewing Room

Racks Ironing Bd Cases

Clos. Sewing Mach

Ironer

LAUNDRY SEWING ROOM ADJACENT TO KITCHEN

LAUNDRY PLANNING

Fig. 140

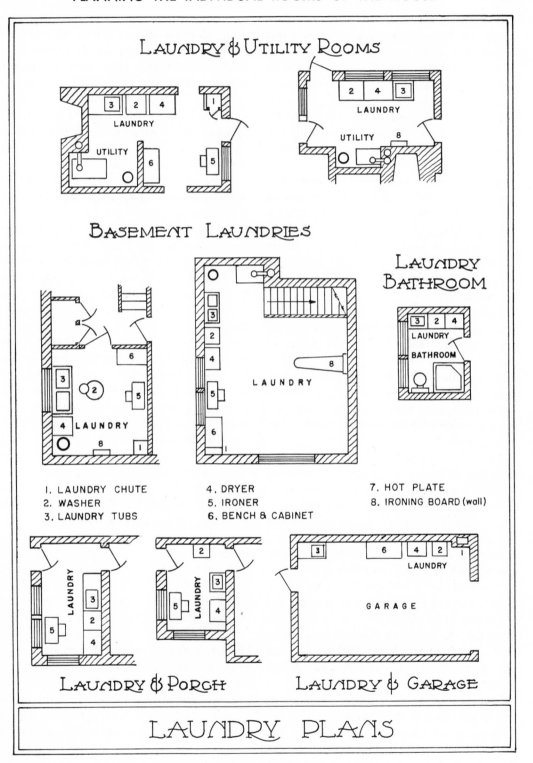

LAUNDRY & UTILITY ROOMS

BASEMENT LAUNDRIES

LAUNDRY BATHROOM

1. LAUNDRY CHUTE
2. WASHER
3. LAUNDRY TUBS

4. DRYER
5. IRONER
6. BENCH & CABINET

7. HOT PLATE
8. IRONING BOARD (wall)

LAUNDRY & PORCH   LAUNDRY & GARAGE

LAUNDRY PLANS

Fig. 141

If there is no available first-floor space within the house, laundry equipment might be installed in a double garage; piping connections and additional wiring are necessary and if the climate is cold the garage would have to be well heated. An automatic drier is practically a requirement here, otherwise the car will have to be moved outside in bad weather to allow clothes to dry by hanging in the garage.

In spite of the advantages of a first-floor laundry, a basement laundry is necessary in many homes; while this means stair climbing and more lifting of clothes, there is the desirable feature of plenty of work space. Bright colors and good lighting can do a lot toward improving the work surroundings in the basement.

Laundry Equipment. A laundry requires four main pieces of equipment: (1) washing machine, (2) clothes drier, (3) ironer or mangle, and (4) the ironing board. Add to these a hamper into which the clothes chute empties, a sorting table or center, cabinets for supplies, a hot plate for boiling linens and making starch, and you have the usual equipment provided.

The laundering process takes the following sequence. Soiled linen and clothing are sorted by fabrics and colors. Some pieces are boiled to sterilize them, some are washed in lukewarm water to minimize shrinkage, the rest are washed in batches of white goods and colored materials. After washing, rinsing, starching when needed, and after excess water is removed by a wringer or spinner, the clothes are run through a drier or hung out of doors. The goods to be ironed are sprinkled and rolled, then ironed by machine or by hand, hung up for final drying, and placed in the proper closets and storage spaces (Fig. 142).

Sequence of Work Centers. Equipment should be arranged in sequence to satisfy the working requirements. (1) *Receiving and sorting:* Close to the laundry entrance door through which soiled clothes are brought in

to be cleaned, or directly beneath a clothes chute, there should be a sorting table or work top large enough to lay out the clothes to be washed into sorted piles. Portable baskets may be substituted if preferred, and storage space provided for the baskets under the work top. (2) *Cleaning Center:* Various elements of the cleaning process should be made accessible to the sorting center. These include: (*a*) a sink or laundry tray for hand washing of delicate fabrics, and as a source of water for sprinkling, preparing starch, and spot cleaning; (*b*) a work top equipped with various solvents and cleaners for spot cleaning; (*c*) a hot plate and starch kettle for preparing starch; (*d*) a boiler for sterilizing handkerchiefs, face cloths, and so on; (*e*) the washing machine with wringer or spin drier; and (*f*) a second work top or group of hampers or baskets for receiving the sorted damp pieces for the drier. (3) *Drying center:* Ideally every home should have a gas or electric clothes drier since laundering must be done in bad weather as often as in good weather. A sunny outdoor drying yard is desirable for whitening and bleaching linens, but the sun also fades colored fabrics. It is desirable to include a ceiling drying rack indoors or for hanging freshly ironed clothes. An automatic drier is sanitary, faster, and permits a flexible laundering schedule. (4) *Finishing center:* Upon return of the clothes from the drier or drying yard they should be brought to a work top for sorting, sprinkling, and rolling. The ironing devices and equipment should be handy and in good light. There should be drying racks upon which finished articles may be hung for final drying.

Each center should be equipped with shelves, racks, or cupboards containing supplies and utensils needed at each stage of the process. Cleaning fluids, soaps, bluing, starches, and so on, should be stored at the cleaning center; iron wax, sprinkling bottles, irons, shoulder boards, and similar accessories should be stored at the finishing center.

Considerations in Planning. (1) Have the

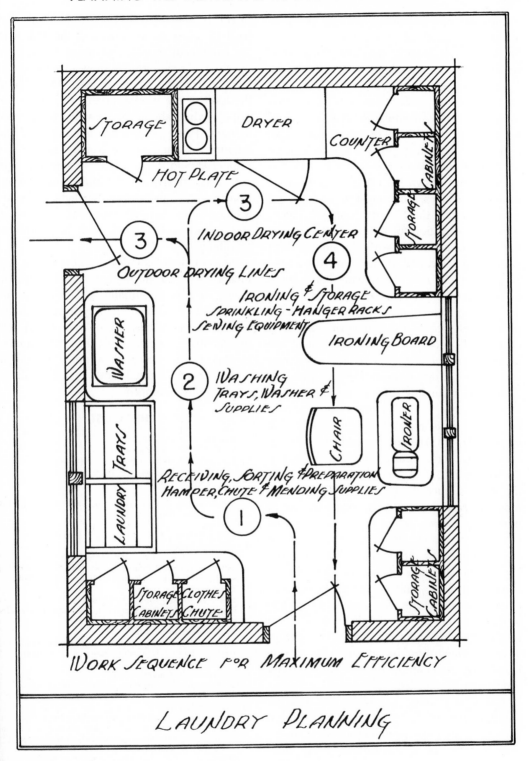

LAUNDRY PLANNING

Fig. 142

laundry as near an outside door as possible, unless you have an automatic drier. (2) Though double laundry tubs are always convenient, you can get along with a single tub if you have an automatic washer. (3) The least expensive washer has a wringer that swings over the washtub. With this type of machine the tub should be set at least 2 ft. 0 in. from the wall to provide standing space for convenient use of the wringer. (4) Because of the design of many nonautomatic washing machines, work must move from left to right rather than in the opposite, more convenient direction for right-handed persons. Thus the sequence of work, beginning with the sorting table and ending with the washbasket or racks near the outside door, needs to be arranged from left to right. However, the ironing center may be arranged in a right to left sequence, with sprinkling table next to the door, then ironing board and ironer. A movable table saves space because you can roll it into position for the three jobs of sorting, sprinkling, and laying out clothes after ironing. (5) The clothes chute should be located as near the laundry sorting table as possible. (6) The sorting table for sorting, sprinkling, stain removing, and starching should be 5 ft. 0 in. to 7 ft. 0 in. long with the work surface 25 in. wide. (7) Portable bins on casters should be provided to fit under the sorting tables. (8) The washing center consists of stationary tubs and an electric outlet for the washer. (9) The ironing center provides space for the electric ironer and chair, built-in ironing board, and an electric outlet for the ironer. (10) The sewing center allows ample space for a sewing machine and chair. (11) The storage space provided must be adequate for storing laundering necessities, ironed clothes, and articles to be mended.

Electrical Wiring. (1) When planning the wiring of the laundry center, you will want at least three double-convenience outlets in the wall for the use of the washer, drier, iron, ironer, radio, portable fan, and clock. For safety as well as convenience, the rule has been to locate these outlets on the wall near the equipment served, and about 40 in. from the floor. Recent studies show that the outlet for the iron should be at least 36 in. from the level of the ironing board. (2) A central ceiling fixture should be provided for general lighting. Panel or bracket lighting over the laundry tubs and at the ironing and sewing centers should be arranged so that the light will shine clearly on washtubs and washer, ironing board and ironer. Daylight bulbs are a convenience because they tend to show up stains and soiled spots and help prevent scorching.

The modern laundry is not unlike the modern kitchen in its layout and appointments. It may be equally well designed and attractively decorated. It may have washable walls and a cove based floor free of dark and inaccessible corners; or by lack of planning it may be a corner of a dingy basement, damp, poorly lighted and heated, and inconveniently arranged.

CHECK LIST

1. Laundry type and location
   a) First floor ( ); basement ( )
   b) Combined with: kitchen ( ); bathroom ( ); recreation room ( ); sewing room ( ); children's play room ( ); garage ( )
2. Windows:
   casement ( ); double hung ( ); fixed sash ( ); sliding ( ); glass block ( )
3. Lighting:
   ceiling fixture ( ); strip lighting ( ); wall brackets ( )
4. Electrical outlets for:
   electric clock ( ); floor and table lamps ( ); iron ( ); ironer ( ); hot plate ( ); washer ( ); drier ( ); ventilator ( ); food freezer ( ); sewing machine ( )
5. Equipment will include:
   sink ( ); laundry tubs ( ); ironer ( ); drier ( ); washing machine ( ); hot plate ( ); ventilator ( ); sewing machine ( ); sorting table ( )
6. Built-in units to include:
   cabinets ( ); supply shelves ( ); drying racks ( ); clothes chute ( ); sorting table ( ); hampers ( ); ironing board ( )
7. Equipment placement:
   a) Receiving and sorting center: clothes chute ( ); hampers ( ); ventilated bin ( ); sorting table ( ); cabinets ( )
   b) Cleaning center: sink ( ); laundry trays ( ); work top for spot cleaning ( ); hot plate ( ); washing machine: automatic washer ( ); wringer type ( ); spin-drier type ( )
   c) Drying center: automatic drier ( ); indoor drying rack ( ); outdoor drying yard ( )

d) Finishing center: flat ironer ( ); mangle ( ); ironing board ( ); electric iron ( ); drying rack ( );
sprinkling work space ( ); cabinets for supplies ( )

CLOSETS AND STORAGE ROOMS

If the trend toward efficiency and order
evidenced in the planning of the modern
home is completely developed there will be
a planned space for everything (Fig. 143).
Normal living produces an enormous number of accumulated possessions that are too
useful to be thrown away, and too seldom
used to require a convenient location. Trunks
need space whether they are empty or filled.
Summer clothing does not come out of storage the same day winter clothing goes in;
there is an in-between season when both are
needed. Skis, sleds, toboggans, skates, tricycles, baseball bats, tennis rackets, fishing
tackle, lawn mowers, garden equipment, and
so on, each requires space of its own type
and size. Porch and terrace furniture and
garden implements must be cared for and
stored. It is not enough to provide storage
space. In addition each space must be
planned to accommodate each and every item
you own or will own. The space should be
provided with the necessary rods, shelves,
hooks, bins, drawers, holders, compartments,
and so on, fitted to use all the space to its
maximum usefulness. So-called waste space
is not wasted if it serves to store unused but
wanted possessions. Attics and basements are
not unnecessarily expensive or outmoded if
they are planned and equipped to store those
things needed infrequently. A livable house
must be a storehouse (Fig. 144).

The formative stages of house planning is
the time to plan for storage space, and the
most realistic way is to list the things you
need to store, such as:

1. **Apparel:**
   Summer, winter, shoes, hats, blankets, underwear,
   etc.
2. **Athletic equipment:**
   Golf clubs, skis, skates, bicycles, sleds, tennis
   rackets, tricycles, wagons, etc.
3. **Sports equipment:**
   Fishing tackle, boats, guns, trailers, etc.

4. **Game equipment:**
   Ping pong tables, archery sets, badminton sets,
   croquet sets, card tables, etc.
5. **Amusement equipment:**
   Record players, records, cameras, movie equipment,
   etc.
6. **Bathroom supplies:**
   Medicines, toilet articles, health lamps, heaters, etc.
7. **Books and magazines:**
   Current, old files, photographs, scrapbooks, etc.
8. **Luggage and trunks**
9. **Work shop and hobby:**
   Supplies, equipment, etc.
10. **Cleaning equipment:**
    Brooms, vacuum cleaners, brushes, mops, cleaning
    supplies.
11. **Cooking utensils:**
    Pots, pans, roasters, broilers, ovens, electric mixer,
    toasters, casseroles, etc.
12. **Recipe files**
13. **Foodstuffs:**
    Fresh, dry, canned, frozen.
14. **Hobby collections:**
    Stamps, glassware, dishes, shaving mugs, etc.
15. **Linens:**
    Sheets, pillowcases, towels, blankets, washcloths, etc.
16. **Silverware**
17. **Dead storage:**
    Old photographs, albums, letters, etc.
18. **Work, sport, and athletic clothing**
19. **Rainy weather clothing:**
    Raincoats, umbrellas, etc.

A closet as distinguished from a store-
room is essentially a place to keep supplies,
clothing, or other things frequently used. It
must have accessibility as its first requirement, and have properly designed means of
holding or supporting the contents as the
second requirement. Finally space-saving
features should also be included. Before a
good plan of a closet can be developed, the
planner must know what is to be stored.
Each major type of closet must be considered, and the best of that kind planned.
A bedroom closet should store without
crowding and keep accessible the following
types of things:

1. (a) wife's closet: dresses, gowns, skirts, blouses, evening wraps, suits, etc.; (b) husband's closet: suits,
   trousers, slacks, sport coats, etc.
2. Pajamas, night gowns, dressing gowns, robes, house
   dresses, work clothes, etc.
3. Hats, neckties, scarfs, gloves, collars, accessories, etc.
4. Shoes
5. Miscellaneous items such as socks, stockings, lingerie,
   underwear, shirts, jewelry, etc.

The choice between built-in storage
(wardrobes), and the use of portable furniture (dressing tables, dressers, chests of
drawers. vanities, and so on) is largely a

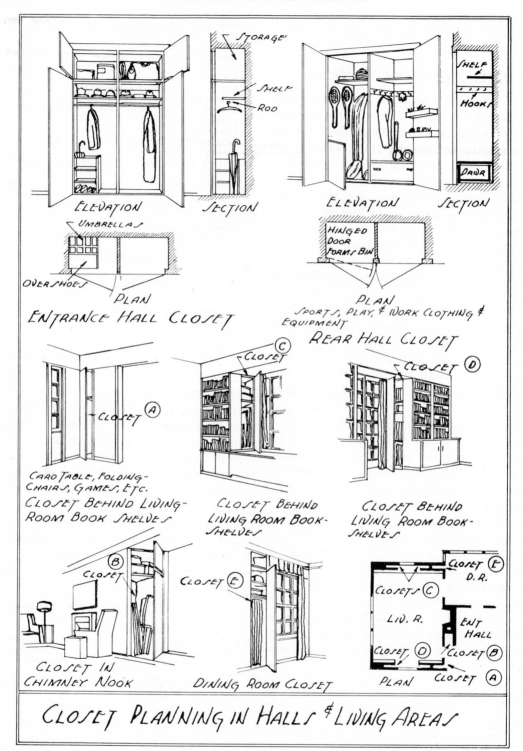

CLOSET PLANNING IN HALLS & LIVING AREAS

Fig. 143

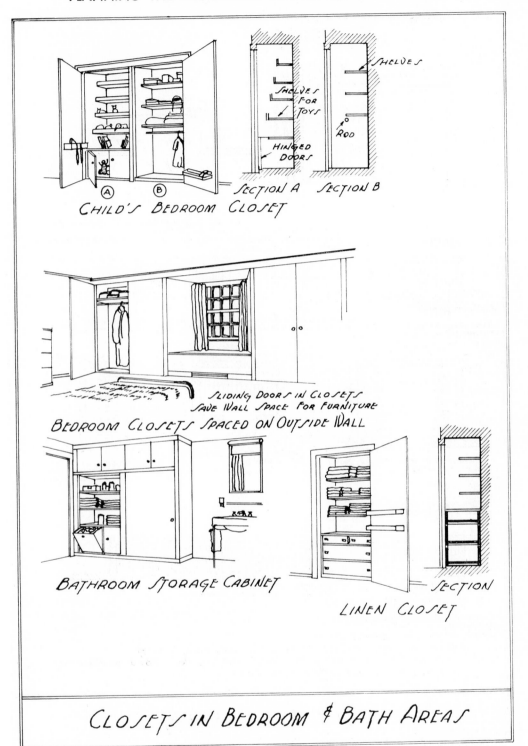

CHILD'S BEDROOM CLOSET

SECTION A   SECTION B

SHELVES
SHELVES FOR TOYS
HINGED DOORS
ROD

SLIDING DOORS IN CLOSETS SAVE WALL SPACE FOR FURNITURE

BEDROOM CLOSETS SPACED ON OUTSIDE WALL

BATHROOM STORAGE CABINET

LINEN CLOSET   SECTION

CLOSETS IN BEDROOM & BATH AREAS

Fig. 144

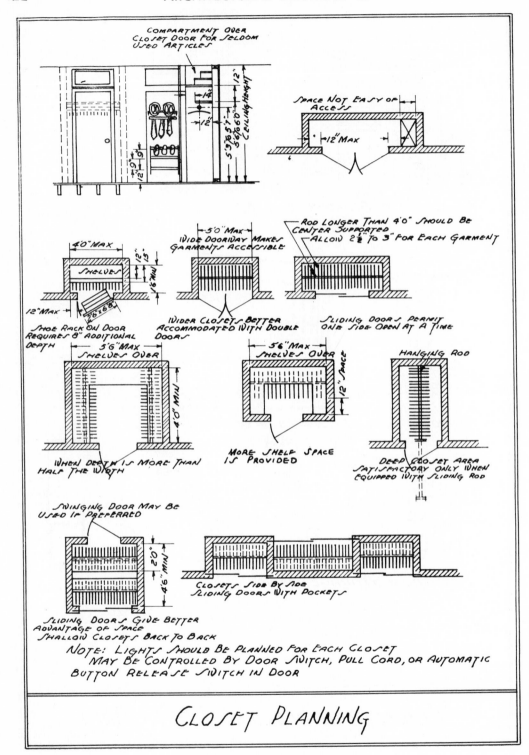

Fig. 145

matter of personal preference. If you already own suitable furniture, the built-in equipment has no advantage except possible economy of floor space. If furniture must be purchased for the purpose, the cost will be about the same as for built-in storage.

A closet in which hangers are to be suspended from a pole or bar parallel to the face of the closet, must not be less than 20 in. deep, and should preferably be from 22 to 24 in. deep. Each garment requires from 1½ to 3 in. of rod length (Fig. 145). The closet doors should be arranged to expose the whole width of the closet, for it is more economical to stand in the bedroom when getting things out of the closet, than to provide floor space behind a single closet door to get access to all of the hangers or shelves. A rod hung 5 ft. 0 in. to 5 ft. 6 in. from the floor will hold any dress or suit conveniently, and a shelf or two may be placed above the hanger rods for hats, gloves, accessories, and storage. By hanging short garments at one end of the closet, and long ones at the other end, room is provided below the short garments for shoes. Access to shelves above the height of the closet doors is made difficult because of the necessity of standing on a step or stool and reaching to the space. To overcome this, the main closet doors may be run to a maximum height of 7 ft. 6 in., and the highest shelf spaced at 6 ft. 9 in. from the floor. By running the closet doors to the ceiling all the space above the hanger rod may be utilized. Usually this is better accomplished by using the usual-height closet doors, with smaller doors above to give access to the storage of little used or out-of-season articles. The doors of the closet are arranged to swing into the room, or they may slide past each other. Hinged doors sometimes interfere with the furniture placement in the room and sometimes provide poor lighting in the closet, but they provide usable space on the closet side of the door. Sliding doors expose only a part of the closet at a time and save floor space, but the inside of the door cannot be utilized.

Specialized storage space in the form of closets will call for the following units:

1. **Bed closets: disappearing beds used in small apartments particularly.**
2. **Broom closets: in the service hall on both first and second floors where possible; the floor area should be large enough to accommodate a vacuum cleaner.**
3. **Cedar closets: side walls and ceiling lined with ¾-in. aromatic red cedar, or cedar-treated paint or plaster.**
4. **China closets: dining room or breakfast room.**
5. **Clothes closets: located in all bedrooms — two in master bedroom or one double closet.**
6. **Coat closet: near entrance door.**
7. **Linen closets: near bedrooms and bath.**
8. **Bathroom supply: all towels, face cloths, medical and personal supplies used in bathrooms should be stored in closets within the bathroom.**

The total space required for adequate storage becomes an appreciable part of the whole of the house and deserves careful planning to make each cubic foot do its utmost toward justifying its cost. In planning your new home, take advantage of all those waste spaces so often overlooked. For example there is frequently unused space on the second floor where the roof cuts into the full headroom. If regular height storage is not possible a small cedar closet can be built in to take suits, children's clothes, and bedding. Luggage can be placed in closets under the stairs, cupboards for towel storage can often be placed around the tub in the bathroom.

Much thought needs to be given to the use to which each cupboard is to be put. The spaces between shelves will vary to suit conditions. By providing the right equipment each closet or cupboard can be made flexible for various uses. Adjustable metal strips can be used to hold the shelves in a cupboard so that the shelves can be raised or lowered as needed. Long-handled coat hangers can be utilized to hang winter garments in a high closet above those in general use. Umbrella racks can be placed on the doors.

The depth of a woman's wardrobe is not as important as the fact that it should be carefully divided for use: one section for long housecoats, evening dresses, and evening wraps; one for street coats and dresses;

and one for suits, skirts, and blouses. Sweaters should be stored in drawers and small hats and shoes on shelves. Women's handbags can be arranged on a rack on the closet door.

ASSIGNMENT

Planning the Individual Rooms of the House

This unit is developed for the purpose of informing the student of the considerations involved in planning the separate rooms making up the house. Most of the students know by experience the changes advisable to remodel the house they are now living in. The parents by their experience can usually advise the student on what they would consider an ideal room such as the kitchen arrangement, and also on their idea of a plan for a model house. A wealth of experience can be gained by reading the articles on this subject, found in numerous magazines.

Keeping in mind the problems of your own family, criticize the floor plans found in textbooks and magazines. Include both the favorable and unfavorable criticisms.

PROBLEMS FOR CLASS DISCUSSION

1. Read all the good articles in your home magazines on planning the several rooms of the house. Send for some of the free literature supplied by equipment firms on the arrangement of rooms.
2. Make up a scrapbook of the advertisements showing room arrangements and decoration.
3. Look through the magazines for advertisements of labor-saving devices. Locate the fixtures you would include in a model home.
4. Look through the furniture catalogues and furnish your rooms with the furniture best suited to the purse and to the style of room.
5. What are the considerations to be given to the planning of the individual rooms of the house?
6. If you were to remodel your house what changes would you like to make? Show by sketches.
7. Would you include a recreation room in a house you planned to build? Where would you put it?
8. What are the changes made in the interior arrangement of the modern houses which are an improvement over those planned a few years ago.
9. What arrangement would you prefer for your basement plan?
10. If you were compelled to eliminate one room from your home, which do you feel you could best do without?

UNIT
XIX

Understanding the Architect's Drawings

THE PRELIMINARY STAGE OF PLANNING

Before any work is done on the drafting of plans, the architect or draftsman first secures all definite information relative to the proposed building. In this preliminary stage of the planning, the client outlines to the architect his desires and ideas by discussing the building's purpose, its general plan and design, its feasibility, location, environment, general types of construction, equipment, time of expected occupancy, architectural style, kind of finish and interior decoration, type of heating, system of artificial lighting, limit of cost, means of financing, and so on. To organize the rooms into a definite plan, consideration must be given to the site, its orientation with respect to the sun, its outlook and views, its relation to streets, the location of the garage, gardens, terraces, or porches that may be a part of the whole plan.

The second step in a series of freehand sketches, drawn at no particular scale, of floor plan arrangements, elevations, and all other details requiring study (Figs. 151–158, 205, 208, and 212). The architect will probably develop several schemes, arrangements, styles, and so on before he attempts to make a finished drawing (Figs. 157, 158, and 212). The prospective homeowner or student of drawing will study current home magazines for ideas and make simple sketches to record the suggestions he gets from the magazines. Finally he consolidates these ideas

into one sketch illustrating how these suggestions are going to be incorporated into the plans to be drawn (Figs. 157, 158, and 212). These "thumbnail" sketches are developed by trained designers with a technique of indication that gets across the idea, although on close inspection no "detail" is found, and they are not intended to be elaborate sketches.

There are no set rules for making these sketches, nor is there insistence on conventional arrangement of views or a precise method of indication. The ingenuity of the person making the sketches and the problem involved govern the technique.

PLAN LAYOUT STUDIES

A. Location Plans

1. *Survey plan.* A survey is a plan of the lot showing its exact dimensions and levels, location of trees and boundaries in relation to the streets and alleys, the location and level of existing sewers, water mains, gas service, electrical service, and so on (Fig. 148). These plans are drawn by licensed surveyors and are made in the form of a finished drawing rather than by a sketch.

2. *Plot plan.* This plan is similar to the survey plan, except that the survey plan shows a lot as it is before building work is started and the plot plan shows the lot as it should appear after the building is completed with landscaping, walks, drives, property lines, contours, available utilities, location of trees, building lines, and other pertinent data (Fig. 149). It should also show a plan of the building in outline, primarily to locate the house on the lot. Distances of the outline of the building to the boundary lines of the property are dimensioned so that the proper authorities can check and approve the location, and to give the contractor exact information as to where to make the excavations.

3. *Landscape plans.* A more elaborate plan which indicates not only the boundary lines of the lot and the location of the buildings on it, but also the proposed arrangement

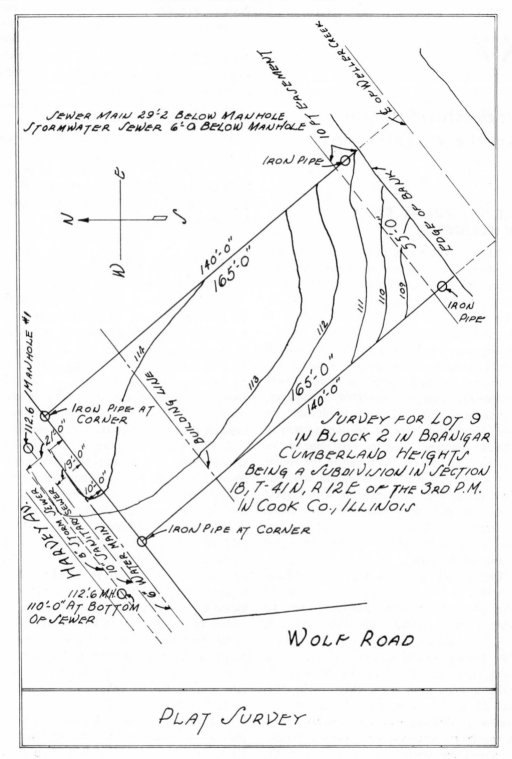

Fig. 148

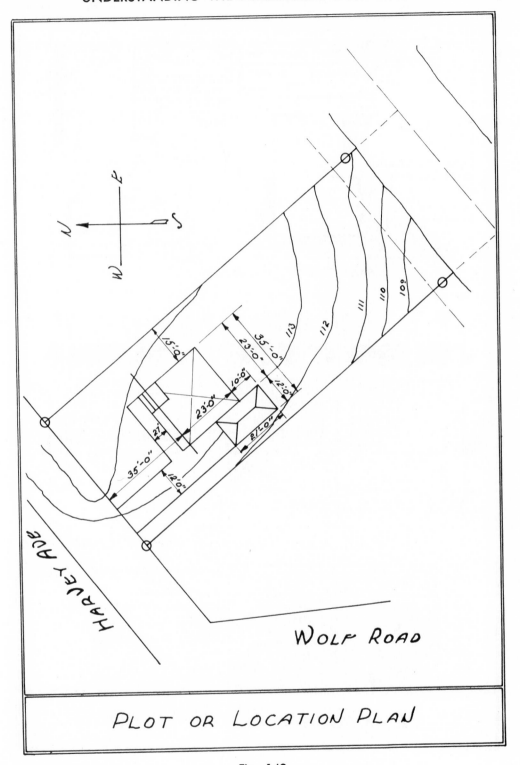

Fig. 149

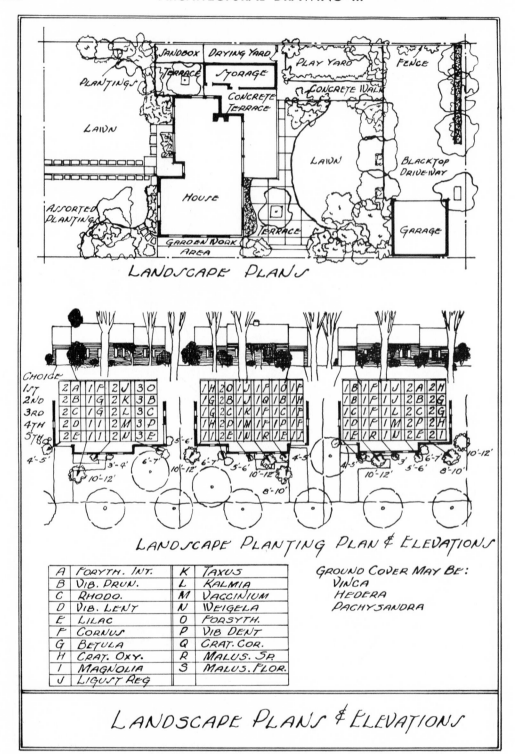

LANDSCAPE PLANS

LANDSCAPE PLANTING PLAN & ELEVATIONS

A	FORYTH. INT.	K	TAXUS
B	VIB. PRUN.	L	KALMIA
C	RHODO.	M	VACCINIUM
D	VIB. LENT	N	WEIGELA
E	LILAC	O	FORSYTH.
F	CORNUS	P	VIB DENT
G	BETULA	Q	CRAT. COR.
H	CRAT. OXY.	R	MALUS. SP.
I	MAGNOLIA	S	MALUS. FLOR.
J	LIGUST REG		

GROUND COVER MAY BE:
VINCA
HEDERA
PACHYSANDRA

LANDSCAPE PLANS & ELEVATIONS

Fig. 150

of trees, shrubbery, flower beds, garden space, lawns, drying yards, and so on (Fig. 150).

B. Floor Plan Studies

Some authorities maintain that before the actual plans are drawn, a decision must be reached as to the general appearance of the completed building. Other authorities are of the opinion that no consideration should be given to the style of house until after the best possible plan has been worked out to fit all requirements. Whichever of the two theories is correct, it is certain that careful study must be given to the final consolidation of ideas that becomes the plan.

After consideration has been given to the planning of each room as to its functions, size, furniture arrangement, closets, and coordination into the total floor plan; each room has been given its preferred orientation in relation to sunlight (Figs. 64, 65, 151); the site considered as to its good and poor aspects, and its relation to street and lot lines; the garage has been given its due importance (Figs. 66, 67, 68, and 69); thought has been directed toward gardens, terraces, porches, and the general landscaping of the property; you have noted down your wants and desires; out of this seemingly impossible tangle of shapes, dimensions, and exposures must evolve a livable house.

The easiest and most accurate way to set about making sketches of the floor plan is to make them on cross section or graph paper (Fig. 152). Each one of the squares can be taken as representing a certain number of inches or feet each way, and thus the constant use of a ruler or scale may be avoided and time saved. Probably the easiest way is to let each square represent a measurement of one foot or two feet in each direction. In these sketches refinements such as thicknesses of walls, locations of windows, and similar details are omitted. What you are after is the general proportions and relationship of rooms to each other. Place the points of the compass where they belong, indicate

the prevailing wind, sun, view, and other orientation factors (Fig. 151). Then begin with the living room and co-ordinate the plan of the house to it by drawing the location of the living room partition walls. This requires a "give and take" attitude for the ideal can only be approached and never reached (Fig. 153). It is a case of reaching the best possible solution of the multiplicity of considerations. When you have a plan that is a composite of all the best ideas test your plan out by drawing it to scale, using drawing tools. Ordinarily this calls for quite a little revision of the spaces allotted because of the differences between the indications on the thumbnail sketch or the graph paper sketch and actual measurements which are made to scale. A common error of the student is to pay too much attention to small details such as the spacing of doors and windows, instead of concentrating on the harmony of the more important elements such as the co-ordination of the rooms and related circulation and traffic, and seeing to it that the rooms are the right size and shape (Figs. 100 and 101). To fit in your furniture, cut diagrams of it out of cardboard drawn to the same scale at which the plans are drawn, and arrange the furniture in the plan checking the possible convenient arrangements.

C. Analysis of Plan

A good plan which meets all the necessary requirements of shape and size should also be analyzed with regard to its observance of the following principles of good planning:

1. *Accessibility.* One of the fundamental principles of good floor planning is to provide easy access to all portions of it, and each part should be so located that privacy and comfort are not neglected. There should be a passageway provided between any two rooms of the house without passing through a third room. Entrances should be provided to allow for privacy.

2. *Circulation.* This involves the additional thought of sufficiently large passages

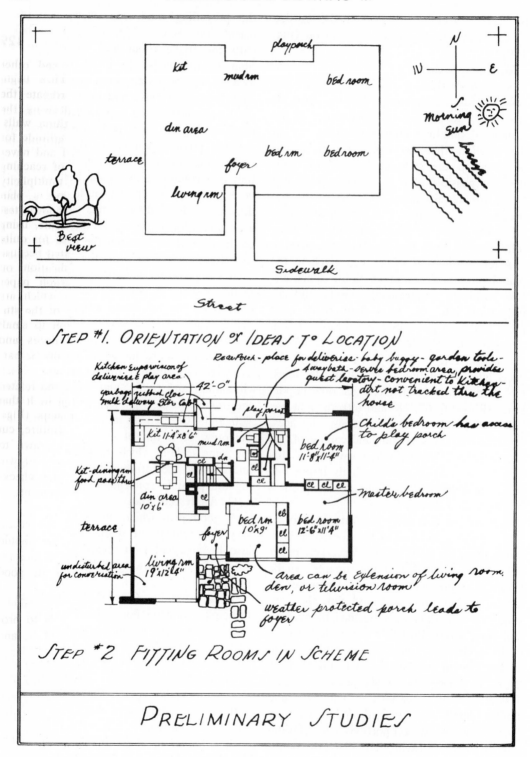

Fig. 151

and the routing of traffic through the house that energy and time may be economized. See "Planning for Good Traffic Circulation," p. 342, and Unit IX, "Planning the Individual Rooms of the House."

3. *Economy of floor space.* How to apportion the available floor space in the most economical manner to best serve the needs of the family is an important consideration. Factors involved are sizes of rooms, location of rooms, shapes of rooms; sizes, shapes, and locations of hallways; storage space and closets; sizes and location of windows and doors; and many other matters.

4. *Utility.* Space should be planned with reference to its use.

5. *Flexibility.* It is desirable that as much space as possible be arranged so that more than one use can be made of it.

6. *Orientation.* As to the most desirable direction or exposure for each room of the house, no uniform rules can be made to apply (Figs. 64, 65, and 151). Differences in climate, prevailing winds, elevation of the site, and direction of appropriate views require consideration. Preferences and peculiarities of members of the family, amount of time spent at home, and ages of the occupants are important factors. Generally it is better to have the sunlight travel from the kitchen and dining room early in the morning to the living room and bedrooms later in the day. The desire to take advantage of a view of a mountain, lake, city, or valley may become the determining factor. A desire for privacy and seclusion may be satisfied in the placement and arrangement of the plan. Individuality and uniqueness may be desirable.

7. *Natural lighting.* There may be a danger of providing too little light in the home. Excess in size and quantity of windows tends to destroy a homelike atmosphere and the restfulness of the home, and disturbs the designing of the elevations. See Unit V, Windows, pp. 128–154.

8. *Planning electrical service.* It probably will be profitable in money and satisfaction to consult expert advice with this phase of planning. See "Modern Lighting and Electrical Installation," pp. 325–342.

9. *Location of furniture and fixtures.* A plan in which the possibilities of the location of furniture is not considered can be of little satisfaction or use. The method of using scale templets of the individual pieces will give the relative amount of space occupied (Figs. 103–108, 159). See "Planning Rooms to Accommodate Furniture," p. 342.

10. *Heating the house.* The method of heating and type of heating plant will be determined by climatic conditions, size of building, kinds of building material used, cost, and individual preference. See "Heating the House," pp. 280–307.

11. *Types and sizes of doors.* The location of the doors in the plan requires special consideration since the comfort and privacy of accessibility and circulation are affected, not to mention the need of moving furniture in and out of the room. See Unit VIII, "Doors," pp. 162–171.

D. Elevation Studies

It is not profitable to attempt to carry a set of floor plans to completion without giving consideration to the appearance of the outside of the house. The appearance of the outside is represented through the drawing of the elevations (Figs. 152 and 155). The type and location of windows, placing of doors, design and location of balconies, dormers, porches, roof pitch, roof overhang, all influence the design of the exterior of the house and cannot be visualized without being drawn to scale.

Several sketches of the elevations should be drawn on squared paper in order that the proportions and scale and general appearance of the elevation can be studied (Figs. 152, 155, 173–175). These should be studies of ideas rather than an attempt at a consolidation of planning. The technique used by architects in making these sketches

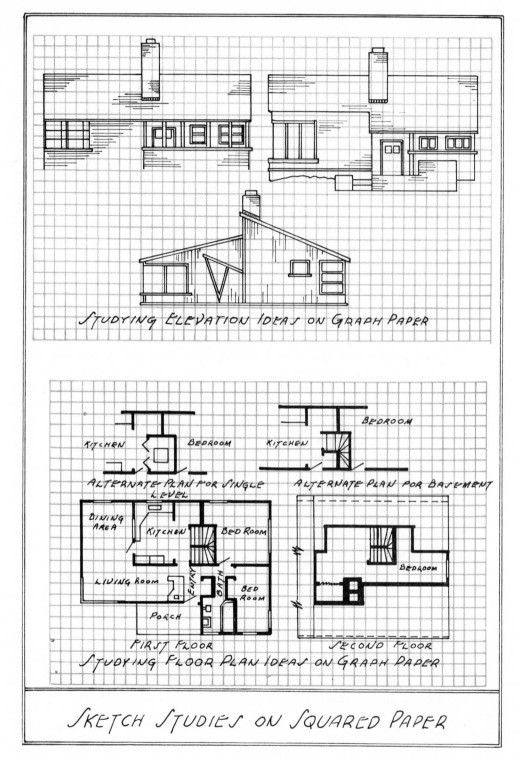

STUDYING ELEVATION IDEAS ON GRAPH PAPER

KITCHEN   BEDROOM

ALTERNATE PLAN FOR SINGLE LEVEL

BEDROOM

KITCHEN

ALTERNATE PLAN FOR BASEMENT

DINING AREA

KITCHEN   BED ROOM

LIVING ROOM   ENTRY   BATH   BED ROOM

PORCH

FIRST FLOOR

BEDROOM

SECOND FLOOR

STUDYING FLOOR PLAN IDEAS ON GRAPH PAPER

SKETCH STUDIES ON SQUARED PAPER

Fig. 152

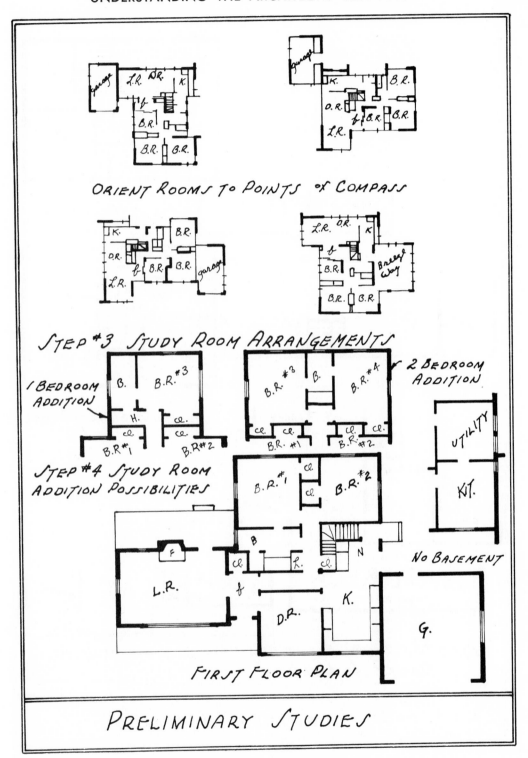

Fig. 153

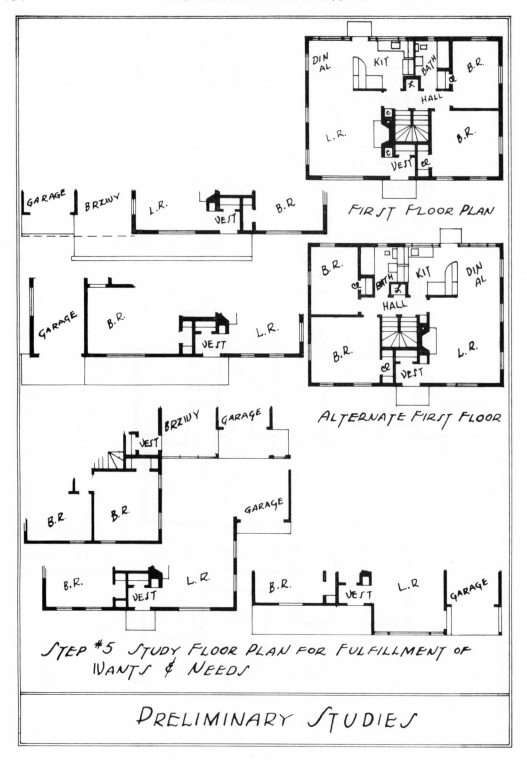

FIRST FLOOR PLAN

ALTERNATE FIRST FLOOR

STEP #5 STUDY FLOOR PLAN FOR FULFILLMENT OF WANTS & NEEDS

PRELIMINARY STUDIES

Fig. 154

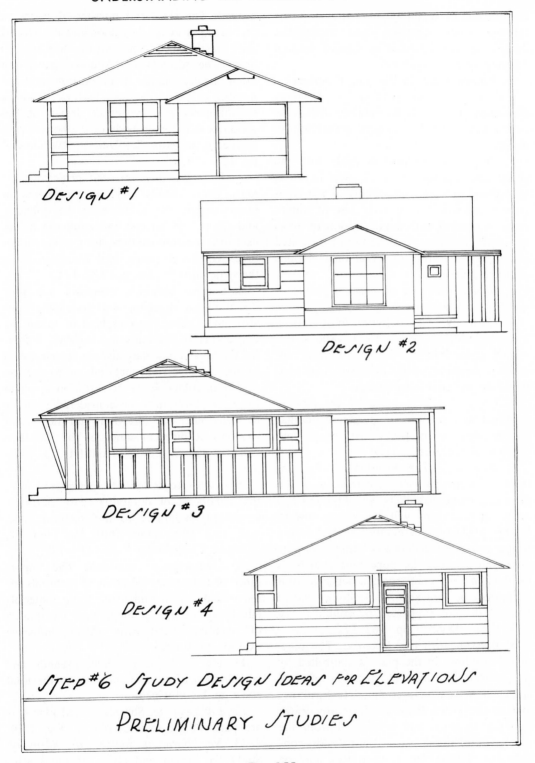

DESIGN #1

DESIGN #2

DESIGN #3

DESIGN #4

STEP #6 STUDY DESIGN IDEAS FOR ELEVATIONS

PRELIMINARY STUDIES

Fig. 155

is difficult to acquire, and attained only through study, practice, and experience. Ability to indicate what is wanted without drawing detail is essential.

E. Fundamentals in Planning Exteriors

To approach the problem of designing elevations one should be familiar with some of the fundamental principles underlying all design:

1. *Proportion.* Proportion deals with the shape and size of the total area in view, with the sizes and relationships of the component and subordinate parts. Use of square areas, repetition, horizontal division of areas into equal divisions, and the use of unrelated structural parts are some common violations of good proportion.

2. *Balance.* Balance produces a feeling of stability, rest, and permanence.

3. *Harmony.* The designer must refrain from introducing details from various unrelated styles into one house, or using unsuitable ornamentation, or color combinations, or material combinations.

4. *Unity.* Unity is achieved by relating principal and subordinate points of emphasis, as well as by the proper shape and division of the area in view.

5. *Doorways.* The location of the entrance, its design and ornamentation are most important. Simplicity, stability, and sincerity in treatment will contribute toward lasting satisfaction. A number of devices are in use to make the doorway express its purpose and improve its appearance, such as overhanging the main roof, a separate roof supported by brackets or trellises, and a balcony or roof supported by columns. See Unit VIII, "Doors," pp. 162–171.

6. *Window sizes and locations.* The placing of windows in the plan is controlled by the interior arrangement, location of wall spaces necessary to accommodate furniture, and so on. When these windows are drawn into the elevation and considered from the standpoint of the design of the exterior, considerable shifting and readjustment may be needed. The sizes and number of panes in the windows in the first floor and the second floor are designed to present the best appearance. The second floor window panes are often slightly smaller in proportion, and the number of panes reduced. Dormer windows should carry out the exact design of the windows in the main body of the house using smaller scale parts. See Unit V, "Windows," pp. 128–155.

7. *Balconies, porches, and projecting details.* These details serve two purposes in house design: (1) to increase the comfort, and (2) to add interest and emphasis to the exterior. Window shutters, iron grilles, lamp brackets, flower boxes, and moldings serve the same purposes. See pp. 172–174.

8. *Casting shadows.* Shadows are produced by overhanging and protruding constructions. These shadows tend to soften the appearance of the walls and surfaces. Softening the appearance may also be accomplished by the use of certain materials or by the use of certain colors. Even the direction in which the house faces must be considered in order to determine the direction and degree of shadows at different times of the day. See "Shades and Shadows," Unit III, pp. 545–550.

9. *Roofs.* Roofs must be considered from the standpoint of durability, cost, harmony in design, suitability to architectural style, and color effect (Fig. 160). See Unit IV, "Cornice Construction," pp. 119–127.

10. *Character of materials.* The importance of the proper selection of materials for the outside finish and using these materials effectively is not to be minimized. The quality of restfulness and calm should influence exterior treatments.

11. *Use of color.* The hue, strength, and combination of colors contribute to the total effect to be obtained.

12. *Landscaping.* Shrubbery and plantings are parts of the exterior design (Fig. 150).

13. *Neighborhood factors of harmony.* Study the design and styles of the houses

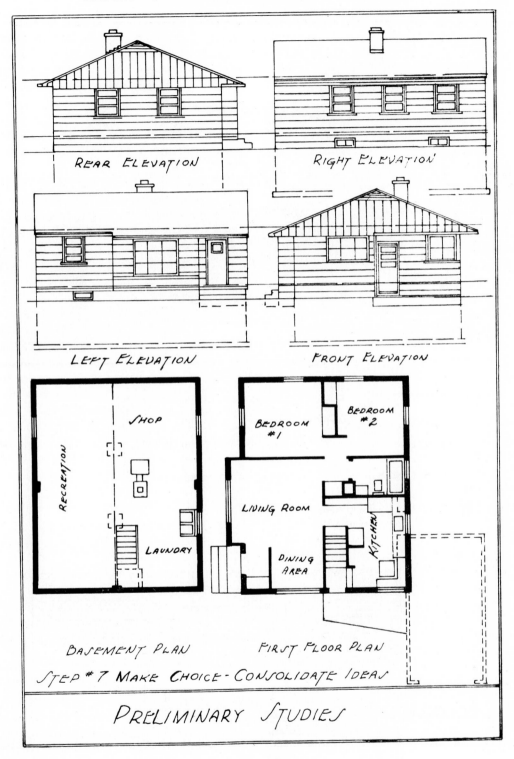

REAR ELEVATION

RIGHT ELEVATION

LEFT ELEVATION

FRONT ELEVATION

SHOP

RECREATION

LAUNDRY

BEDROOM #1

BEDROOM #2

LIVING ROOM

KITCHEN

DINING AREA

BASEMENT PLAN

FIRST FLOOR PLAN

STEP #7 MAKE CHOICE - CONSOLIDATE IDEAS

PRELIMINARY STUDIES

Fig. 156

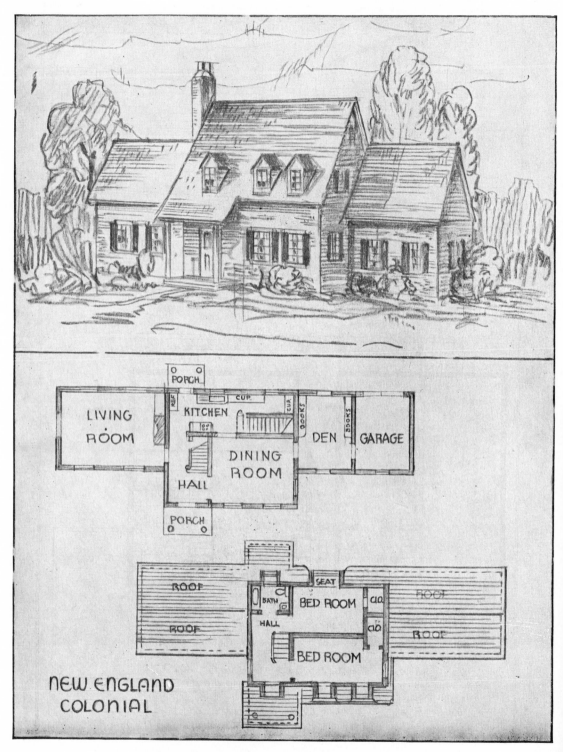

PORCH

LIVING ROOM

KITCHEN   CUP.

CUP.

DEN   GARAGE

HALL

DINING ROOM

PORCH

ROOF

SEAT

ROOF

BATH   BED ROOM   CLO.

ROOF

HALL   CLO.

ROOF

BED ROOM

NEW ENGLAND COLONIAL

Fig. 157.   Rough pencil sketches for a house.

of the neighborhood into which the house is to be placed. The things to be noted in this study are: architectural styles, building materials, distances from the street, contour and character of the site, trees, and other natural factors.

F. Finished Sketches

When plans are being made for a building, the first set of drawings usually consists of a set of finished sketches (Fig. 159). Enough of the dimensions and details are represented so that the ideas in plan and elevation are sufficiently worked out and presented to be used as a basis for the working drawings. Sometimes several sketches, each differing in some respects from the others, must be neatly executed before a draftsman or client is entirely satisfied with the preliminary studies (Figs. 157, 158, and 212).

THE BASIC STAGE OF PLANNING

When the client accepts the ideas presented by the architect in the preliminary planning stage, the architect makes his general studies of the assignment to determine the plan, design, and related data he will recommend to his client. He investigates the various possibilities of the design, location on the lot, materials, methods of construction; he familiarizes himself with the conditions of the problem; and he examines the laws and ordinances, codes, rules, and regulations of governmental authorities and of the insurance companies involved.

Next, the basic drawings are drawn at small scale sufficient to illustrate his conclusions and fix the plan and design in all essentials. These basic drawings and recommendations are submitted to the client for suggestion and approval. If the client desires changes he must allow ample opportunity for the architect to make further study after which the client gives his approval. After the client has approved the basic drawings he should not require any changes of the drawings without adequately compensating the architect for the work involved (Fig. 159).

The services rendered by the architect during the preliminary and basic drawing stages are the most valuable of his services for they settle the elements of the plan and design; the general types of materials to be used; the methods of construction; the general equipment to be installed; and, determine the amount of money the client is willing to spend on the assignment.

THE WORKING DRAWING STAGE

During this stage the architect develops the working drawings, specifications, general contract, and bid forms. These technical drawings and legal documents are the expressions of the architect's ideas from which the cost of the assignment can be determined, and the building constructed. Working drawings should be the logical developments of the approved preliminary studies and include all essential architectural and engineering drawings. They should show plans, elevations, sections of the structures, details of the work, and indicate the various materials as to where and how they are to be used. The specifications should describe the types and qualities of the materials and their finish, and the manner of their construction, assembly, and erection. The general contract should describe the conditions under which the work should be done. The bid forms are prepared by the architect for the express purpose of selecting a contractor capable of doing the work under the provisions of the specifications and the contract. The architect receives the bids for his client and advises him on the acceptance. The architect's drawings and specifications remain his property at all times. He is required to furnish a copy of each to his client, but the cost of making and delivering the copies is paid by the client.

Architectural Working Drawings. The principles of drawing are similar for all kinds of industry, but each branch requires its own

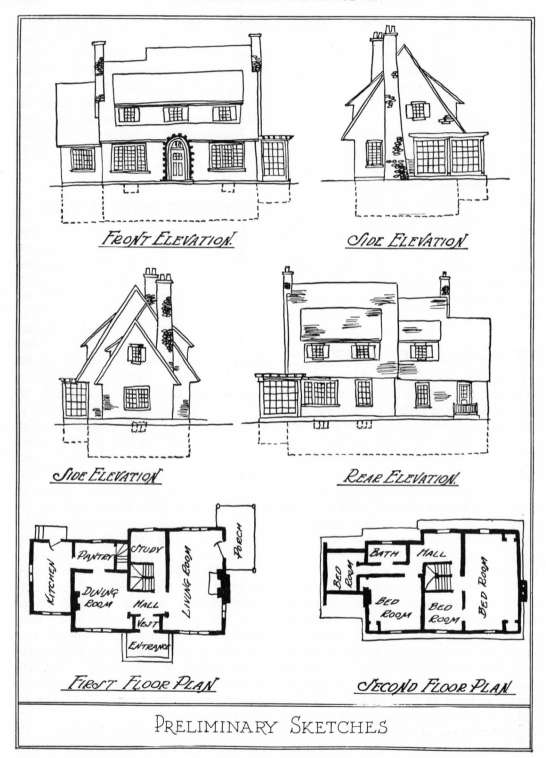

FRONT ELEVATION.

SIDE ELEVATION

SIDE ELEVATION

REAR ELEVATION.

FIRST FLOOR PLAN

SECOND FLOOR PLAN

PRELIMINARY SKETCHES

Fig. 158

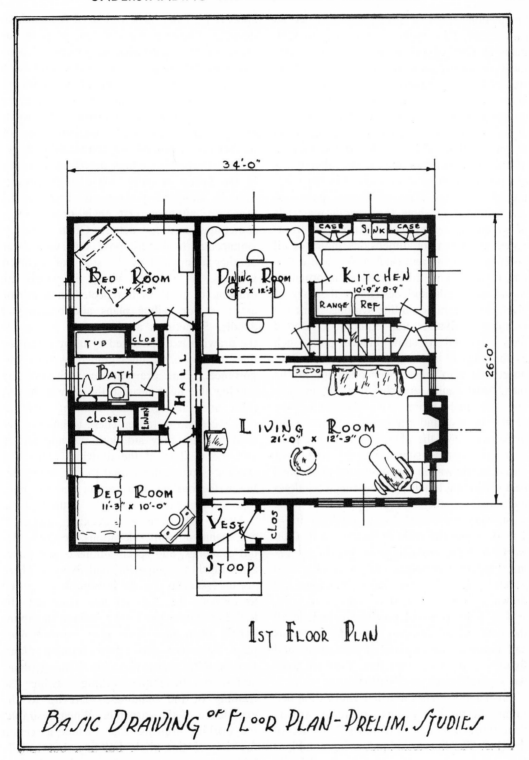

1st Floor Plan

Basic Drawing of Floor Plan—Prelim. Studies

Fig. 159

application of these principles to meet its own needs. This applies particularly to such items as scale, dimensioning, symbols, treatment of views, and so on. Because of the size of building structures a smaller scale is necessary to fit the drawings to the size of the sheet. Conventional symbols are used for doors and windows and other various kinds of information. This speeds up the making of the drawings and makes the plan quick of interpretation to those trained in the reading of drawings. The walls and partitions are sectioned to show the various materials of which the several constructions are composed. A system of dimensions indicates all necessary spacing and thicknesses, and a system of notes and titles provides information regarding details and designates the uses of given areas. Simple outline symbols mark the location of fixtures and equipment. Dotted lines are used to show hidden parts such as the edge of footings below the basement floor, and also edges over openings in the plan. Steel beams are shown as heavy dot-and-dash lines representing the center line of the beams, and these lines always refer to beams above the plan, never below. Thus a row of beams supporting the first floor would be shown on the basement plan. Steel beams forming lintels over basement windows are shown on the basement plan. The scale most commonly used for plans is ¼ in. = 1 ft. 0 in. but the scale of ³⁄₁₆ in = 1 ft. 0 in. works to better advantage on the 11 by 17-in. standard size sheet and is coming into general use. Plans of large buildings are drawn at ⅛ in. = 1 ft. 0 in., and even ¹⁄₁₆ in. = 1 ft. 0 in. It is not possible to include all the notes of information regarding materials and finishes, specification of equipment and fixtures, and so on; therefore, they are written separately as specifications.

Freehand sketches and lettering as applied to architectural drawings are more artistic than those used in some other branches of drawing. The line techniques using combinations of finer lines give an entirely different appearance from those produced for machine drawing. They serve a different purpose because of the differences in process of construction. Where architectural drawings need be accurate in placement of windows to 2-in. measurement and measurements varying up to ½ in. on a floor dimension of a room are permitted and only nominal sizes of lumber are in general use, the machine drawing must represent a high degree of accuracy in the fitting of parts. Third angle projection is standard practice in architectural drawings, although first angle projection is sometimes used for details. Often it is advantageous to superimpose one view over another as applied by the study of revolved sections. A "reflected view," in which the drawing is made as if reflected in a mirror are used for ceiling plans and ornamental details. Sometimes an important outline of the drawing is emphasized by using a heavier line and the other lines graded by their importance. Some drawings are "shaded" by making the lines nearest the viewer heavy, thick lines and gradually thinning them as they recede in distance. These techniques are used because they aid both the appearance and the reading of the drawings. This line shading is particularly used to distinguish between the outline of a section and the lines representing parts beyond the cutting plane.

Under the term of "working drawings" are included plans, elevations, sections, detail drawings, and specifications of the materials, finishes, equipment, and fixtures. These are necessary to give the information required to execute the contract and construct the building. These plans may include the foundation plan, first floor plan, second floor plan, basement plan, floor framing plans, roof framing plans, elevation framing plans, and so on. In simple working drawings the framing of the building is left up to the experience of the carpenter. When desirable, the working drawings may include a section drawing of the whole building, but usually in house construction a "vertical section" of one wall of the house is drawn. See Unit VI, "Wall Sections," pp. 155–160.

Large details of such parts as are not shown with sufficient clearness on small scale drawings are often used to show the framing of sills, cornices, windows, stairways, fireplaces, cabinets, and so on. These details are best grouped so that each sheet contains the references made on one sheet of plans or elevations. As a general rule, things which are related should be shown together, and information prepared for each trade should be grouped together as much as possible. Drawings are usually made with one plan or one elevation on a sheet to allow for the making of the drawing at the most convenient working size, but often the sheets are combined for compactness. In larger buildings the work becomes so complicated that it is advantageous to draw special plans for each trade, in addition to the general plans. Special plans are often drawn for structural steel, heating, plumbing, and wiring. See "Heating the House," p. 280 ff., "Plumbing Fixtures in a House," p. 307 ff., "Modern Wiring and Electrical Installation," p. 325 ff. To be able to prepare good detail drawings the draftsman needs much ingenuity, good technique, experience in construction and access to reference material giving information on construction details. The draftsman must also be familiar with local and state building codes, and the legal requirements prescribed.

The construction and equipment of a modern building is so complex that no one person can plan the building in all its details. The engineer and architect are mutually dependent upon each other for answers to questions of strength, mechanical apparatus, construction, design, and so on. The architect is usually associated with an architectural engineer who designs the framework and its structural details, lighting and wiring systems, plumbing, heating, air conditioning, and so on. In large buildings, specialized engineers are employed to design each separate functional system of the building. For this reason each person employed in an architect's office is usually a specialist doing just one phase of the total work, such as preliminary sketches, perspective, stair layout, detailing, acoustics, lighting, heating, ventilation, insulation, legal contracts, specifications, supervision, and so on. Because of this specialization most architectural offices are an "association" of architectural specialists. In home planning it is necessary for the planner to consult with tradesmen in the specialized fields to obtain the information necessary for the making of the drawings, or often the tradesmen are called in to make their own layout drawings as the construction progresses. It is necessary to make a plumbing layout drawing and lay certain pipes before the foundation walls and basement floor are poured. Pipes are placed in the walls at time of construction (or provision made for them), but the fixtures may be installed later in the finishing process. Wiring layouts need to be made by the electrician in the planning stage, since most of the wiring is done during the framing of the construction.

In modern building construction, many parts of the building are fabricated, ready for installation, by firms specializing in the manufacture of that particular element. Windows are usually completely fabricated by a millwork company ready for installation. Full details about sizes and styles available and other information are supplied by the company and the architect draws his plans to fit the prefabricated unit. Very few details need be drawn in plans for small buildings because few of the details such as windows, doors, and so on are custom built. A few years ago the stairway required an expert stair builder while now the millwork company supplies the parts and the finishing carpenter assembles and installs them. Prefabricated parts of the house now include such items as doors and frames, windows, stairways, fireplace linings, cabinets of all kinds, bookcases, breakfast nook furniture, and even chimneys. Because of this progress it is no longer necessary to represent these parts by detail drawings unless it is desired that they be custom built.

It is possible for a prospective home builder to go to a contractor with a plan and a picture cut from a magazine or copied from a book. If both parties are honest, a working agreement may be made satisfactorily to cover the planning, costs, construction, and so on, involved, but there are so many chances for a misunderstanding and dispute that it is worth the cost and effort to make or have made a set of working drawings to serve as a record of what was agreed upon, and what exactly is to be built. Most cities require a set of working drawings before approval can be made for a building permit. Some cities go so far as to require that the drawings be made by a licensed architect.

Architectural Floor Plans. One of the most important steps in planning a house is the laying out of floor plans, which require more than the representation of lines and shapes on paper. Careful thought must be given to site planning, room planning, and room arrangements considered as one problem. To organize the rooms into a definite plan you must consider the site, its orientation with respect to the travel of the sun, its outlook and views, its relation to the streets, and finally the proper location of the garage and any outdoor living space such as gardens, terraces, or porches that may be a part of the whole scheme (Figs. 66–69 and 151).

Next comes the final planning of the arrangement of the house itself. Each room should have been previously considered as to its function, size, arrangement of furniture, closets, and relationship to the total plan. All this planning depends primarily upon two things: (1) the needs of the family who plan to live in the house, and (2) the amount of money which can be spent in building. It has been seen that in the average house there are three essential first floor rooms, namely, kitchen, living room, and dining room which must be arranged in combination with the entrance hall, stairs, closets, and so on (Fig. 160). The number of different ways in which these three rooms and the entrance hall can be arranged is more or less limited, especially when consideration is given to the fact that the dining room or dining alcove must in every case be in such position that it is directly accessible to the kitchen, with only a partition and door or a serving pantry between. The entrance may be placed near the center of the front wall, with the hallway between the living room and the dining room, which is desirable for a Georgian style of house. This arrangement, using a large portion of one of the outside walls which might have been useful for natural lighting, has more or less wasted valuable space on the front entrance hall (which has little utility), but there are some advantages in having such an arrangement. These plans are simple rectangles, nearly square and therefore economical to build with the least possible amount of outside wall space. The ell-shaped plan is somewhat more costly than a simple rectangular plan because of the extra corners which are required, as well as the additional outside wall surface and roof areas.

In any good plan the rooms must be placed with proper relation to each other and to the entrances, so that related rooms will be fairly close to each other. Thus the living room may be separated from the dining room by a hall, but there should be no hallway between a dining room and kitchen. It is essential that one should be able to pass from any bedroom to a bathroom without passing through any other room than a hallway or corridor. It is desirable to be able to go to the front door from the kitchen without passing through the living room or dining room, but where the stairway is placed in the living room this is not possible. Access to the basement from the kitchen without

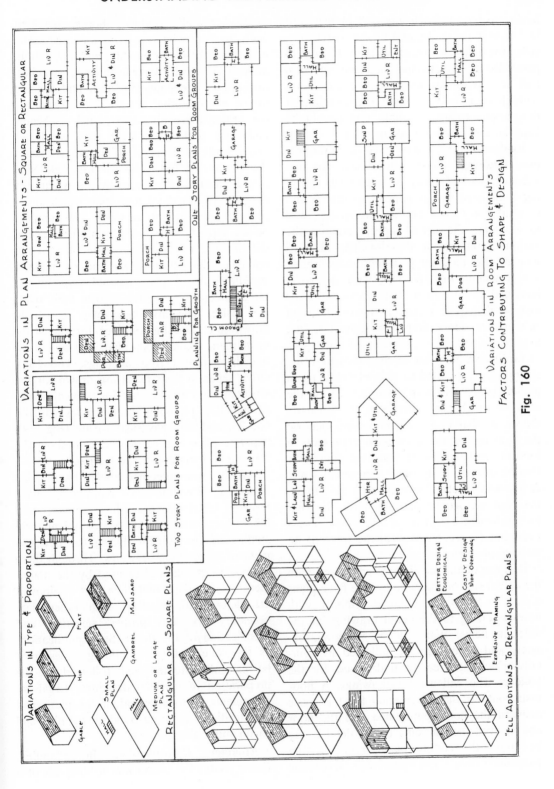

Fig. 160

having to pass through any part of the front hall is very desirable, and access to the outside from the basement without having to pass through the kitchen or front entrance hall is a great advantage. These considerations have a bearing upon the location of the various rooms and halls and should be kept in mind when making plans.

Explanation of Plans Used in Architectural Drawing. Persons who have not had a background of study in mechanical drawing sometimes find it difficult to understand or read floor plans as they are drawn, and to visualize the actual appearance of the various rooms from the drawings. Try to imagine that the floor plan represents a horizontal section or top view, with the walls imagined as cut about 3 ft. above the floor and parallel to it, in order that details such as windows, doors, fireplaces, stairways, etc., may be shown. Even a top view of each piece of furniture which can be simplified by using symbols may be used to help visualize room planning. Since it is impossible to draw the plan of the house actual size it is usually drawn so that each quarter of an inch on the drawing of the floor plan represents a foot on the actual house. But floor plans may also be drawn to any other convenient scale. A pictorial sketch, which looks as though the wall were only partially built, is what the draftsman has in mind when he draws a plan, but he represents it in the form of an orthographic plan.

Because of the small scale compared with the actual size of the building, the floor plans are made up of conventional symbols, with notes referring to the detail drawings of the different items. Walls, doors, windows, fixtures, and so on are all indicated by symbols which are readily understood by the builders who will use the drawings. A floor plan contains the information for the space between the floor represented and the floor above, even though some of the details may be above the cutting plane used for that particular floor. The plan will show the location of all windows, doors, partition walls, radiators, built-in fixtures and cabinets, inlets and outlets for heating and ventilation, outlets for electrical convenience, switches, material of the floor, direction and spacing of the joists of that floor level, information concerning the ceiling above such as beams and light outlets. A floor plan is always drawn with the front of the building toward the bottom of the sheet (or the right side of the sheet depending upon the placing of the title strip or block and upon which direction the drawing is to be read). The compass points should be indicated on the drawing showing the relationship of the plan to the points of the compass. All the sheets in a complete set of plans should face in the same direction, since this makes their reading easier. The first floor plan is usually drawn first, and the outlines for the basement plan, second floor plan, and so on are traced or drawn from it (Figs. 166–169). Often separate floor plans are drawn for the representation of the heating system (Figs. 82 and 83), plumbing system (Figs. 86, 89, 90, 95, and 96), electrical wiring (Fig. 99). Separate plans are often drawn to show the framing construction to the carpenter.

Architectural reference books, handbooks, American Institute of Architects' files, Sweet's Catalogs, magazine articles, and other literature should be conscientiously studied by the student during the development of all working drawings. Through these references, standard sizes used by the manufacturers for their materials and equipment are determined, together with other data necessary for the proper selection and specification of the items. Such publications as the state and local building codes must be carefully studied and followed in the preparation of working drawings. Legal requirements as to approval of the plans and specifications, securing building permits, and so on must also be met.

Modular   Co-ordination   in   Planning. Every contractor knows that a blueprint of a

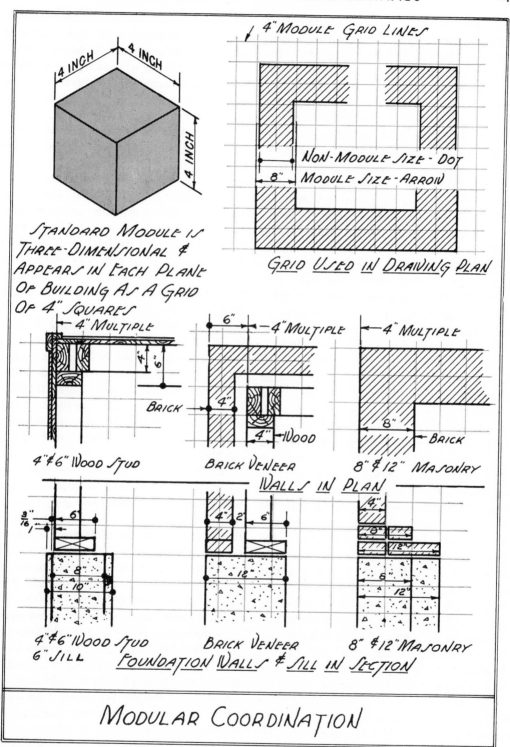

STANDARD MODULE IS THREE-DIMENSIONAL & APPEARS IN EACH PLANE OF BUILDING AS A GRID OF 4" SQUARES

GRID USED IN DRAWING PLAN

WALLS IN PLAN

4" & 6" WOOD STUD   BRICK VENEER   8" & 12" MASONRY

4" & 6" WOOD STUD
6" SILL   FOUNDATION WALLS & SILL IN SECTION

MODULAR COORDINATION

Fig. 161

house plan is not a home. The contractor brings lumber, wallboard, cement, bricks, windows, doors, cabinets, hardware, and plumbing, heating, and lighting fixtures from all parts of the country to the building site. Installed by workmen of different industries, these parts must arrive at the site on a synchronized time schedule, and each part must fit. This co-ordination of workmen and materials is a problem requiring continuous study and solution by the building industry. New materials, new workmen, and new methods must be constantly co-ordinated at the home site if each home is to be built at the lowest possible cost.

In the past, building products were manufactured in a wide variety of sizes. This resulted in time-consuming cutting and fitting of related products in the field, in order to build according to the dimensions in the plan. If these component parts were made of a size and shape so that they could be fitted together without cutting on the job the cost of construction and the cost of planning the construction is lower than it would be otherwise. Under the "modular system" of designing homes, all measurements are based in 4-in. multiples (Fig. 161). The determination of the size module involved extensive research and study by a committee of the American Standards Association under the sponsorship of the American Institute of Architects and the Producers Council Inc. In general, too large a module would restrict the flexibility of building layout and of sizes of products so as to make its application impractical. On the other hand, the larger the module the greater would be the simplification and economy of standardization. Building materials are related to this 4-in. grid only in planning as it affects their co-ordination with other materials. Since they must be joined by mortar, nails, bolts, or must overlap as in the case of shingles and clapboards, the building parts are only rarely made to some multiple of the 4-in. module. From a practical viewpoint it must be understood that not

all manufacturers are producing materials in the 4-in. multiple, nor is such standardization ever likely to happen or be intended. Size co-ordination of building materials and equipment is achieved by selection from the available sizes, followed by a fitting of the details into the modular grid.

Two systems of dimensioning are used in architectural drawing: (1) representing details by actual size of members, or (2) using nominal sizes (Fig. 162). Studding 2 by 4 in. is commonly used in both exterior and partition walls; these sizes are nominal dimensions. The actual size is 1⅝ by 3⅝ in. Nominal sizes of a modular brick are 2⅔ by 4 by 8 in., to be laid with ⅜ in. mortar joints, is actually 2⁵⁄₁₆ by 3⅝ by 7⅝ in. If the mortar joints are to be ½ in. instead of ⅜ in., the brick sizes are correspondingly smaller and the actual thickness of a nominal 8-in. wall is 7½ in. The student must determine which sizes of brick are available in the territory where the building is to be erected. It is usual that the interior and exterior treatment, or finish, is not considered in the calculation of the nominal size of any wall thickness; only the structural members enter into the calculations.

A symmetrical location of walls and openings with respect to the grid is desirable to accomplish standardization (Fig. 163). For wall thicknesses, only one reference to a grid line is possible if the walls are (1) centered on the grid lines, or (2) centered between grid lines (Fig. 164). Any other method of positioning walls results in too many possibilities of location of details on the grid. Vertical positioning is usually accomplished by locating floor levels on the grid lines (Fig. 163). Openings need not be symmetrical in their vertical positioning, since head and sill details are different but the different-sized openings are usually positioned with all the heads on the same grid reference line. Adjustments for variations in thicknesses are made at the intersections of the ceiling and wall for that particular story.

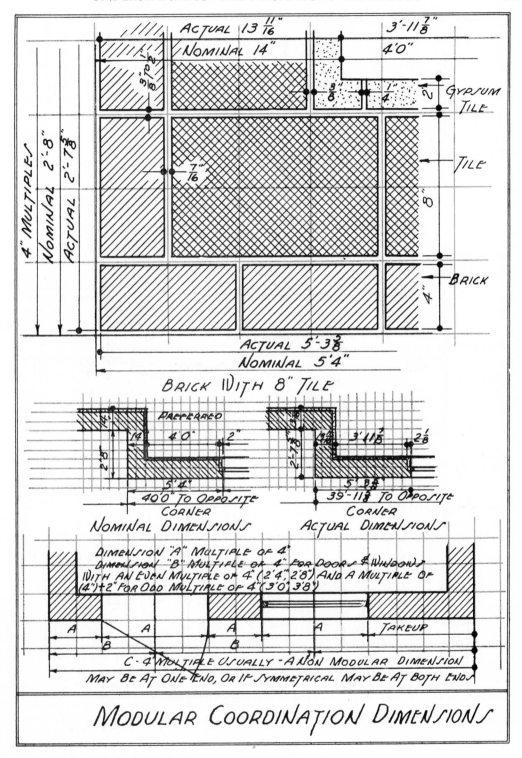

Fig. 162

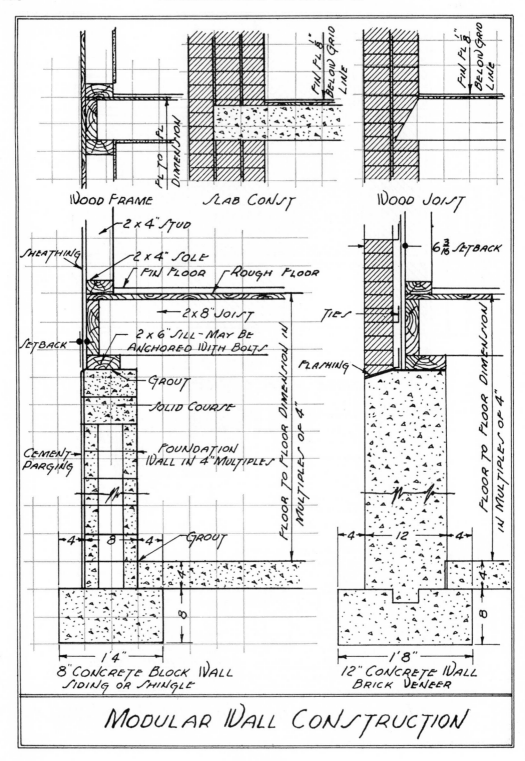

WOOD FRAME   SLAB CONST   WOOD JOIST

MODULAR WALL CONSTRUCTION

Fig. 163

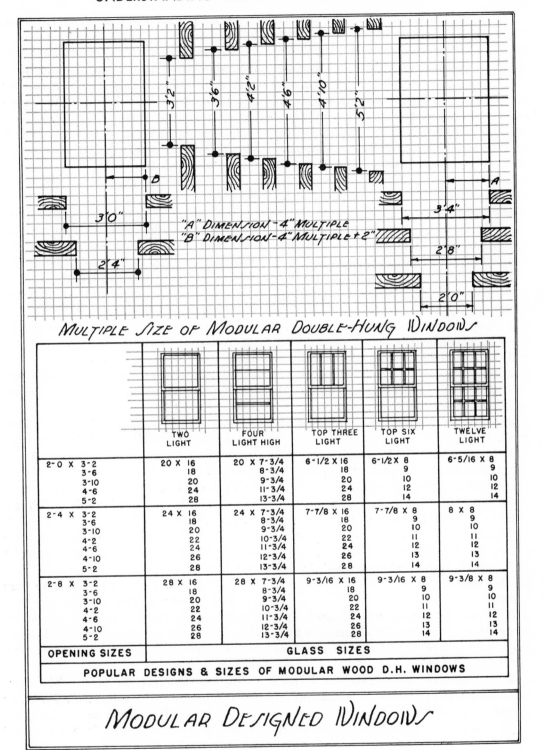

MULTIPLE SIZE OF MODULAR DOUBLE-HUNG WINDOWS

"A" DIMENSION - 4" MULTIPLE
"B" DIMENSION - 4" MULTIPLE + 2"

	TWO LIGHT	FOUR LIGHT HIGH	TOP THREE LIGHT	TOP SIX LIGHT	TWELVE LIGHT
2-0 X 3-2	20 X 16	20 X 7-3/4	6-1/2 X 16	6-1/2 X 8	6-5/16 X 8
3-6	18	8-3/4	18	9	9
3-10	20	9-3/4	20	10	10
4-6	24	11-3/4	24	12	12
5-2	28	13-3/4	28	14	14
2-4 X 3-2	24 X 16	24 X 7-3/4	7-7/8 X 16	7-7/8 X 8	8 X 8
3-6	18	8-3/4	18	9	9
3-10	20	9-3/4	20	10	10
4-2	22	10-3/4	22	11	11
4-6	24	11-3/4	24	12	12
4-10	26	12-3/4	26	13	13
5-2	28	13-3/4	28	14	14
2-8 X 3-2	28 X 16	28 X 7-3/4	9-3/16 X 16	9-3/16 X 8	9-3/8 X 8
3-6	18	8-3/4	18	9	9
3-10	20	9-3/4	20	10	10
4-2	22	10-3/4	22	11	11
4-6	24	11-3/4	24	12	12
4-10	26	12-3/4	26	13	13
5-2	28	13-3/4	28	14	14
OPENING SIZES	GLASS SIZES				

POPULAR DESIGNS & SIZES OF MODULAR WOOD D.H. WINDOWS

MODULAR DESIGNED WINDOWS

Fig. 164

Modular sizes of many building products (bricks, glazed tile, concrete masonry, glass blocks, wood and metal windows and doors) are now available throughout the country. This change to a modular size for building materials and equipment has encouraged architects and builders to apply the principles of modular co-ordination and to receive the benefits from the use of these co-ordinated sizes. Advantages of this module system of layout are many and varied, although the advantages for different industries differ widely. Some of these advantages are:

1. The module is large enough for manufacturers to reduce the number of stock sizes and still meet customer's demands.

2. It is small enough for ample freedom in architectural design and for flexibility in equipment layout.

3. It agrees with the dimensions of a great many building materials already standardized, and is applicable to present construction practices.

4. It is a unit of measurement with which architects, builders, masons, carpenters, and others in the building trades are already familiar.

5. It approximates 10 centimeters (3.9 in.), the basis of measurement proposed by metric system countries working on standardization.

6. No attempt is made at standardization of houses as to size, shape, arrangement, or design. No individuality is sacrificed.

7. It leads to nationwide standards instead of sizes fixed by local customs in different sections of the country.

8. It increases the demand for stock sizes in preference to custom sizes because of their lower purchase price and ease of construction or installation.

9. A lower cost of manufacture is possible compared to custom manufacturing of special detail and size.

10. Improved precision and uniformity of quality result from improved manufacturing processes.

Among the advantages to the architect and builder who use the module sizes are these:

1. A simplified method of making building layouts appreciably reduces drafting time.

2. Alternate materials, construction, and specifications can be used without the necessity of redrawing details.

3. The necessity of drawing details of standardized constructions, and stock manufacture is eliminated.

4. Easier supervision of the job results from standard building practice.

5. A unity of structural design results from the application of a single dimensional unit, both vertically and horizontally to the building structure, its openings, finish, and even to various exterior features.

6. Estimating is simplified by the elimination of fractional inches.

7. The cost of fabrication is lowered by the reduction of cutting and fitting on the job.

8. Uniformity of building practices and better control of assembly and installation are other advantages.

Sometimes in drawing plans, elevations, and details to a small scale, it is clumsy and inconvenient to use a 4-in. module at this scale size. The module may be taken in the multiples of 4 in. but using a larger unit of measure such as a 12-in. grid. With the module 16 times 4 in. or 5 ft. 4 in., it is called a "large planning module" and the center line of the walls coincide with the grid lines.

In dimensioning drawings that have been drawn using the modular system, it is customary to use arrowheads where the dimension line terminates on one of the grid lines, and dots where it terminates on points other than grid lines.

Steps in Drawing the Plans. The plans are usually drawn on a pencil tracing paper so that succeeding plans may be drawn by tracing over the first plan for the principal dimensions, thus saving time in the measuring and laying out stage.

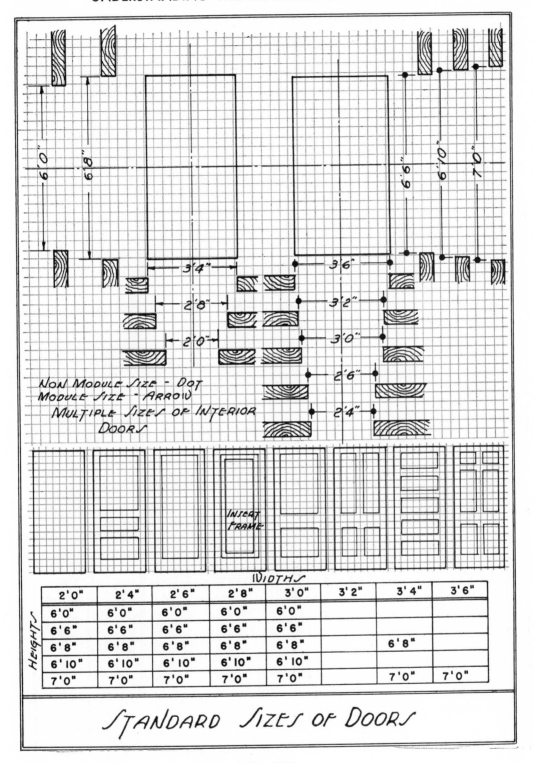

WIDTHS							
2'0"	2'4"	2'6"	2'8"	3'0"	3'2"	3'4"	3'6"
6'0"	6'0"	6'0"	6'0"	6'0"			
6'6"	6'6"	6'6"	6'6"	6'6"			
6'8"	6'8"	6'8"	6'8"	6'8"		6'8"	
6'10"	6'10"	6'10"	6'10"	6'10"			
7'0"	7'0"	7'0"	7'0"	7'0"		7'0"	7'0"

STANDARD SIZES OF DOORS

Fig. 165

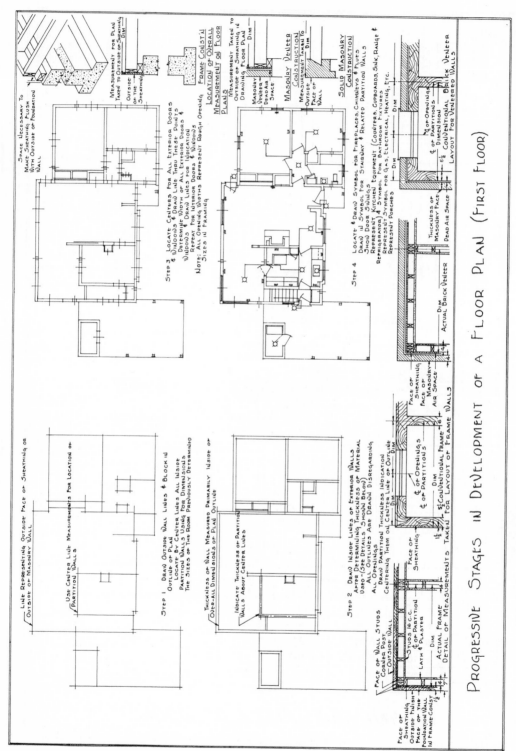

PROGRESSIVE STAGES IN DEVELOPMENT OF A FLOOR PLAN (FIRST FLOOR)

Fig. 166

Layout stage. All lines are drawn *very lightly* and of indefinite length, thus simplifying the making of corrections and saving time. A 2H pencil with a comparatively sharp conical point is to be recommended for layout on tracing paper.

1. Draw outside wall lines the total length and width of the building. Measurements are usually taken to the outside of wall in masonry buildings, and to the outside of the sheathing in frame buildings (Step 1, Fig. 166).

2. Draw the inside of exterior walls after determining the thickness of the building material to be used. A frame wall is drawn 7 in. thick, including siding, sheathing, studs, lath and plaster. Masonry walls are drawn 8 in. or 12 in. for brick and 18 in. for stone. All dimensions are dependent upon the materials used and the standards recommended for their use.

3. Locate center lines for all interior partitions. Determine thickness of partitions and draw in light outlines. A wood frame partition is usually represented at 6-in. thickness. Partitions are outlined with no attempt to consider locations of openings (Step 2, Fig. 166).

4. Locate the center of all exterior doors and windows, and draw a line through these points. No conventional representation of the center line is necessary at this time. Widths of these openings should only be temporarily located because their exact location will be determined during the layout drawing of the elevations of the house so that they will complement the appearance and design of the exterior of the wall and total building. After their proper location has been determined, then the lines representing the widths of the openings may finally be drawn on the plan and proper symbols and indications used.

5. Locate center lines for interior door openings, draw in the proper width, and erase the partition layout lines in the opening. A check should be made to see that the doors do not interfere with furniture grouping and locations, that doors do not interfere with each other, that traffic is routed efficiently, and that the swing of the door is correct (Step 3, Fig. 166).

6. Locate and draw in the fireplace, chimney, and flue. Only the conventional symbol of a fireplace is used. Give the overall and most important dimensions. The fireplace detail drawing will give complete information concerning construction. This symbol should be checked later against the detail drawing to be sure that they agree as to size, location, and so on.

7. Stairways should be drawn next, with partitions and framing calculated and located. It is suggested that the detail drawing of the stairway be laid out so that the rise and run of the stairway be calculated, as well as the rise and the width of tread. The rise, or height from one step to the next, will vary in size depending upon the type of building and whether the stairway is an interior or exterior construction, and the incline to be used will be determined by the proportion given to the rise and width of tread, and the space given between floors. The lower the rise the lower the incline, and the longer the stride in ascending or descending. On the plan, the lines drawn represent the edge of the risers and are as far apart as the width of the tread. The entire flight is not indicated on one floor, but is stopped at about half the flight to show what is under it. In most plans the stairs are all located one over another to save on wasted space. Each floor plan thus shows part of the stairways leading both up and down from the floor plan represented. Always indicate the direction and number of risers in the stairway by an arrow and note.

8. Kitchen equipment should be drawn in next. Be careful to keep the representations to scale, and arrange the kitchen equipment for work efficiency.

9. Draw in the front and rear steps and porches.

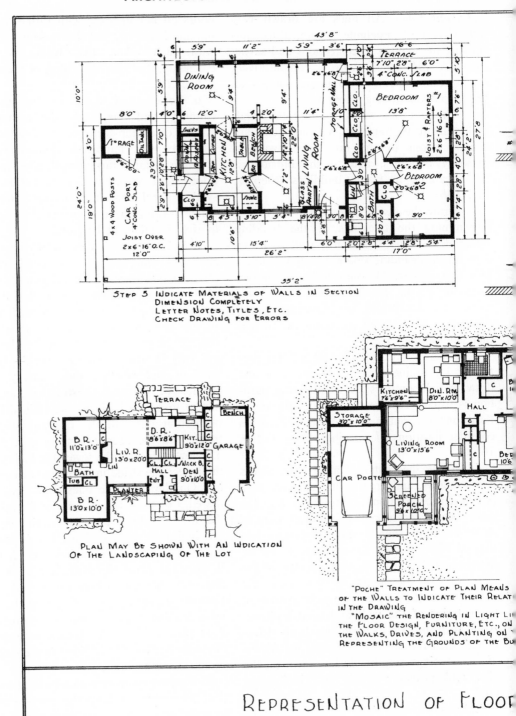

STEP 5 INDICATE MATERIALS OF WALLS IN SECTION
DIMENSION COMPLETELY
LETTER NOTES, TITLES, ETC.
CHECK DRAWING FOR ERRORS

PLAN MAY BE SHOWN WITH AN INDICATION
OF THE LANDSCAPING OF THE LOT

"POCHE" TREATMENT OF PLAN MEANS
OF THE WALLS TO INDICATE THEIR RELAT
IN THE DRAWING
   "MOSAIC" THE RENDERING IN LIGHT LI
THE FLOOR DESIGN, FURNITURE, ETC., ON
THE WALKS, DRIVES, AND PLANTING ON
REPRESENTING THE GROUNDS OF THE BU

REPRESENTATION OF FLOOR

Fig. 167

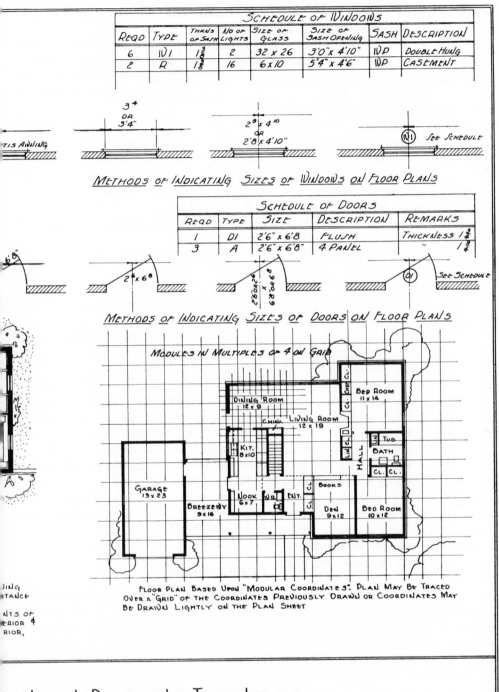

Schedule of Windows							
Reqd	Type	Thkns of Sash	No of Lights	Size of Glass	Size of Sash Opening	Sash	Description
6	W1	1⅜	2	32 x 26	3'0" x 4'10"	WP	Double-Hung
2	R	1⅜	16	6 x 10	5'4" x 4'6"	WP	Casement

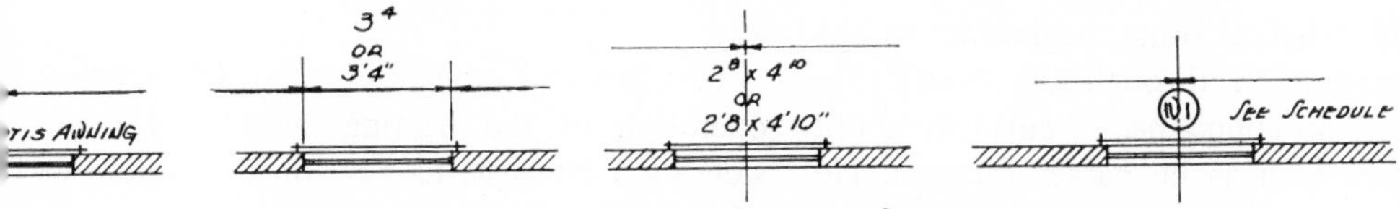

...tis Awning
3⁴
or
3'4"
2⁸ x 4¹⁰
or
2'8 x 4'10"
W1
See Schedule

Methods of Indicating Sizes of Windows on Floor Plans

Schedule of Doors				
Reqd	Type	Size	Description	Remarks
1	D1	2'6" x 6'8	Flush	Thickness 1¾
3	A	2'6" x 6'8"	4 Panel	" 1¾

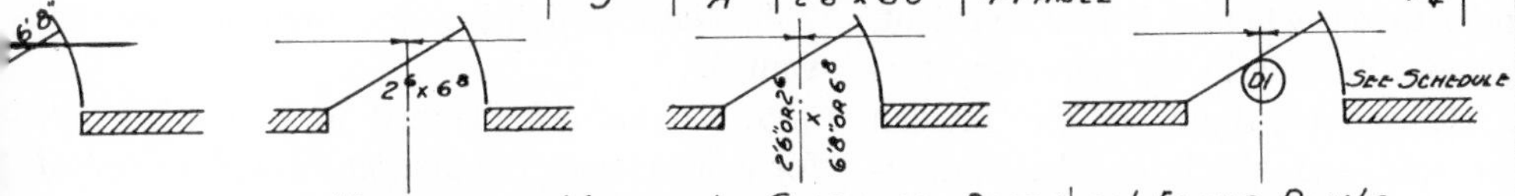

6'8"
2⁶ x 6⁸
2'6" or 2⁶ x 6'8" or 6⁸
D1
See Schedule

Methods of Indicating Sizes of Doors on Floor Plans

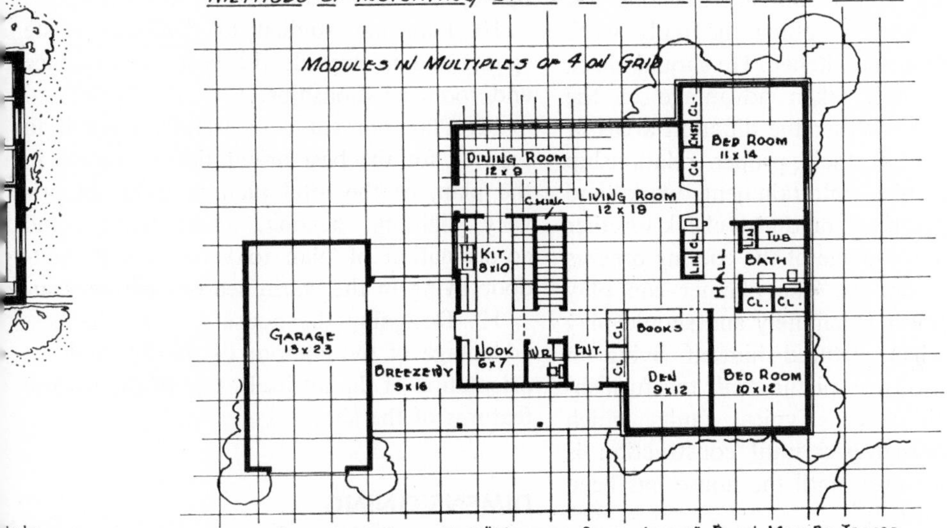

Modules in Multiples of 4 on Grid
Dining Room 12 x 9
Living Room 12 x 19
China
Bed Room 11 x 14
CL.
CHST.
Kit. 8 x 10
LIN
Tub
Bath
Hall
CL.
Garage 13 x 23
Breezeway 9 x 16
Nook 6 x 7
WR
Ent.
Books
Den 9 x 12
Bed Room 10 x 12

Floor Plan Based Upon "Modular Coordinates". Plan May Be Traced Over a "Grid" of the Coordinates Previously Drawn or Coordinates May Be Drawn Lightly on the Plan Sheet

...ing
...tance

...nts of
...erior &
...rior,

...ans in Different Techniques

Fig. 167

10. Locate electrical outlets, fixtures, switches with the proper symbols (Step 4, Fig. 166).

Checking for planning faults. The planner must visualize the relation of room to room, the location of windows, the location of doors, and trace a route beginning at the front door and on through the house. He must assume an abundance of curiosity about every square inch as he passes through. He must go through all openings shown on the plan, but think of them as doorways, and visualize the partition walls. Doors must be tried to make sure they swing the most convenient way. He should sit in different parts of the room to see whether it is convenient, pleasant, and will contain the necessary furnishings. He should stand at the kitchen cabinet or sink and check on the convenience, lighting, and so on; and see how far you have to walk in doing the daily work accomplished in the kitchen. He should check to see if he has taken advantage of the best views, see whether the different areas of the house are in their proper relationship for privacy, quiet, entertainment, work, and so on. The planner should also check whether he has taken advantage of the cooling breezes for summer comfort. The planner can play this game almost indefinitely and should play it until he has pictured himself living in every room and has pictured all the furnishings in their place. Typical faults which often go undiscovered until construction is under way, or even until the house has been lived in, are listed:

1. Doors are often placed where they interfere with each other, or present an awkward direction of swing (Figs. 109 and 124).

2. Stairways planned without enough headroom, or in such a way that furniture cannot be maneuvered up them (Fig. 30).

3. Closets indicated under a stairway where there is not enough height to place the door shown on the plan. (Twelve steps are necessary for average allowance.)

4. Passageways too narrow to be of practical use.

5. Garages planned too narrow to allow opening of car doors, too short to allow for new models, and not enough room around car to maneuver loading or unloading (Fig. 13).

6. Chimneys poorly located for efficient operation of the heating system. No consideration given as to how they may line up with other floors and thus project into rooms (Figs. 166 and 168).

7. Convenience outlets not placed in such a way that several furniture arrangements can be used.

8. Natural lighting not used to best advantage.

9. Rooms not planned to best advantage for convenience, circulation through to rest of house, or accommodations as to its purpose.

10. Plan not studied to eliminate waste space, and to provide the best use of space and room relationships.

11. Plan not studied carefully enough to provide for the best orientation of rooms in the plan, or the total plan in terms of privacy, lighting, heating, street noises, and co-ordination of plan to accommodate outdoor living in the warm seasons of the year.

12. Designing the house to take the best advantage of the contour of the lot, and the orientation of the lot itself. Use of the natural features of the site.

DIMENSIONING

The general principles of dimensioning a drawing as given in the basic course of mechanical drawing apply to architectural drawings with modification. It is presumed in this text that the student has learned the fundamentals of drawing and especially the principles of dimensioning as a prerequisite to the study advanced in this textbook.

The correct dimensioning of architectural drawings requires a knowledge of the meth-

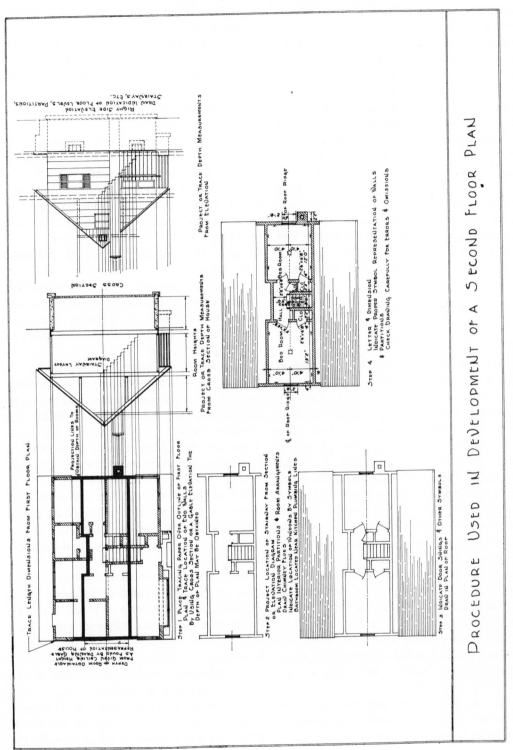

PROCEDURE USED IN DEVELOPMENT OF A SECOND FLOOR PLAN

Fig. 168

ods used in building construction. Dimensions should be so placed that they are most convenient for the workman using them, rather than for the convenience of the draftsman making the drawing. They should be given only on accessible points and in the manner that the workman lays out his work, and chosen so that variations in sizes of materials will not affect the general dimensions. It will be noted that dimensions are placed on all four sides of the plan view, with the dimension figures placed to read from the bottom and right side of the drawing. Architectural draftsmen usually place the dimension figure above the dimension line rather than making a break in the center of the line (Fig. 169). The detail dimensions

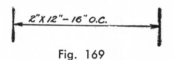

Fig. 169

are kept farther away from the plan than is usual in mechanical drawing since they are often placed at 18 in. in the scale used for the drawing. These practices will vary according to the techniques used by individual draftsmen. Some draftsmen then place the over-all dimension 12 in. outside the detail dimensions. The detail dimensions are given completely along the full wall so that when added they will total the same as the over-all dimension. Any projection such as a porch, fireplace, dinette, or bay window, should be dimensioned independently. If any side of the building is irregular in outline a subtotal should be given, keeping 12 in. between all dimension lines as a minimum. Some draftsmen indicate room sizes by a note lettered in the plan giving width and then length of the room, but in finished drawings it is safer to run dimension lines to the center of the partitions. These lines should run entirely through the building so that this total can be checked against the over-all dimension.

Compared with the dimensioning tech-

niques employed in other fields of drawing, architectural working drawings will seem overdimensioned. No dimension needed by a tradesman should be omitted on an architectural drawing, even though that dimension could be calculated by the addition or subtraction of other dimensions on the sheet or on other sheets.

It will be noted that most dimensions are kept outside of the plan; that they are given to the outside face of masonry walls, and to the outside of studs (or sheathing) in frame walls; to the center of studs in partition walls; to the center of door and window openings, frame partitions, beams, and columns; that vertical dimensions and glass sizes are given on elevations; and that door and window sizes are given on the plan by a note related to the symbol, or in a schedule which is identified by a letter. Schedules are commonly used to complete a description (Figs. 167, 179–194).

Legibility is of utmost importance in dimensioning. All numerals must be carefully lettered so there can be no possibility of misinterpretation. Arrowheads should be carefully made (architectural draftsmen sometimes use dots or very small circles, or a wider proportioned arrowhead for their purpose). Practice regarding extension or witness lines varies with draftsmen and with the character of the work. In some cases, extension lines are allowed to touch the object; in others a gap is left, as in mechanical drawing.

1. The scale to which a drawing is made must be placed in some conspicuous place, generally in the title strip or block. If several details are drawn to different scales, each detail should indicate the scale to which it is drawn.

2. Preliminary studies are usually drawn at ¼ in. equals 1 ft. scale.

3. Details should be drawn to as large a scale as possible, considering the size of the sheet and the importance of the detail. The

common scales for building details range from ¾ in. equals 1 ft. up to 3 in. equals 1 ft.

4. All drawings should be so dimensioned that it will be unnecessary at any time for the workman to measure the distance to find the dimension.

5. Drawings are always dimensioned actual size regardless of the scale.

6. Floor plans and elevations for residences are usually drawn at a scale of ¼ in. equals 1 ft. but may be drawn to ³⁄₁₆ in. equals 1 ft., ⅛ in. equals 1 ft., or ¹⁄₁₆ in. equals 1 ft.

7. Dimensions and notes should be placed at least ¼ in. away from the drawing.

8. Plans are dimensioned on all four sides. Dimensions indicating horizontal measurements should be read from the bottom of the sheet.

9. All notes should be placed either horizontally or vertically.

10. On architectural drawings, dimension lines are made continuous and the dimension figure is placed above the line (see Fig. 169).

11. On architectural drawings, dimensions of 12 in. and over are given in feet and inches.

12. Over-all dimensions as well as detail dimensions of parts should be given. When possible, a series of dimensions should be given along one straight line across the drawing.

13. A horizontal division line should be used for fractions, but the slanting division is acceptable.

14. Over-all dimensions should be placed well outside the drawing, shorter dimensions being placed inside.

15. All dimensions should be subordinate to the shape description.

16. Dimensions never should be put on center lines.

17. All distances, such as windows, piers, and so on, must be tied up to center lines or working edges. Dimensions should always be given to the face of masonry walls, to the outside of studs in outer frame walls (or outside of sheathing), to the center of frame partitions, to the center line of beams, girders, and columns, and to the center line of door and window openings. These dimensions should be given in such a way that variations in stock sizes will not affect the results.

18. Center lines should be placed through the centers of all circles, openings, and symmetrical drawings.

19. Drawings should be dimensioned to center lines of circles and not to circumferences. Circles are dimensioned by their diameters, arcs by their radii. All radii should be marked R. or Rad. and all diameters Dia.

20. Break section lines for dimension or note if placed within a sectioned area.

21. All dimension drawings should be completely figured for the workman. Such dimensions as will be needed by the workman in laying out the work must be given.

22. To find the over-all, all detail dimensions should be added, instead of scaling the drawing to find the distance.

23. Story height must be dimensioned from finished floor to finished floor.

24. Drawings must be checked to see that complete dimensions are given for all openings — width and height of sill above the finished floor.

25. The swing of doors and windows should be shown. The thickness of doors is not always given in plans, the specifications usually covering same, but where doors vary considerably, it may be an additional help to show sizes on plans. Often door and window sizes are given by a schedule shown on the plan.

26. Sizes of glass in windows are usually placed on the elevation.

27. Doors and width of openings are shown on the plans.

28. Work should be done to the com-

mercial or stock sizes of lumber, windows, doors, and so on.

29. Doors vary from 1⅛ to 1¾ in. thick. The 1⅛-in. thickness is used for very light construction, 1⅜ in. for interior doors, and 1¾ in. for exterior doors.

30. In width and height doors vary from 2 by 6 ft. to 3 by 8 ft.

31. Doors are always measured by width, height, and thickness. Example: 2 ft. 6 in. by 6 ft. 8 in. by 1⅜ in.

32. A sash usually indicates only one piece to fill an opening.

33. The term *window* indicates two pieces — the upper and the lower sashes.

34. When ordering sash, the size of glass, the number of lights, opening, thickness, and plain or check rail should be given.

35. When referring to window frames, sash, glass, door, or any opening on an elevation, width is given first; height, second, and may be expressed as 30 x 24, 30/24, or 30–24, meaning in each case 30 in. wide and 24 in. high.

36. Heights of windows vary according to the type of building, the average practice being to place the sill 20 to 24 in. above the finished floor for 9-ft. ceilings.

37. When possible, the tops of doors and windows should line up for height.

38. Bedroom window sills vary from 18 to 20 in. in height. Dining-room and living-room windows may be slightly higher.

39. Kitchen windows should clear the top of sink.

40. A key to the symbols used for materials should always accompany every drawing, regardless of an accepted set of conventions.

41. On every complete set of plans, the size, spacing, and direction of joists should be shown. This may be done on a partial section at the side of an elevation, or it may be shown on the floor plans (see Fig. 169). It is especially useful where the directions of the floor joists change several times on the same floor. Unless the word *above* appears

directly below the line it shall be understood to apply to the joist of the floor on which the note is put.

42. The names of the various rooms in plans and elevations should be inserted between light guide lines ⅛ to 3/16 in. apart (proportional to the size of the drawing), placed centrally in the room and parallel to the front lines of the house.

43. All dimensions of partitions should be given to centers, or from center to outside walls.

44. Dimension notes and figures should be made proportional to the size of the drawing.

45. Height of "Front, Rear, and Side Elevations" should be 3/16 in.

46. All subtitles on details should be proportional to the size of the drawing and their importance.

47. All notes on drawings should be made with capital letters between light guide lines spaced from 1/16 in. to ⅛ in. high depending on the containing area.

48. No attempt should be made to draw in each brick, tile, shingle, or siding, as the case may be, on elevations. It is necessary simply to spot in a few small, irregular areas of the material, always placing a note to name the material, these notes to be 1/16 to ⅛ in. high.

In representing objects that are larger than can be drawn to their actual or full size, it is necessary to reduce the size of the drawing in some regular proportion, and the architect's scale is used for the purpose. The scale ¼ in. equals 1 ft. 0 in. is the usual one used for house plans and is referred to by architects as "quarter scale." This term should not be confused with the term "quarter size" as the former means ¼ in. equals 1 ft. while the latter means ¼ in. equals 1 in. In architectural drawing the statement will be given in terms of in. to the ft. It should always be remembered that, in stating the scale, the first figure refers to the drawing and the second to the object drawn. The important thing in drawing to scale is to think of each dimension as being

SCALES ON ARCHITECTURAL DRAWINGS

Scale = 12" = 1'–0", 1 Foot, 1 Ft. (Full size).
     6" = 1'–0", 1 Foot, 1 Ft. (Half size), ($\frac{1}{2}$ size).
     3" = 1'–0", 1 Foot, 1 Ft. (Quarter size), ($\frac{1}{4}$ size).
     1½" = 1'–0", 1 Foot, 1 Ft. (Eighth size), ($\frac{1}{8}$ size).
     1" = 1'–0", 1 Foot, 1 Ft. (One-twelfth size), ($\frac{1}{12}$ size).
     ¾" = 1'–0", 1 Foot, 1 Ft. (One-sixteenth size), ($\frac{1}{16}$ size).
     ½" = 1'–0", 1 Foot, 1 Ft. (One-twenty-fourth size), ($\frac{1}{24}$ size).
     ⅜" = 1'–0", 1 Foot, 1 Ft. (One-thirty-second size), ($\frac{1}{32}$ size).
     ¼" = 1'–0", 1 Foot, 1 Ft. (One-forty-eighth size), ($\frac{1}{48}$ size).
     $\frac{3}{16}$" = 1'–0", 1 Foot, 1 Ft. (One-sixty-fourth size), ($\frac{1}{64}$ size).
     ⅛" = 1'–0", 1 Foot, 1 Ft. (One-ninety-sixth size), ($\frac{1}{96}$ size).
     $\frac{3}{32}$" = 1'–0", 1 Foot, 1 Ft. (One-one hundred twenty-eighth size), ($\frac{1}{128}$ size).
     $\frac{1}{16}$" = 1'–0", 1 Foot, 1 Ft. (One-one hundred ninety-second size), ($\frac{1}{192}$ size).

in its full size and not in the reduced (or enlarged) size it happens to be drawn to on the paper. Some of the statements of scale as indicated on architectural drawings are shown above.

Notes and Specifications. There should be on architectural drawings clear, explicit notes regarding materials, construction, and finish even though they may be included in the specifications. The builder may overlook a mention in the specifications but will see a reference or note on a drawing calling attention to the explanation in the specifications. A schedule is a systematic way of presenting information given in notes, for they give in tabular form the detailed information taken from the specifications, thus making the information more convenient to the workman. These schedules are usually placed on a plan drawing and include information on finish, hardware, doors, windows, and so on (Fig. 167).

NOTE: Since the floor plans are only in the layout stage, no attempt should be made to darken them in as finished drawings as yet. All of the drawings included in the complete set of working drawings are drawn lightly until all the *planning* has been done and all the work carefully checked for all errors. This finishing stage used in the making of a set of plans will be indicated later in its proper order of working.

Second Floor Planning. The first floor plan is usually drawn first on tracing paper and drawn *very lightly* so that errors may be easily corrected (Fig. 168). Next a piece of tracing paper may be fastened over the top of the first floor plan. Utilizing the main outlines of the first floor plan as a guide the usable outline of the exterior walls may be drawn in *lightly*. Some variation is to be expected since full room heights are not always possible and they must be obtained from a gable elevation drawing, or from a vertical wall section. Often a roof plan is necessary before a planning of an elevation drawing can be made. The outline of the outside wall will be influenced by possible room heights, dormer windows, chimney locations, and so on. The partition walls will not necessarily match those of the first floor even though a "bearing partition" should be used on the first floor plan. Most often this bearing partition may be duplicated on the second floor by the careful planning of hallway partitions which are extended as a support for the roof. In good planning the windows on the second floor are placed as often as possible above those on the first floor, giving a better appearance in design and also making a saving in the framing when the balloon frame is used since the studs are doubled around the opening and continued for the full height of the house. If a bathroom is to be planned for the second floor, it should be arranged directly over the plumbing in the

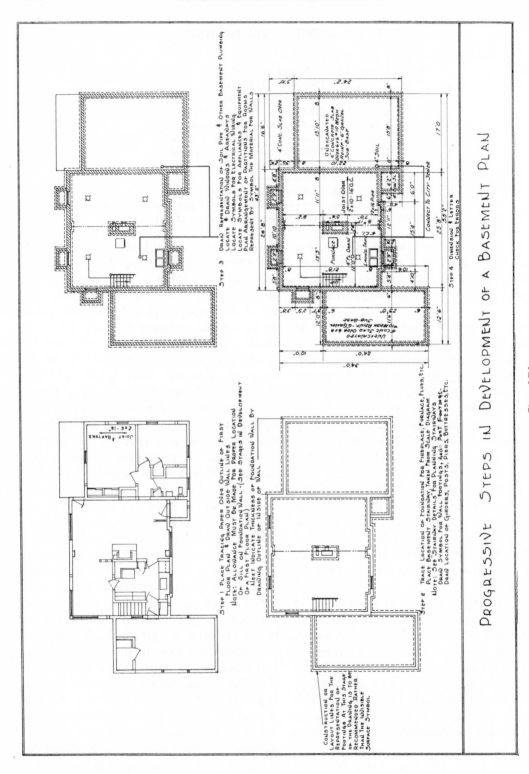

Fig. 170

PROGRESSIVE STEPS IN DEVELOPMENT OF A BASEMENT PLAN

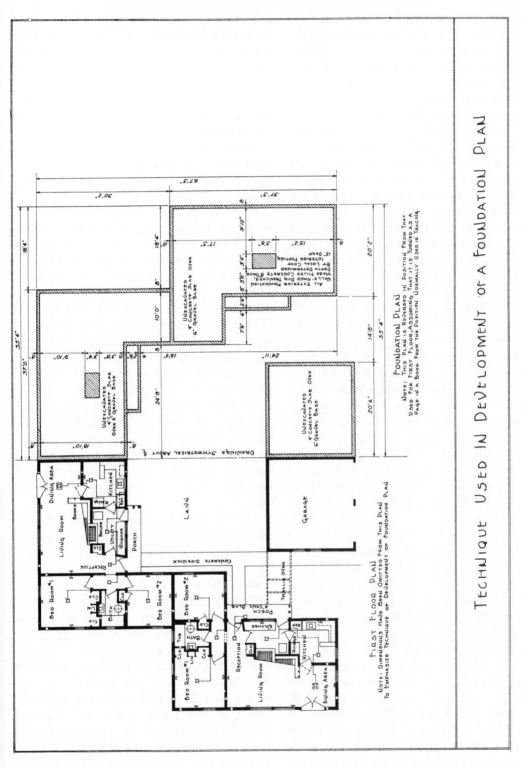

Technique Used In Development of a Foundation Plan

Fig. 171

kitchen or the first floor bathroom for economy reasons. It is also most important to study the stairway location that the upstairs hallway can be as centrally located as possible, providing easy access to all rooms.

Basement Planning. Similar procedure is followed in drawing the plans for the basement, for the outline can be traced from the first floor plans (Fig. 170). The outside of the foundation wall should be aligned with the measurement indicating the outside of the sheathing on the first floor plan (Fig. 171). The thickness of the wall then is determined by the material used in making the foundation wall. A footing must be properly proportioned to strengthen the foundation wall and indicated on the drawing. Some portions of the basement may be left unexcavated but foundations and footings are shown on the plan for these areas. Walls and footings must be provided for such areas as areaways around the basement windows, stair wells for outside stairways, porches, and steps for both front and side doors. The basement plan is often used to indicate the plans for plumbing, and heating systems while in larger buildings separate plans are drawn for each trade. In small buildings the tradesman usually plans his own layout from the floor plan of the house. The basement plan usually provides an area for the heating plant, an area for fuel storage (the oil tank is often placed underground and outside of the basement), storage for fruit and vegetables, laundry, hobby rooms, work areas, and recreation rooms. The foundation walls must in every case extend below the frost level of the particular area in which the house is to be built.

Foundation walls with footings are required between excavated and unexcavated parts of the plan, not only to support the girder and joists but also to act as retaining walls for unexcavated earth. Openings 2 ft. 0 in. wide should be provided to unexcavated areas. Twelve inch vent openings are left in the foundation walls of unexcavated areas for air circulation and for drying any moisture.

The draftsman is usually unable to complete a plan without some idea of the elevations and associated details. It would be impossible to know whether the basement windows will require areaways unless the difference in height of the windows and the distance between the top of the foundation wall and the finished grade line is known.

The outline of the chimney can be traced from the first floor plan and located by dimensions from the inner faces of the foundation walls.

Often the span from wall to wall in the basement is too long for ordinary length joists. Such a condition requires a support in the form of a girder so that two or more joists may be used to span the basement. Even if the joists are long enough they may sag and require support. Eight-inch steel I beams are often used to support the joists with 4-in. lally columns set on 24-in. concrete footings supporting the I beam at approximately 8 ft. 0 in. intervals. To make the top of the girder level with the foundation wall, it is necessary to notch the wall at both ends so that the girder can be set in the wall. A minimum of 4-in. bearing surface for the I beam is required in the wall. Where large openings occur in the plan as for the garage door, no foundation wall or footing is required but is often used.

Dimensioning the basement plan is similar to that followed for the first floor plan, except that dimensions are taken from one outside face to the other outside face of the concrete wall, or from the inside face of the concrete wall for interior dimensions. Dimensions for windows or vents are those of the rough opening size, or the face of masonry to the face of masonry.

Roof Plan. In small homes the roof plan may be indicated on the second floor plan or the first floor plan depending upon the height of the house. Lines are indicated around the outline of the plan representing the overhang of the roof beyond the walls, and lines then drawn within this area representing the intersections of the various planes. There are situations requiring that the plan of the roof be drawn before elevations can be completed, because the intersection points can only be found in the plan. Sometimes in larger buildings a separate plan is drawn for the roof (Figs. 196 and 198).

Framing Plans. A complete set of working drawings does not always include framing plans since the floor plans, elevations, and details are generally sufficient for a competent builder to build the house. The architect or draftsman must, however, understand the principles of framing and must have a working knowledge of the methods used in framing in order to do a good job in house planning. It is the responsibility of the architect to supervise the builder in correct framing and construction so that the job is accomplished according to accepted practice and local building codes. See Unit I, "House Construction."

In drawing the framing plans the student must know the structural members used in framing and know the purpose of each. (For examples of these see Figures 184–192.) Spacing of joists and ceiling beams is usually 16 in. from center to center. Sometimes, however, it is necessary to place the joists at fixed positions that do not fall on the 16-in. spacings because of a partition located between two joists. In such cases joists must often be placed in multiples of twos or threes directly under the partition for additional bracing and strength. Such construction should always be used under a bearing partition. Headers are similar to joists except that they are used around openings such as the opening for the stair well and those around the fireplace and chimney. Headers are placed at right angles to the regular joists and are used to carry the load of the ends of those joists cut to make the opening. These headers are doubled regardless of their length. Headers resting on the sill around the foundation wall need not be doubled. Tail beams are the joists cut to butt against the headers around openings. The longer the tail beams, the greater the load

distribution to the header. The beams running parallel to the joists and at right angles to the header, framing the sides of the opening are called trimmers. Trimmers are regular floor joists but are doubled. To keep the joists in alignment and to help to distribute the load, 1 by 3-in. or 1¼ by 3-in. pieces are nailed crosswise between the joists. This procedure is called cross bridging. If joist spans are 10 ft. 0 in. or under, one row of cross bridging should be used as a minimum. In spans greater than 14 ft. 0 in. two rows of bridging are necessary, since this bridging should not be further than 7 ft. 0 in. to 8 ft. 0 in. apart.

In drawing a floor framing plan, trace the outline of the foundation wall from the basement plan, then locate the sill set back from the wall far enough to allow room for the sheathing to come flush. Next draw in the supporting girder if the width of the house requires it. The joists usually run crosswise of the plan or across the narrow way to make use of shorter lengths and making the floor stronger. The girder usually divides the width but may be conveniently located under the partition walls. Draw in the joists, headers, trimmers, and tail beams at their proper spacing. Where overhead partitions are parallel to the floor joists, draw the joists double for the extra support. Keep joists and all framing members a minimum distance of 2 in. from the brickwork of a chimney. The double header for the hearth should be 1 ft. 8 in. from the face of the fireplace to allow for the hearth. Where the span of the joists exceeds 14 ft. 0 in. the joists are spaced at 12 in. on centers to give added strength to a floor supporting heavier equipment, such as furnace, refrigerator, piano, automatic washing machine.

The second floor framing plan is developed in much the same manner as that for the first floor except that the foundation wall is not represented. Instead a 2 by 4-in. plate is nailed to the first floor, and the studs forming the first floor walls and partitions rest on

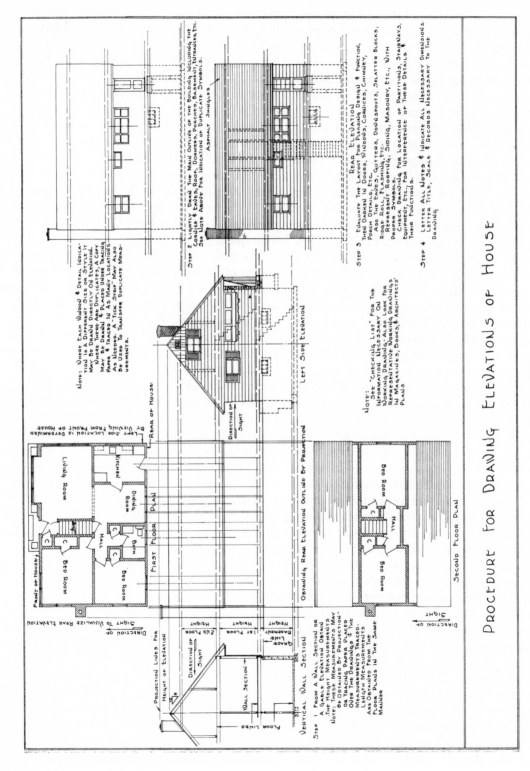

PROCEDURE FOR DRAWING ELEVATIONS OF HOUSE

Fig. 172

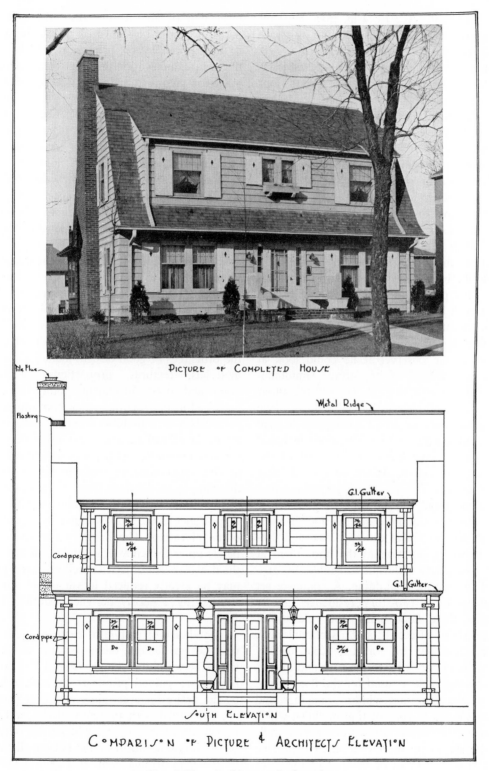

PICTURE OF COMPLETED HOUSE

COMPARISON OF PICTURE & ARCHITECTS ELEVATION

Fig. 173. Architectural elevations.

this sole or sill. A 2 by 4-in. plate caps off the top of the studs and the ceiling joists are supported on this structure. Bearing partitions supporting the ends of the ceiling joists should also be indicated on this second floor framing plan. The stairwell can be traced from the first floor plan, and the proper headroom allowed. The headers and trimmers are doubled for extra support.

Architectural Elevations. Most people who are interested in building houses feel competent to set their ideas on paper in the form of floor plans from which houses can be built by the tradesmen (Fig. 167). There is another step which must be taken in the form of drawings and other information which will enable the builders to carry out the construction. This procedure calls for a person familiar with building construction.

An elevation is one of the views of an upright side of the building drawn as it would appear to the observer if he could look at every square foot of its surface simultaneously, and could not see any of the other three sides at the same time (Fig. 173). Since most houses are square or rectangular in plan there will usually be four elevations included in a plan of the house. Every part of the exterior wall can be drawn on one of these four drawings. When a plan is irregular, other elevations parallel to the walls may be necessary. The elevation indicates the floor heights, heights and widths of the openings, and outside finish. In addition to the floor plan, at least two exterior elevations should be provided to describe a building. A complete set of plans for a two-story residence usually includes three floor plans, four elevations, several sheets of details, and a sectional view.

The elevations are drawn to scale, usually ¼ in., ³⁄₁₆ in., or ⅛ in. to the foot and always to the same scale as used for the floor plans. All of the door and window openings and other features of construction or finish which occur on the outside surface of exterior walls can be shown on the elevation in their true scale size. The offset or amount of recess or

projection of any feature from the face of the wall cannot be shown on an elevation. It is this principle of projection which distinguishes an elevation drawing from a photograph or picture drawing, which produces a picture of a building rather than a single plane representation (Fig. 173). The elevation drawings must agree with the plans in giving the general dimensions of the house and the location of openings on each floor, as well as such features as cornices, water tables, corner trim, balconies, porches, terraces, bay windows, and stairways. Taken together the plans and elevations give the length, width, and height of every part of the house.

It is the ability on the part of the designer to see the house in his mind's eye before it has been built which makes it possible for him to draw the elevations. An elevation is more difficult for the beginner to visualize than a plan, for attention is here directed to the principles of good design, including color, materials, textures, proportions, balance, unity, and so on. Visualizing ability must be exercised to imagine the actual appearance or perspective of a building from its elevations. Roofs in elevations are often misleading to persons unfamiliar with projection drawings, as the appearance of roofs in single plane drawings is so different from the appearance of the roofs when the building is finished. Appearance is the first essential in the design of an elevation. The merit of the style depends upon the knowledge and good taste of the designer. An otherwise well-arranged plan may be greatly reduced in value and attractiveness by a poorly designed exterior (Fig. 174).

The choice of a style of elevation depends upon several factors, the importance of which varies between individuals (Fig. 175). Some people are guided primarily by cost, others by the desire for a certain style. Most people are concerned with the convenience and arrangement of rooms and will let the outside of the house conform to the pattern dictated by the plan arrangement. If a central hall is

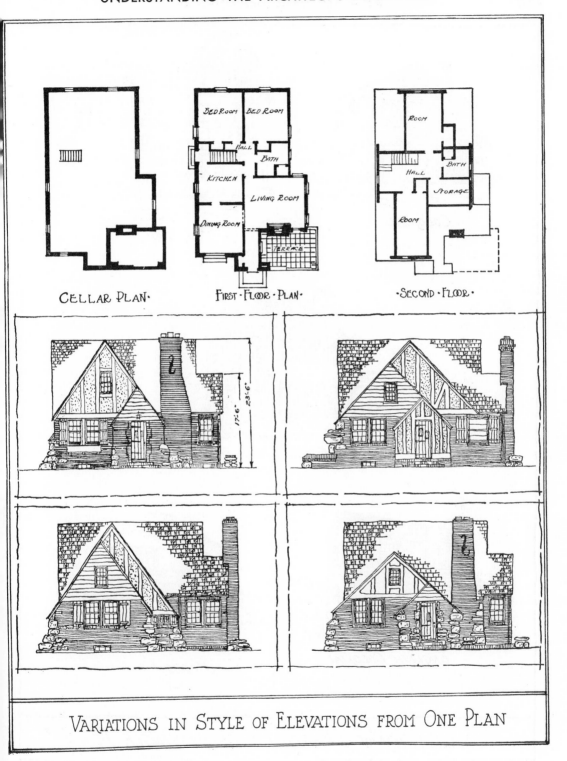

CELLAR PLAN·   ·FIRST·FLOOR·PLAN·   ·SECOND·FLOOR·

VARIATIONS IN STYLE OF ELEVATIONS FROM ONE PLAN

Fig. 174

COLONIAL

GEORGIAN

FRENCH MANOR

ENGLISH COLONIAL

MODERN

VARIATIONS POSSIBLE FROM SINGLE PLAN

Fig. 175

used, the exterior will probably develop into one of the formal styles such as Modern, Georgian, or Cape Cod. A rambling floor plan is best adapted to one of the English exteriors or Modern. If a central court is used, a California style will adapt itself. The Modern style can be adapted to any arrangement featuring large window areas which may extend to, and around the corner of the building. The flat roof makes for a square, boxlike appearance which can be improved by giving consideration to the relative height of walls and the spacing of windows. A few possible variations worked out from a single floor plan are shown in Figures 174 and 175.

The choice of material is governed by style and by cost. Most styles can be used with or applied to any one of several materials, or in combinations. Brick and siding, brick and stone, brick and stucco, shingles and siding, for instance, all can be used in combinations and in interesting design. The type of roof is also to be given careful thought, particularly in those styles requiring large roof areas. Materials will often vary in cost depending upon nearness to the source of the material.

When the choice of style has been carefully thought out, several sketches should be made before a final choice is made. These sketches should be corrected and changes studied before the resulting choice will produce a satisfactory design (Figs. 152 and 155). It is best to make sketches on tracing paper through which the lines of the drawing are visible, and to place a sheet of tracing paper over the work done each time a change or new study is desired. Sometimes these thumbnail sketches are made on graph or cross-section paper which saves time in keeping the sketches to proportion. The use of graph paper makes it convenient to locate the openings on elevations in the correct proportions corresponding to their locations on the sketch studies of the plan. If the sketches of both plan and elevation have been drawn on squared paper, the openings and features can be readily drawn to agree in plan and elevation, in showing the location and size. The elevations show the heights of all openings in the exterior walls as well as the height of these features above the finished level of the floors. The distances from the tops of the openings to the finished ceiling levels are shown. In starting a sketch it is important to draw the horizontal lines representing the levels of the floors and ceilings.

It is necessary to have an understanding of the standard sizes of wall openings such as for windows and doors, and the sizes for trim which may be used in the exterior treatment. Outside doors are usually 2 ft. 8 in. by 6 ft. 8 in., 2 ft. 10 in. by 6 ft. 8 in., 3 ft. 0 in. by 6 ft. 8 in., 2 ft. 8 in. by 7 ft. 0 in., 2 ft. 10 in. by 7 ft. 0 in., and 3 ft. 0 in. by 7 ft. 0 in. The larger sizes are used at the front entrance and the smaller sizes at the rear or side entrance. Exterior doors must be carefully planned to accommodate carrying furniture through them. A millwork catalog should be available so that standard stock sizes of doors are used because they are more economical. A study should be made of the sizes ordinarily used in house construction. The sizes of windows are usually about 2 ft. 6 in. by 3 ft. 6 in. up to 3 ft. 0 in. by 4 ft. 0 in. for double-hung windows, but half windows and three-quarter windows are used for particular situations. Casement windows of either wood or steel may be of various widths and heights as found in the catalogs. If the windows are divided into panes, each pane will usually be about 8 in. by 10 in. or 12 in. high. The windows may be made up in a variety of styles to fit the individual taste.

Exterior moldings are found in the cornice, casings around doors and windows, water table, belt courses, porch columns, caps, bases, and so on. Their use affords a decorative treatment of otherwise bare surfaces and also indicates the style used. Their projecting, receding, or curved planes produce the softening effects of shade and shadows. Most moldings are based upon the classic Greek or

Roman curves. Stock moldings carried by lumberyards and millwork companies are not always found in these carefully designed shapes, so care must be taken to insure good proportions.

If the walls of a house are made of brick it is necessary in the finished elevations to work out carefully the sizes and locations of openings so that the brickwork can be built around the openings with as few odd or cut sizes of brick as possible. Such planning will improve the appearance and reduce the cost. Some openings may have brick arches over the heads supported by steel angle lintels. The bricks may be laid on end, on edge, or on their face giving variety in design. The sills may be of brick, wood, stone, or concrete, and may be the width of the opening or may extend into the wall on each side. Although bricks are approximately of the same size, those made in different parts of the country or in different yards vary in size. Both the width and height dimensions of openings should measure up to an even numbered whole or uncut bricks and joints. The thickness of the mortar joints are adapted to the size of the brick, and the area to be covered. Thus the opening size is made to a multiple or module of 8 in., sometimes to a multiple of 4 in. when headers are used. Bricks may be represented by horizontal lines spaced approximately the thickness of bricks apart. A few vertical joints may be represented to add interest to the drawing. These representations may be artistically arranged in patches with a note added to explain the symbol. In some places the actual representation of bricks may be needed. See Plate 1, page 24.

The shingles are indicated in elevation by horizontal lines spaced a distance apart to represent the amount of shingle exposed to the weather. A few vertical lines may be drawn to make the drawing more artistic and interesting, but none of these representations are given by actual measurement. The representation need not completely cover the roof, but may be placed in scattered patches inter-estingly arranged and a note used to explain the symbol. Often wavy or jagged lines and breaks are carefully added to the representation. Flashing is shown around all locations where the intersections of roof occur. The roof height is obtained by a projection of a gable end of the house, and is determined by the room needed on the second floor and attic and by the style of house. Sometimes a roof framing plan is necessary to help draw the elevation. Each material used on a roof has its own symbol. Each material is usually adapted to a certain style of house. Where roofs are designed to different combinations of pitches and at different heights, these distinctions must be clearly shown in the elevation. The representation of these materials is similarly made on wall elevations. The actual spacing of shingles, siding, etc., must be given in the specifications, and can also be shown in the notes used on elevation drawings. The finish at the ridge of the roof should be clearly shown.

The window elevations should be carefully drawn to size and detail. If these drawings are all made on tracing paper, it is necessary to draw only once each representation of a window. This window drawing may be drawn on a scrap of paper, aligned in its proper location, and traced on the elevation drawing of the building. Thus it is necessary to draw an elevation drawing on the scrap of paper each time a window varies to size, kind, or detail. At this stage of the drawing, spacing and location of the windows may then be considered according to the accommodation of the room arrangement inside the house, and to the appearance and design on the outside of the house, and to the spacing between framing members. The design of the window and location in the wall and in the room must be carefully studied so that it fulfills its purpose and harmonizes with the style of the house. The modern tendency is to simplify the trim used in the construction of a house. The finish at the corners of a building should be studied and represented. Gutters and downspouts are indicated by symbol and note on elevations. The elevation of gable ends of houses shows the representation of trim following the sloping lines where the walls meet the roofs, and the finish of the end of the roof proper. In brick walls the trim may consist of arches over the windows and quoins at the corners of the building, or there may be practically no trim used. The monotonous appearance of walls and surfaces may be improved by several devices in design and construction. Brickwork on walls may be relieved by a variety in the bonding of the bricks, types of joints used, color of brick, finish and size of brick, and other interesting variations.

Foundation walls and footings are studied in relation to the ground level or grade, and everything below the grade level is shown by dotted lines. Windows placed below grade get their light from areaways. The basement wall height is adjusted to meet conditions such as the style of house, amount of height needed in the basement, frost level, flood conditions, and so on. The basement height may be adjusted in placing the first floor joists above the top of the basement wall. Foundation walls must be indicated under entrance steps, unexcavated area, porches, and so on. The depth of the foundation wall must be carried below frost level which varies with the climate of the locality.

Steps in Drawing an Elevation. A person who is not familiar with the layout and proper procedure of drawing an elevation often has difficulty in obtaining a satisfactory result because he attempts to put in too much detail. By breaking the procedure down into logical sequence the representation may be simplified (Fig. 172). The steps of procedure used in making an elevation are as follows:

1. Become familiar with the floor plan representations and the details of the side of the building to be drawn. The elevation will be drawn to the same scale as the floor plans and actually the width dimensions are traced from the plan. The drawing of the elevations and plans should be carried on together with no attempt made to finish one drawing before proceeding to the other. You should not attempt to complete the plans and then proceed to the elevations. The drawings if made on tracing paper can be laid over each other and locations made and measurements traced through. This particularly applies to all adjustments necessary to represent all openings from plan to elevation and from elevation to plan. The elevations should indicate everything on the outside of the building from the grade line to the chimney caps. The basement wall and all stairs which are hidden are indicated by dotted lines.

2. Decide on the story heights and mark these distances on your sheet. Draw in the floor lines. These floor lines are often inked in for convenience. If the elevation is symmetrical, draw in center lines and ink them.

3. Draw in the grade line representing the surface of the ground. This line should be plainly noted.

4. Draw a wall section at the side of the sheet, starting with the foundation and showing the grade line, floor heights, section of a typical window, section of a water table, section of the cornice, and an indication of the pitch of the roof. Projection lines are used to transfer the vertical measurements from this section across to the elevation drawing. It usually is necessary to draw an end or gable elevation to obtain the true height of the roof, so that a great deal of time can be saved if the front and side elevations can be drawn on the same sheet and developed simultaneously. This procedure is not always possible when the front elevation has a wide frontage. The heights of the windows from the finished floor level are 2 ft. 6 in., 2 ft. 10 in., 3 ft. 0 in., or 3 ft. 10 in., and the minimum head height from the finished floor should be 7 ft. 0 in. The minimum head height is regulated by building code in some areas. The tops of the windows and doors are usually aligned to the same height.

5. Windows, doors, corners of the building, and all vertical ends of the elevation may

be projected or traced from the floor plans. Some draftsmen use a tick strip and transfer the measurements for these vertical lines from the plan to this strip. By placing this strip accurately on the elevation the measurements can be readily transferred.

6. After the windows are blocked in, the details such as muntins, meeting rail, and trim around the outside of the window may be drawn. If the location of the window as roughly blocked in the plan does not meet all requirements of both interior and exterior planning, the window location may be correctly drawn in the elevation and then relocated on the plan by tracing. Leave the center lines in all openings and columns. This gives the drawing a neat appearance and is a great help in drawing the details. A recommended procedure in drawing in several windows of the same size and style is to draw a complete elevation of the window on a small scrap of paper. This drawing must be drawn to the same scale as used on the rest of the plan and elevation. Move this loose drawing under the center lines used to locate the window in the elevation (these center lines have been traced from the location of the window given on the plan). After these openings have been properly located in the elevation, then the symbols may be relocated to agree on the floor plan.

7. Project the cornice details from the section to the elevation. Cornices around dormer windows, porches, and so on are usually in smaller detail and must be kept in proportion.

8. Draw in the front entrance. Work from center lines. Use the same method as in tracing in a window elevation. This eliminates erasing on the drawing plate.

9. Draw in the porches. Pergola effect porches look well on a house with a flat roof. Keep the detail in agreement with the main body of the house. Lattice work softens the lines of a porch if it is well placed and carefully designed.

10. Draw in the dormer windows. Large dormers should be very carefully treated. Dormer windows should have the same general design as the windows in the main portion of the house. The shape of the dormer roof should also correspond with the shape of the main roof.

11. If the stairway is next to an outside wall, it is often shown by dotted lines on that wall to which it is adjacent. This will help on the placement of windows to light the stairway and landings, and also aids in the detailing of the stairway.

12. Draw the trim, moldings, ornament and finish, and all details needed to make the elevation complete. It is common practice to draw a little of the ornament and then add a note stating that the ornament is to be repeated, rather than to draw the ornament in detail on the whole elevation.

13. Siding is indicated on a frame house by horizontal lines. The spacing of these lines indicates the amount of surface to the weather. An explanatory note describing the siding should be added. For brickwork, stone, and similar finishes horizontal lines are used to indicate the joints, with enough vertical joints shown to give the material a realistic appearance. It is not necessary to cover the entire elevation with these elevation symbols for materials, rather they should be located in patches which give an artistic touch to the appearance of the drawing. Dot the stonework and crosshatch the metal flashings.

14. Footings and foundation walls below grade, including areaways, are indicated by dotted lines.

15. The ends of the siding boards at the corners may be mitered for a finish, or may be butted against a corner board. The ends of the siding boards may also be cut square and the joint covered with metal corners which are available. This choice is left to the discretion of the draftsman. Although mitered corners have a more pleasing effect, there is more work required in this kind of construction than if corner boards are used.

16. The chimney must be carefully de-

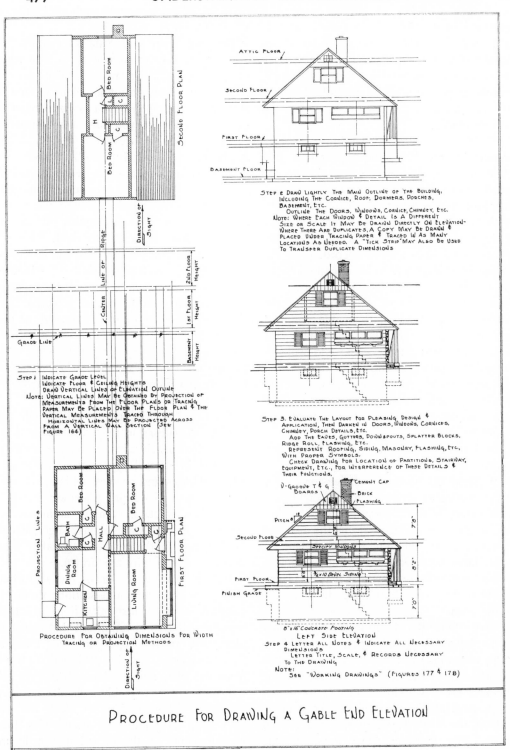

PROCEDURE FOR DRAWING A GABLE END ELEVATION

Fig. 176

signed to accomplish its purpose and also contribute to the design and appearance of the house. It should be drawn a minimum distance of 2 ft. 0 in. above the highest portion of the roof. Its location is traced through from the plans and must be carefully checked. The cap should be carefully designed for use and appearance.

17. The roof must be carefully designed for pitch, construction, and appearance. The height of the roof is usually correctly represented on one of the gable end elevations and then projected across to indicate the height on the other elevations. The representation of the shingles is shown on the elevation by horizontal lines spaced according to the amount of shingle left to the weather. Since this is not a true distance but a projected distance the amount of shingle left to the weather is measured on the gable end and then projected to the other elevations. This one measurement on the gable end will determine the spacing of the lines. Most draftsmen represent the roof covering by sight and appearance rather than by true projection and their several techniques of representation should be studied.

18. Insert all notes and titles in proportion to their importance.

19. Show all necessary dimensions, such as the heights of windows, room height, and all necessary vertical dimensions. Indicate the size of glass on the window in the form of a fraction, that is, place width over height.

20. Draw and letter-in a window and a door schedule. These schedules may be placed on either the sheets containing the elevation or the plan.

NOTE: Since the elevation drawing is only in the layout stage, no attempt should be made at this time to darken it in as a finished drawing. All of the drawings included in the complete set of working drawings are drawn lightly until all the *planning* has been done, and all the work carefully checked for all errors. The finishing stage including the proper darkening of lines used in the making

of a set of plans will be indicated later in its proper order of working.

Drawing Rear and Side Elevations. A common mistake of students is to draw some of the elevations in reverse. This can be avoided by turning the floor plans around so that the wall of the plan to be drawn in elevation is toward you, and then comparing the plans with the elevation while it is still in the layout stage (Fig. 172). Drawing the rear elevation can also be accomplished by turning the tracing of the floor plans with the drawing on the side toward the board, or upside down. To accomplish this do not turn the sheet from left to right. Turn the sheet over so that the rear wall will be toward you. Vertical ends, the width of windows, and doors can then be traced or projected from the plan, and the heights projected from the front elevation or traced through as preferred. The side elevations can be developed in a similar way by proper reversal when placing the plans (Fig. 176). The heights for the side elevations can be projected from the front elevation or traced through.

NOTE: The beginning student will find that the elevations in the layout stage if left in very light pencil layout technique, although complete in general appearance, will require minor changes and corrections later on when roof pitches and framing plans are drawn. It is common practice, even for architects and experienced draftsmen, to make slight changes in drawings in the layout stage after other drawings and details are drawn.

Before starting to draw the elevations, enough of the plans and sections should be roughed in to furnish elevation layout dimensions. It is very important that elevation, plan, and section agree in size, therefore these distances must be projected or traced from the plan and section rather than laid out with a scale. Ticking off the measurements for the wanted points along the edge of a strip of paper and transferring these measurements to the elevation also insures accuracy.

Fundamental Principles in Designing Exteriors (Fenestration). Regardless of whether the plans and elevations are spoken of as separate and independent kinds of drawings, they are so closely related that one cannot be considered without thinking in terms of the other. For this reason the two kinds of drawings are drawn simultaneously, particularly during the layout stage. In developing the plans thought must be given to the exterior appearance. The elevations must be thought of in three dimensions, and they must represent the plan in its prerequisites of utility and appearance through the location of its windows, placing of doors, design and location of bays, gables, chimneys, and projections. These details all influence the exterior appearance and cannot be visualized as they would actually appear without having been correctly represented in the working drawings. To approach the problem of designing elevations it is necessary to become familiar with some of the fundamental principles of design. Design and style do not mean purposeless ornament. Design is a fulfillment of the purpose for which the object or construction is intended with truthful expression of the limitations of the material of which it is constructed. For any style selected there are a few principles of design which must be followed:

1. *Proportion of mass* deals with the shape and size of the total area in sight, with the sizes and relationships of the major and minor divisions. The use of squares and circles for areas, repetition of dimensions of equal size, horizontal division of areas into equal spaces, and use of unrelated structural parts (small homes with large, stubby columns; heavy and wide cornice projections; and large brackets) are some of the common violations of this principle.

2. *Unity* is obtained by observing dominant and subordinate points of emphasis or variation of treatment, as well as by shape and division of the primary mass. To accomplish unity some feature (such as a front entrance or a main gable) must predominate, and other minor details contribute to the design.

3. *Balance* expresses itself in a feeling of stability, rest, and permanence. It is accomplished by arranging portions of the design either symmetrically or unsymmetrically about a center line. In unsymmetrical design a smaller window a greater distance from a centered entrance will balance a larger one near the center, but on the opposite side. The symmetrical design is accomplished by centering an entrance and placing windows of equal size and location on each side.

4. *Harmony* is obtained by adhering strictly to the forms and details of the particular style selected, and avoiding unrelated combinations in the form of foreign elements, unsuitable ornamentation, or color combinations.

A few simple rules may generally be applied in elevation design:

1. Choose some feature to be predominant, such as an entrance, and center it on the elevation, grouping all subordinate features about it. Naturally, the plan and elevation must be in agreement in planning.

2. Details of the building, such as windows, should be lined up vertically on the first and second floors. This gives a better appearance, adds strength to the structure (studs may be doubled around openings and carried from one floor to another), and it is more economical in construction.

3. Structural supports should never be placed in the center of an elevation.

4. Grouped details such as windows, doorways, and arches should be used in odd number multiples.

5. Openings placed near the corners or ends tend to indicate weakness in design.

6. Proportions of windows, doors, archways, and all openings look best when proportioned twice as high as they are wide.

Doorways. The doorway and its immediate surroundings form a center of interest to the approaching visitor. The walk leading up to the entrance, the landscape plantings, the hardware details, lighting, all contribute to the impression given the visitor, which may be of formal dignity or of almost extreme simplicity, and can be controlled by the draftsman or designer. Entrances may be private or service type and should be designed in such a way as to leave no doubt in the mind of the person approaching the house. Lighting should illuminate the doorway and the approach and clearly show the street number.

Outside entrance doorways should be at least 3 ft. 0 in. wide for the convenience of moving furniture and appliances in or out of the house. A tall narrow door gives a feeling of severity which does not contribute to the design of an entrance. A means of observing a visitor on the outside of the door should be provided by means of a small window in the door, or by sidelighted panels. These lights also improve the lighting of the entrance hall. Generally some sort of shelter is suggested at the doorway to keep out rain and snow and give some protection to the visitor. Sometimes the doorway is recessed into the wall to form this shelter.

Placement and Kinds of Windows. The problem of designing the window must be viewed from both sides of the wall. Daylight must be admitted to the rooms at the proper location and in amount as near the ideal as possible. The location and size of the window will depend upon how the light is to be used, how the furniture will be arranged adjacent to the windows, and how the windows will appear on the outside design of the house. Minimum window sizes and amount of light are often specified in city building codes. Correct designing will require that the windows be placed to give consideration to their use in the rooms as well as to their appearance on the exterior of the building.

The glass area of the window may be undivided, or it may be divided into a number of panes (or lights) by means of muntins. When properly proportioned, these small panes present an interesting pattern that is more pleasing than a large undivided glass area. They are, however, more difficult to clean.

The proportion of window height to width must be in harmony with the wall area. Seen from the outside, the design, location, and proportion of windows have a most important effect on the appearance of the house. Windows too large will tend to dwarf the house, and very small ones will make the house appear larger than it really is. The house will tend to appear formal, stiff, or simple and cozy, as the windows are made tall and narrow, or broad and low. The quantity and type of detail, or its absence, will make the window pleasant and hospitable or demanding and stiff in appearance. Second story windows should be located directly above those of the first story, or they should be centered over the blank wall spaces below.

There are several types of windows suited to house planning, but the three most commonly used are the double-hung, casement, and fixed sash. In the double-hung window, the heavy meeting rail where the two sash overlap puts a horizontal line across the window that has the effect of making it appear more squatty than a casement window of the same proportions. Even painting the wood muntins a light color does not counteract this effect entirely.

Vertical Heights Affecting Design. It is generally agreed that the nearer the first floor of a house can be kept to the ground level the better the house will look since it will give the impression of growing out of the ground and being in harmony with it. The first floor of a house can be kept low and the basement still get light through windows by using areaways. If areaways are not wanted the alternative is to have the basement window sills above ground level by using a basement wall which extends enough above the outside ground level to allow sufficient space to use windows above grade.

The height of the ceilings is clearly a matter to be determined by those people interested in the design of the house. In the past it was considered that high ceilings made the house airy and cool during the warmer months, while now the tendency is to make the ceilings lower since this helps reduce the cost. Local building codes sometimes specify minimum ceiling heights. Generally the trend in design now is to keep the house low in height and extend it horizontally rather than vertically. Emphasis on the horizontal trim placed on the design of the house contributes to this styling. Wider cornices, windows wider and shorter in height with horizontal muntins, a rowlock course of brick projecting from the face of the wall and running around the wall of the house, and shutters to decorate the house are all contributing factors to this emphasis.

Roofs. The type and the contour of the roof play an important part in the impression created by the design of the house. Some of the roof styles may be combined with different shapes of floor plans; others are limited to one particular style. The roof line cannot be shown until a plan of the roof has been worked out from the floor plan, and the pitch decided upon in an elevation. The material and color of the roof must be considered from the standpoint of durability, as compared to original cost. Harmony in design, and the effect of color are other important elements of roof design to be considered.

Chimneys. Entirely independent from their utilitarian purpose chimneys play a most important part in the exterior design of a building. Chimneys placed on an outside wall are often made a feature of the house and trimmed at the top with a decorative cap. Where several flues are placed in one chimney the chimney cap should be designed to give a solid substantial appearance. In order to prevent downdrafts chimneys must rise at least two feet above the highest ridge line of the house. This requirement sometimes is a determining factor in its place-

ment for appearance. The chimney is also placed close to the heating plant. The chimney's location affects to some extent the styling of the house, and the efficiency of the heating plant.

Porches, Balconies, Grilles, and Other Details. Avoid meaningless ornamentation. Where these features are more decorative than useful each part must be studied carefully to determine whether they belong in the design. To insure privacy in the modern home, porches are usually placed to face the lawn or garden and often are in the forms of patios, breezeways, and other outdoor living areas. In some types of houses more formal porches are still to be seen occasionally. Window boxes, iron grilles, flower boxes, and lamp brackets can be used effectively if their design and placement are carefully studied. Unbroken wall spaces are not inherently monotonous and often contribute to the quality of restfulness and sincerity which should influence elevation design.

Exterior Finish and Materials. The proper selection of the outside finish and building materials is most important when planning the elevations of the home. Whether it be brick, frame, stone, or a combination of these materials, the design must be considered carefully to guard against violations of the elementary principles of good design. Simplicity and restraint in design and in the use of ornamental effects are points to keep in mind when developing the design.

Using Natural Shades and Shadows. Shadows are important elements in the design of the exterior, and are obtained by producing overhangs and offsets in construction. To plan for effective use of shadows, the direction in which the house faces must be considered in order to determine the direction and amount of shadow at different hours of the day.

Skillful Use of Color. The color, tone, and skillful combination of these help greatly in producing the total effect.

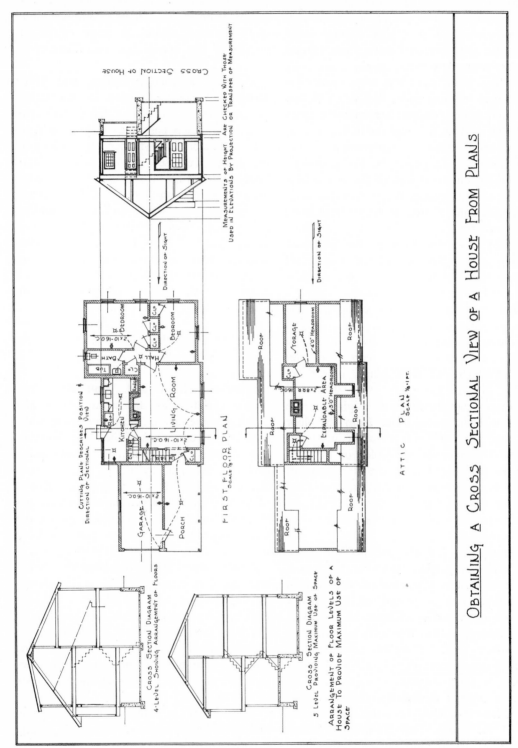

OBTAINING A CROSS SECTIONAL VIEW OF A HOUSE FROM PLANS

Fig. 177

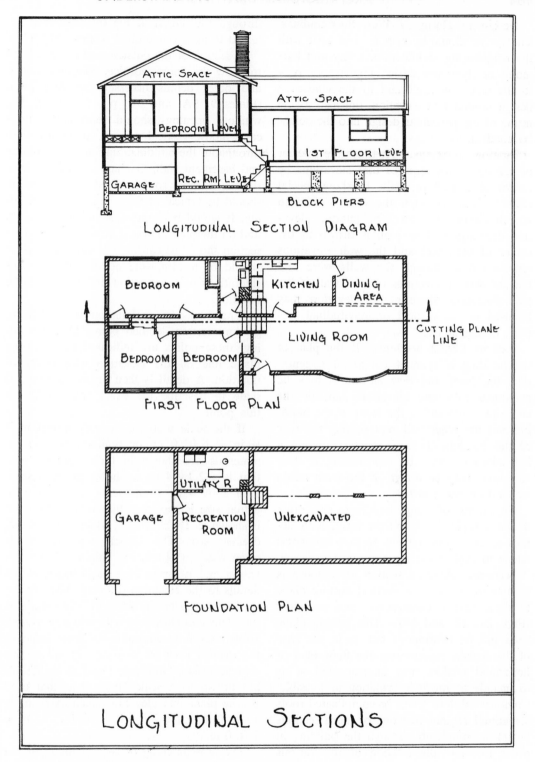

LONGITUDINAL SECTION DIAGRAM

FIRST FLOOR PLAN

FOUNDATION PLAN

LONGITUDINAL SECTIONS

Fig. 178

Design in Harmony With Surroundings.
The design should be kept in good taste with the neighboring architecture. Unity and harmony in style and design applies not only to the elevation itself and to the landscape design around that elevation, but also to the fitting of the particular design into the neighborhood surroundings.

Interior Elevations. At times the interior of certain rooms requires that elevations be drawn of a wall or walls to show special features. This is often the case of kitchen and bathroom interiors. In interior elevation drawings a floor plan is drawn in the center of the sheet and the wall elevations represented as though the walls were laid flat and were projections of each wall of the plan. Sometimes these interior elevations may be used in the vertical or longitudinal sections of the house.

Half or Partial Sections. If the plan of the building is symmetrical about a center line, the front and rear elevations may be combined into one elevation, half of the elevation representing the front of the building and the other half representing the rear of the building. In a U-shaped building a half elevation may be represented, or half elevations may be drawn of the front wings which face the court.

Elevations of long buildings are often drawn completely in outline form, with details given of one typical portion and notes added to explain the repetition of the design.

Sections. A cross section of a house is an interior view on a vertical cutting plane to show interior construction and treatment (Figs. 21, 22, and 177). This cutting plane need not be continuous but as in the case of the section representing the floor plan or horizontal section, may be staggered so as to include as much information as possible. Complicated floor levels or complicated roofs sometimes require that one or more sections be taken completely through the building in order to show the relation of the various parts to each other. If the section is cut through the length of the building, it is referred to as a longitudinal section (Fig. 178).

A section of the outside wall is often used to show the floors, cornice, windows, doors, and other details necessary of description (Plates 9, 9A, and 9B, pp. 156–158). The window openings should represent a typical window vertical section commonly used throughout the building. Similarly, the footing and basement wall, first and other floor constructions, and roof and eave construction should be typical of those used on the building. It would be impossible in most cases to find on the plan the point at which the typical section should be considered, since the section should be a composite of all ordinary considerations of construction detail used on the building.

Where specific explanation is needed regarding certain detailed points of the building, these points are indicated by a cutting plane line on the elevation with reference notation. A detail is then drawn to enlarged scale to describe the exact construction at this point.

If the scale used for drawing a section is ¼ in. = 1 ft. 0 in. or smaller, the sizes of materials are shown in their nominal size, that is a 2 by 4 in. is shown in small scale as a 2 by 4 in. If the scale is enlarged the actual size is shown — that is, a 2 by 4 in. is shown as 1⅝ by 3⅝ in., which is the actual dressed size. The vertical wall section is often used to obtain the heights of the elevation and it serves as a basis in projecting details to the elevation drawing. The vertical section should be drawn to the same scale as the plans and elevations with which it is used. Sometimes it is advisable to draw some of the details, such as moldings, in actual size representation. Otherwise many of the details are drawn to a scale larger than that used on the plans and elevations such as ¾ in. = 1 ft. 0 in., 1½ in. = 1 ft. 0 in., 3 in. = 1 ft. 0 in.

The crosshatching or section lining of the materials shown in section is most important, since it makes the drawing easier for the workman to read and understand. It is important that the symbols for rough and finished lumber be properly used and that the symbols be kept in their correct scale and proportional size.

When making sectional drawings, the draftsman must keep in mind that the building procedure is being recorded on paper, that they are drawn by proceeding exactly as the workman does when actually constructing the building. The draftsman must carefully draw all materials to their correct size, build up the details by using the correct dimensions, so that all heights shown on the section will be correct when used in construction. These measurements must all be measured with a scale and not judged "by eye" or guesswork. The exact construction wanted should be shown by the section drawing.

Details. After the plans, elevations, and sections for a house have been drawn, larger scale drawings of such parts as are not indicated with sufficient construction information are necessary. These are called "detail drawings" or "details" and are intended to serve as a guide to the tradesmen for the more decorative parts of the construction. This part of the construction is known as "finish," when they occur on the outside of the building they are known as "exterior finish," and for the inside they are called "interior finish." It is this fine "detail" of exterior and interior finish which makes the difference in appearance and design (see "House Construction" units, II to XII).

Many years ago the builders were master tradesmen of great skill and long experience. Early buildings were entrusted entirely in their hands without benefit of complete working drawings as now considered necessary. Each builder had his particular way of building which could be identified much as we now use a trademark. In our age it is necessary to specify just how we want each part of the work finished, what size and shape we require for each molding, and what materials should be used. Such drawings are prepared by the architect or draftsman, and the result depends entirely upon his skill and good taste (Figs. 186 and 187).

A detail consists of the necessary views to best describe the construction. Often a single section showing the design, materials, and construction of parts of the building will give the information needed. Many combinations of drawings are used by draftsman familiar with the needs in building construction. Exterior details may consist of the following: chimney caps, dormer windows, gable returns, gable finish, eave finish, cornice, window frames, sash and trim, shutters and blinds, storm sash, screens, porch finish, bay window, front entrance, and so on. Interior details may be required of the following: window trim, door trim, baseboard finish, interior cornices and moldings, paneling, custom built cabinets, bookcases and shelving, fireplace and mantel trim, stairs and trim, and so on. The plan of the building and its construction requirements will determine the number and kinds of drawings to be drawn. Details are located on the sheet and in such a way in groups that each sheet contains the reference notations pertaining to the details and the particular sheet where the details may be found. The reference notes are more often indicated on the elevation drawings so the elevations and details are often shown on the same sheet.

The scales most commonly used for drawing detail drawings are ¾ in. = 1 ft. 0 in., ⅜ in. = 1 ft. 0 in., ½ in. = 1 ft. 0 in., 1 in. = 1 ft. 0 in., 1½ in. = 1 ft. 0 in., or 3 in. = 1 ft. 0 in. Details are to be drawn at a scale no larger than is necessary to describe the construction clearly. It is not unusual to draw the parts of the views and sections at a much larger scale than the general plan and elevation drawings, so as to illustrate more clearly the construction and sizes.

The necessary dimensions of width, height, and depth of the detail to be drawn are taken from the plan, section, and elevations. They should be laid out in light lines, representing the actual parts and construction. The individual construction members of the detail, framing, moldings, and so on, should all be included as the drawing progresses. Actual sizes and shapes should always be represented in the detail drawings.

As the building progresses, the scale working drawings and details are supplemented by full-size drawings of special moldings and millwork details, ornamental ironwork, and so on. These full-size drawings are usually made in soft pencil on tracing paper and blueprinted, all of which must be carefully checked against measurements of the building as given in the general drawings.

Details of Special Features Used in Construction. The architect, specialized engineers, and the tradesmen are dependent upon each other. Such questions as strength and qualities of materials, mechanical apparatus, and construction problems belong in the work assigned to specialized engineers, while planning arrangement, appearance, and good construction are intended for the work of the architect or architectural draftsman. There are many specialized fields of work which the architect cannot be expected to know; and, for these, specialists are called in for advice. These engineers often include heating, lighting, drainage, ventilation, and so on.

In modern building construction, many parts are used which are manufactured by firms specializing in one particular item, and these items are carried in stock by dealers in the community. Among the many such items available are doors, windows, cabinets used in making up kitchen interiors, ventilators, chimneys, patented fireplace liners, stairways, heating and ventilating systems, electrical and mechanical equipment, and so on. There is little question of the advantages to be gained from the use of these stock items. If stock items are to be used, the designer should carefully consider the de-

sirability and limitations of the articles. He should be sure that costs are weighed against the consideration given to utility and beauty.

It is necessary for the designer to be aware of the latest developments in the new materials, designs, and items and to be able to judge properly the merit of their use. He will need to keep up in his knowledge of woods, metals, plastics, glass, and their new applications.

Prospective buyers of homes are attracted to various new installations of equipment as the noteworthy features of a house rather than to the arrangement, construction, resale possibilities, and other more important considerations. Unusual application of materials and equipment should be evaluated after the plan, design, construction, and workmanship of the house have been judged.

Most stock items have limitations of size and design. If stock windows are to be used, the sizes, number and division of panes will be limited to the size and style of available windows carried in dealer's stock. The use of these stock items sometimes involves alteration of the plan to accommodate these particular items. This requires that a kitchen, for example, be planned to fit the cabinets rather than having the cabinets fit the kitchen. The selling point in favor of stock items is usually the lower initial cost. The point that should be carefully considered is the superior construction, finish, and fulfillment of need which can be realized by having cabinets built to fit the kitchen. Common sense evaluation is necessary in choosing these items so that their advantages are weighed against their limitations.

TRACING PLANS IN ELEVATIONS

A tracing is a copy of the original drawing which is made by placing transparent tracing paper, vellum, or tracing cloth over the drawing and tracing all lines and lettering. The best of the materials used is the tracing cloth, but its high cost limits its use. Where a tracing is expected to give long wear and withstand hard usage, cloth is recommended. A tracing which is to be used only a few times may be made on tracing paper. Vellum is a tough, wear-resisting paper that is not easily torn. Tracing paper is easily torn and cracked.

Tracing may be done with a medium soft pencil or in ink. The standard ink is black india ink. Colored inks are sometimes used to bring out the details but this is not advisable for beginners.

Tracing papers and cloths are slightly oily. This causes the ink to flow unevenly unless the proper care is exercised. Soapstone, tracing powder, talcum powder, or chalk dust may be dusted over the surface before attempting to ink. If tracing cloth is used, generally the dull side is placed up although the smooth side may be used and to the advantage that mistakes are easier to erase.

The weights of lines used are very important to show up the contrasts between the important lines and the subordinate lines. The first in importance are the border lines and title block boundaries. Next come the actual drawing outlines and symbols. Then partitions, stairs, and lesser symbols, door and window identifications, remainder of symbols, and invisible lines. Lastly, the dimension and extension lines, crosshatching, and conventional symbols.

PROCEDURE IN TRACING A DRAWING

1. Trace border lines.
2. Trace circular object lines in heavy ink lines.
3. Trace horizontal object lines in heavy ink lines.
4. Trace vertical object lines in heavy ink lines.
5. Trace inclined object lines in heavy ink lines.
6. Trace light circles.
7. Trace light horizontal lines.
8. Trace light vertical lines.
9. Trace light inclined lines.
10. Trace horizontal dimension lines.
11. Trace vertical dimension lines.
12. Trace inclined dimension lines.
13. Draw guide lines for lettering (in pencil).
14. Ink-in dimension figures, lettering, arrowheads, and all freehand work.
15. Check drawings for mistakes.

CHECKING THE WORKING DRAWINGS FOR ERRORS IN DIMENSION, DESIGN, AND CONSTRUCTION

As the draftsman develops his layout of the drawings he continually checks from plan to elevation to detail. Before the lines of the drawing are darkened in the final stage prior to blueprinting, the design of all structural parts should be checked for strength, and fulfillment of requirements, and for accuracy of draftsmanship and to see that all needs and wishes of the client are provided for. These layouts should be carefully checked by a responsible person trained for giving constructive and accurate criticism. Checking should be done in a definite order, following each item separately and systematically. This order will be decided by the checker's preferences and by the conditions and requirements of the problem. The specifications should also be checked against the plans. The following is suggested as a guide:

I. **General**
Sheet number, date, scale, etc.
Cardinal points of the compass, usually located on the plot plan
Title of drawing, south elevation, front elevation, detail of cornice, and so on
Legend of symbols used
Window, door, finish schedules

II. **Dimensions of Architectural Features**
Widths of all openings
Reveals
Center lines

Angles

Main over-all dimensions on the plans, that all plans agree

Location dimensions on plans, seeing that all openings line up vertically

Dimensions of construction and finish on details correspond to those on plans and fit into adjacent construction. Large-scale details made as the work progresses must be checked against general drawings

Projection of balconies

Sizes of rooms

Belt courses and projections

Stair dimensions, both as to rise and run and to the headroom

Vertical dimensions on elevations and sections

Glass sizes on windows and glazed doors

Door sizes and see that doors are described by note, schedule, drawing, or specification

Window sizes and see that windows are described by note, schedule, drawing, or specification

Design, length, and specification of steel lintels over windows and doors as shown on elevations, and compare with large-size detail drawings

Size and location of all ducts and flues

Kind and location of wiring outlets

Clearances for all mechanical equipment

Relation of the elevations to the grade or building line

Thicknesses of all walls

Furring

Framing for fireplace

Framing over all interior openings

III. Finish of All Rooms

Kinds of floors

Trim

Base

Paneling

Kind of ceilings

Coves

Cornices

Reveals

Slopes of floors (basement, garage)

IV. Windows

(Usually covered in "Window Schedule" on elevation drawings, giving sizes, number of panes, number required, and location)

Size

Description

Shutters — holdbacks

Screens — access to clean both sides

Interior shades — covered in specifications

Venetian blinds — covered in specifications

V. Doors

(Usually covered in door schedule on elevation drawings, giving number required, thickness, width, height, description, and location)

Size

Description

Swing

Type

VI. Stairs

Headroom

Newels — size, and description

Handrails — size, and description

Materials

Width of treads

Thickness of treads, and risers

Number of risers and height

Nosing

Balusters

VII. Exterior Stairs

Width of treads
(thickness, if wood)

Number of risers and height

Buttresses or ramps

Anchoring of railing

Nosing

Material

VIII. Ceilings

Cornices

Lights

Coves

Heights

Furring

Beams

IX. Roofs

Direction of slope

Pitch of gutters

Leaders

Flashing (valleys, chimneys, etc.)

X. Plot Plan

Survey

property description — lot, block, tract, city, street number, easements

Property lines — dimensions, angles, stakes

Topography — present grades and detours, bench mark

Public improvements — streets, sidewalks, drives, parkway

Utilities — water, gas, sewer, electricity, telephone

Private improvements — existing buildings, trees, shrubs, walls, fences

Compass — relationship

Scale

New work

Buildings — location dimensions, elevations

Revised topography — new or finish contours and grades, legend of contours and grades

Stormwater disposal — storm sewers, drain pipes, spill blocks, dry wells

Sanitary sewage disposal — sewer connection, septic tank, cesspool, grease trap

Driveway — dimensions and material, private curb, public curb

Garden accessories — walks, walls, steps, gutters

Service yard — drying yard, incinerator, milk delivery, fuel delivery, grocery delivery

XI. Basement Plan

Title, scale, compass relationship

Dimensions

Foundations — concrete walls, sheathing line above footings (dotted), post and column footings, foundation section lining, porch and terrace walls, slabs, vents and areaways, underpinning, pier and footings, garden walls

Chimneys — footings, ash pit and cleanout door, flues

Framing — joists above, size and direction, posts, piers, and beams

Steel — columns and beams, size and number

Unexcavated portion — crawl holes and space, foundation wall, footings, and ventilating grilles

Excavated rooms — title, foundation walls, footings, floor, wood partitions

Furnace room — furnace, water heater, fuel storage, chimney and flues, pipe runs and risers, gas and power outlets, fuel delivery

Plumbing — sump pump, cleanouts, water softener, soil, waste, and vent pipes

Electrical — legend of symbols, meter and panel board, convenience and power outlets, lights, switches

Heating and ventilating — roof vents, ground vents, blower fans, concealing risers and off-sets, ventilators

Incinerator — gas outlet

XII. Foundation Sections

Title, scale

Typical section — footing and wall dimensions, reinforcing in footing and wall, asphalt slab or plastic covering in unexcavated portion, basement floor — 4 in. reinforced, water table, calking, asphalt mopping on outside of concrete foundation, sill setting, joists and blocking, furred ceilings, studs, waterproofing, beams over openings

Masonry veneer section — studs, sheathing, paper, veneer, masonry 3 in. above grade, flashing, and steel lintels at openings

Porch slab section — pitched to drain

Stud partition foundation — masonry wall to plate, 4 to 6 in. above floor

Underpinning walls

Pier footings

Wood post, steel column footings

Basement walls — crawl holes

Special sections — stair slab, door thresholds, areaway and opening, areaway grating, concrete beams and columns, steel beams carrying wood or concrete floor, retaining walls, weep holes, coal chute, garden walls and steps, incinerator

XIII. Floor Plans

Title, scale, compass relationships

Section lining

Dimensions — continuous and closed about building, to face of masonry walls, to outside of sheathing, to center of inside partitions, to center line of doors, windows, openings

Walls — stud sizes, posts, furred walls dimensioned, veneers crosshatched

Framing — joists above, size and direction, special joist framing dotted, overhangs dotted

Steel — beams, size and number; columns, size and number

Chimneys — material indicated; flue and ash drop, sizes; furnace, water heater, and incinerator flues, sizes; hearth, ash dump, fireplace

Stairs — number of risers, height of riser, width of tread, thickness of tread, run of stairway, handrail

Doors and windows — type, swing, size, number, thickness, material, and glazing; swing of screens (dotted); notation for opening; mirror doors noted; threshold material noted; sliding door and screen pockets; curtain and blind pockets

Rooms — title and size; floor material; beams; built-in cases; joists, direction and spacing

Closets — shelves and rod, number of shelves, card table storage, wardrobes, cleaning closet, off-season closet

Deck and balconies — title and size, drain, railing

Electrical — legend and symbols used; meter and panel board; convenience and power outlets; outside lights; switches; bells, pushbuttons; telephone; radio; television

Plumbing — gas meter; gas outlets — range, water heater, unit heaters; special soils, wastes, and vents; water softener

Heating — risers, floor and wall registers; unit heaters

Porches, terraces, patios — floor material; drainage; railings; lattices and trellises; hoods; roof, and pitches

Walks, walls, stairs, drives — material; dimensions

Garage — finish of floor, pitch of floor, drainage, workbench, hose bib, storage cases

Roof plan — ridge and hips, decks, material, chimney and saddles, diverters

Door and window schedule — sash — number, size, type, thickness, material, glazing, muntin; screen — type, thickness, material; doors — number, size, type, thickness, material, glazing

XIV. General Considerations in Floor Planning

Basement — foundation walls, sewer, windows, outside entrance, hot water heater, floor drain, laundry equipment, fuel storage, chimney cleanout, lights, location of switches, outlets for electrical equipment, shutoff valves for water and heating pipes, heating system

Attic — attic stairs, ventilation, lighting fixtures, location of switches, floor

Living Room — adequate size, ceiling beams, windows, doorways, wall space for all furniture, floor finish, fireplace symbol, electrical outlets, location of radiators and registers, wall fixtures, ceiling lights, location of switches, built-in cabinets, swing and arrangement of doors, convenience of location, view and exposure, trim finish

Dining room — adequate size, windows and exposure, doorways, swing and arrangement of doors, convenience to kitchen, wall space for furniture, built-in cabinets, electrical outlets, location of radiators or registers, ceiling beams, wall fixtures, ceiling lights, location of switches, floor and trim finish

Kitchen — adequate size, door arrangement and swing, convenience to dining room, efficient arrangement, windows and exposure, sink and cabinets, counter top surface material, location of furniture and equipment, gas stove vent pipe or stove hood with exhaust fan, electrical outlets, lighting fixtures, location of switches, storage space, breakfast snack bar, built-in cabinets, ventilating fan, cabinet and trim finish

Bedrooms — adequate size, exposure, windows, door arrangement and swing, convenience to bathroom, space for convenient arrangement of furniture, location of radiators or registers, electrical outlets, lighting fixtures, location of switches, closet space, mirror closet door

Bathroom — tile floor and walls, adequate size, outside window, door arrangement and swing ventilation, electrical outlets, location of switches, medicine cabinet with built-in mirror door, convenient location, built-in cabinets, storage space, equipment location

Closets — adequate size, door arrangement and swing, sliding doors, shelf space, hangers, hooks, fixtures, lights, location and kind of switch

Miscellaneous — radio wiring, telephone wiring, intercom wiring; hallways — lighting, location of switches, size, etc.; front vestibule — adequate size, lighting, location of switches, etc.; coat closet at entrance — door swing, etc.; clothes chute; stairway to admit carrying up of furniture; concrete driveway accommodating fuel delivery; cross ventilation; concrete walks; driveway; garage; downspouts

XV. Exterior Elevations

Title and scale

Dimensions — finish floor lines, head of door and window openings, roof plate heights

Lines and levels — center lines, finish floor lines, stair landings, balconies, finish grade, natural grade, footings, areas, openings below grade, basement floor, sump pits, sidewalk levels, curbs, ridges, eaves, decks, beams, low point of porch floors

Walls — brick, stone, concrete, plaster, siding, boarding, shingles; steel lintels over openings in veneered walls; masonry grilles; fireplace and flues; wood posts and beams, size and finish; arches — radius lines, spring lines, thrusts, centers; masonry courses — stone, brick, terra cotta, marble, joining of sills and heads, bond stones; notes on ornaments; bond stones — Lewis bolts on section; no unnecessary repetition of ornament or detail; gas and electric meter openings

Doors and windows — panels and glass design, shutters, wood and masonry trim

Roof — material and pitch; gable ends; vents, screens; cornice and gutter; downspout — size and shape; splash block; dormers — galvanized iron valleys and flashing; cupolas; metal roofs and flashings; metal copings; ridge and end finish

Drainage of rainwater — leaders, conductor heads, size of gutters, hanging and concealed roof drainage on plan, drainage of areas (dotted), drainage of basement (dotted), drainage of sump pumps (dotted), splash blocks, leader straps

Dot in stairways, footings, pits, hidden roofs, chimneys, flues, areas, roof lines, raised floors, furred ceilings

Vents to crawl space

Access to crawl space

Headroom in gables or under slanting roofs where rooms will be built in the future

Check height of all chimneys for draft

Check all soil pipes for ventilation

Nearness of soil pipes to windows

Roof vents away from windows

Water outlets, hose bibs

Meter boxes

Section lines, projections and setbacks, sunken or raised panels

Diameter of columns, width of pilasters

Height of columns

Height of railings

Height of belt courses, copings, cornices

Height of bases

Grilles over basement windows and other openings

Street names and house number

Awnings

Screens

Blinds, and holdbacks

Exterior lighting

Exterior electrical outlets

Dormer and gable cheeks — material, support on framing construction below

Projecting hoods — entrances, balconies

Flashing and counter flashing

Pitch of gutters

Roof or attic ventilation

Steel angle lintels

Stone or other lintels

XVI. Interior Elevations

Title and scale

Dimensions — ceiling heights, cases and seats, radii of curved openings, fireplace openings, electrical outlets, equipment and fixtures

Walls — material and finish

Doors, windows, and openings — material of trim, curtain and blind pocket

Bays and recesses — material of trim, rough framing

Ceilings — furring, exposed beams and rafters

Trim — base and shoe, door and window casings, cornices and quarter rounds, beams, wood lintels, carved moldings

Cases — china, book, book shelving

Mantels — firebox facing and pattern, masonry facing, over-mantel treatment, carvings

Stairs — strings, treads, nosing, risers, railing and handrail, newel

Plaster — cornices and beams, ornamental

Electrical — convenience outlets, switches, brackets, telephone

Heating — registers, radiators, controls

Kitchen — sink, splashboard, soap dishes, recesses; cabinet space provided with two doors through which pipes can be reached; removable wall panel for access to water pipes; towel racks; counter tops and back; case drawers, doors, toe space, shelves, bins; cabinets; desk; pass door to pantry; cornice mold; typical case section; ventilator fan; refrigerator vent; range, hood, vent, fan, back; pot and pan cabinet, shelves, lid racks, tray compartments, hook strips; glazed light in pantry door; convenience outlets, clock fan, toaster, mixer; incinerator or garbage disposal

Pantry — sink, counter tops, cases, similar to kitchen; cupboard doors glazed; lined silverware drawers; table linen drawers; tray compartments; table leaves storage

Service porch — vegetable drawers, counter, storage, garbage can or incinerator chute

Laundry — laundry chute, wash trays, ironing board, gas plate; convenience outlets, washer, drier, ironer; cases; drying lines

Linen room — cases, glazed doors, adjustable shelves; counter, pull-out boards; sink; ironing board; convenience outlet, iron; drying rack

Dressing and Powder Rooms — dressing table, glass top; mirror door, triplicate mirror; shoe closet; hat closet; tray cupboard; pullout closet rods

Baths — lavatory, tub, water closet, soap and tumbler holder; convenience outlet; medicine cabinet and lights, wall switch; access to plumbing pipes, cleanouts, and valves; wall finish; floor finish

XVII. Small Scale Sections
Title and scale
Finish floor lines
Natural and finish grades
Foundation walls and piers
Floor framing
Stairs
Furred ceiling
Decks and balconies
Roof — truss, dormer, hood
Chimney, fireplace and flues
Porch and terrace

XVIII. Heating and Ventilation Plans
Roof vents
Ground vents
Ceiling grilles
Blower, fans
Concealing of risers and offsets
Ventilators
Location of all radiators, sq. ft., size of radiators, number of columns, height, type
Location of registers, size, outlet or inlet
Recesses — size of pocket, size of grille

XIX. Plumbing and Roof Drainage
Soil pipes — size, vents, cleanouts
Rain water drain pipes
Place soil pipes independent of partition joists
Floor drains
Water taps
Hose bibs
List and description of all fixtures

XX. Roof Plate and Cornice Detail
Run rafters in the same direction as ceiling joists
Show relation to window lintel
Ties between roof rafters and ceiling joists
Relation to finished wall or building line

XXI. Chimney and Fireplace Detail
Corbel out to support first section of flue lining
Size of throat and length
Smoke chamber
Passage of other flues

XXII. Electrical Plans
Location of ceiling outlets
Wall brackets — height from floor
Base plugs, floor plugs
Electric range outlet
Switches — 2-way or 3-way and their location
Meter box — fuses, circuit breakers, main switch
Telephones, telephone extensions
Radio — radio extensions, ground, and aerial
Push buttons at doors
Doorbells, buzzers, chimes
Doorbell transformer
Floor buzzers — dining room and other places

FINAL STAGE REQUIRED IN THE MAKING OF WORKING DRAWINGS

The last step is reached when the working drawing has been completely lettered and dimensioned, with window and door schedules, and all information required by the builder to complete the building (Figs. 179–184). The drawings have been developed and carried through the processes of thinking and planning until now they are ready to be darkened and completed. A careful check should have been made for all errors, and these should be corrected. The last step and procedure is to *darken* the drawings with architectural line technique, and letter them with single stroke Roman lettering as used by architects. It is this stage which develops all of the study and layout into finished drawings ready for the blueprinting process.

Architectural Technique. Technique is the kind and quality of lines used in making a drawing; the methods of dimensioning; the character of the figures, letters, and arrowheads used; the style and character of lettering; and the general spacing or grouping of the views, dimensions, lettering, and so on.

Architectural drawing permits a greater freedom in technique than other kinds of drawing. Lines when meeting at right angles, or nearly so, are overlapped a short distance. This practice, if carefully done, adds to the artistic appearance of the drawing and saves considerable time. Care must be taken that the overlap is uniform and not too long. Some drawings are "shaded" by making the lines nearest the viewer heavy thick lines, and by making lines which represent parts farther away thinner. The lines are graded in thickness according to their distance from the viewer. Such lines of different widths are particularly used to distinguish between the outline of a section and the lines representing parts beyond the cutting plane. Different widths of lines are also commonly used in drawing elevations because they give a more pictorial effect. In drawing, the thickness of a line should be uniform throughout its length. Lines may vary in different parts of the same drawing, and in different drawings, according to the amount of detail shown, but in all cases the finished line must be dark (black), clear, and in character. All the lines in a finished drawing should be of a character and intensity that they will produce the best possible blueprints.

The standard architectural letter is the Old Roman, as originally found on Trajan's Column (see Unit II, "Architectural Lettering," p. 11 f.). It will be noticed that the strokes of the lettering are not uniform in thickness, the sloping strokes from the left downward to the right being heaviest except in the case of the Z. The type of lettering most commonly used in architectural drawing for notes and titles is a single line adaptation of the Old Roman letter. A vertical letter is more commonly used, although some draftsman prefer the sloping letter. The letters are all kept of uniform weight and serifs (small finishing strokes) are sometimes used on the end of the straight-line strokes. Much individuality is permissible in architectural lettering. The letters may be made compressed or extended, especially the straight line letters, while the round letters like the O, C, and Q may be made in varying sizes, from a very small character to the full round. In the composition of words, the lines of the letters and the spaces between the letters should be such as to give an effect of even spacing. This cannot be accomplished, however, by actually spacing letters the same distance apart because of the variety in the forms of the letters and the illusion produced. All figures should be made clearly and distinctly to prevent misreading.

The division line between the numerator and denominator of fractions may be made horizontal or sloping to fit the style of lettering. Guide lines should always be drawn for the top and bottom of the letters. Notes may be made ³⁄₃₂ or ⅛ in. in height, subtitles ³⁄₁₆ or ¼ in., and the size of titles depends much upon the size of the drawing and the space available.

The test of this final step of producing a working drawing is the quality of its drawing and planning. Two objectives must be met in developing a set of working drawings:

1. The proper procedure in developing a complete set of working drawings.

2. The considerations met in developing a suitable house plan for a particular family.

It has been said that it takes the planning and building of five houses, and the living in each of them before a house can be built which might approach an ideal. A perfect house cannot be built, but we attempt to plan each house as nearly perfect as we individually know how to make it. It is the continued repetition of the proper procedure of planning a house which should attain the objectives so that each plan you produce will be better than the one before.

ASSIGNMENT

This unit is intended to explain the architect's drawings to the student and to help him visualize the house that would result from the plan. In learning to read floor plans the student will need to practice with a wide variety of plans. In addition to plans included in this unit, it will be well to study others that you will find in magazines.

PROBLEMS FOR CLASS DISCUSSION

1. Describe the size and relationship of rooms in a home you know.
2. How does the architect convey his ideas to the contractor?
3. If you were planning to remodel your house, how would you determine whether or not your ideas were practical?
4. How might the ability to understand floor-plan drawings help you in working with the architect?
5. Keeping in mind the problems of your own family, criticize the floor plans found in this unit of work. Be sure to include both favorable and unfavorable criticisms.
6. Visit buildings in the process of construction for which blueprints are available. Study both the plans and the buildings to see whether you can locate any changes from the original drawing.

Suggested Problem Assignments

ASSIGNMENT

House Planning Procedure

Plate 1, Preliminary Sketch

The first step in drawing a complete set of plans for the building of a house is to think of the lot on which the house is to be built (Figs. 148 and 149). If you have already purchased the property you will know exactly the advantages and limitations of the lot and you can plan your house accordingly, but if you are planning an imaginary house you must consider the type of lot you would like to have. The architect must consider the location of the street (Figs. 66, 68, and 69), the orientation of the lot (Figs. 64 and 65), arrangement of the rooms (Figs. 151–154), and the style of the exterior (Figs. 151 and 155–158).

With this actual or imagined information in mind draw an outline sketch of your lot on paper. It does not have to be drawn exactly to scale since you are merely thinking locations through the medium of a rough freehand sketch. Next, place the house roughly where you think you would like to have it (Fig. 149). Most houses are placed at the side and front of the lot so that space is provided on the other side and back for gardening. Plan the location of your driveway since this will determine the location of the service portion of your house (Figs. 66, 68, and 69). Plan your house in rela-

tion to scenery that your best view may be seen from an outdoor garden or from an important window of the house.

Locate the rooms in relation to the points of the compass, the view, the working divisions of your house, and the garden (Figs. 64 and 65). The living room should be given a south and west exposure where possible. The dining room should face the east to get the rising sun. The first floor should have a toilet and lavatory, and a hall space from the front door and stairway to the kitchen. Plenty of window space should be given to all rooms. Bedrooms should be given ample closet space as well as ventilation. The bathroom or upper hall should have a linen closet. Sufficient wall space should be provided for all furniture. It is necessary to consider the requirements of the family and how they may be provided for. Think about how you live, both everyday and when you entertain.

Make a list of all the rooms you want in your house, with a description under each of the way it is to be used and the furniture you expect to place in it, plus the things to be stored in the closets.

Sketch a geometric form representing the outline of the whole house and then fit in the rooms (Fig. 151). The second-floor room partitions should line up rather closely above the partitions of the first floor rooms. This is important both for economy and for strength in the building.

Each student should submit an original sketch of the house he expects to plan, after having studied all available information on house planning obtained through the study of books, magazines, and so on (Fig. 157). The preliminary sketches consist of the principal floor plans accompanied by either the elevations, or a perspective of the exterior (Figs. 155 and 156). These drawings are usually done in a sketchy manner to show the general scheme clearly. The walls are usually represented with single line thickness in this drawing. The elevations are sketched rather roughly at first until an approximate design has been developed. The kinds of

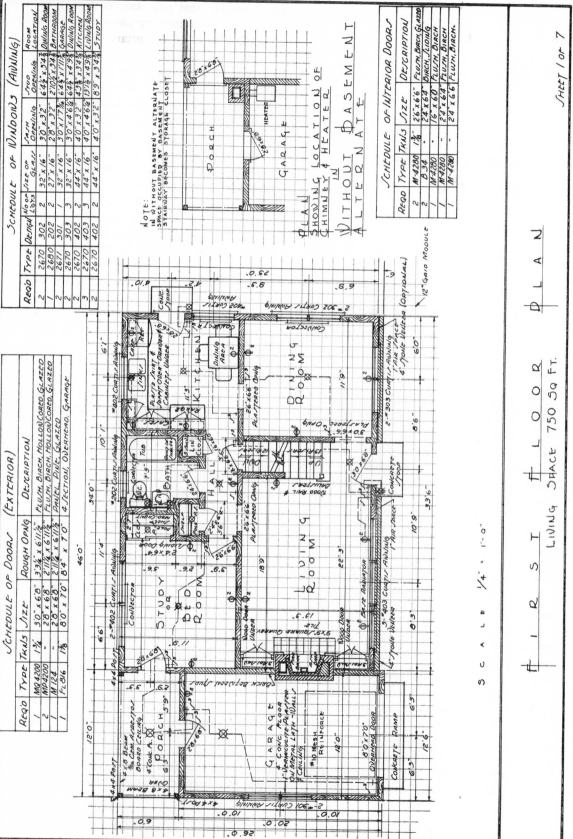

Fig. 179

sketches used in connection with architectural working drawings are:

1. Thumbnail sketches
2. Plan layout studies
3. Elevation design studies
4. Finished sketches

Plate 2, First Floor Plan

After these preliminary studies have been made the student is prepared to start the scale layout of the first floor plan. Of course certain changes and adjustments must be made in the scale layout of the floor plan concerning the arrangement and general dimensions of the rooms because the scale drawing will never quite work out like the preliminary sketch. It is for this reason that all the drawings are laid out *very lightly* so that corrections may be easily made. The drawings are not darkened in as finished drawings until all working drawings are completed and checked carefully for all errors.

The first-floor plan is as a rule planned and drawn first, because there are many important things which depend on the layout of the first floor plan. Some of the important things to consider are, the layout of the various rooms, partitions, windows, doors, stairways, and plumbing on this particular floor (Figs. 166 and 179). In completing the first floor plan layout, window and door sizes must be determined by reference to catalog stock sizes, and these sizes should appear on the plan at the window and door symbols or be listed in separate schedules. Bathroom fixtures, kitchen equipment, and built-in features should be selected from plumbing and millwork catalogs available to the student. The stairway must be laid out to scale, and the proper number of risers figured accurately with their proper dimensions. This stair detail may only need to be started to get the needed information and may be finished later. Information relative to the stair flight may also be checked by drawing an outline of it on the elevation drawings. Lighting fixtures and switches must be planned and the proper symbols located in the plan. Interior trim must be specified and heating arrangements located. In determining the size of a room, the draftsman must know something of the size and type of furniture that is to go into it. This information in turn necessitates a knowledge of the likes and dislikes of the owner, who is influenced either by his tastes or his pocketbook. A well-planned home will satisfy the habits and mode of living of the family occupying it.

The plans of the house must not be developed too far before the elevations are laid out. It is customary to develop the plans and the elevations together, because this method saves considerable time and minimizes the possibility of mistakes.

In preparing the layout of the first floor, block in the outline of the building with a light continuous line, disregarding door and window openings temporarily. Next draw the center line for all partition walls. The outside wall thickness, which is approximately 7 in. for a frame house, may then be drawn, and the thickness of partitions, which is approximately 6 in., may be drawn. Door and window openings are located by center lines and their widths determined from the stock catalog sizes. In order to draw the window symbols in the plan the draftsman must know the type and size of the window to be used. The type of window selected is generally one that will conform to the design or appearance of the building. The sizes of windows for the various rooms must meet requirements for light and air. The light requirements for a room call for a minimum glass area equal to 10 per cent of the floor area. The requirements for air are that the windows can be opened to a minimum area equal to 5 per cent of the floor area.

The widths of the windows and doors on the plan are those of the rough openings. The draftsman may show by means of dimensions on the plan, the actual sash openings and the actual widths of doors, provided

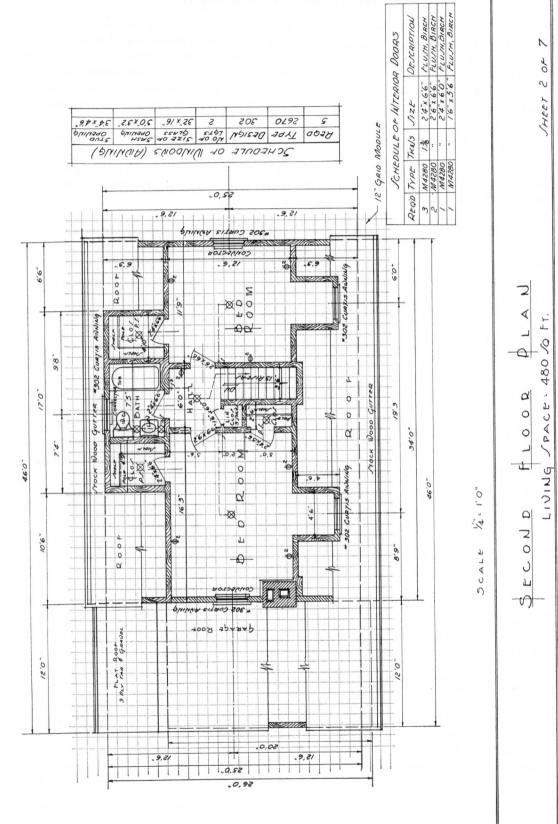

SCHEDULE OF WINDOWS (AWNING)

REQD	TYPE DESIGN	NO. OF LGTS	SIZE OF GLASS OPENING	SIZE OF SASH OPENING	STUD OPENING
5	2670	302	2	32" x 16"	30" x 32"	34" x 46"

SCHEDULE OF INTERIOR DOORS

REQD	TYPE	TRN'S	SIZE	DESCRIPTION
3	M4280	1¾	2'4" x 6'6"	FLUSH, BIRCH
2	M4280	"	2'6" x 6'6"	FLUSH, BIRCH
1	M4280	"	2'4" x 6'0"	FLUSH, BIRCH
1	N4280	"	1'6" x 5'6"	FLUSH, BIRCH

SHEET 2 OF 7

SCALE ¼" = 1' 0"

SECOND FLOOR PLAN

LIVING SPACE = 480 SQ FT.

Fig. 180

The beginning draftsman will find that the elevation drawings in the layout stage, although complete in general appearance, will require minor changes and corrections later on when the roof pitches and framing plans are studied. It is common practice, even for architects and experienced draftsmen, to make changes in the elevation and floor plan layout drawings after the framing plans, elevations, and detail drawings are started because of the discovered errors in the checking process (Fig. 182).

Plates 6 and 7, End Elevations

A common mistake of students is to draw some of the elevations of the building in reverse. This is best avoided by turning the plans around so that the elevation being drawn is toward you, and comparing the plans with the elevation while the elevation is still in the layout stage (Figs. 182 and 183). Enough of the plans and sections should have been completed to furnish elevation layout dimensions (Fig. 176). It is very important that elevation, plan, and section drawings agree in respect to the over-all size, and certain details, such as windows and door sizes and locations; therefore these distances should be projected to the elevation from the plan and section rather than laid out with a scale. By placing the tracing paper successively over the floor plans and section, this projection of measurements or distances is easily accomplished. If these drawings are tacked down to other drawing boards and are not easily available, use the edge of a strip of paper as a "tick" strip to lay off marks representing the wanted points, and transfer these measurements to the elevations.

Many of the small distances on an elevation, like muntin strips in a window are put in by eye (often using single lines to represent them). Symbolized details on the plan, such as doors and window sash, are also represented by single lines. The reason for this is that the eye is very sensitive and critical of propor-

tional distances. Of course all important measurements must be accurately scaled.

It is often advantageous to draw a front and an end elevation on the same sheet because many of the measurements and details may be projected across from one elevation to the other. This is particularly true of the height of the roof which is to be represented on the front elevation by projecting from the end elevation. Other combinations may be worked out on a single sheet to save time in drawing and to insure accuracy.

Plate 8, Rear Elevation

In preparing to draw the rear elevation it is best to fasten the tracing paper over the first floor plan after the plan is laid upside down (with the drawing side of the tracing paper toward the board) (Fig. 172). Do not turn the plan from left to right but rather from top to bottom. Vertical ends, windows, and doors can then be projected from the plan, and the heights can be stepped off from the front elevation (Fig. 183).

Plate 9, First Floor Framing Plan

A complete set of working drawings does not, as a rule, include framing plans. The floor plans, elevations, and details are usually sufficient for the builder. It is the responsibility of the architect to supervise the builder in the structural elements of the building and see that the job is carried out to accepted practice and prescribed building codes. The framing plans are especially important to the student because by studying framing plans he can become familiar with the principles and practices of house construction. An understanding of house framing is necessary in order to prepare the other drawings satisfactorily (Figs. 184 and 185).

In drawing the first floor framing plan, trace the outline of the foundation wall from the basement plan, then locate the sill as taken from a detail or section. The sill loca-

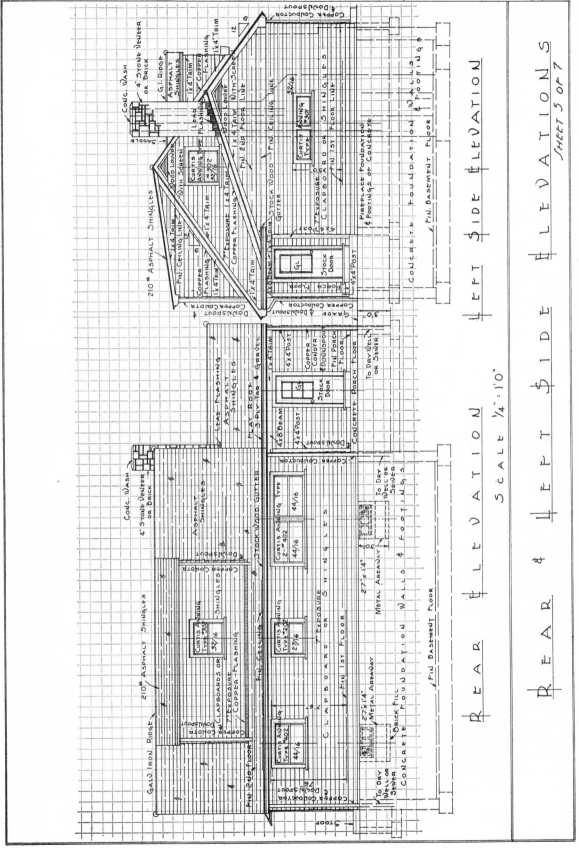

REAR ELEVATION

SCALE ¼" = 1'0"

REAR & LEFT SIDE ELEVATIONS

LEFT SIDE ELEVATION

REAR & LEFT SIDE ELEVATIONS

SHEET 5 OF 7

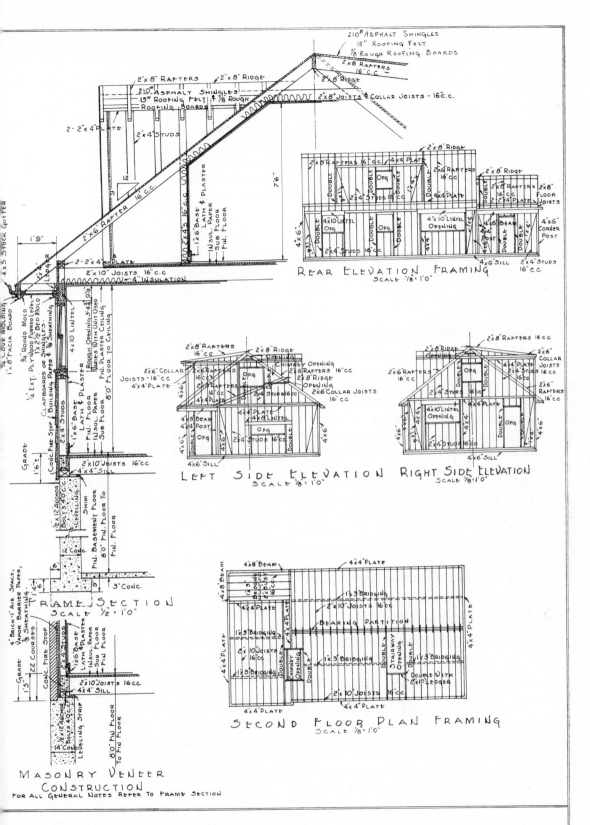

TYPICAL FRAMING CONSTRUCTION

SHEET 6 OF 7

Fig. 184

tion will be ⅞ in. inside the outer face of the foundation wall for a frame house. Next trace the girder and draw in the supporting columns. Draw in the joists, headers, trimmers, and tail beams as indicated by the plan. Where partitions overhead are parallel to the floor joists, draw double joists. When partitions run at right angles to the joists no extra support is required. If two partitions are close together, as in closets running parallel to each other near the center of the span, greater support is necessary. In this case joists should be spaced 12 in. instead of the usual 16 in.

Plate 10, Second Floor Framing Plan

The second floor framing plan is developed very much like the first floor framing plan except that the foundation wall need not be drawn (Fig. 184). In the platform or Western framing a 2 by 4-in. double plate, on which the ceiling joists and the header rest, is shown around the building and can be traced from the first floor plan. In the balloon framing these joists rest on a "ribbon" or "ledger board." Bearing partitions supporting the ends of ceiling joists should be indicated on this plan.

Plate 11, Front Elevation Framing Plan

Plate 12, Right End Elevation Framing Plan

Plate 13, Left End Elevation Framing Plan

Plate 14, Rear Elevation Framing Plan

Proceed in about the same manner the carpenter follows in framing the house (Figs. 184 and 185). Represent the sill, joists, and headers. On each corner represented indicate the framing for the corner posts. Space the studs the proper distance apart and double the studs around the openings. Show the difference in construction as a result of the different methods of framing used for the first and second floors. Draw in the cornice, the plate, the ridge of the roof, and the supporting rafters. Much of the information may be obtained from the elevation, floor framing plan, and the detail drawings, by tracing the measurements through the sheet of tracing paper.

Plate 15, Roof Plan

The roof plan serves a very minor function in the planning of a small home, and seldom is a part of a complete set of plans. The roof plan is often represented on the floor plans by indicating the outside outlines of the roof and the ridges for the various parts of the plan (Fig. 180).

The roof plan is important to the student and architectural draftsman when the plans and elevations are being developed. It would be difficult to draw a longitudinal section with its different ridge levels without the elevations; nor could the ridges of the elevations finally be drawn without the floor plan, because the floor plan determines the roof outlines. The roof plan must receive full consideration in the early stages of planning.

Plate 16, Roof Framing Plan

Before beginning the roof framing plan it is essential to understand the need of each framing member (Figs. 192 and 194). The rafters serve the same purpose for the roof as do the joists for the floors: the rafters provide a support for the roofing boards and materials. They extend from the ridge to the eave without interruption and must have a minimum bearing surface of 3 in. on the plate. The ridge is the horizontal member against which the rafters are supported at the peak of the roof. Its purpose is to align and hold the rafters in place. The depth or width of the ridge board should at least equal the length of the ridge cut of the rafters and usually 1-in. lumber is sufficient thickness.

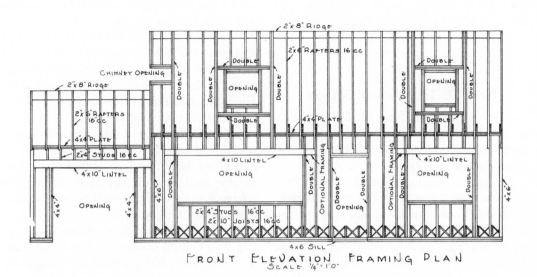

FRONT ELEVATION FRAMING PLAN
Scale ¼" = 1'0"

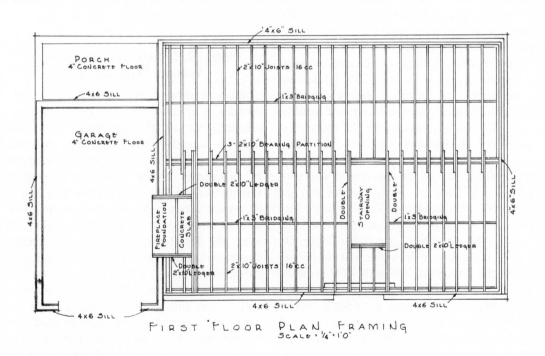

FIRST FLOOR PLAN FRAMING
Scale = ¼" = 1'0"

TYPICAL FRAMING PLANS

Fig. 185

Plate 17, Roof Pitches

Various roof heights and pitches are selected for appearance and proportion of the different elevations. Select the pitch that comes nearest to the desired ridge height for appearance or for usable attic space if this is a factor in the planning.

Plate 18, Longitudinal Section

This section gives the builder a picture of the relative position of floor levels and floor constructions as well as the wall and roof details (Fig. 178).

A sheet of tracing paper is placed over the first floor plan and the vertical ends, partitions, doors, windows, and stairway can be projected. The draftsman will have at hand for reference all previously laid out drawings. To begin the section, the grade line, the correct distance of the finished floor level from the grade line, and the ceiling level should be drawn. These dimensions should be obtained from the elevations. First develop that part of the section representing the first floor, temporarily neglecting the basement and roof. Construct the sill at the floor level taking into consideration all the parts included such as the plate, header, joists, subfloor, and finished floor. The sill is supported by the foundation wall. The thickness of the foundation wall may be obtained from the basement plan. The outside face of the foundation wall projects ⅞ in. from the outer face of the sill to receive the sheathing. Keep it flush with the outside face of the foundation wall. This ⅞ in. is the allowance for a frame house. On top of the subfloor draw the sole which receives the wall studs. The wall section should include the windows and door representations. This window section need not be drawn in detail since it is enough to show the sill of the window, the meeting rail, and the head. More complete information may be obtained from a detail drawing of the window. Note that the draftsman is required to look at the elevation to get the exact height of the window from the finished floor before he is able to represent it correctly in the longitudinal section. Since the joists are usually placed to run across the short dimensions of the building, they will be represented in end section in the longitudinal section drawing and be properly spaced. Since the sectional cut is taken through the center of the stair well opening, no joists are represented in this open area. The location of these joists can be taken from the floor framing plans.

After the floor joists are properly represented, the footings, foundation walls, basement floor levels, and excavated and unexcavated levels may be indicated with careful reference to the drawings that give the correct information. Ceiling joists, rafters, fireplace and chimney, interior doors, partitions, stairway, and built-in furniture and equipment are drawn in place. Reference should continually be made to manufacturers' data and the other drawings of the series making up the complete set of working drawings.

Plate 19, Typical Cross Section or Vertical Wall Section

When drawing these sections, the draftsman keeps in mind that he is giving on paper certain important information the builder will need in actually constructing the building. This means that the sections should be drawn by proceeding as the workman does when actually constructing the building. The draftsman must carefully lay out all stock material to actual size, build up the floor thicknesses using the actual dimensions, so that heights shown on the section will be correct for construction purposes. The draftsman must not guess or approximate any of these distances since errors will occur in trying to make the materials fit properly if the measurements are not accurate. After the layout of the required ceiling heights and door and window openings, the problem involved in making these sections is simply fitting the best and simplest

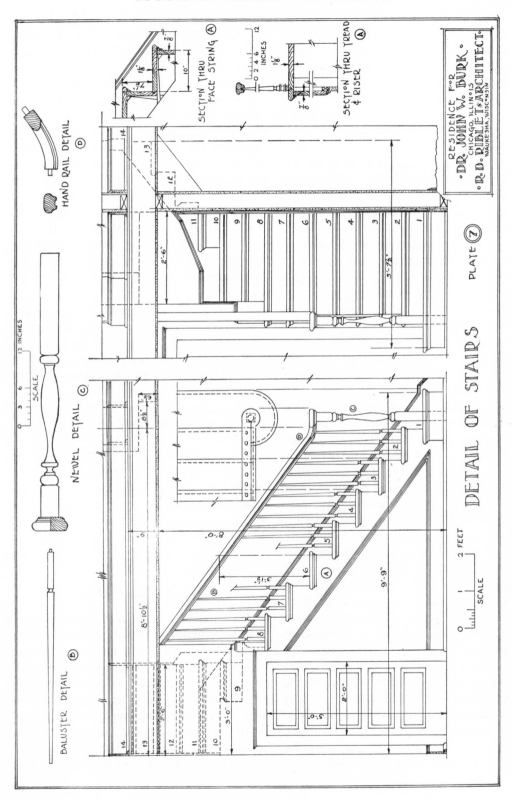

Fig. 186

construction into the space allotted (Figs. 21, 22, and 178). These sections are drawn to the same scale as the plans and elevations and are used to determine the method of construction and all necessary height dimensions. Sections are of three kinds:

1. *Vertical wall section.* This is a section of the outside wall to show the floors, footings, foundation wall, sill, water table, windows, doors, cornice, and so on (Plates 9–11, p. 156 f, Figs. 184, 190, 192, 194–196, and 198). The window openings represent a typical window (the window most commonly used throughout the building). For most simple buildings this section is all that is required and it is commonly placed on a sheet with an elevation drawing so that the vertical heights and detail may be projected from it.

2. *Detail Section.* Where explanation is needed regarding certain construction details of the building, these areas requiring explanation are indicated on the plans or elevations by an identified cutting plane line. This line indicates where the section is obtained and the arrows indicate the direction in which the section is viewed. An enlarged section is drawn and a note added, "refer to section A-B." This note identifies the detail section with the section line in the plan or elevation.

Good details, drawn as a part of the set of working drawings, are most important to the workman. Their purpose is to represent the design and construction of special features of the building. Many years of experience are needed to become a thoroughly competent detailer.

A detail consists of the representation of the views necessary to describe the object, and the dimensions necessary to construct it, with whatever enlarged sections are necessary to describe the design, materials, and construction of that particular portion of the building. Some of the subjects which may require detailing are doors, windows, stairways, cornices, bay windows, sills, fireplaces, cabinetwork, and so on. The plan of the particular building being drawn will govern

the number and kinds of parts to be detailed. The more details that are drawn the better and more complete the information given to the workman.

Construction details are large-scale or full-size working drawings showing the important parts of a building that are difficult to show clearly or accurately on the small-scale drawings. For the most part they are sectional drawings showing the construction behind the sectioned surface. The scales most commonly used for drawing details are: ¾ in. = 1 ft. 0 in., ⅜ in. = 1 ft. 0 in., ½ in. = 1 ft. 0 in., 1 in. = 1 ft. 0 in., 1½ in. = 1 ft. 0 in., and 3 in. = 1 ft. 0 in. Details should be drawn at a scale no larger than is necessary to describe clearly the construction of all parts.

The required dimensions for the length, width, height, or thickness of the detail to be drawn usually are taken from the plan, section, and elevations. After they are laid out in light lines at the proper scale, the next step consists of filling in the construction, design, etc. This should be done by visualizing and drawing the actual parts used in the construction itself.

3. *Cross Section.* Complicated floor levels or roofs sometimes require that one or more sections be taken completely through the building in order to show the relation of various parts to each other (Figs. 21, 22, 23, 177, 184, 192, and 196.

Plate 20, Stair Details

A diagrammatic section may be drawn to show the required headroom. Dimensions may be indicated to show how the headroom may be determined. The riser and tread are shown, as well as the required height for a handrail, although this may vary according to the design and specific conditions involved. Three details are necessary for the drawing of a stairway (Fig. 186, Plate 14, p. 181):

1. The elevation shows the outside finish

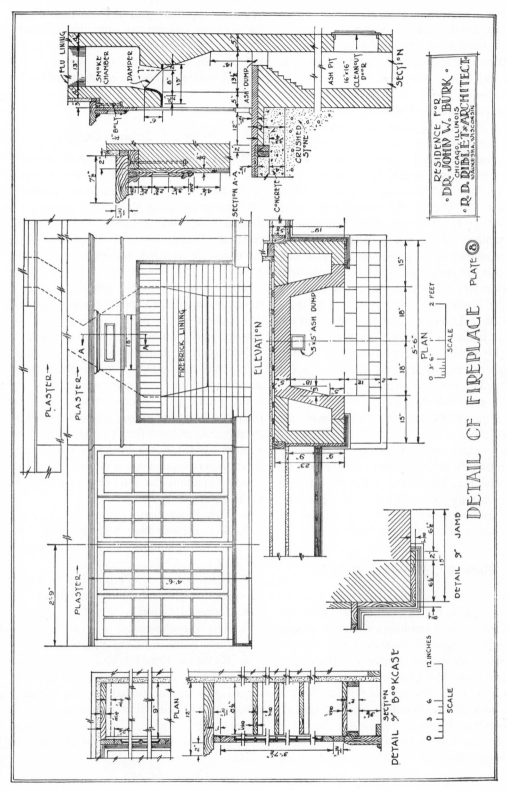

Fig. 187

of the stairway which consists of the newel, balusters, handrail, tread, nosing, stringboard, and the finish of the wall between the run of the stairway and the floor. In laying out the risers and treads, one must know the height from floor to floor and the height of the riser decided upon. There are several rules for determining the riser and tread dimensions. For ordinary houses a good rule is two risers plus one tread equals 25 in., 7½ in. being a good riser height. If the height from floor to floor and the height of the riser to be used are known, the number of risers required can be figured mathematically. When the number of risers is determined, the method shown in a geometric diagram can be applied to space the risers between floors. The elevation also shows the newel post and how the handrail is fastened to it. The spacing of the balusters is shown and also how the stringer is fastened at the floor level.

2. A sectional view shows a section through the riser and tread; this view is cut parallel with the wall string.

3. A sectional view should also be cut at right angles to the run and parallel with the face of the step.

The section through the stringers shows the construction at the wall and the outside edge, the location of the balusters, and the rough carriage or stringers. The riser and tread section shows clearly the details and construction of the riser and tread.

Plate 21, Fireplace Details

Since the fireplace detail drawing is to be used as a guide by the mason who constructs the fireplace, both the interior and exterior of the fireplace must be shown. A vertical section which shows the interior construction is always given. The plan at the floor line is given in section, with separate details for the jamb, mantel, and pilaster. An elevation of the fireplace is always given to show the exterior details of construction (Fig. 187).

The plan shows the width and depth of the opening, together with the location of the furnace flue coming up from the basement. The elevation shows the height of the opening, the finished mantel, and the wall. The vertical section shows the construction behind the cut surface.

Plate 22, Cabinet Details

A plan and elevation showing the location and heights of the cabinets is essential. When ready-made fixtures are ordered and installed, the draftsman need show only over-all dimensions of such fixtures. If custom-built cabinets are to be installed, complete working drawings are required. See Plates 16, 17, and 17A.

These drawings should give the joint construction, moldings, drawer details, vertical end section of the cabinet, elevation of the cabinet, and plan section of the cabinet.

NOTE: It is understood that the requirements for a complete set of plans varies according to the size and complexity of the house plan. In a school drawing class the number of working drawings is also influenced by the time allotted the drawing class within a given semester, the length of period, and the number of meetings per week. As a suggested minimum the following plates are to be required:

1. First Floor Plan

2. Second Floor Plan (Used because of the influence on planning when a stairway is involved.)

3. Basement Plan (Foundation plan may be substituted in a one-story building.)

4. Front Elevation

5. Side Elevation

6. First Floor Framing Plan

7. Elevation Framing

8. Stairway Details (Some other plate on details may be substituted such as cornices, windows, and sills, if a one-story house is used.)

9. Fireplace Details (Substitution may be made.)

10. Cabinet Details (Substitution may be made.)

Other combinations of plates to be drawn may be assigned by the drawing instructor.

ALTERNATE PROBLEM ASSIGNMENTS

High school classes in drawing are organized on many different plans of operation. Some schools have 45-minute class periods but allot shop and laboratory classes a double period, others operate on the 60-minute length period with all classes on equal time. Some schools offer shop and/or drawing classes 5 days a week; others have classes meeting only certain days of the week. In the smaller schools only a semester of drawing may be offered in which mechanical, architectural, and machine drawing are combined into a semester unit course. In the larger high schools, architectural drawing is an elective course offered for from four to six semesters time. It is because of these variations in time allotment that the author has offered the following shorter, simpler, and accelerated architectural drawing course for schools with less time allotted for architectural drawing. This shorter course is based upon the construction of a residential garage, a building so simple that it is easy for any student to learn to draw a good set of architectural working drawings. Because a garage is such a common structure every student should be able to see one close at hand and study carefully its construction because most of the framework is usually exposed.

To make a complete set of plans one requires information about the following: an understanding of blueprint reading or an understanding of the principles of mechanical drawing and their application to architectural drawing; an understanding of conventional standards and symbols; architectural technique; lettering in the Roman alphabet; use of catalogs and handbooks for standard sizes and constructions; and the kinds of drawings required by builders (plans, details, elevations, framing plans, and so on) (Figs. 179–187, 190–193, and 194–198).

It is difficult to place specific material in the textbook in the sequence in which it may be used by all teachers and in all variations in courses. By placing this accelerated short unit on architectural drawing and explaining the drawings needed for a complete set of plans for a garage in this location in the textbook, it is hoped that it will be of value to courses of limited time, as well as an introductory course for schools devoting more time in the specialized and technical subjects. The study given previously in the textbook relating to development of a set of plans for a house will be of value whether a simple garage construction is used or whether a more involved assignment requiring a complete set of plans for a house is used. Reference may be profitably made to the information provided in the textbook.

VARIATIONS IN ASSIGNMENTS MAY BE MADE BY DRAWING: (Figs. 190–193)

I. Single-car frame garage
   A. Doors
      1. sliding
      2. swinging
      3. overhead
   B. Windows
      1. fixed sash
      2. double hung
      3. awning
      4. sliding
      5. casement
   C. Roof
      1. gable
      2. hip
      3. shed or flat
II. Single-car brick garage
   Same as outlined for single car frame garage given above
III. Double-car frame (Figs. 194–197)
   Same as outlined for single car frame garage given above
IV. Double-car brick (Fig. 198)
   Same as outlined for single car frame garage given above

Other variation in assignments involving other types of common construction might be suggested. Variations in designs may be gotten from booklets obtained from lumber companies, gardening magazines, household magazines, books, and from original student designs. Individual student assignments may

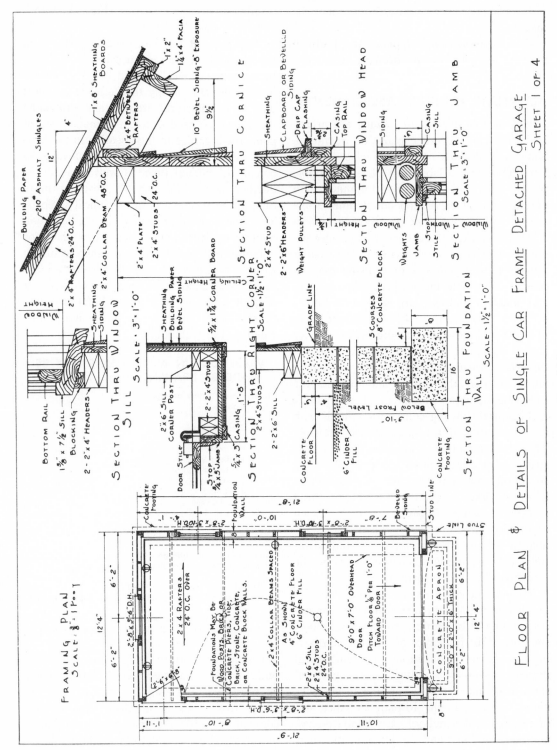

FLOOR PLAN & DETAILS OF SINGLE CAR FRAME DETACHED GARAGE

SHEET 1 OF 4

Fig. 190

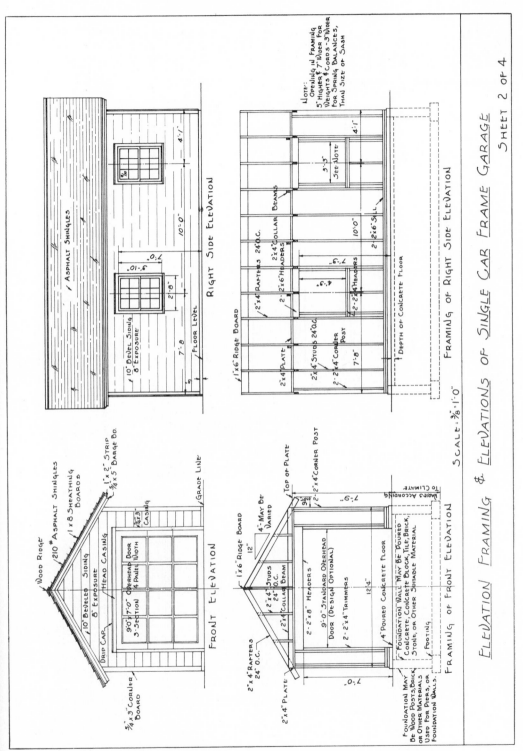

Fig. 191

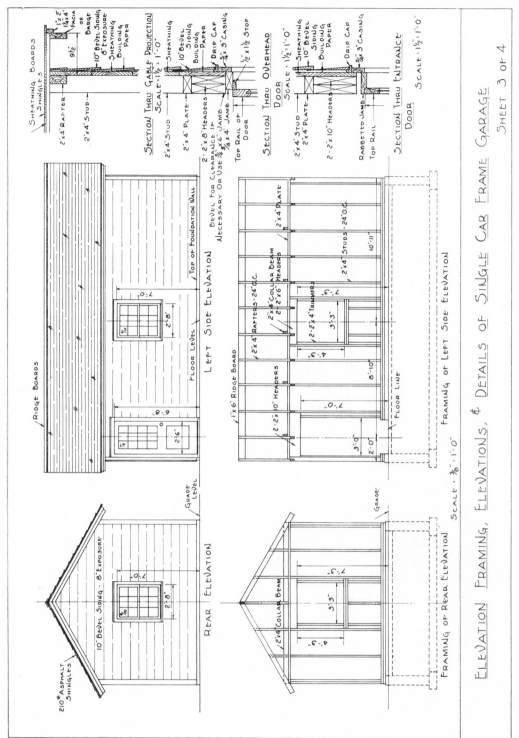

ELEVATION FRAMING, ELEVATIONS, & DETAILS OF SINGLE CAR FRAME GARAGE

SHEET 3 OF 4

Fig. 192

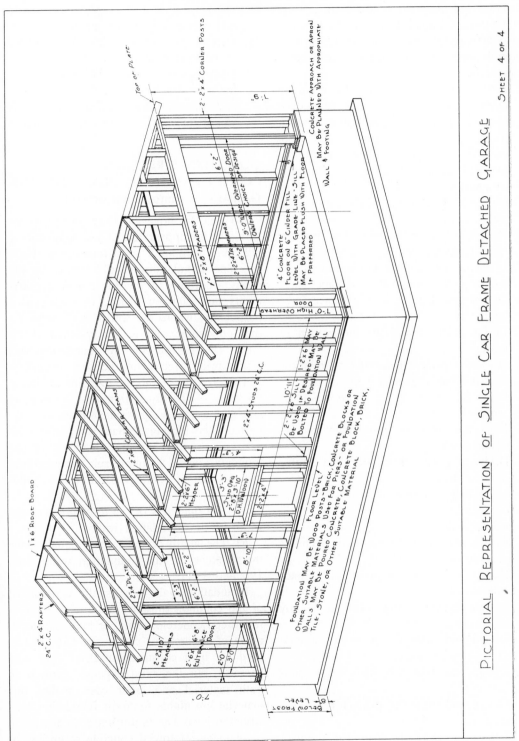

Fig. 193

PICTORIAL REPRESENTATION OF SINGLE CAR FRAME DETACHED GARAGE

SHEET 4 OF 4

be varied with different styles, such as English, Cottage, Colonial, Spanish, and Modern. These assignments may also be adapted to materials such as frame, stucco, brick, stone, or concrete.

1. Design and draw the plans for a garden arbor. Lawn accessories such as outdoor fireplace, greenhouse, slat house or arbor for potting and growing flowers, tool shed, or screened portable porch, may be included in this planning or designing assignment.
2. Design and draw the plans for a lawn trellis.
3. Design and draw the plans for an ornamental garden gate.
4. Design a garden wall which would harmonize with your ideal of a home.
5. Design a wall and motor entrance for a large estate.
6. Design a rustic well for the garden or lawn.
7. Draw the plans for a boy's room using an available attic space.
8. Draw the plans for a children's playroom or nursery.
9. Draw the plans for a basement recreational room.
10. Design a garage that will serve double purpose as:
    a) recreational room
    b) laundry
    c) gardening center
11. Design and draw the plans for a child's playhouse.
12. Design and draw the plans for a roadside stand.
13. Design and draw the plans for a boy scout cabin.
14. Design and draw the plans for a land or real estate office.
15. Design and draw the plans for a summer cottage.
16. Design and draw the plans for a filling station.
17. Design and draw the plans for a single-story ranch type house.
18. Design and draw a complete set of plans and details for a two-story house.
19. Design and draw the plans for a bi-level or tri-level house.
20. Draw necessary plans to remodel the house in which you live. Include changes and improvements which you believe would make it a more desirable home.

GOOD CONSTRUCTION A CONSIDERATION IN PLANNING THE GARAGE (Frame Construction)

No matter how carefully designed the garage is for appearance, it will soon start to fall apart without a good foundation. Footings and foundations should always be put down according to the local code requirements and climatic needs. In some cases, particularly where the soil is hard or rocky, the foundation wall is not widened at the base. The portion of the foundation wall which rests directly on the soil or rock is still referred to as the footing. The minimum thickness of the foundation wall depends, of course, on the weight which must be supported. The footing is made proportionately larger in width than the thickness of the foundation wall. A simple rule for determining the size of footings for a frame building is:

a) The thickness of the footing equals the width of the foundation wall.

b) The width of the footing equals twice the thickness of the foundation wall (Figs. 190 and 194).

Foundation walls are usually constructed of the common masonry materials. Plain or reinforced concrete, stone, or building blocks made of concrete or cinder are most widely used for light construction. Brick may also be used, but the extra expense involved in both material and labor costs makes this material unsuitable for most foundation construction jobs. The footings are usually made of plain or reinforced concrete regardless of the material used in the foundation wall itself.

To prevent upheaval and the subsequent settling of the foundation due to the freezing and thawing of the underlying soil, all footings must be located below the frost line. This frost line is the maximum depth to which the ground freezes in the winter. This depth varies throughout the country. It is dependent on the latitude and the climatic conditions in each specific locality.

In order to indicate the height of the top of the foundation wall above the ground, a heavy line is drawn in the elevation drawings. This line is called a *grade line* and a dimension is placed indicating the distance the foundation wall extends above grade. If the line on the drawing is used to indicate the height of the ground before the building is started, it is called a *present grade line*. When called a *finish grade line*, it indicates the line or height on the foundation to which the ground will be leveled after the building has been completed (Figs. 190, 192, 194, 195, and 198).

Recommended floor for the modern garage is concrete slab at least 4 in. thick and equipped with a drain (Fig. 194). This type of floor has great strength, can be laid in a short time, and is relatively inexpensive. These floors are often reinforced with heavy wire mesh. To prevent water from collecting under the slab floor and to allow any water present to drain off, a layer or fill of cinders, gravel, or crushed rock at least 4 in. deep should be used as a base. The top of the floor may be slanted or pitched toward the center where a drain may be provided, or toward the front to allow the water to drain out of the garage. The floor may be pitched toward the rear and the water drained out through a 3-in. drain tile set in the foundation wall. The concrete slab should extend at least 2 ft. 0 in. in front of the garage to form an apron sloping to the driveway. An expansion joint should be provided between the apron and the driveway. One popular floor with slab and foundation in one unit is the thick-edge reinforced slab. These are 18 to 24 in. thick at the outside edges with the underside arched to a minimum of 4 in. at the center.

To anchor the frame walls of a structure to a masonry foundation, anchor bolts are embedded in the foundation wall while it is being built. The threaded ends of the anchor bolts are extended above the foundation a distance equal to the thickness of the sill plus a sufficient allowance for a washer and a nut to be attached above the sill. The 2 by 4 or 2 by 6 lumber which rests horizontally on the foundation wall and forms the support or bearing surface for the wall of the garage is called a *sill*. In house construction the sill supports the joists and floor as well. The sill may be a single timber or may be built up of two or more thicknesses of 2-in. stock. In the average frame construction the sill is set ⅞ in. inside the outside face of the foundation wall to allow for the sheathing.

Wood doors are made in fixed standard sizes and are stocked by lumber dealers. The width and height of a standard door varies in multiples of 2 in. For example a typical door is 2 ft. 6 in. by 6 ft. 8 in. The next larger size would be 2 ft. 8 in. by 6 ft. 8 in. The doors are stocked in thicknesses varying from 1⅜ to 1¾ in. and in a variety of woods and numerous designs. The heavier doors are used for exterior entrances while the lighter ones are used for the interior of the building. To indicate doors in plans and elevations the proper symbols should be used and all information obtained from manufacturer's catalogs (Fig. 192). See Unit VIII, "House Construction."

Windows, like doors, are standard accessories. They are purchased as prefabricated units, and are installed directly into the openings provided in the structure. See Unit V, House Construction. They are made in standard sizes which vary in width, height, trim, and design. The most common types used in garages are the double-hung, casement, and single or fixed sash. The double-hung window is divided horizontally into two parts, with each part or *sash* sliding past the other in its own channel in the window frame. Each sash may contain a single pane of glass or it may be divided into smaller panes by the thin vertical and horizontal members which are called muntins. In addition to the proper symbol for a window shown in plan, a notation of the window size is placed on the drawing. The abbreviation D. H. is often placed after the note if the window is a double-hung window so that there will be no doubt of the type of window specified. The size of a single pane is indicated on the symbol in elevation by a fraction of width/over height. Often the window will be dimensioned for total height of the window, and a dimension given for placement of the window for height in the wall measured from the floor. The casement type of window has become increasingly popular in light constructions. This type of window consists of one, two, or more panes of glass in the window sash. The sash is hinged along one side. In the more expensive types of casement windows, the opening or closing is done by means of a small crank which is attached to the window sill. The fixed-sash window is widely used in garage construction. This window is used for its decorative effect and for providing light. Since it cannot be opened or closed, it has no value as a source of ventilation.

The vertical members of walls and partitions are called *studs* (Figs. 193 and 197). These studs, when they run the height of the structure from the sill directly to the plate, are called common studs. The studs are set flush with the outside edge of the sill and are often spaced 16 in. apart measured from the center of one stud to the center of the next. The dimension is noted on the drawing as 16 in. O.C. The one-story detached garage may be framed with 2 by 4's spaced 24 in. O.C., depending on the size and type of structure. However, any variation in center distance should be in multiples of 4 in. such as 16, 20, 24 in. since lumber comes in these multiples of length and can be cut to length with minimum waste.

A *corner post* is the structural member which is located at the corners of a frame structure to provide a nailing surface for the outside sheathing and for the inside lath. In a light frame building a single 2 by 4 may provide sufficient strength and nailing surface if the inside is not finished with lath or other finish. In a structure where the inside is not finished and where a single 2 by 4 does not provide the required strength and nailing surface, two 2 by 4's may be used in several combinations as corner posts. When the structure has both exterior sheathing and inside lath, two or more studs are combined to furnish the desired nailing surfaces.

The horizontal member which is nailed directly to the upper ends of the studs is called a *plate*. It is on this exterior wall that the rafters are supported. The plate is usually made of two 2 by 4 timbers. In many cases, however, where the wall is a nonbearing inner partition which must only support its own weight, a single 2 by 4 is used. This single 2 by 4 is sometimes referred to as a *cap*.

The outside of exterior studs is usually covered with sheathing boards, which are usually tongued and grooved, or by a composition sheathing panel. Rafters are usually covered by common boards or sheets of plywood. In some structures such as sheds or garages the sheathing is often omitted, although these will help the owner avoid hard starting of the car in cold weather. In very cold climmates, insulation is desirable. The sheathing serves three purposes: (1) it helps to brace and strengthen the walls; (2) it helps to insulate and make the structure weatherproof; (3) it provides nailing surface for the exterior siding. (The same applies for sheathing or roof boards under the roofing materials.) The sheathing may be applied either horizontally or diagonally. Diagonal sheathing, while it is more costly in labor and material, is by far the stronger. When nailed properly, diagonally sheathed walls are from four to seven times as stiff and from seven to eight times as strong as horizontally sheathed walls.

Wood finish which is applied to the sheathing to form the exterior wall of a frame structure is of two general types: shingle, and siding. Wood shingles are of tapered cross section and are made in lengths of 16, 18, and 24 in. and in random widths from 2½ to 16 in. Each row of shingles overlaps the previous row leaving from 6 in. to 12 in. of the shingle exposed or "to the weather." The random widths permit each new row of shingles to be applied so that the openings formed by the butting of the adjacent shingles do not align with the openings in the under row. Thus, wind and rain do not have easy entrance through the exterior wall. Siding is the name given to the long strips of lumber used for exterior finish of the walls. This material comes in a variety of cross-sectional shapes ranging in width from 4 to 12 in. When using *clapboard* or beveled siding, the drawing must contain a note which gives the number of inches the siding must be exposed "to the weather." This notation is not necessary when using *drop siding* since the bottom edge of each strip laps over the top of the preceding strip. Each of the two types is tapered in cross section as are shingles, and they are usually applied over some type of sheathing in house construction. In much garage construction, however, such siding is applied directly to the studs. *Novelty siding* and *ship-lap* siding are used extensively in low cost constructions. Both of these siding materials are thicker than either beveled siding, or drop siding. With these siding materials, each strip is lapped over the preceding one so that it makes an effective seal against wind or rain.

The vertical boards sometimes used at the corners of frame buildings are called *corner boards.* In an inexpensive type of frame structure the corner boards are often nailed directly over the siding. This is practical when using either shiplap or novelty siding which is of uniform thickness. When using clapboard, beveled siding, drop siding or other

exterior wall materials which are of tapered cross section, the corner boards are nailed in place before the siding is applied. The siding strips are then cut to fit between the corner boards and the door and window casings. Shaped metal strips are sometimes used instead of corner boards when beveled siding is used. These metal corner strips cover the openings formed on exterior corners where the beveled siding meets. Another purpose of the metal strips or wood corner boards is to trim the corner for appearance in addition to sealing the open break at the corners against the weather.

It is most important that the garage area be properly lighted for both the inside and outside uses required of it. A light on the exterior over the door, operated by a three-way switch for both house and garage entrance, makes it easier to get the car in the garage and for the driver and others to enter the house. A light inside the garage is necessary for the placing of and the removal of articles carried in the car. Several outlets should be provided for an extension cord for inspection of the car or as a source of power for electrical tools. Lights and outlets should be conveniently located to accommodate all work areas.

Some provision for heating the garage in very cold weather will pay for itself many times over in the convenience of starting the motor. Several electrical devices are on the market for keeping the oil warm for easier starting but these do not keep the cooling system protected. Ventilation of the garage is most essential for the prevention of possible accidents through the escape of carbon monoxide gas while the motor is running. If the car owner does his own minor repairs or his cleaning and polishing there is need for good lighting. One window is essential, two are better for both light and ventilation.

The driveway to the garage should be of cement or blacktop construction. The driveway may be a wide one where the available space is not at a premium. A drive where only the concrete is in two tracks is sometimes used but not to be recommended. If the area permits the drive should not be in a straight line, for a graceful curve is much more attractive and the added expense is negligible. A widened space or apron at the entrance to the garage provides a convenient place for turning the car as well as for washing and polishing it. The width of the apron should be wide enough for one to work on both sides of the car without being required to step off of the concrete, and wide enough that the car can be maneuvered in position easily. The apron should be laid with an easy grade for drainage so that there will be no accumulations of water after rains or car washings (Fig. 14).

FRAMING PLANS AND ELEVATIONS (Figs. 191, 192, 194, 195, 196, 198)

The average construction job is too involved to be explained clearly and adequately by the representation of a few views given in a set of drawings. To explain the construction further, the draftsman or architect uses conventional symbols, detail drawings, sectional views, plans, elevations, and at times pictorial representations. In addition, written specifications usually accompany a set of drawings.

Framing plans and elevations are included with a set of plans to explain further the construction to be used. In some sections of the country, building codes call for framing plans and elevations before a permit is given and construction can be started. In these framing plans the draftsman strips away the outer finish of the structure so that he may show the number, size, spacing and direction of studs, joists, rafters and other structural parts of a frame building. In addition the framing plans show the location, size, and framing details for the rough opening in the frame which is provided for doors and windows. The cross-sectional size, that is, the width and thickness of the structural members, is given in whole inches and represents

the nominal sizes. The widths and thicknesses usually vary in multiples of 2 in. The actual size of stock is less than the nominal size by the amount of stock that is removed in the milling or finishing operations. The actual width and thickness may be from ⅜ to ½ in. less than the nominal size.

When framing a building, the designer must provide room in the frame for the insertion of windows and doors. These openings in the walls are called *rough openings*. The rough openings are always larger than the units for which they are provided, with the actual size of the opening dependent on the type of window, door, or finish trim used. Millwork catalogs, which should be available to the drafting room, provide information on the necessary increase in size of the rough opening over the stock unit size. When studs are cut to make an opening, the studs on either side of the opening must support the weight which the cut studs would have carried. To help support this weight, the studs around the openings are doubled. If the doubled studs run the full length from the sole to the plate, they are called *trimmers*. If one or both are cut shorter than the full length or common stud, they are called *jack studs*. Some type of support is necessary to support and finish off the top and bottom of the opening formed by the jack studs. These studs below the opening are supported directly on the sole. For the jack studs above the openings, the support is made of double 2 by 4's laid preferably on edge because they can support more weight without sagging, and they are called *headers*. Over a small door or window two 2 by 4's are used as a header. However, when the opening is over 3 ft. 0 in., two 2 by 6's or larger are recommended. Where the opening, such as in a window, does not reach to the floor, doubled 2 by 4's called a *rough sill* are used across the bottom of the opening. These lower 2 by 4's may be set flat.

The type of roof formed by two flat surfaces intersecting at a ridge is called a *gable roof*. The end wall which runs up to the

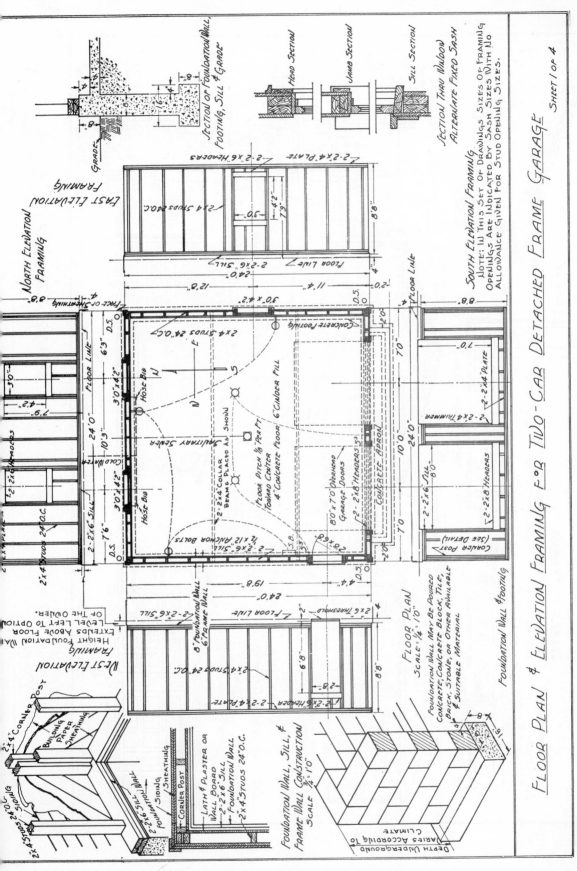

Section of Foundation Wall, Footing, Sill & Grade

Section Thru Window, Alternate Fixed Sash

Head Section

Jamb Section

Sill Section

South Elevation Framing
Note: In this set of drawings sizes of framing openings are indicated by sash sizes with no allowance given for stud opening sizes.

East Elevation Framing

North Elevation Framing

West Elevation Framing

Height Foundation Wall Extends Above Floor Level Left To Option Of The Owner.

Floor Plan
Scale 1/4"=1'-0"

Foundation Wall May Be Poured Concrete, Concrete Block, Tile, Brick, Stone, or Other Available & Suitable Material

Foundation Wall, Sill & Frame Wall Construction
Scale 3/4"=1'-0"

Depth Underground Varies According To Climate

FLOOR PLAN & ELEVATION FRAMING FOR TWO-CAR DETACHED FRAME GARAGE   Sheet 1 of 4

Fig. 194

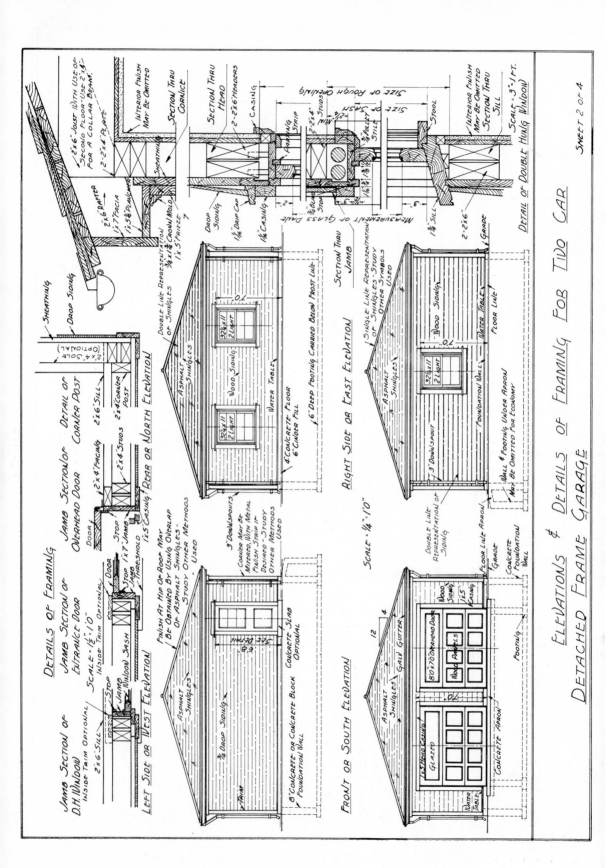

ELEVATIONS & DETAILS OF FRAMING FOR TWO CAR

DETACHED FRAME GARAGE

SHEET 2 OF 4

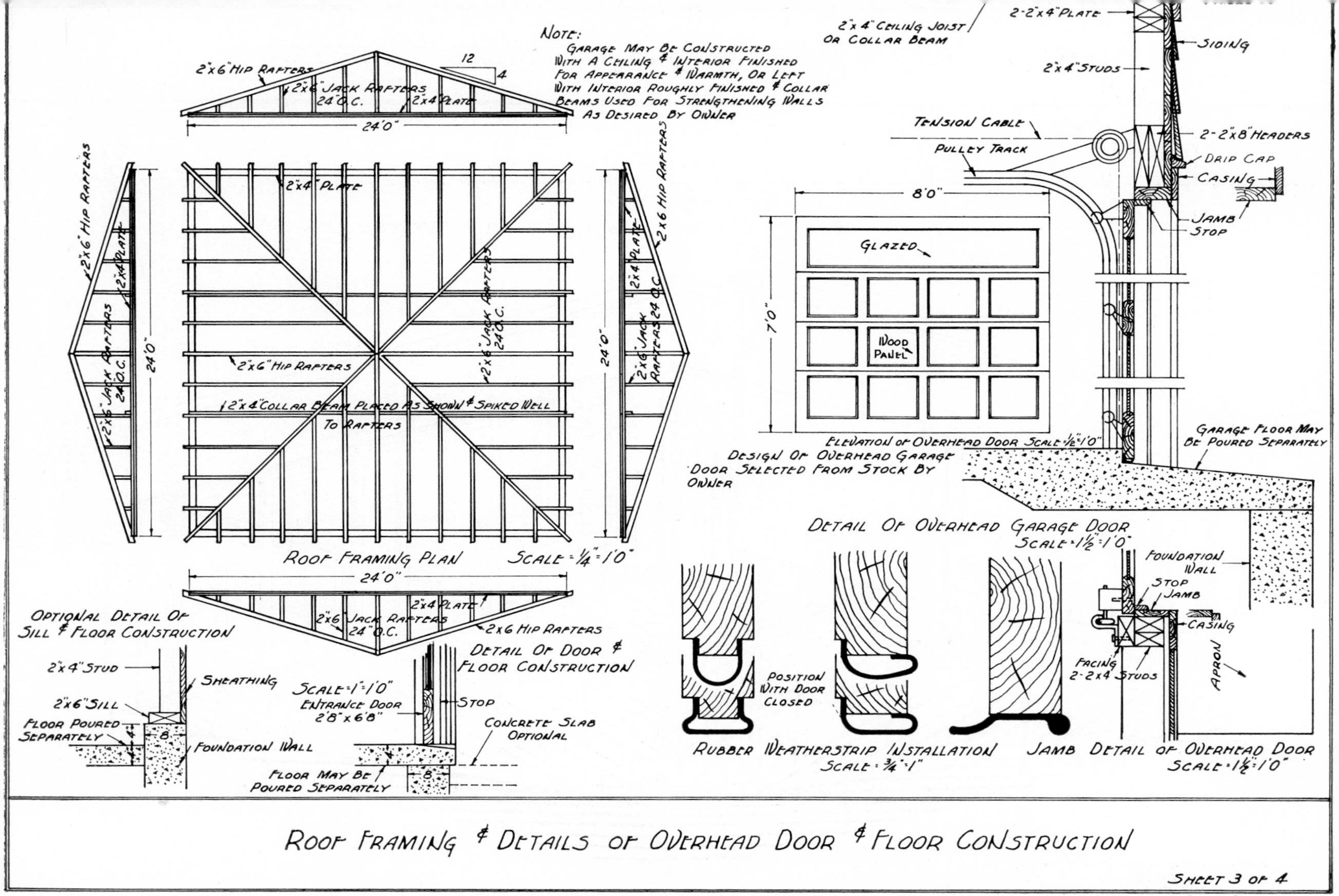
NOTE:
GARAGE MAY BE CONSTRUCTED WITH A CEILING & INTERIOR FINISHED FOR APPEARANCE & WARMTH, OR LEFT WITH INTERIOR ROUGHLY FINISHED & COLLAR BEAMS USED FOR STRENGTHENING WALLS AS DESIRED BY OWNER
2"x6" HIP RAFTERS
2"x6" JACK RAFTERS 24" O.C.
2"x4" PLATE
12
4
24'0"
2"x4" PLATE
2"x6" HIP RAFTERS
2"x6" JACK RAFTERS 24" O.C.
2"x4" COLLAR BEAM PLACED AS SHOWN & SPIKED WELL TO RAFTERS
2x6 HIP RAFTERS
2x4 PLATE
2x6 JACK RAFTERS 24" O.C.
ROOF FRAMING PLAN
SCALE = 1/4" = 1'0"
OPTIONAL DETAIL OF SILL & FLOOR CONSTRUCTION
2"x4" STUD
SHEATHING
2"x6" SILL
FLOOR POURED SEPARATELY
FOUNDATION WALL
DETAIL OF DOOR & FLOOR CONSTRUCTION
SCALE = 1" = 1'0"
ENTRANCE DOOR 2'8" x 6'8"
STOP
CONCRETE SLAB OPTIONAL
FLOOR MAY BE POURED SEPARATELY
2"x4" CEILING JOIST OR COLLAR BEAM
2-2"x4" PLATE
SIDING
2"x4" STUDS
TENSION CABLE
PULLEY TRACK
2-2"x8" HEADERS
DRIP CAP
CASING
JAMB
STOP
8'0"
7'0"
GLAZED
WOOD PANEL
ELEVATION OF OVERHEAD DOOR SCALE 1/2" = 1'0"
DESIGN OF OVERHEAD GARAGE DOOR SELECTED FROM STOCK BY OWNER
GARAGE FLOOR MAY BE POURED SEPARATELY
DETAIL OF OVERHEAD GARAGE DOOR
SCALE = 1 1/2" = 1'0"
POSITION WITH DOOR CLOSED
RUBBER WEATHERSTRIP INSTALLATION
SCALE = 3/4" = 1"
FOUNDATION WALL
STOP
JAMB
CASING
FACING 2-2x4 STUDS
APRON
JAMB DETAIL OF OVERHEAD DOOR
SCALE = 1 1/2" = 1'0"
ROOF FRAMING & DETAILS OF OVERHEAD DOOR & FLOOR CONSTRUCTION
SHEET 3 OF 4

Fig. 196

Note:
Collar Beams Have Been Omitted From This
Pictorial Drawing To Keep The Main Details Of
Construction As Clearly & Simply Illustrated
For The Student As Possible.

2×6"Hip Rafters

8'.8"

7'.0"

2'.0"

24'.0"

2'.0"

2-2×8" Headers

8'0" Wide Overhead To Be
Garage Door Design To
Selected From Stock By
Owner

10'.0"

7'.0"

1"×1"×3/16" L Angle For Corner
Reinforcement

Concrete Apron

7'.0" High Overhead Door

2×6" Rafters

2×6"
24"O.C.

2-2×6"
Headers

28"Wide
Door

2×6 Threshold
May Be Omitted
If Desired

8" Poured Concrete Foundation Wall &
Footing Carried Below Frost Level- May Be
Concrete Block or Other Suitable Materials

24'.0"

4"

6'.8" High Door

30"×42"
Window

Exposed Concrete When Required

2×4 Studs 24"O.C.

Floor

2-2×6 Sill

2-2×4 Plate

3-2×4's
Built Up Corner Posts

Level

Below Frost

6"

3"

Framing For Two-Car Detached Garage
Scale 3/8"=1'.0"

Pictorial Representation of Construction of Detached Garage

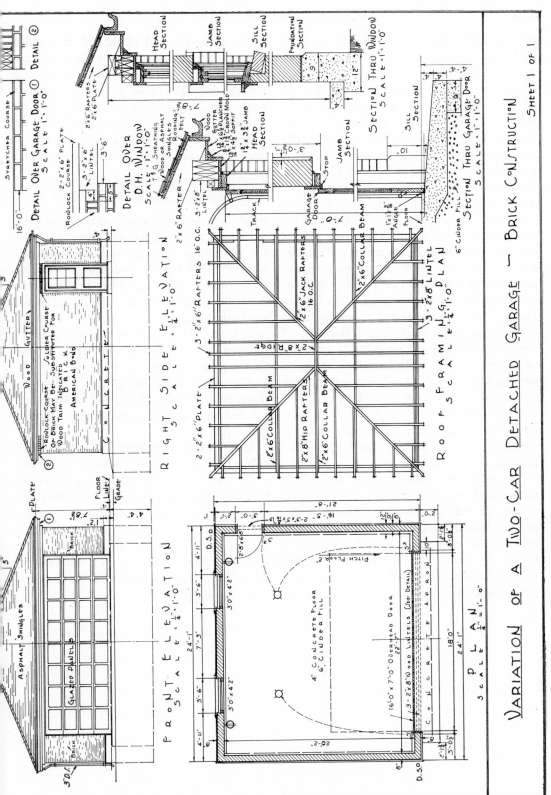

VARIATION OF A TWO-CAR DETACHED GARAGE — BRICK CONSTRUCTION

Fig. 198

ridge is called the gable end. This type of roof adds height and beauty to a structure and may be varied by using the several pitches or angles. The comparatively steep slope of this type of roof allows rain water or water from melted snow to run off immediately so that no damage results from an accumulation. Most detached garages use this type of roof. The *hip roof* slopes from all four walls. It is usually brought to a point at the top, but it may be finished with a ridge or a flat deck.

Asphalt shingles are used almost exclusively as a roof covering because of the durability and fireproof nature of the composition. Wood shingles were at one time the most widely used roof covering but are not recommended because they are quite inflammable. Composition shingles are specified according to their weight per 100 sq. ft. of area covered. They are available in a variety of designs, colors, and sizes. The exposure or "to-the-weather" dimension of asphalt shingles depends on the type of shingle used and its tab length. The shingle lines indicated on the elevation drawings are only symbolic representations and are not actual representations of the courses.

The members which form the framework of the roof are called *rafters*. The *common rafters* run from the plate to the ridge board and are usually spaced 16 or 24 in. apart (O.C.). The rafters may extend beyond and below the plate. The linear length of the rafter beyond the building is called the *projection* and the horizontal distance from the sheathing to the end of the rafter is called the *overhang*. There are two ways of measuring and specifying the angle at which the rafters rise. The first and most common method is by specifying a certain height in inches for each foot of *run* or horizontal of the rafter. The second method of specifying this angle is a fraction representing the ratio of:

$$\frac{\text{Total Rise (height of roof from plate)}}{\text{Total Span (distance between plates)}}. \text{ The}$$

weight of the roof acting against the plate has a tendency to spread the rafters and push the wall out. To counteract this tendency, a tie or *collar beam* is fastened to both rafters to form a triangle. Collar beams can be 2 by 4's, or 2 by 6's and should be spaced no farther than 6 ft. 0 in. O.C. In many structures, such as houses, and garages with rooms above, floor or ceiling joists which rest on the plate are used.

The size and spacing dimensions and the direction of joists, rafters, and collar beams are indicated on the plan which is directly below the beams.

Exterior trim on a frame building is usually applied at the *eaves* and *cornices,* the *gable ends,* the *corners* and around the doors and windows. The trim is applied for two purposes: to cover the rough construction and for its decorative effect. The trim at the cornice is used to close the juncture of the roof rafters and the walls. In a *flush cornice* the rafters are cut off flush with the plate and there is no overhang.

UNIT
XXI

Legal Documents

The legal side of the building problem is somewhat confusing to the inexperienced. Documents written in legal phraseology are somewhat complicated to the owner who is asked for his signature.

Proposals, contracts, bonds, and other legal papers are very simple when analyzed. These contract forms have been standardized by the American Institute of Architects.

The contract is the first legal paper the owner is asked to sign. After the bid to be accepted has been decided upon, the building contract must be signed by the owner and contractor. This contract is an agreement in which one party agrees to perform certain work and the other party agrees to pay him for the work and services rendered. The standard form used is the *standard form of agreement* recommended by the American Institute of Architects.

When the plans and specifications are ready for bids, many architects send an invitation for proposal to the various contractors whom he believes advisable to invite. Each contractor is given a standard proposal form on which to enter his bid.

When a large house is to be built, it is quite common to require the contractor to furnish a bond assuring that he will faithfully carry out the agreement.

After a contract is let for the building of the new house and the contractor is ready to begin work, it is necessary to take out a *building permit*. The permit states in a general way the character of the work and

the cost of the building, the fee required for the document being a certain percentage of the cost of the house. Special permits are issued for the remodeling of an old house. Other permits required are the plumbing and electric permits.

When payments are made to a contractor as the work goes on, it is usually required that he give the owner a *waiver of lien* from himself and all other firms who have furnished materials to him.

When the contractor has performed sufficient work to entitle him to a payment, this is done upon receipt from the architect of a certificate of payment due the contractor. This is really a requisition upon the owner for the required amount with a detailed statement of what the money was paid for. This serves as a receipt when in the hands of the owner.

Some architects enter into a private contract with the owner as to the compensation the architect is to receive, stating the work he is to perform and the amounts of the various payments due him from time to time as the work progresses.

SPECIFICATIONS

A contract on specifications should be thought of as a conversation between the owner, the contractor, and the architect. During the conversation, the architect tells the contractor just how certain details are to be accomplished, and what materials are to be used. This conversation must be recorded so that all three participants have a copy.

Specifying materials and products definitely by trade or manufacturer's name will accomplish the best results. With this system there is no trouble for the owner to determine who is legitimately low.

It is better to add a few more notes and a detail drawing, referring to them in the specifications, than to attempt to explain and cover them by specification. The more that is covered in the drawings, the less danger of forgetting something. Details covered by drawings do not need to be repeated in the specifications, but only referred to. For example, if some trim is shown in detail it is only necessary to mention the kind of wood to be used and the finish in the specifications.

The method usually used by the architect in writing a set of specifications for a house, is to take from his files specifications for a similar house designed at some previous period, following it as a model for the new specifications.

In writing specifications it is customary in the offices of most architects to write separate specifications for each branch of work. Thus there are mason's specifications, carpenter's specifications, plumbing specifications, and so on. Even when a general contract is let for the entire work, the general contractor usually sublets portions of the work, such as the plumbing, electrical, heating, and so on, and it is a great convenience for him to have separate specifications for the different branches. Thus he hands the plumbing specifications to the plumber, the painting specifications to the painter, instead of giving them a set of specifications for the entire building.

Although each of the branch specifications is written separately, when one contract for the whole job is let, the separate specifications are bound together into one, and the contract with the general contractor is made for the complete building.

Many of the separate specifications contain more than one branch of work. For instance, masonry specifications include excavation, bricklaying, plastering, and so on. The mason who takes the contract frequently does not do the plastering but sublets this contract to other contractors. He does take the entire contract for masonry, however, and he is responsible for the entire masonry contract.

ASSIGNMENT

Specification Sheets

Specification sheets should be drawn up for the house as planned in the previous unit. Several samples of specification sheets should be at hand to be used as a guide for the students. Contract forms as standardized by the American Institute of Architects may be found in any of the better architectural handbooks. Particular attention should be directed toward the relationship of the working drawings and the specification sheets.

PROBLEMS FOR CLASS DISCUSSION

1. What is the relationship which exists between the working drawings and the specifications?
2. Why are the specification sheets necessary? Who uses them?
3. Obtain, if possible, some blank forms used by architects in drawing up contracts.
4. What regulations do you find in your building code for your city? Obtain a copy of this code for your classroom.
5. What regulations are imposed by the state for residences?

ARCHITECTURAL DRAWING IV

Preliminary Studies in Getting Out a Complete Set of Plans

The average client who comes to the architect's office builds but once in a lifetime and, as a rule, is entirely unfamiliar with the working drawings as used by builders. He may be able to read a blueprint so far as the general layout of the rooms is concerned, and may understand the elevation drawings if they are simple in form, but if there are irregular masses with several gables of different pitches, he is confused. Because of this difficulty of expressing the idea of the plans and elevations of the building, the practice of preparing sketches and rendered perspective drawings has grown.

A person who desires to build a house should consult a reliable architect, giving him in general an idea of what he, wants in regard to the style of house, number of rooms, and amount of money available for the purpose. The architect usually discovers through questioning and through outside information, his client's habits, mode of living, type of friends, and, roughly, his income. With his client's personality and general make-up in mind, he makes several pencil sketches of floor plans and elevations and submits them for study and approval. These small sketches are usually made at about ⅛-in. scale. From these rough sketches, several "thumb-nail" perspective sketches are made giving the floor plans and the proposed exterior of the house. As the design takes more definite form, accurate but simple instrumental perspectives are made. These perspectives are rendered by casting the shadows and often in the natural colors of the building and surroundings.

Freehand studies are often made of such details as the chimneys, dormer windows, front entrances, and so on. Even while the building is being erected sketches are occasionally needed to explain details to the client or the contractor.

A plot plan should be made for all working drawings. This plan should show the property lines and locate the buildings with reference to them. The walks, driveways, and landscape plan should be included.

PRACTICE STROKES IN SKETCHING

Sharpen the pencil by cutting away the wood at a long slope, being careful not to cut the lead, but exposing it about three eighths of an inch. Next, wear the point down on fine sandpaper holding the pencil at an angle of about 45 degrees with the paper. The point is then smoothed by rubbing it on rough paper until each stroke gives a firm, even tone (see Fig. 201). For broad strokes the flattened side of the lead is used, for occasional sharp, decisive touches the pencil may be held on its sharp edge.

The student must be able to draw individual lines of a great variety. Long, sweeping strokes, bold, vigorous lines, crisp dashes, straight lines, curved lines, are drawn with directness and vigor and not in a laborious manner. All strokes should receive full pressure and begin and end in a crisp, painted-

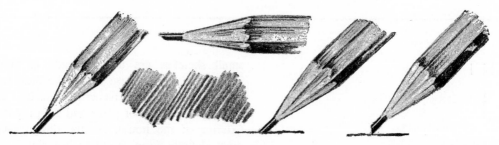

Fig. 201

like stroke. Allow some strokes to fade out so gradually that the ends are lost in the tones of the paper, and accent others at the ends by using extra pressure as the pencil touches or leaves the paper. Make lines with broad and fine points, with various grades of pencils, and on all sorts of paper.

In the horizontal, vertical, and oblique strokes, bear down hard, "ironing out" the paper with the lead until you get an even, firm tone of the desired value. (See Figs. 202 and 203.)

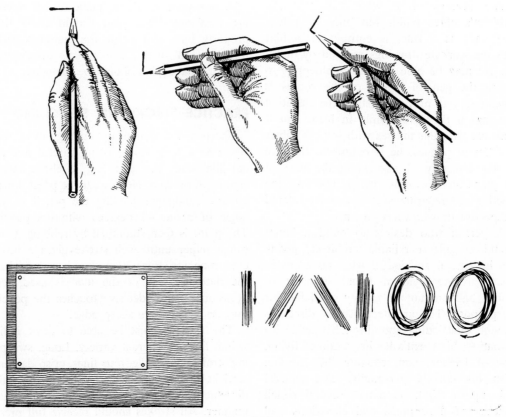

Fig. 202

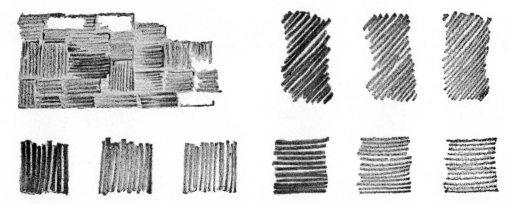

Fig. 203

For the stone wall, 2H, HB, and 2B pencils are used, the direction of the stroke being changed occasionally to give variety and indicate the direction of laying the stones. Accent may be obtained with the sharp edge of the soft pencil. Allow a little of the paper to show occasionally. Strokes for foliage are made in a free manner. They are of various lengths, forming the shape of the bush, tree, grass, and so on. The masses should be kept simple but interesting in shape. (See Figure 204).

ASSIGNMENT

Plate 1, Practice Strokes Used in Sketching (Pencil)

Make a drawing consisting of the strokes used in sketches. Make lines with broad and fine points, with various grades of pencils.

The Supplementary Plate 1A, may be assigned to advanced students.

Fig. 204

Plate 1

Supplementary Plate 1A

UNIT

II

Representation of Details

The easiest way of learning to render a freehand perspective sketch is to become familiar with the methods of indicating the smaller details. One should learn to represent such materials as brick, stones, shingles, slate, and clapboards, and then progress to the representation of details such as chimneys, doors, windows, and cornices. There is no one correct method of representing these details, for the distance from the object is to be considered as well as the amount of elaboration which would be advisable. In the representation of a complete building the details must be so subordinated that they will blend nicely.

STONEWORK

The method of representation will vary according to the light and shade of the wall, consideration of the distance of the object from the eye, the angle of projection used in the representation, tone of the individual stones, texture of the stone, size of the stone, shape of the stone, and the method of laying the stones in a wall (see Plate 3). Some stones are laid as they are brought from the quarries, and others are carefully finished to give the wall almost the appearance of being plastered. The mortar between the joints varies from none at all to elaborate methods of finishing. The important consideration is that it is not the representation of the individual stones which counts, but that the effect of the entire wall must be obtained.

BRICKWORK

The chief difference between the representation of brickwork and stonework is in the smallness of the units of the bricks (see Plates 2, 3, and 4). The average brick is represented by a rectangle 2 in. high, 4 in. wide, and 8 in. long. The various bonds used in brickwork must be suggested in the rendering. It is advisable to vary the method of indication in the different parts of the same drawing, in order to avoid monotony.

STUCCO OR CONCRETE

A little stippling or a few groups of sketchy strokes here and there are all that is needed to represent the smooth surfaces of the stucco or concrete. The bare paper usually serves for the representation of the light surfaces. Shade lines are represented by almost any arrangement of vertical and inclined lines.

CLAPBOARD

Usually nothing is needed to represent the clapboards other than the horizontal lines of shadow under each one (see Fig. 205 and Plate 2).

SHINGLES

The clapboard representation with the addition of a few vertical lines will serve for the shingles (see Fig. 205 and Plate 2).

ROOF INDICATIONS

The planes of the roof are foreshortened in appearance, especially when viewed from the ground, so that roof representation is largely a matter of experimentation (see Fig. 205 and Plate 2). The treatment depends upon the distance from the subject, the kind of roofing material, the age of the material, and the method of laying. Slate is represented in much the same manner as

HORIZONTAL METHOD

OUTLINE METHOD

FREE LINE METHOD

METHOD OF INDICATING ROOFS

Fig. 205

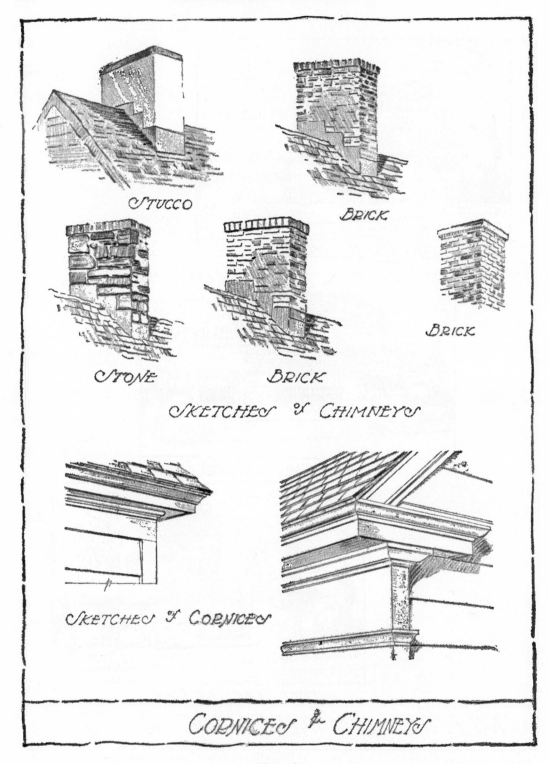

STUCCO

BRICK

STONE

BRICK

BRICK

SKETCHES OF CHIMNEYS

SKETCHES OF CORNICES

CORNICES & CHIMNEYS

Plate 2

CLOUDS

ROOFS

CHIMNEYS

WATER

DETAILS & ACCESSORIES

Supplementary Plate 2A

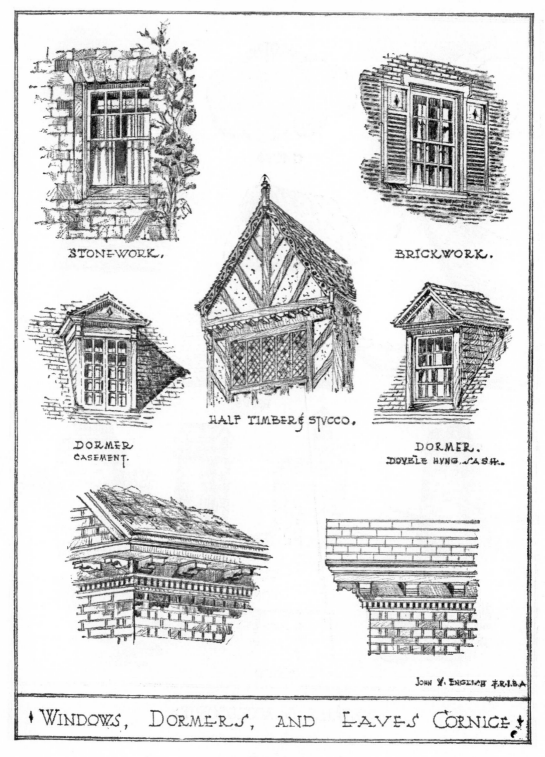

STONEWORK.

BRICKWORK.

HALF TIMBER & STUCCO.

DORMER.
CASEMENT.

DORMER.
DOUBLE HUNG SASH.

JOHN V. ENGLISH F.R.I.B.A

WINDOWS, DORMERS, AND EAVES CORNICE

Plate 3

shingles. No attempt should be made to show every course of slate or shingles, for if this is done the value is almost sure to become either too complicated or too dark. Avoid breaking the tone into too many conspicuous spots.

CHIMNEY REPRESENTATION

No other detail of a house is more worthy of study than the chimney, together with the parts of the house directly adjacent to it. Plate 2 will offer the best chance for the student to test his skill in the representation of various materials as they appear in close relationship to each other.

CORNICE REPRESENTATION

In a sketch the student must work for an effect of reality, and even though certain details are necessarily slighted, the light and shade and the tone and texture of the materials must be given the relative values as might be found in nature (see Plates 2 and 3). In sketching the cornice do not over-darken the projecting portions, for it is the contrast of the light fascia board against the shadow below which gives the desired sense of projection.

WINDOW REPRESENTATION

Windows and doors are a bit harder to draw than most of the house details because the light and shade of the glazed surfaces are changeable in their appearance (see Fig. 205 and Plate 3). Before attempting finished renderings of doors and windows the student should carefully observe the appearance of these details under actual conditions. This observation will bring out the leading characteristics of glass. The first consideration is the transparency of glass, which allows a showing of the draperies and shades within as though the panes of glass were non-existent. The other consideration, and the

one which causes much of the trouble for the beginner, is the power that glass has to reflect, giving very often a shiny effect to the window. As a rule the two characteristics appear in combination in a window.

The beginner must first decide in sketching as to whether the glass is to be shown light or dark and this depends largely upon the surrounding material. The best way to determine which windows should be dark and which light is by making a preliminary study on tracing paper before starting the final rendering. As a rule those windows nearest the spectator should show not only the strongest contrast but also the greatest amount of detail. Treat the woodwork very broadly merely suggesting by one or two lines all the various members of which the sash and frame are composed. The sash bars will be sufficiently indicated by a single line representing the shady side, and an indication of the shadow on the glass. Sashes are, as a rule, left white.

The shadows cast by the frame and by the sashes on the shades are made quite prominent which adds greatly to the effect. The shadows of the shutters are strongly emphasized.

REPRESENTATION OF TREES, SHRUBS, AND OTHER ACCESSORIES

In this representation it is important that the student become familiar with the trees, shrubs, vines, etc., of his neighborhood by strict observation. He should observe the general mass of each, analyzing the skeleton of the trunk, limbs, branches, twigs, and leaves, as well as the contrasts of light and shade. Such observation will show that trees are representative of the geometric shapes (see Figure 206). The contour of the tree should be given in correct proportion, and be indicated by a few strokes of the pen or by delicate pencil lines, with a representation of the main lines of growth of the framework, such as the trunk and branches (see

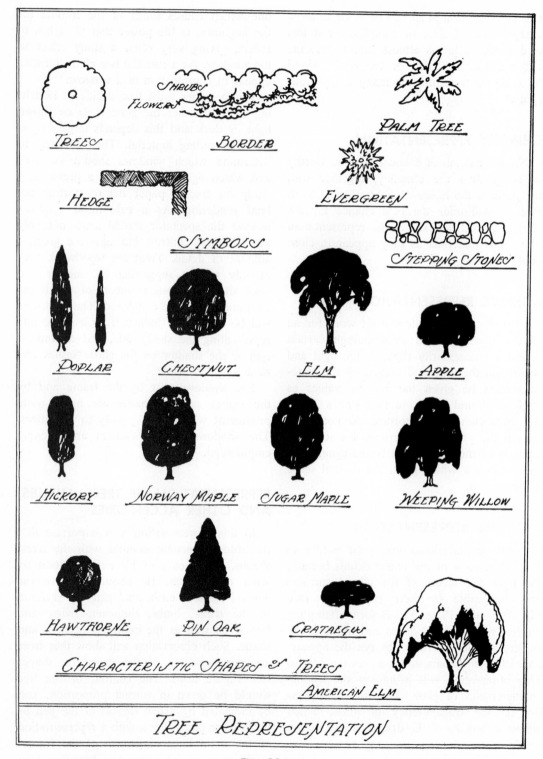

Fig. 206

REPRESENTATION of DOORWAYS

Plate 4

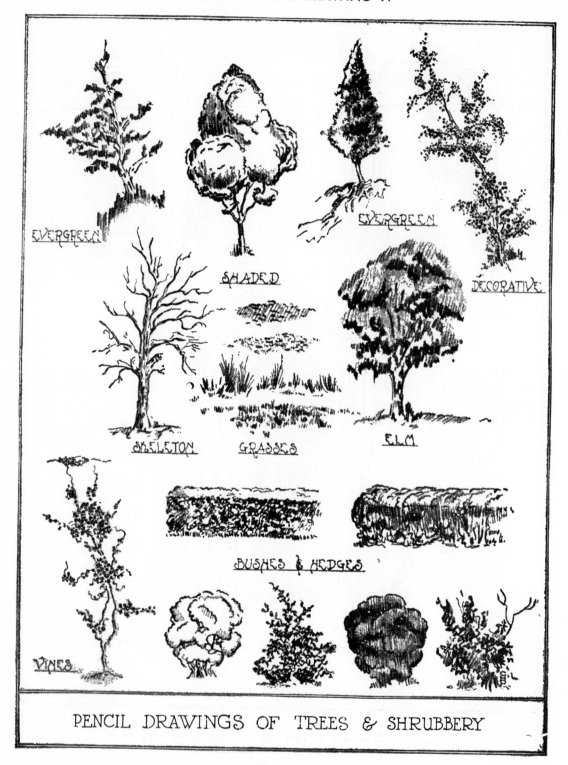

PENCIL DRAWINGS OF TREES & SHRUBBERY

Plate 5

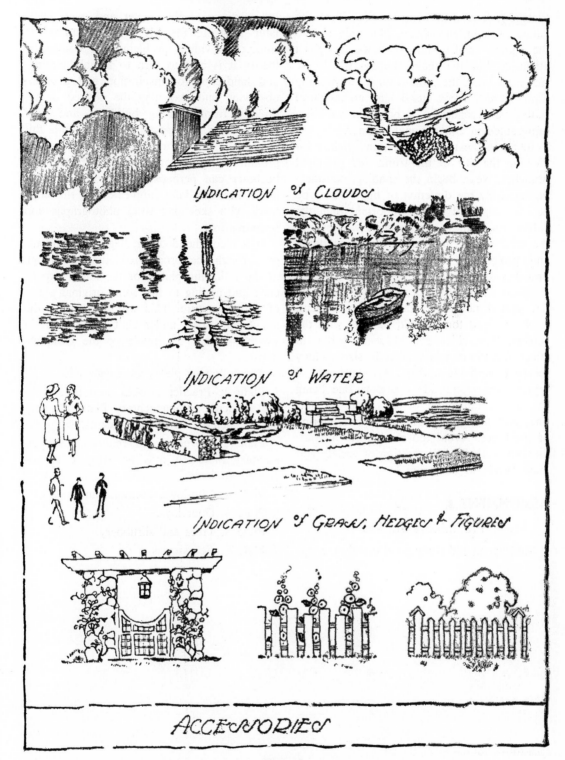

INDICATION of CLOUDS

INDICATION of WATER

INDICATION of GRASS, HEDGES & FIGURES

ACCESSORIES

Plate 6

Plate 5). The next consideration is of the values of light and shade. Not only should the minor shades and shadows be given attention, but the main shadow which the tree casts upon the ground must be carefully represented. Trees used in architectural settings are generally of common varieties, represented in conventional manner.

Block in the main proportions, lightly indicating the line of the trunk and principal branches. Next, begin the shading, considering carefully the direction of light. The type of line employed is less important than the values, for if these are properly worked out the tree will seem modeled to show depth and projection. Suggest roundness in the branches and the trunk.

Clouds, like other accessories (see Plate 6), should never be made too prominent. Each line and tone should balance with the subject. The skies should seem softer in effect and the clouds smaller in size as they recede toward the horizon. Two methods of representing clouds are common, one being the simple indication of the form by outline, and the other a naturalistic rendering of the tones. Avoid too mechanical an outline but work for a suggestion of variety and mass as found in nature.

ASSIGNMENT

Preliminary Studies

Students should study good sketches, copying portions of them over and over again, later applying the ideas thus acquired to similar individual problems. Of course, in theory it is best to turn to actual buildings and landscape for inspiration and practice, observing and sketching the desired details directly from existing buildings and their surroundings. The average student finds this rather difficult work without considerable preliminary preparation, and therefore, the beginner can perhaps learn more by copying at first and later supplementing this copy work with sketching from photographs and from nature.

It is recommended that beginning students go through the process of copying enough of the following plates for the initial experience and adding to this some original plates of similar nature. This will lead up to the assignment given under Unit IV, p. 551, in which sketches are made of the complete house.

The following plates are suggested:

Plate 1, Practice strokes used in sketching (pencil). Supplementary Plate 1A may be assigned to advanced students.

Plate 2, Cornices and chimneys. Supplementary Plate 2A may be assigned to advanced students.

Plate 3, Windows, dormers, and eaves.

Plate 4, Doorways.

Plate 5, Trees and shrubbery.

Plate 6, Accessories.

Shades and Shadows

Shades and shadows are used for the natural appearance they give to the drawing. Although the natural tone and color of the materials in the buildings and their settings are of great importance, so much of the effect of the structure depends on its shadows that the study of light and shades deserves special study which is not within the scope dealt with in this section.

So many separate influences affect the lighting of all objects, such as the reflecting and absorbing powers of the different surfaces and materials, the shifting of clouds, reflections of trees, etc., that individual study and observation of nature at first hand is recommended to the student. One excellent method of studying the changing effects of light on a building is by a series of snapshots taken from some fixed position at intervals during the day.

THE USE OF CONVENTIONAL SHADOWS

Inasmuch as the lighting of most architectural objects will be by the direct rays of the sun's light, the sun is by common convention used as the source of light in architectural drawing. On account of the great distance of the sun from the earth its rays may be taken virtually as parallel to one another (see Figs. 207–211).

The usual practice of dealing with architectural shades and shadows is to assume that the rays of light produced by the sun make an angle of 45 degrees with the horizontal and vertical planes of projection. It has been customary in architectural practice to consider the direction of light as being parallel to that diagonal of a cube drawn from the upper left front corner to the lower right back corner, the bottom of the cube being parallel to the ground and its front parallel to the front plane.

According to the character of the objects which cast or receive the shadows, the method must be adapted. Of these several methods the following are the most applicable in dealing with architectural forms:

1. By means of oblique projection.
2. By means of auxiliary shadows.
3. By the slicing method.

The method of oblique projection consists of simply drawing the 45-degree lines representing the ray tangent to an object or passing through its shade edges, to find the points of the shade line, and in finding the point where these rays strike any other object involved in the problem. Many of the architectural shadows may be cast by this method.

ASSIGNMENT

Because of the application of shades and shadows to both freehand sketching as done in the preliminary studies of a house plan and also in the rendering of the perspective drawing, the student should spend some time in applying the principles to orthographic details of the house. Some time should also be spent in representing the shades and shadows on a few perspective representations of details such as cornices, windows, and so on.

The amount of time to be spent upon this unit is to be left to the judgment of the teacher. This unit is a complete study in itself, and only a brief amount of time can be allowed for experience except as the student may be able to apply it in the unit on *rendering*.

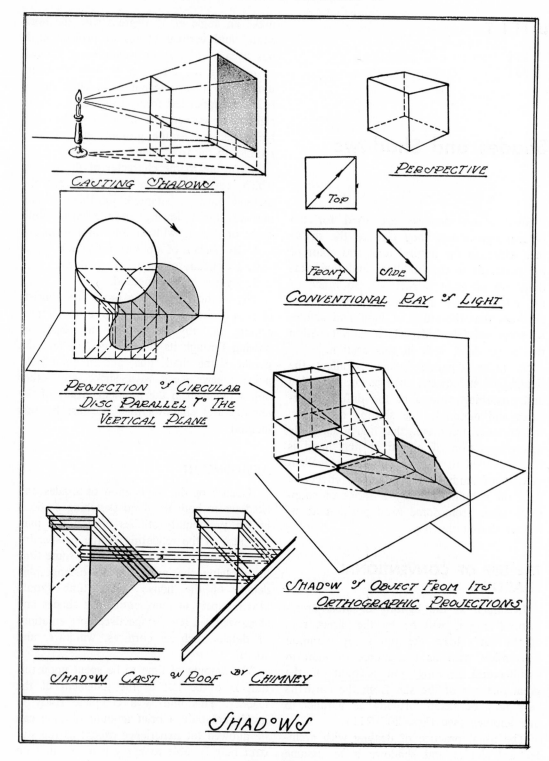

CASTING SHADOWS

PERSPECTIVE

Top

FRONT   SIDE

CONVENTIONAL RAY OF LIGHT

PROJECTION OF CIRCULAR DISC PARALLEL TO THE VERTICAL PLANE

SHADOW OF OBJECT FROM ITS ORTHOGRAPHIC PROJECTIONS

SHADOW CAST ON ROOF BY CHIMNEY

SHADOWS

Fig. 207

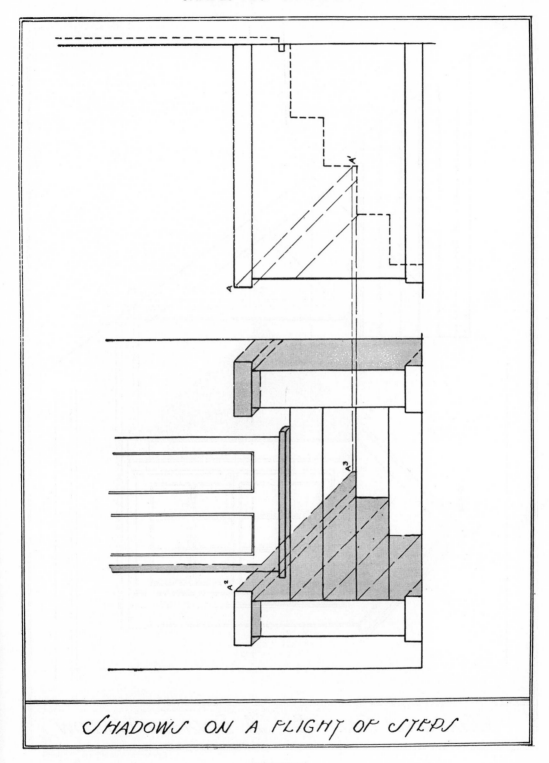

SHADOWS ON A FLIGHT OF STEPS

Fig. 208

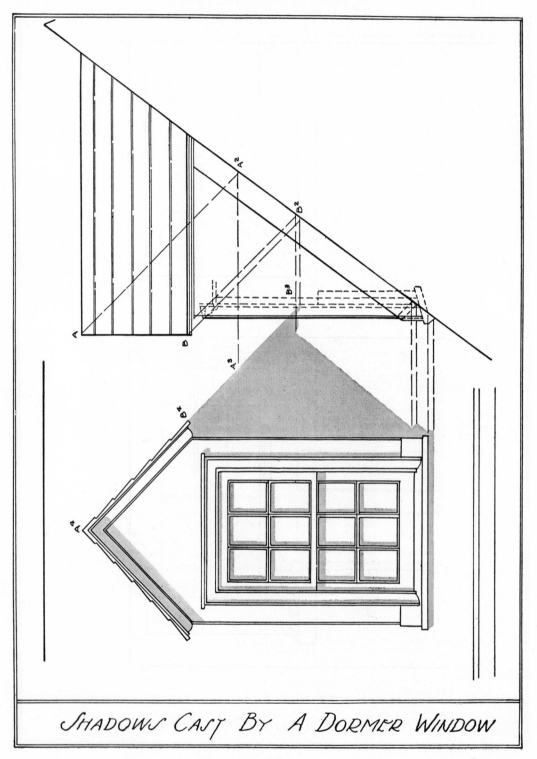

SHADOWS CAST BY A DORMER WINDOW

Fig. 209

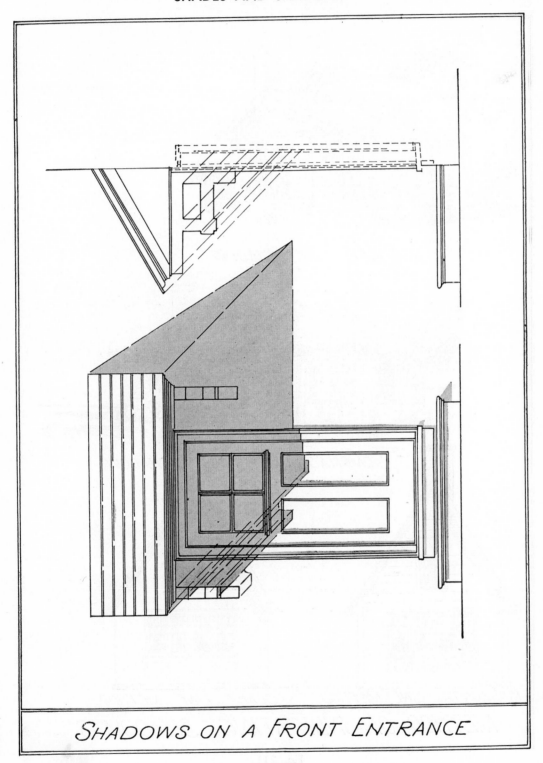

SHADOWS ON A FRONT ENTRANCE

Fig. 210

VERTICAL LINE SHADING

EMPHASIZING BRICK IN SHADOW

HORIZONTAL LINE METHOD   SLANT LINE METHOD

METHOD OF INDICATING SHADOWS

Fig. 211

Rendering Drawings of a House

UNITY

The most important consideration for the student is the determination and arrangement of values of the separate details. All of the details must be so related and so blended together that they become a single unit. Unless each detail is given just the right amount of attention that is proportionate to its importance, the composition will fail as a complete unit. Failure to give sufficient emphasis to the important details causes a loss of force to the entire building. Unity in architectural sketching is often injured because certain accessories are made too important in relation to the building itself. In many rendered sketches of public buildings people are represented on the walks or near entrances of the building, but these figures are left in a somewhat unfinished or conventional representation. Trees are shown in a conventional and an inconspicuous manner; clouds are often either omitted or only lightly indicated, and the shadows are simplified (see Fig. 212).

BALANCE

Balance refers to the restfulness which results from having all the parts of the sketch arranged so that each receives its proportionate amount of attention. In order to study the composition as a whole for balance, a trial sketch should be attempted to study the finished sketch as a whole. By turning a sketch upside down, viewed in a mirror, or standing on end, one may tell as to whether the balance is good and if not that necessary adjustments should be made. If some parts are too prominent, they may be toned down or other parts may be accented until a balance is restored to the sketch.

EMPHASIS

In a rendered sketch it is permissible to omit certain portions if they are of minor importance, and emphasize other details of greater interest. It is generally assumed that the artist is looking in one fixed direction. He gazes at some interesting object and selects some prominent feature, and makes this the center of interest for the sketch. The sharpest details and strongest contrasts are drawn at this point, the drawing growing less distinct toward the edges of the paper. This follows very closely the principle of focus on the camera.

Different methods are needed for obtaining the desired emphasis when using different mediums. In color work, the eye may be compelled or attracted to some particular spot of interest by the medium of some bright and contrasting hue. In pen drawing, the artist is required to obtain the effect through the strong contrasts of light and dark. A white spot against a dark background always attracts the eye. Likewise, a black spot against a light background draws attention. An application of this principle is in the sketching of a white house with a dark background of trees and shrubbery, or the reverse, using a dark building against a lightly outlined background (see Fig. 213).

When starting a perspective, decide which way you wish the house to face for best results. It is usually better to use the front elevation with the most interesting end of the house. Another point worth considering is that it is best to draw the sketch as from a distance so that the receding lines are not

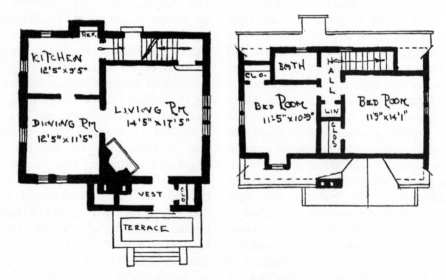

Fig. 212.   Simple pencil sketch of perspective and floor plans.

so acute as to appear clumsy. Sketch a pleasing surrounding for the house perspective, keeping it in harmony with the style of architecture. A path or groups of lines should be used to direct the attention toward the center of interest in combination with a background which gradually fades in the distance. Care must be exercised that these incidentals are not too prominent, otherwise they will defeat their purpose.

Plate 7.   Pencil rendering.

ASSIGNMENT

Plate 7, Rendering Drawing of a House

Application is here made of the previous units of study in sketching. The several details of the house are now united, and thought given to the important elements. This unit becomes a practical application of the previous study units. Perspective is considered in a practical study as the eye would picture the entire unit (see Unit V, p. 554 ff); shades and shadows are cast (see Unit III, p. 545 ff); points of interest or emphasis are located; material representations are indicated.

The several styles of houses are sketched that the student may study the important details of house styles as well as the representations of the several different materials in common use for these particular styles.

Make a complete freehand rendering of one of the following: Spanish Mission, English Colonial, Dutch Colonial, or of a Modern House (see Fig. 212 and Plate 7).

PROBLEMS FOR CLASS DISCUSSION

1. How are these rendered freehand perspectives used by the architect?
2. How are these sketches affected by the individual style used by the architect?
3. Make up a scrapbook of clippings of the several sketches found in magazines and newspapers, including details, accessories, complete house perspective, and so on.
4. Get a few representative sketches from architects for classroom display.

U N I T

V

Perspective Drawing

Before beginning the study of perspective projection, some consideration should be given to the theory upon which this projection is based. One of the most important examples of the theory, and one which is the keynote to the whole study of perspective, has been noticed by everyone. *The length of any line seen on the picture plane varies inversely as the distance of that line from the eye. The area of any surface on the picture plane varies inversely as the square of its distance from the eye.* This fact is illustrated in a practical way when one stands in the center of a straight section of a railroad track. On looking up the track, the rails appear to converge and meet at a point in the distance, while on looking above at the wires on the telegraph poles, they appear to converge and disappear at the same point, and the lines of the fence boards and the telegraph all diminish and finally disappear in the distance in a similar manner. The apparent width of the track and the height of the telegraph poles obey the first rule of perspective set forth, and finally meet in a point at an infinite distance away.

Horizontal lines that are parallel with the picture plane always appear parallel in perspective as shown by the ties of the railroad tracks, which appear to diminish in length and in distance apart, but remain parallel with each other until they disappear in the distance. The same is observable in the telegraph poles and the fence posts. Hence the following rules are given:

Rule I

1. All lines parallel with the picture plane, whether vertical, horizontal, or inclined to the ground line, retain their normal directions in perspective drawing.

2. All lines or surfaces of objects in contact with the picture plane appear their full normal size in perspective.

3. All lines or surfaces of objects beyond the picture plane appear smaller than normal in perspective drawing.

4. All lines or surfaces beyond the picture plane and parallel with it can be drawn to the same scale; but smaller than those in contact with the picture plane.

Rule II

1. All lines not parallel with the picture plane, but parallel with one another, appear to converge as they recede from the eye. The point toward which any set of parallel lines converges is called the vanishing point.

2. When parallel lines are perpendicular to the picture plane, the vanishing point is directly in front of and on a level with the eye; in this position it corresponds to the center of vision.

Hence, lines perpendicular to the picture plane and below the level of the eye slant upward as shown by the rails, and above the level of the eye slant downward as shown by the telegraph wires.

Rule III

1. When the parallel lines are horizontal, but at an angle with the picture plane, their vanishing point is on a level with the eye but to the right or left of the center of vision, according to the angle that the lines make with the picture plane.

2. When parallel lines are horizontal and incline at an angle of 45 degrees to the picture plane, their vanishing point is to the right or left of the center of vision a distance equal to the distance of the station point from the picure plane.

A perspective drawing of an object is a representation of the outline of the object when observed from a given point. If the perspective is rendered in outline only it is

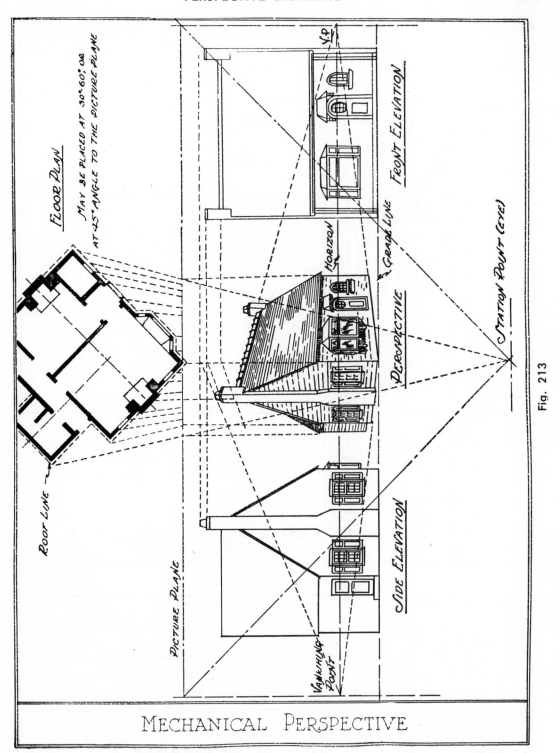

Fig. 213

MECHANICAL PERSPECTIVE

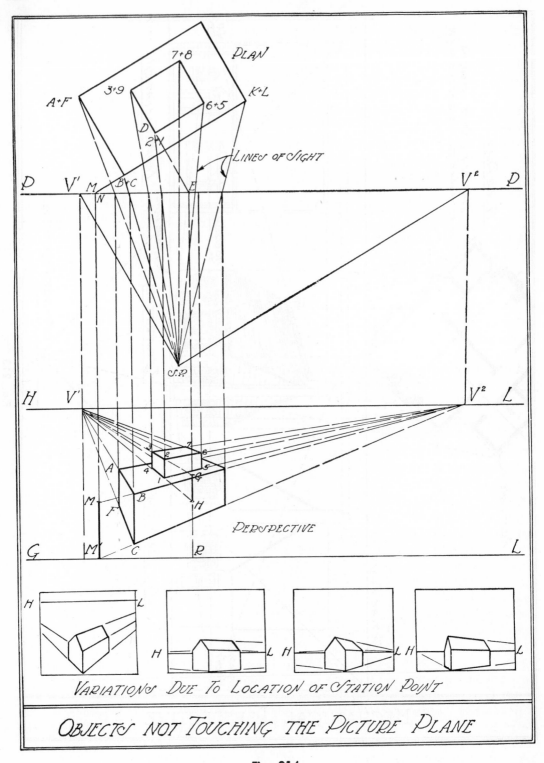

PLAN

LINES OF SIGHT

PERSPECTIVE

VARIATIONS DUE TO LOCATION OF STATION POINT

OBJECTS NOT TOUCHING THE PICTURE PLANE

Fig. 214

known as an *outline perspective;* but if it is shaded in order to express the light values of the several parts it is a *shaded* or *rendered* perspective.

It is important that the architect and builder be able to think in perspective, because the architect expresses his thoughts to his client through this medium. Perspective also helps the architect and builder to visualize the finished object.

The student must first become familiar with the terms used in the construction of these pictorial drawings. In making perspective drawings, the plane on which the drawing is expressed is assumed to be between the eye and the object (see Fig. 213). In perspective drawing this plane is called a *picture plane* and is usually marked with the letters P.P., and the point from which the object is viewed is called the *station point* or *eye* and is lettered S.P. The intersection of the picture plane with the ground is called the *ground* or *grade line* and is lettered G.L. All receding parallel lines which vanish at one point are marked V.P.L. or V.P.R. The receding parallel horizontal lines vanish at one point on the horizon line and this line is marked H.L.

To construct a perspective drawing of a house, the floor plan is placed to a 30–60 deg. or at a 45-deg. angle to the picture plane line (see Fig. 213). This angle depends upon what details of the elevation are to be shown, placing of the position of the perspective, shape of house, and the like. Locate the station point a distance of two to three times the height of the house away from the picture plane. From this point draw the lines which are parallel with the respective sides of the house on the floor plan, until they intersect with the picture plane line. Place the front and end elevations of the house on the sheet so they lie in the middle third of the distance between the station point and the picture plane. The horizon line may be from 3 ft. 6 in. to 6 ft. 6 in. above the grade line. Drop perpendiculars from the points

formed by the lines parallel with the sides of the floor plan to their intersection with the horizon line. These intersections are the true vanishing points. Next draw the lines of sight from the points on the plan to the station point. Where these lines of sight intersect the picture plane line drop perpendiculars to the perspective view. Draw horizontal lines from elevation to the perpendicular corner line of the floor plan, and from these points to their respective vanishing points. The intersection of these lines with the perpendiculars locates the points of the perspective. After the principal lines have been located, much of the detail may be sketched in without definitely locating its component parts.

OBJECTS NOT TOUCHING THE PICTURE PLANE

It sometimes happens that no line of the object lies in the picture plane. In this case some vertical line of the object must be extended until it intersects the picture plane, forming by this intersection an auxiliary line of measure. In Figure 214 the base of the block is extended in one direction and the upper block extended in the other direction for comparison.

Draw the sight lines from the station point to the plan of the base block, and from their intersection with the picture plane line drop perpendiculars to the perspective view. Since this rectangular solid does not touch the picture plane, we cannot measure its height directly along any of these lines. One way of determining this height is to consider one vertical face of the cube as being brought forward to the picture plane line and meeting it at M in plan. In a case like this, B–M must be brought down parallel to S.P.–V^1 or S.P.–V^2 in plan. Drop perpendicular from the point M to the ground line. Now line M–M^1 is in the picture plane and distances may be measured along it. From R measure up the height of the base block and mark,

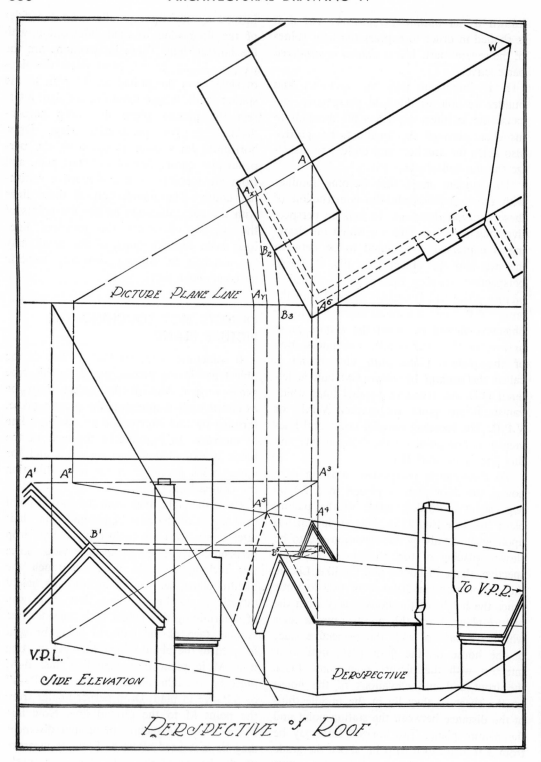

PICTURE PLANE LINE

PERSPECTIVE OF ROOF

Fig. 215

and from H measure off the height of the upper block. Draw lines from B and C to V^1. From the same points draw lines to V^2. Finish the drawing of the block in like manner.

Instead of being some distance behind the picture plane, the block might have been partly in front of the picture plane. This point is illustrated by the representation of the roofs on a floor plan. This cornice projection is usually placed beyond the picture plane. In any case, find the intersection with the picture plane of some vertical face of the block or plan. This intersection will show the true vertical height of the block.

DRAWING THE ROOF IN PERSPECTIVE

Extend the inclined line AW, which forms the ridge of the roof, until it intersects the picture plane. This is explained under "Objects Not Touching the Picture Plane" (see also Fig. 215). From this intersection drop a vertical line, as indicated in Figure 215. This vertical line may be considered to be a line of measure for an imaginary vertical plane passing through the ridge of the house as indicated by the dotted construction lines of the drawing. On this line of measure, lay off the ridge point of the roof A^1, extending the line to point A^3 on the measuring line. Connect point A^2 to V.P.R., and where this construction line crosses the vertical construction line A the ridge point A^4 is located. This line represents the ridge of the roof on this gable.

Since a complete study of instrumental or freehand perspective is beyond the scope of this volume, reference is given to several good books on the subject. Knowledge of the fundamental principles of freehand and instrumental perspective is essential to one who hopes to make architectural perspective drawings correctly.

ASSIGNMENT

It may be well at this time to start on the perspective described in the assignment of Unit VI for Plate 8.

UNIT VI

Rendering the Perspective Drawing

To draw the perspective, the student chooses a station point and an eye level which he believes will show the house to best advantage. If the site for the house has not been selected one is composed which seems suitable. Often the site has been purchased and the driveways, paths, streets, or sidewalks may be used as a natural setting.

Next lay tracing paper over the instrumental layout and work out a thoughtful composition. In doing this strive to express the architecture honestly, accurately, and pleasingly (see Figs. 217 and 218). Nothing should be placed on the drawing unless it contributes toward this expression. The trees and foliage do not exist for any other reason than to contribute toward the setting for the house. One advantage to this system lies in the fact that should the rendering be spoiled it is easy to begin over, and no mechanical lines show in the finished drawing. When the drawing is completed it can be mounted on heavy cardboard.

Another method, and the more common one, is to make the layout on the final paper, using a fairly hard pencil and drawing not only the outline of the large portions but also the window molding, clapboard lines, and other such details. After this is completed the drawing should be gone over with a soft eraser until the lines are just visible as a guide for the freehand work.

With these facts in mind, the student must next decide upon the direction of light. A knowledge of the subject of shades and shadows is a great help in this work. The shadows now may be lightly laid out in outline. In this the customary study of shades and shadows is not sufficient so the student must thoughtfully draw the shadows as best he can. The effect of the finished result is the test so that nature is not always exactly copied in this respect.

After the direction of the light has been decided and the shadow forms outlined, a key to the tone values should be decided upon. In pencil and pen-and-ink drawings these tones are expressed as black, gray, and white. Tones of these same colors must be used to represent the shades and shadows. There are several procedures from this point; the student may put in the darkest tones of the whole drawing, later adding enough gray tones to complete the picture, or he may put in the gray tones first, adding the dark tones and sharp accents to finish the drawing. In building these tones the beginner must beware of too many small lines as they often produce a spotted effect. It is best to vary the length and character of the lines so as to produce an interesting variety. Observation and practice will teach the student the best way to indicate wood, masonry, glass, and other materials (see Figs. 217 and 218).

Many artists complete their work as they proceed, beginning at the center of interest and working out, or beginning at the top and gradually working toward the bottom. The latter method has an advantage in that the drawing can be kept clean more easily than by other methods, but it is a more difficult method to keep the tone values balanced.

The danger in rendering is overcomplication of tone. This produces monotony, rather than variety and interest.

Fig. 216.   Rendered perspective.

Fig. 217.   Rendered perspective.

RENDERING THE PERSPECTIVE DRAWING IN COLOR

Rendering as applied to architectural drawing refers to the application of colors or tones to the drawing, showing the shades and shadows, drawing in the sky and the surrounding landscape so as to produce an attractive and realistic effect. This rendering may be done in the various mediums such as pencil, crayon, pen and ink, washes of color, washes of colored ink, and tinted papers.

In order to make a satisfactory rendered drawing, the student must be able to make a drawing in the proper technique required for that branch of drawing, and he must be able to represent shades and shadows correctly.

MATERIALS REQUIRED

A standard size drawing board and straightedges of sufficient size are needed. The T square and triangles should be straight, true, and clean. The paper used may be colored or white. Cold-pressed paper, face side up, should be used. Tracing paper is used when making studies. Drawings are made on the paper with a soft pencil of HB or F grade. A minimum amount of erasing should be done so as not to injure the surface of the paper. Art gum may be used very lightly, and lumps of stale bread and sponge rubber also are used satisfactorily. Large, soft sponges are used for the application and distribution of the water. All lines of the drawing are inked in with a diluted ink so that they resemble pencil lines. This ink may be used in stick or prepared form as desired. A ruling pen and bow pen are used to make the lines on the drawing. Writing pens are used for drawing curved lines, ornament, and lettering. Brushes are used to make all washes on a drawing that is rendered in ink or water color. Sable or camel's-hair brushes of No. 3 and No. 6 sizes will be found satisfactory for the average size drawing. Blotters are very useful when rendering to pick up the ink or color which may have been accidentally dropped on the drawing, and to pick up the surplus water or wash which may be carried over a line unintentionally. Paste is used to secure the paper to the board.

PREPARATION OF THE MATERIALS FOR RENDERING

The drawing paper must be stretched tightly on the drawing board. To do this, lay the paper face up on the board, and turn the edges up all around for a distance of ¾ in. Then wet the entire surface evenly, using a sponge filled with clean water. Now apply strong paste to the upturned edge, and remove all surplus water with the sponge. Next turn the paper face up and stretch it as tightly as possible. Rub down the edge with some hard object, and place enough thumbtacks around the edges to hold the paper securely. The paper should then be covered for protection from dirt and allowed to dry and tighten.

MAKING THE DRAWING ON STRETCHED PAPER

Often a study is made first on tracing paper and then is transferred to the cold-pressed paper. To do this, the design is fully drawn on the tracing paper with a lead pencil, and then is laid on top of the paper to be used for rendering with the pencil lines toward the stretched paper. The study is then fastened securely with thumbtacks as tightly as possible. It is then transferred to the stretched paper by rubbing every line with some hard rounded object. This, of course, reverses the view originally made. If this is objectionable, trace the lines on tracing paper with a soft pencil, also on the back of the tracing. Then, when the tracing is tacked down on the stretched, hard pressed paper, and is rubbed with the hard rounded object as already directed, the view will appear as originally drawn. After the transferring is complete, the tracing paper is removed and the lines of the drawing are strengthened with a diluted ink. The outlines of the shades and shadows should be drawn in their proper places if they were not transferred from the tracing. All lettering which is to show on the rendering should next be inked in, after which the pencil lines are erased by rubbing the entire surface lightly with art gum or sponge rubber. The drawing is then taken to the sink and clear water run over it. The darker lines may be dabbed with a wet sponge until all of the loose ink is removed. This must all be done quickly and the water soaked from the edges so that the hold of the paste is not loosened. The drawing is again allowed to dry thoroughly.

APPLYING FLAT WASHES

Have three or four water-color pans or saucers at hand, in which to dilute the ink for the proper tones for the washes. The several tones to be used should be tested before starting to work on the drawing. To test the tone, try some of the ink on a scrap of the same paper as used for the plate. Allow each color to dry, because they show up differently when wet. If the tone is too dark add water, and if it is too light add more ink. Always clean out the brushes in clear water before using them for any purpose.

Place the drawing board at an incline of 2 to 3 in. so that the wash will spread out more uniformly. Fill the brushes with ink and begin the wash in the upper left-hand corner. Draw the full brush across the portion to be rendered, leaving a pool of ink along the bottom of the wash strip. Stir the liquid thoroughly before filling the brush for the second strip, and apply a brushful along the bottom of the pool above, helping the fluid to flow down the surface of the paper and forming a new pool. This process is repeated as many times as necessary to cover the surface. No pool should be allowed to stand any longer than necessary. The last wash across at the bottom should pick up all of the surplus water.

RENDERING IN WATER COLORS

The same methods are followed in water-color rendering as those described for the use of ink. The drawing must be carefully made, shadows shown, accessories and lettering neatly drawn, and the drawing cleaned and washed. Instead of using ink in the different tones the separate blended colors are used. In applying colors it is better to mix them. Before applying a color to the drawing it should be tested for intensity and tone. It is always better to apply a color that is too light than one that is too strong. The light wash may be darkened by applying a second or third coat. The dark color must be washed off and new washes applied to all parts of the drawing. Light washes may be altered in color or intensified as desired by the addition of the complementary and opposite colors.

APPLICATION OF COLORED INKS WITH A PEN

When a number of colors are to be employed on one drawing, the bottles should be arranged in some convenient and orderly way so that each color may be easily found when needed. It is also convenient to have a separate pen for each color, with a holder of the corresponding color. The ends of the holders may be scraped and dyed to color by dipping them in their respective colors. The subject may be lightly sketched in pencil or with a pen dipped into diluted ink. The lighter values are built up first. All areas of one color should be inked, so far as is possible, at one time. After the lighter tones have been applied, the darker or stronger colors should be added, reserving the black until the last.

Any amount of variety may be included in the rendering of architectural drawings. Experiment until satisfactory results are obtained.

A few of the more common combinations of the various mediums follow:

1. Thin lead colored pencils in the various color combinations on white paper.

2. Black pencils or crayons on white paper with washes of gray added.

3. Black pencils or crayons with color washes added.

4. Thin colored pencils used on the tinted papers.

5. Thin colored pencils used on the tinted papers with highlights added.

6. Combinations of pencils with ink or ink with wash colors on white and tinted papers.

For the inexperienced a few hints as to what combinations of color to use may be helpful:

1. A simple blue sky: Prussian blue, Antwerp blue, or Cobalt blue.

2. Clouds: Light red. For the distance use lighter tones with a little addition of carmine or green.

3. Dark portion of clouds: Light red and blue.

4. Roads and paths: Yellow ocher and light red with a little blue to gray added to it.

5. Cast shadows: Cobalt and light red or carmine with a little green added.

6. Grass in sunlight: Yellow and light green or emerald.

7. Grass in shadow: Prussian blue and Indian red; or Prussian blue or burnt Sienna.

8. Gray roofs in sunlight: Light red and blue.

COLOR COMBINATIONS

Primary, Secondary, and Complementary Colors. The three primary colors are yellow, red, and blue, and cannot be made by a combination or mixture of any other colors (see Fig. 218). Yellow is the most luminous color. It is cheerful, brilliant, and stimulating, and has great carrying quality. Red is rich, warm, and aggressive, and is the color of danger, passion, violence, and energy. It should never be used in that part of the design where emphasis is undesirable. Blue, on the contrary, is known as a cool, or receding, color because it is quiet and reposeful in its effect and seems to give greater depth or distance.

The colors directly obtained from the three primaries are also three in number and are called secondary colors. They are orange, derived from equal parts of red and yellow, a perfect orange being just halfway between red and yellow in the color scale; violet, derived from red and blue; and green, obtained from blue and yellow. These colors are warm, or advancing, as the red or yellow elements predominate in their composition; or they are cool or receding, as the blue element predominates. All the graduations of orange are warm and advancing because both elements are of that nature. Greens and violets, however, may be either warm and advancing or cool and receding in varying degrees, depending upon whether the warm or cool elements in their composition are the stronger.

Tertiary colors are those obtained from two secondary colors and are also three in number: citrine, slate, and russet. The quaternary colors, those in the fourth order of derivation, are each composed of two tertiary colors.

That which is called complementary relation exists between each one of the primary colors and the secondary colors derived from the other two primary colors, so that complementaries have no elements in common. Thus, for example, orange is the complementary of blue, because orange is composed of the two primaries red and yellow and there is no blue in it. The secondary orange and the primary blue, therefore, are said to be complementary colors because, while they

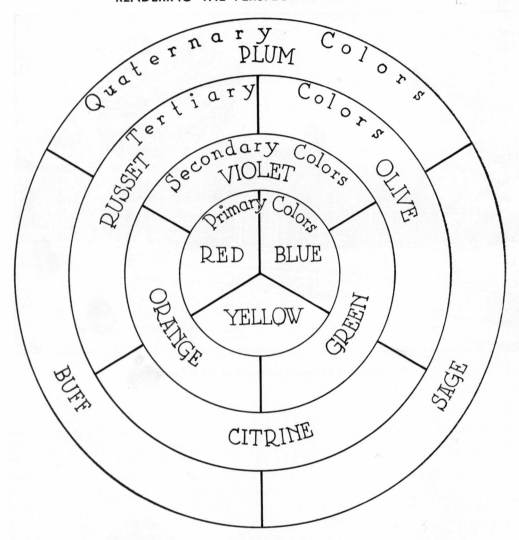

Fig. 218

have no elements in common, between them they complete or round out a representation of all the primary elements. The complementary relationship can exist only between primaries and secondaries; there are three pairs of complementaries: (1) orange and blue, (2) green and red, and (3) violet and yellow.

The tertiary colors each have some portion of every one of the primaries. Thus we see russet, consisting of two secondaries violet and orange, accounts for one strain

of yellow through its orange parent, and one strain of red and one strain of blue through its violet parent. In other words, russet is two parts red, one part yellow, and one part blue.

In the circular chart, it can be seen at a glance not only which colors are complementaries, but also which colors are by their nature and derivation opposed to other colors. By pivoting a ruler or straightedge on the center of the circle and swinging it as you have occasion, the exact degree of

Plate 8.   A student's perspective for a house.

Plate 8A

any opposing color will appear directly opposite along the straight edge of the ruler on one or another circumference of the concentric circles. Thus, if you wish to find the opposing color of blue-green, you will see that directly opposite it, in a straight line, is red-orange.

The term *value* might be defined as relative lightness or darkness, without regard to any particular color. Scale, in color, is a relative correspondence in the intensity of depth of the colors used. The terms *key* and *pitch* relate to the degree of intensity or brilliance of a color. *Shades* are degrees or *tones* of a color darker or deeper than the normal or standard color. *Tints* are degrees or tones lighter and higher than standards. These definitions are important, and it would be well for you to keep them in mind.

ASSIGNMENT

Plate 8, Perspective and Rendering of House Designed in Architectural Drawing III

Only a very brief introduction to the study of perspective may be given in this short unit of work, and no effort has been made to cover the subject in all of its details. It must be remembered that this course is for the purpose of determining the natural talent and ability of the student to determine the advisability of his further study in preparation to become an architect. No effort, therefore, has been directed toward mastery of each of the units presented. They are complete studies in themselves and are to be for study in the higher institutions of special training.

A mechanical perspective drawing is made of the house as drawn in the previous semes-

ter. This perspective drawing is completely rendered for the shades and shadows, material representations, foliage, and so on. If the mechanical perspective is drawn on a good grade of drawing paper this perspective may be rendered in color by the student, using water colors, crayons, and so on. Tracing paper may then be used to trace the house in perspective, and these tracings may then be rendered in pencil, ink, and so on. This gives a completed study of all the previous units of the preliminary studies.

This course has purposely been placed at the end of other studies such as the conventional representations, details, and house planning, and only those students interested in becoming architects are given this type of tryout work. The author is aware of the fact that this preliminary work is done first by an architect but feels that since only the mature student can attempt work of this type, and since all students taking architectural drawing are not planning to become architects, it is not desirable to attempt this study sooner than the senior year.

PROBLEMS FOR CLASS DISCUSSION

1. Of what value is a perspective drawing to the client? The architect?
2. How are measurements made on a perspective drawing?
3. Obtain, if possible, an architect's rendered perspective of some proposed building. This may be framed and made a part of the decoration of the room. Samples of each method of rendering may be obtained.
4. Obtain a book on "Architectural Composition" and report to the class emphasizing the common errors made by students.

U N I T
VII

Display Drawings

The object of the display drawing is to give a realistic representation of the appearance of the proposed building for competitive purposes. In most competitions not only is a perspective required but plans are asked for as well, and sometimes elevations, sections, details, interiors, and even a plot plan. They are "rendered" on Whatman's eggshell, tracing, or other white paper, in water color, pen-and-ink, crayon, pencil, giving the effect of color, or light and shade. Accessories, such as figures surrounding buildings and foliage, are often used to give the relative sizes and the pictorial effect.

When a perspective drawing and plans, and perhaps a detail, are grouped on one sheet, the perspective is really the important consideration. As this perspective is usually the largest single unit it should be placed on the paper in a commanding position, which usually means toward the top. The better method of locating this perspective on the sheet is to block out the outline of the building perspective on a separate sheet and shift this sketch to the various positions on the display sheet, until a logical and interesting arrangement is found. Even the location of the necessary lettering should be carefully studied.

In rendering the plans for display purpose the tints and shadows are often used to show the plan in relief. The rooms are all shown and a line is drawn around the inside of each room. This line gives a certain degree of finish to the plan. A line also may be drawn around the outside of the plan. This line serves to outline the wall against the background. A graded wash is run over the grounds and when dry the indication of the foliage is drawn. Furniture symbols located in the room make the plan more interesting. The walls are blacked in with jet black ink and the other lines with diluted ink. When the walls are blacked in, the drawing cannot be washed. It is a good idea to leave the blackening of the wall until the remainder of the drawing has been satisfactorily completed. The term *poche* used in this process, means simply the blackening of the walls to indicate their relative importance on the drawing.

The architect must be familiar with perspective drawing, since he uses it both in the preliminary study of his problem and in showing his client the finished appearance of the proposed residence.

ASSIGNMENT

Plate 9, Display Drawing

The object of the display drawing is to give a realistic representation of the appearance of the proposed building for competitive purposes. First-hand studies of these drawings may be made at home shows given in the larger cities.

This unit may be used as a complete review of the procedure in the units of *house planning* and *preliminary studies,* or it may be used to develop original design of such projects as city memorials, parks, community centers, and schools.

Emphasis is placed upon the finish given to a competitive drawing as compared to a working drawing.

For this unit the student is to draw a display type of drawing of the house drawn in the unit of "house planning" in Architectural Drawing III.

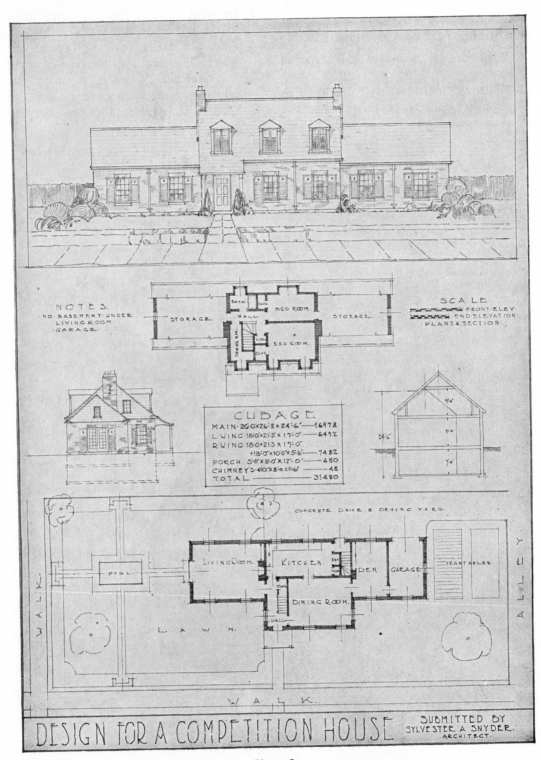

NOTES.
NO·BASEMENT·UNDER
LIVING·ROOM·
GARAGE·

SCALE
FRONT·ELEV·
END·ELEVATION·
PLANS·&·SECTION·

STORAGE. HALL BED ROOM STORAGE.

BED ROOM.

CUBAGE
MAIN·26'0"X26'-8"X24'-6"——16978
L·WING·18'-0"X21'-3"X17'-0"——6492
R·WING·18'-0"X21'-3"X17'-0"
+18'-0"X10'-0"X5'-6"——7482
PORCH·5'-0"X8'-0"X12'-0"——480
CHIMNEY·3'-4"X8'-0"X11'-6"——48
TOTAL————31480

CONCRETE DRIVE & DRYING YARD.

LIVING ROOM. KITCHEN. DEN GARAGE VEGETABLES.

POOL.

DINING ROOM.

LAWN. HALL

WALK ALLEY

WALK.

DESIGN FOR A COMPETITION HOUSE

SUBMITTED BY
SYLVESTER A SNYDER.
ARCHITECT.

Plate 9

PROBLEMS FOR CLASS DISCUSSION

1. What use is made of this type of drawing?
2. Notice the individual style developed by several architects in their competitive drawings.
3. Of what value is this free competition to the profession?
4. Attend a home show in one of the larger cities and see this type of work at first hand. Notice in particular the criticisms made upon the drawings.
5. Obtain, if possible, a display drawing made by an architect.

UNIT

VIII

Models

The secret of any pictorial house model is the keeping of all parts to proportion or scale. Sixteenth scale is used for the model of large areas and its detail must be greatly limited. Eighth scale is the best to use when making a model of both house and its surrounding areas. Half-inch scale is sometimes specified for some flower-show competitions, but this is too large except for models of very small houses. The usual scale for models of moderate size is one quarter or three sixteenths. This scale best fits the sizes as specified for working drawing plans of the house (see Figs. 220–223).

In making the actual scale house model, a heavy rough Upson board is used. Blueprints are taken of the drawings of the ele-vations of the house and are pasted to the board with a good paste or by a shellac procedure. The blue-line prints on a white background serve best for this purpose. The boards are then cut out to the shape of the several elevations, care being taken that the full wall heights are used which includes that portion under the cornice projection. If plain Upson board is to be used, the elevations of the doors and windows may be traced in with carbon paper. If blue-line prints are used, the lines are already in for the wall openings. If regular blueprints are used, it is better to trace the lines in with colored pencil, or strips may be pasted on to represent the openings. Also, window and door glass openings may be cut out and glassine paper, ruled with mullions, glued on the back side of each cut opening. If not cut out, the glass portions may be tinted with a faint wash to represent the glass and shadows.

Roof intersections must be carefully worked out that the gables will match nicely. If a dormer window is to be built in, be sure to lay the paper to the full roof as in the plain roof construction and then cut out the opening for the window. Careful consideration of the several problems involved will improve the appearance of the model. The

C. K. Pritchett, Somerset Area Vocational School, Kentucky

Fig. 219. A house model.

571

Fig. 220. Pictorial house modeling.

roof may then be given a weathered appearance.

Shutters may be cut out to shape, painted, and glued in place. Terraces, chimneys, window boxes, and so on may be made of single thicknesses of the board and glued in place and rendered with the proper representation and colors.

When the several sections of the house are ready to be assembled, they may be glued and supported with brads, or little glued strips may be fitted to the corners.

The lawn may be symbolized by a piece of green blotting paper glued onto a board, or the board itself may be painted green and given a sawdust finish. To apply the sawdust to the board, cover all the grass areas with a good heavy shellac or thin liquid glue. As you shellac, sprinkle the grass areas thickly with sawdust. When the shellac is thoroughly dry stand the board on end to shake off the excess sawdust. The grass is then given its color by spraying the sawdust with watercolor paint through a fly spray gun or some other blower and sprayer arrangement. Powdered water-color paint is the cheapest and may be purchased at any good hardware store. An eighth of a pound

of emerald green and chrome yellow is more than enough. Mix these together to give a good yellow green, which is more effective and pleasing than a bluish green.

Clumps of Grape Nuts will do for an indication of the spring vegetable garden, although Japanese sea moss bought at the dime stores is good for representing topped vegetables. The stamens of larger artificial flowers make good tulips, or, if covered with Cream of Wheat, fairly acceptable hyacinths. Tall spikes of flowers can be made of dried grasses or of paper and wire dipped into glue and then covered with the tiny candies used for cake frosting. Foliage can be made by working with green crepe paper or green rubber sponge purchased at the dime store.

The gravel paths around the vegetable garden are painted with shellac and then are covered with fine gray sand. Stone walls may be drawn on cardboard, painted, cut out with a sharp knife, and glued in place. The wire fences may be made of wire screening. The pergola may be constructed of small sticks of the proper scale, which can be obtained at any good school supply store. The wooden fence should be made of small swab sticks or matches. Small spools are

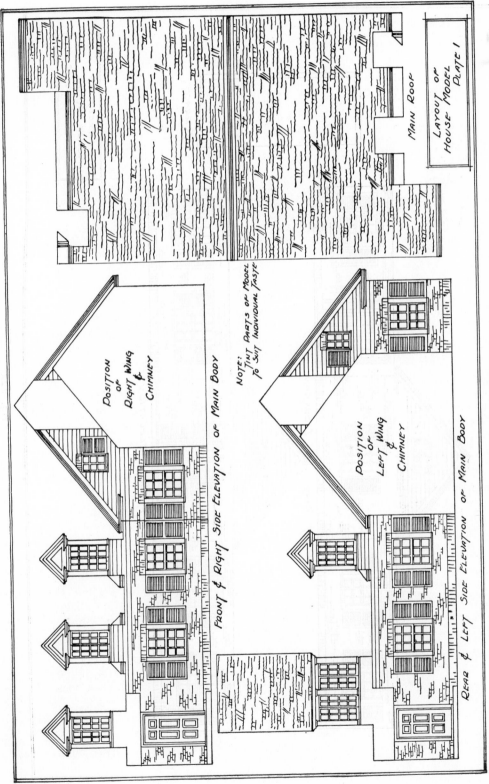

MAIN ROOF

LAYOUT OF HOUSE MODEL PLATE 1

NOTE: TINT PARTS OF MODEL TO SUIT INDIVIDUAL TASTE

POSITION OF RIGHT WING & CHIMNEY

FRONT & RIGHT SIDE ELEVATION OF MAIN BODY

POSITION OF LEFT WING & CHIMNEY

REAR & LEFT SIDE ELEVATION OF MAIN BODY

Fig. 221

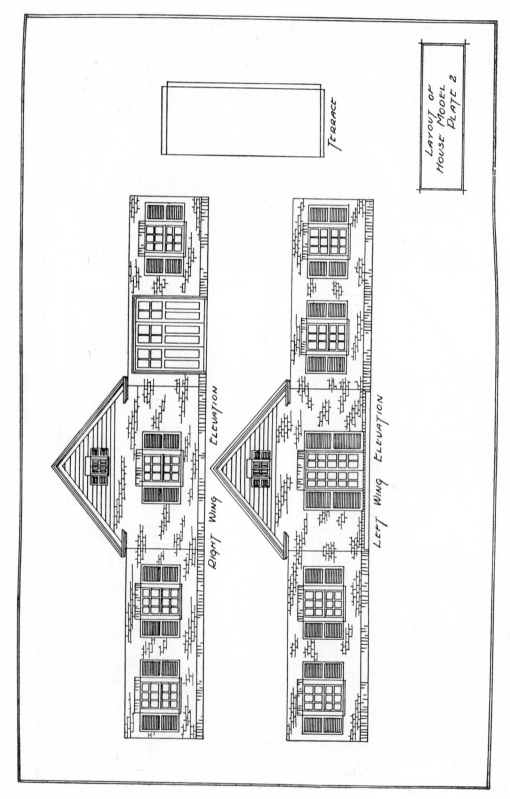

Fig. 222

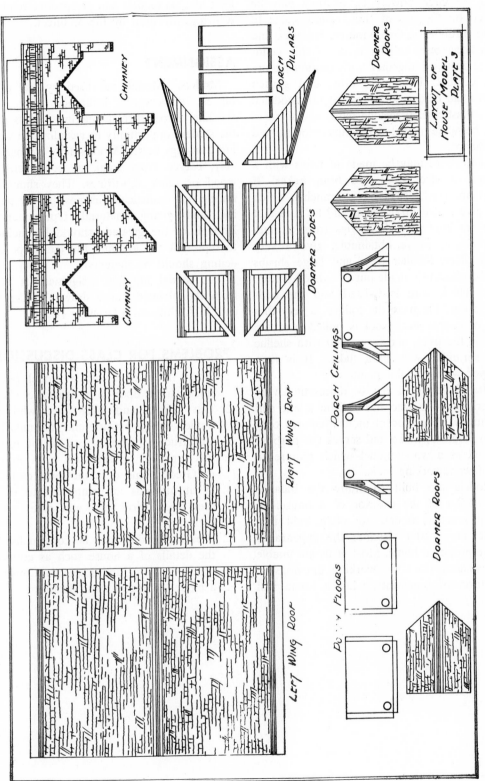

Fig. 223

used for large flowerpots, or they may be placed on the top of thin, round sticks to make birdhouses. Greenhouses, lanterns, and such accessories can be made of thin cellophane fastened together with motion-picture film cement. Fountains, urns, and garden figures can be carved out of soap or modeled from Plasticine. Flagstone paths and terraces may be made of real slate chips or of painted cardboard.

Large trees may be made of twigs with a foliage of steel wool and bran flakes. If twigs are used, select those branches which will give a structural effect, and be sure that they are kept to scale. Twigs from a blueberry bush, where obtainable, give a very good effect. Smaller trees and large shrubs can be effectively made out of twisted picture wire. Thick wire is twisted and the ends frayed out. To make the foliage, a very thin film of coarse steel wool is pulled over the tops of the trees, and is sprayed with shellac and sprinkled with bran flakes. It is then sprayed with oil color paint.

The whole model may be represented very cleverly by one who has artistic talent and originality. This type of model requires only a few hours to make and serves the purpose as well as a wood model which requires a kit of woodworking tools.

Models are built to study the balance and design of the exterior of a house. In actual practice models are often built that clients may better visualize the appearance of the proposed home. Most of us are unable to visualize, from the working drawings in the form of blueprints, what a home will look like, so models and perspective rendered drawings are used by the architect.

ASSIGNMENT

Models. Models are used by real estate offices, lumberyards, insurance offices, and the like. Experience in making models gives the student opportunity to visualize the working drawings better. Models may be made of clay, carved from soap, or constructed of wood or other substitutes. They should be finished as realistically as possible by painting and giving material representations. Enough of the grounds should be included to represent the lot, and the landscape gardening should be included.

The model for this assignment is made from the planned house drawn by the student in Architectural Drawing III.

PROBLEMS FOR CLASS DISCUSSION

1. What influence would a model of the house have upon a prospective client?
2. List offices and businesses who use models for advertising and salesmanship.
3. Construct a model of one of the historical types of houses such as a Roman or Greek home or a medieval castle.
4. What methods are employed to represent trees, shrubbery, and other accessories?
5. Working models may be constructed for the details of a house such as cornices, windows, doors, and fireplaces. Construct a model of one of these details.

INDEX

INVENTORY 74

FALL 77

INVENTORY 1983